*Warman's*

# TENTH ANTIQUES
# AND
# THEIR CURRENT PRICES

BY

EDWIN G. WARMAN

*A Check List and Guide of*
*Comparative Prices for*
*Antique Dealers and Collectors*

Published by
**E. G. WARMAN PUBLISHING INC.**
UNIONTOWN, PENNSYLVANIA 15401

1970

# Introduction

The "Tenth Antiques and Their Current Prices" is the largest and most complete book in the series to be issued to date. It has been increased in content by almost 100 pages. An important new feature is a section on English Antique Furniture. The compiler made two trips to London to secure photographs and to check the various antique markets. The bottle section has been greatly enlarged. A new section has been added on numerous patterns of Sterling Silver Flatware. New items have been added to most existing groups and twenty new categories have been included in this latest publication.

Prices have continued to rise since the last edition of Antiques and Their Current Prices (Ninth edition) was published. It appears that some investors as well as collectors are coming into the market and buying prime antiques and highly desirable collectors' items in glass and china. Prices have continued to increase on art, colored and cut glass. Carnival glass has lost considerable ground in value because of numerous reproductions which have been made in the last two or three years. Recently, a collector's market has developed for barbed wire and glass telephone pole insulators. The bottle market has been booming, however, it appears that peak prices will be reached within the next year because of the numerous new issues and the problem collectors have in storing their items in this category. Furniture remains one of the favorites of collectors and investors and prices continue to increase. The entire antique market seems to be firm and the prospect for continued prosperity in the field appears rosy unless some sudden monetary or economic catastrophe should appear on the horizon.

Prices incorporated within the volume are current retail values determined by compiling all retail quotations available to the author and arriving at an average price. Retail prices vary in different parts of the country (depending on abundance, scarcity, distance from wholesale sources and other factors) and do not always correspond with the prices listed herein. The primary purpose of this book is, therefore, to be considered a guide to prices rather than a final authority.

Every effort has been exerted to accurately record prices. However, in the event of clerical, typographical, or any other errors, the compiler/publisher declines to assume any liability or responsibility for any loss or losses incurred by the purchasers or users of this volume.

A voluminous amount of correspondence is received requesting appraisals on items not listed or which appear to the owner to be unique. It is impossible to answer each request personally because of other matters demanding attention. It is suggested that local dealers, or dealers exhibiting in antique shows, be contacted for answers to such questions. Library books prove invaluable aids in securing desired information.

Compiling a volume of this type, especially with the regularity we have established in the past, is a costly and colossal task. The assistance of many interested and cooperative people is needed. Appreciation and thanks are due those who have furnished information, illustrations and other material. It would be impossible to name every individual. Special thanks and recognition are given the following: Mr. B. H. Leffingwell, Antiques, Rochester, New York; Mrs. June Stout, Antiques, R. D. #2, Prosperity, Pennsylvania; Mrs. Ada Haas, National Trail Antiques, Route 40 East, Farmington, Pennsylvania; Mr. James Watt, Great Falls, Virginia; Mrs. Edna A. Carl, Pittsburgh, Pennsylvania; Henry Cohen, Manager, Thieves Market, Alexandria, Virginia. Also, we would like to thank the following dealers at Thieves Market, Alexandria, Virginia for their cooperation: Hazel's Findit Antiques, Blanton's Antiques, Raymie's Antiques, Blanche Dobkin Antiques, Marie Evans' Antiques, Fullhouse Antiques and Forrest L. Newton Antiques. We also want to express our appreciation to Mr. John F. Gates, Photographer, Uniontown, Pennsylvania, and Mr. Geo. Steinbach, London, England, for photographs.

EDWIN G. WARMAN
Uniontown, Pa.

# PATTERN GLASS

**— Section One —**

## CLEAR GLASS PATTERNS

Quotations listed on Pattern Glass are retail prices for pieces in perfect condition. All prices are on clear glass. The Colored Glass Section follows this group and is designated as "Section Two." Each pattern is illustrated with an original drawing or photograph. Items marked with an asterisk (*) have been, or are now being produced.

## ACTRESS

| | | |
|---|---|---|
| Bowl, footed, 6'' | $ | 18.25 |
| Butter dish | | 38.50 |
| Cake stand | | 35.25 |
| Celery | | 36.00 |
| Cheese dish, covered | | 53.25 |
| Compote | | |
| a. Covered, high standard | | 55.00 |
| b. Covered, low standard | | 46.75 |
| c. Open, 10'' | | 33.00 |
| Creamer | | 24.75 |
| Goblet | | 25.25 |
| Honey dish, covered | | 33.00 |
| Marmalade jar | | 26.75 |
| *Pickle | | 12.00 |
| Pitcher | | |
| a. Milk | | 72.00 |
| b. Water | | 55.00 |
| Platter | | |
| a. Pinafore, 9¼ x 12¾'', oval | | 22.00 |
| b. Miss Nielson center | | 23.75 |
| Sauce | | |
| a. Flat | | 7.75 |
| b. Footed | | 10.00 |
| Shakers, pair | | 19.00 |
| Spooner | | 15.50 |
| Sugar bowl | | 38.50 |
| Tray, bread | | 23.75 |

*Reproduced Item

## ALABAMA
### (Beaded Bull's Eye and Drape)

| | | |
|---|---|---|
| Butter dish, covered | $ | 12.25 |
| Compote, open, 5'' | | 10.00 |

| | |
|---|---|
| Creamer | 11.00 |
| Honey dish | 6.25 |
| Pickle | 6.25 |
| Spooner | 6.75 |
| Sugar bowl, covered | 13.25 |

## AMAZON
### (Sawtooth Band)

| | | |
|---|---|---|
| Banana stand | $ | 20.00 |
| Bowl, open | | 6.75 |
| Butter dish | | 14.00 |
| Cake stand | | 15.50 |
| Celery | | 9.25 |
| Champagne | | 9.50 |
| Claret | | 9.00 |
| Compote | | |
| a. Jelly, 5½'' | | 11.25 |
| b. Open, high standard | | 18.50 |
| Cordial | | 10.00 |
| Creamer | | 13.25 |
| Flower vase | | 9.50 |
| Goblet | | 10.00 |
| Pitcher | | |
| a. Syrup | | 13.50 |
| b. Water | | 20.00 |
| Sauce, flat, 4½'' | | 5.00 |
| Shakers, pair | | 9.25 |
| Spooner | | 6.75 |
| Sugar bowl | | 14.00 |
| Tumbler | | 6.50 |
| Wine | | 7.25 |

## AMBERETTE
### (See Colored Glass Section)

## ANTHEMION

8

| Bowl, berry, 7'' | $ 7.75 |
|---|---|
| Butter dish | 15.75 |
| Cake plate, 9¼'' | 11.75 |
| Celery | 9.50 |
| Creamer | 13.25 |
| Marmalade jar | 8.25 |
| Pitcher | 15.50 |
| Plate, 10'' | 11.50 |
| Sauce | 4.50 |
| Spooner | 5.50 |
| Sugar bowl | 15.75 |
| Tumbler | 6.50 |

## APOLLO

| Bowl | $ 6.25 |
|---|---|
| Butter dish | 16.00 |
| Cake stand | 12.25 |
| Celery | 9.75 |
| Compote | |
| a. Covered, high standard | 18.25 |
| b. Open, low standard | 12.75 |
| Creamer | 13.00 |
| Goblet | 6.75 |
| Pickle | 5.00 |
| Pitcher, water | 16.50 |
| Sauce | |
| a. Flat | 3.25 |
| b. Footed | 4.50 |
| Spooner | 6.75 |
| Sugar bowl | 16.00 |
| Tray, water | 10.50 |
| Tumbler | 5.25 |

## ARABESQUE

| Butter dish | $ 18.50 |
|---|---|
| Celery | 12.75 |

| Compote | |
|---|---|
| a. Covered, 6'', high standard | 18.50 |
| b. Covered, 8'', low standard | 20.00 |
| c. Covered, 8'', high standard | 22.00 |
| Creamer | 17.75 |
| Goblet | 6.75 |
| Pitcher | 16.25 |
| Sauce | 3.75 |
| Spooner | 7.00 |
| Sugar bowl | 18.50 |

## ARCHED GRAPE

| Butter dish | $ 19.00 |
|---|---|
| Celery | 13.00 |
| Compote | |
| a. Covered, high standard | 23.50 |
| b. Covered, low standard | 18.50 |
| Cordial | 7.50 |
| Creamer | 15.50 |
| Goblet | 8.50 |
| Pitcher | 20.50 |
| Sauce | 3.25 |
| Spooner | 7.25 |
| Sugar bowl | 19.00 |
| Wine | 5.25 |

## ARGUS
### (Flint Glass)

| Ale glass | $ 20.50 |
|---|---|
| Bitters bottle | 15.50 |
| Bowl, 5½'' | 16.50 |
| Butter dish | 24.50 |
| Celery | 35.00 |
| Champagne | 14.50 |

| | |
|---|---|
| Cordial | 11.00 |
| Creamer | 30.00 |
| Decanter | |
| a. Pint | 35.00 |
| b. Quart | 40.00 |
| Egg cup | 12.75 |
| Goblet | 16.50 |
| Lamp, footed | 26.50 |
| Mug, applied handle (scarce) | 35.00 |
| Salt, open | 8.75 |
| Sauce | 10.00 |
| Spooner | 16.50 |
| Sugar bowl | 27.50 |
| Tumbler | |
| a. Footed | 15.00 |
| b. Jelly | 12.25 |
| c. Water | 14.75 |
| Wine | 13.50 |

## ART

| | |
|---|---|
| Banana dish (scarce) | $ 36.00 |
| Basket, fruit | 22.00 |
| Bowl, berry, 8'' | 11.00 |
| Butter dish | 16.50 |
| Cake stand, 10'' | 18.25 |
| Celery | 15.50 |
| Compote | |
| a. Covered, 7'', footed | 22.00 |
| b. Open, 7½'', footed | 18.25 |
| Cracker jar | 12.00 |
| Creamer | 16.00 |
| Cruet | 13.25 |
| Goblet | 15.50 |
| Mug | 8.25 |
| Pickle | 7.25 |
| Pitcher, water | 21.50 |
| Sauce | 5.00 |
| Spooner | 8.25 |
| Sugar bowl | 17.75 |
| Tumbler | 7.25 |
| Vinegar jug | |
| a. ½ pint | 9.00 |
| b. 3 pints | 10.00 |

## ASHBURTON

| | |
|---|---|
| Ale glass | $ 20.00 |
| Bitters bottle | 15.50 |
| Butter dish | 41.00 |
| Celery | |
| a. Plain top | 34.00 |

| | |
|---|---|
| b. Scalloped top | 53.00 |
| *Cordiol | 20.00 |
| Creamer (scarce) | 68.00 |

| | |
|---|---|
| Decanter | |
| a. Pint | 27.00 |
| b. Quart | 30.00 |
| c. 3 pints | 33.00 |
| Egg cup | 11.50 |
| Goblets | |
| a. Flaring sides | 16.50 |
| b. Straight sides | 13.50 |
| Jug | |
| a. Pint | 39.00 |
| b. Quart | 52.00 |
| c. 3 pints | 57.50 |
| Lamp | 27.50 |
| Lemonade glass | 17.00 |
| Mug | 20.00 |
| Sauce | 7.50 |
| Spooner | 11.00 |
| Sugar bowl | 41.00 |
| Toddy jar, covered (rare) | 145.00 |
| Tumbler | |
| a. Jelly | 13.00 |
| b. Water | 22.00 |
| c. Whiskey | 25.00 |
| Wine bottle, with tumble-up | 62.50 |
| Wine | 13.75 |

*Reproduced Item

## ATLANTA
### (Clear Lion Head)

| | |
|---|---|
| Bowl, berry | $ 11.00 |
| Butter dish, covered | 27.00 |
| Cake stand | 21.00 |

| Compote | | |
|---|---|---|
| a. Covered, 5'', square stem | | 33.00 |
| b. Open, 5'', square stem | | 20.00 |
| Creamer | | 16.50 |
| Goblet | | 19.00 |
| Marmalade jar | | 13.25 |
| Pickle | | 7.75 |
| Salt | | 6.75 |
| Sauce | | 6.00 |
| Spooner | | 9.75 |
| Sugar bowl, covered | | 28.00 |
| Toothpick | | 9.00 |

## BABY FACE

| Butter dish | $ 45.00 |
|---|---|
| Cake stand | |
| a. Large | 41.00 |
| b. Small | 58.00 |
| Celery vase | 39.00 |
| Compote | |
| *a. Covered, small | 44.50 |
| b. Open, large | 33.25 |
| Cordial | 33.25 |
| Creamer | 44.00 |
| *Goblet | 45.00 |
| Lamp | 60.00 |
| Pitcher | 69.00 |
| Salt dip | 13.25 |
| Sauce, footed | 13.75 |
| Spooner | 20.00 |
| *Sugar bowl | 44.00 |
| *Wine | 27.50 |

*Reproduced Item

## BABY THUMBPRINT, See Dakota

## BALL AND SWIRL

| Bowl, finger | $ 6.75 |
|---|---|
| Butter dish | 17.75 |
| Cake stand | 14.00 |
| Compote | |
| a. Covered, high standard | 20.00 |
| b. Open, high standard | 15.00 |
| Cordial | 6.50 |
| Creamer | 13.75 |
| Decanter | 14.00 |
| Goblet | 6.50 |

| Mug | | |
|---|---|---|
| a. Large | | 8.25 |
| b. Small | | 6.75 |
| Pitcher | | |
| a. Tankard | | 27.00 |
| b. Water | | 16.50 |
| Sauce, footed | | 5.00 |
| Spooner | | 7.75 |
| Sugar bowl | | 16.50 |
| Tumbler | | 6.25 |
| Wine | | 7.50 |

## BALTIMORE PEAR
### (Gypsy)

| Bowl | | |
|---|---|---|
| a. Berry | $ | 15.50 |
| b. Covered | | 20.50 |
| *Butter dish | | 26.00 |
| *Cake stand | | 22.00 |
| *Celery | | 24.00 |
| Compote | | |
| a. Covered, 6'', high standard | | 42.50 |
| b. Covered, 7'', high standard | | 46.50 |
| c. Covered, 8'', high standard | | 53.00 |
| d. Covered, 8¼'', low standard | | 36.00 |
| e. Open, large | | 26.00 |
| *Creamer | | 18.50 |
| *Goblet | | 14.00 |
| Pickle | | 10.00 |
| *Pitcher, water | | 42.00 |
| Plate | | 13.75 |
| Sauce | | |
| a. Flat | | 5.50 |
| b. Footed, large | | 8.25 |
| *c. Footed, small | | 9.75 |

| | |
|---|---|
| Spooner | 10.50 |
| *Sugar bowl | 27.00 |

*Reproduced Item

## BAMBOO

| | | |
|---|---|---|
| Butter dish | $ | 13.75 |
| Celery | | 8.75 |
| Compote | | |
| a. Covered, 7'' | | 17.75 |
| b. Covered, 8'' | | 20.50 |
| c. Covered, 9'' | | 23.00 |
| Creamer | | 11.00 |
| Dish | | |
| a. Oblong, 7'' | | 5.50 |
| b. Oblong, 8'' | | 6.75 |
| c. Oblong, 9'' | | 7.75 |
| Pitcher, water | | 16.00 |
| Sauce, 4'' | | 3.25 |
| Shakers, pair | | 11.00 |
| Spooner | | 6.75 |
| Sugar bowl, covered | | 14.00 |
| Tumbler | | 6.00 |

## BANDED BUCKLE

| | | |
|---|---|---|
| Butter dish | $ | 19.00 |
| Compote, covered | | 24.50 |
| Cordial | | 8.00 |
| Creamer | | 16.00 |
| Egg Cup | | 9.00 |
| Goblet | | 8.75 |
| Pickle, oval | | 6.00 |
| Pitcher | | |
| a. Syrup | | 15.50 |

| | |
|---|---|
| b. Water | 27.50 |
| Salt, footed | 5.00 |
| Sauce | 4.50 |
| Spooner | 8.75 |
| Sugar bowl | 20.50 |
| Tumbler | 6.50 |
| Wine | 9.50 |

## BARBERRY

| | | |
|---|---|---|
| Bowl, 8'', covered | $ | 13.75 |
| Butter dish | | 22.00 |
| Cake plate | | 16.50 |
| Celery | | 14.00 |
| Compote | | |
| a. Covered, high standard | | 30.25 |
| b. Covered, 8'', low standard | | 24.75 |
| Cordial | | 9.75 |
| Creamer | | 13.75 |
| Dish, oval, 8 x 5½'' | | 10.50 |
| Egg cup | | 8.25 |
| Goblet | | 9.00 |
| Honey dish, 3½'' | | 6.75 |
| Pickle | | 7.50 |
| Pitcher | | 26.50 |
| Plate | | |
| a. 6'' | | 12.00 |
| b. Cup plate size | | 11.00 |
| Salt, footed | | 8.75 |
| Sauce | | |
| a. Flat | | 5.50 |
| b. Footed | | 6.75 |
| Spooner | | 8.25 |
| Sugar bowl | | 21.50 |
| Syrup jug. Pewter top | | 20.50 |
| Wine | | 6.75 |

## BARLEY

| | |
|---|---|
| Butter dish _____ $ | 18.25 |
| Cake stand _____ | 13.25 |
| Celery _____ | 11.25 |
| Compote, covered _____ | 22.00 |
| Cordial _____ | 9.50 |
| Creamer _____ | 11.00 |
| Dish, oval, $6\frac{1}{2}$ x $9\frac{1}{2}$'' _____ | 9.50 |
| Goblet _____ | 9.75 |
| Marmalade jar _____ | 14.00 |
| Pickle, open handles _____ | 7.25 |
| Pitcher _____ | 21.00 |
| Plate, 6'' _____ | 13.00 |
| Platter _____ | 20.00 |
| Sauce | |
|   a. Flat _____ | 5.00 |
|   b. Footed, 4'' _____ | 6.00 |
|   c. Footed, 5'' _____ | 6.75 |
| Spooner _____ | 8.25 |
| Sugar bowl _____ | 19.00 |
| Wine _____ | 7.25 |

### BARRED FORGET-ME-NOT
(See Colored Glass Section)

### BASKETWEAVE
(See Colored Glass Section)

### BEADED ACORN MEDALLION

| | |
|---|---|
| Butter dish _____ $ | 16.50 |
| Compote | |
|   a. Covered, high standard ___ | 25.00 |
|   b. Covered, low standard ___ | 17.75 |
| Creamer _____ | 16.00 |
| Dish, oval _____ | 7.25 |
| Egg cup _____ | 9.50 |
| Goblet _____ | 9.75 |
| Honey dish _____ | 5.50 |
| Pickle _____ | 6.75 |
| Pitcher _____ | 19.00 |
| Plate, 6'' _____ | 8.75 |
| Salt, footed _____ | 4.00 |
| Sauce _____ | 4.00 |
| Spooner _____ | 7.25 |
| Sugar bowl _____ | 18.50 |
| Wine _____ | 5.25 |

### BEADED BAND

| | |
|---|---|
| Butter dish _____ $ | 15.50 |
| Cake stand _____ | 12.75 |
| Celery _____ | 12.00 |
| Compote, covered _____ | 18.25 |

| | |
|---|---|
| Cordial _____ | 9.00 |
| Creamer _____ | 12.75 |
| Goblet _____ | 7.25 |
| Marmalade jar _____ | 12.75 |
| Pickle _____ | 6.25 |
| Platter _____ | 9.50 |
| Sauce _____ | 5.00 |
| Shakers, pair _____ | 10.00 |
| Spooner _____ | 6.25 |
| Sugar bowl _____ | 16.00 |

### BEADED DEWDROP
(Wisconsin)

| | |
|---|---|
| Bowl | |
|   a. Covered, oblong, 6'', 8'' ___ $ | 9.00 |
|   b. Covered, round, 7'', 8'' ___ | 12.75 |
| Butter dish | |
|   a. Handled _____ | 15.50 |
|   b. Large _____ | 12.75 |
|   c. Small _____ | 10.50 |
| Celery _____ | 12.25 |
| Celery tray _____ | 9.75 |
| Compote | |
|   a. Covered, 6', 7'', 8'' ___ | 20.00 |
|   b. Open, $8\frac{1}{2}$'' $9\frac{1}{2}$'', $10\frac{1}{2}$'' ___ | 22.00 |
| Condiment set. 4 pieces in holder__ | 26.50 |
| Creamer | |
|   a. Individual _____ | 6.75 |
|   b. Large _____ | 9.75 |
| Cruet _____ | 9.00 |
| Cup and saucer _____ | 12.75 |
| Dish | |
|   a. Candy _____ | 6.75 |
|   b. Handled, oval, 6'', covered | 12.75 |
|   c. Handled, oval, 6'', open ___ | 7.75 |
|   d. Sweetmeat _____ | 12.75 |
| Goblet _____ | 12.50 |
| Mug _____ | 11.00 |

Pitcher
  a. 3 pints _____ 17.75
  b. ¼ gallon _____ 20.00
Sauce
  a. Handled, 5½'' _____ 4.75
  b. Flat, 4'' _____ 4.00
Shakers
  a. Squatty, pair _____ 11.00
  b. Tall, pair _____ 13.25
Spooner _____ 7.25
Sugar bowl
  a. Large, covered _____ 19.00
  b. Small, covered _____ 16.00
Syrup _____ 12.75
Toothpick holder _____ 5.00
Tumbler _____ 9.00
Wine _____ 9.50

### BEADED GRAPE
#### (See Colored Glass Section)

### BEADED GRAPE MEDALLION

Butter dish _____$ 18.25
Castor bottle _____ 6.75
Celery _____ 21.50
Compote
  a. Covered, 7¼'', 8¼'', large, high
    standard _____ 25.00
  b. Covered, low standard _____ 22.00
  c. Covered, oval, collared base,
    10 x 7'' _____ 28.00
Cordial _____ 13.25
Creamer _____ 23.25
Dish, oval _____ 9.75
Egg cup _____ 11.00
Goblet _____ 10.00
Honey dish _____ 5.50
Lamp, handled _____ 15.50
Pickle _____ 7.25
Pitcher _____ 27.50
Plate, 6'' _____ 10.50
Salt
  a. Footed _____ 7.75
  b. Oval, flat _____ 7.50
  c. Round, flat _____ 6.00
  d. Celery dip _____ 2.75
Sauce _____ 6.00
Spooner _____ 7.75
Sugar bowl _____ 18.75

### BEADED LOOP

Bowl, berry, covered _____$ 11.25
Butter dish _____ 15.50
Cake stand _____ 13.75
Celery _____ 12.25
Compote, open _____ 14.00
Cordial _____ 7.25
Creamer _____ 12.75
Dish, oval _____ 8.25
Goblet _____ 9.00
Mug _____ 8.75
Pickle _____ 8.50
Pitcher
  a. Milk _____ 17.75
  b. Syrup _____ 15.00
  c. Water _____ 16.50
Sauce _____ 3.50
Shakers
  a. Salt and pepper _____ 11.00
  b. Sugar _____ 10.00
Spooner _____ 7.50
Sugar bowl _____ 16.00
Toothpick holder _____ 5.00
Tray, bread _____ 10.50
Tumbler _____ 9.25
Wine _____ 8.00

### BEADED OVAL AND SCROLL

Bowl, 6¼'' _____$ 6.75
Butter dish _____ 13.75
Cake stand _____ 13.00
Compote, high standard _____ 15.50
Cordial _____ 7.75
Creamer _____ 11.00
Dish, oval _____ 6.00
Goblet _____ 7.25

| | |
|---|---|
| Pickle | 5.75 |
| Pitcher | 15.00 |
| Sauce | 3.75 |
| Shakers, pair | 9.75 |
| Spooner | 6.50 |
| Sugar bowl | 14.00 |

## BEADED TULIP
### (Andes)

| | |
|---|---|
| Bowl | $ 10.00 |
| Butter dish | 20.00 |
| Compote, covered, high standard | 20.50 |
| Cake stand | 19.00 |
| Cordial | 10.50 |
| Creamer | 14.00 |
| Dish, oval, 9½'' long | 8.25 |
| Goblet | 9.75 |
| Lamp | 11.50 |
| Marmalade jar | 10.50 |
| Pickle | 7.25 |
| Pitcher | |
| a. Milk | 16.50 |
| b. Water | 20.00 |
| Plate, 6'' | 10.75 |
| Sauce | |
| a. Flat | 4.25 |
| b. Footed | 5.75 |
| Spooner | 8.25 |
| Sugar bowl | 20.00 |
| Tray, water | 16.00 |
| Wine | 8.50 |

## BEARDED MAN
### (Queen Anne)

| | |
|---|---|
| Butter dish | $ 15.50 |
| Celery | 10.50 |
| Compote, covered, 7'', 8'' | 19.00 |

| | |
|---|---|
| Creamer | 11.00 |
| Pitcher, water | 16.50 |
| Sauce, 4½'', footed | 5.00 |
| Spooner | 6.75 |
| Sugar bowl | 16.00 |

## BELLFLOWER

**SINGLE VINE**   **DOUBLE VINE**

| | |
|---|---|
| Bowl | |
| a. Berry, flat, scalloped edge | $ 55.00 |
| b. Flat, 8'' | 58.00 |
| c. Deep | 45.00 |
| Butter dish | |
| a. Beaded edge | 40.00 |
| b. Plain edge | 42.75 |
| c. Scalloped edge | 46.50 |
| Cake stand (rare) | — — |
| Castor bottle | 15.00 |
| Celery | |
| a. Clear marginal band | 62.50 |
| b. Ribbed top | 67.00 |
| Champagne | 29.50 |
| Compote | |
| a. Covered, 8'', high standard | 90.00 |
| b. Covered, 8'', low standard | 70.00 |
| c. Open, 8'', high standard, scalloped top | 42.50 |
| d. Open, low standard, scalloped top | 37.50 |
| e. Open, 9¾'' diameter, 8¼'' high | 40.00 |
| f. Open, low standard, small | 35.00 |
| Cordial | 30.00 |
| Creamer | |
| a. Double vine | 55.00 |
| b. Single vine | 60.00 |
| Decanter | |
| a. Double vine, quart | 65.00 |
| b. Single vine, pint | 62.50 |
| c. Single vine, quart | 60.00 |
| Dish, oval, large | 45.00 |
| Egg cup | 15.00 |
| Goblet | 15.00 |
| Honey dish | 10.00 |
| Lamp | |
| a. All glass | 48.50 |
| b. Bracket lamp | 45.00 |
| c. Marble base | 44.00 |
| Mug, applied handle | 50.00 |
| Pickle, 5 x 7'' (scarce) | 55.00 |

15

Pitcher
| | |
|---|---|
| a. Milk, double vine (scarce) | 325.00 |
| b. Syrup, hexagonal | 67.50 |
| c. Syrup, round | 55.00 |
| d. Water, double vine | 85.00 |
| e. Water, single vine | 79.50 |

| | |
|---|---|
| Plate, 6¼'' | 48.00 |

Salt
| | |
|---|---|
| a. Covered, footed (rare) | 65.00 |
| b. Open, footed | 21.50 |

| | |
|---|---|
| Sauce | 8.75 |

Spooner
| | |
|---|---|
| a. Double vine | 22.50 |
| b. Single vine | 16.50 |

Sugar bowl
| | |
|---|---|
| a. Double vine | 50.00 |
| b. Single vine | 42.50 |

| | |
|---|---|
| Tumbler | 30.00 |
| Whiskey glass | 37.50 |
| Wine | 25.00 |

## BIGLER

| | |
|---|---|
| Bowl | $ 15.50 |
| Celery | 18.25 |
| Cordial | 15.00 |
| Goblet | 11.75 |
| Mug | 18.25 |
| Plate, toddy | 11.50 |
| Salt | 6.75 |
| Tumbler, water | 15.25 |

## BIRD AND STRAWBERRY
### (Bluebird)

Bowl
| | |
|---|---|
| a. 5'' | $ 6.75 |
| b. Berry | 9.75 |

| | |
|---|---|
| Butter dish, covered | 15.50 |

| | |
|---|---|
| Cake stand, 9'' | 12.75 |
| Compote, covered, 6'' | 20.50 |
| Creamer | 11.00 |
| Cup, punch | 6.75 |
| Goblet | 9.00 |
| Pickle dish | 5.50 |
| Sauce, 5¼'' | 3.50 |
| Spooner | 6.50 |
| Sugar bowl, covered | 15.50 |
| Tumbler | 5.25 |
| Wine | 7.75 |

## BLACKBERRY
### (See Colored Glass Section)

## BLAZE

| | |
|---|---|
| Bowl, 7'', 8'' | $ 11.00 |
| Butter dish | 30.00 |
| Celery | 18.25 |
| Champagne | 15.50 |
| Cheese plate | 13.25 |

Compote
| | |
|---|---|
| a. Covered, 7'', 8'', low standard | 29.00 |
| b. Open, 8'', 9'', 10'', high standard | 22.00 |
| c. Open, 8'', 9'', low standard | 19.00 |

| | |
|---|---|
| Cordial | 10.00 |
| Creamer | 22.00 |
| Custard cup | 9.00 |
| Decanter | 22.00 |
| Dish, oval | 9.50 |
| Egg cup | 11.50 |
| Goblet | 13.25 |
| Lemonade glass | 12.00 |
| Pickle | 7.75 |

Plate
| | |
|---|---|
| a. 6'' | 11.50 |
| b. 7'' | 13.25 |

Sauce
| | |
|---|---|
| a. 4'' | 3.75 |
| b. 5'' | 5.00 |

| | |
|---|---|
| Shakers, pair | 13.25 |
| Spooner | 7.75 |
| Sugar bowl | 30.00 |
| Tumbler | 10.50 |
| Wine | 10.00 |

## BLEEDING HEART

Bowl
| | |
|---|---|
| a. Berry, covered, 7¼'', 8¼'' | $ 18.75 |
| b. Waste | 13.25 |

| | |
|---|---|
| Butter dish | 26.50 |
| Cake stand, 9½'' | 23.25 |
| Compote | |
| a. Covered, high standard | 36.00 |
| b. Covered, low standard | 30.75 |
| c. Covered, oval | 38.50 |
| Cordial | 16.00 |
| Creamer | 25.00 |
| Dish, oval | 12.25 |
| Egg cup | 15.75 |
| Goblet | |
| a. Plain stem | 10.00 |
| b. Knob stem | 13.25 |
| Mug | 16.00 |
| Pickle | |
| a. Oval | 12.75 |
| b. Relish dish, 4 sections | 30.00 |
| Pitcher | |
| a. Milk | 40.00 |
| b. Water | 44.50 |
| Plate | 38.50 |
| Platter, oval | 27.50 |
| Salt, oval | 15.50 |
| Sauce | 7.25 |
| Spooner | 9.50 |
| Sugar bowl | 27.50 |
| Tumbler | |
| a. Footed | 18.25 |
| b. Water | 15.25 |
| Wine | 17.75 |

## BLOCK AND FAN

| | |
|---|---|
| Bowl, berry | $ 14.50 |
| Butter dish | 16.50 |
| Cake stand | 12.75 |
| Celery | 9.75 |
| Compote | 16.50 |
| Cordial | 6.75 |
| Creamer | 13.75 |

| | |
|---|---|
| Cruet | |
| a. Large | 10.75 |
| b. Small | 8.75 |
| Goblet | 9.75 |
| Lamp | 10.00 |
| Marmalade jar | 9.75 |
| Pickle | 6.50 |
| Pitcher | 15.50 |
| Plate | 9.75 |
| Sauce | 4.00 |
| Shakers | 10.00 |
| Spooner | 7.25 |
| Sugar bowl | 16.50 |
| Tumbler | 7.25 |

## BLOCK AND PLEAT
### (Three Stories, Persian)

| | |
|---|---|
| Bowl | |
| a. Oval, 8'' | $ 5.50 |
| b. Oval, 9'' | 6.75 |
| c. Oval, 10'' | 7.50 |
| d. Fruit, round, 6'' | 5.00 |
| e. Fruit, round, 7'' | 6.00 |
| f. Fruit, round, 8'' | 6.50 |
| Butter dish, covered | 12.75 |
| Celery | 9.00 |
| Creamer | 8.25 |
| Goblet | 6.75 |
| Mug | 5.50 |
| Pickle, handled | 6.50 |
| Pitcher, water | 13.25 |
| Platter, bread, oval | 9.00 |
| Sauce | |
| a. Flat, 5'' | 3.00 |
| b. Footed, 4'' | 4.00 |
| Spooner | 6.25 |
| Sugar bowl, covered | 11.75 |
| Tumbler | 5.25 |

## BOW-TIE

| | |
|---|---|
| Bowl, open, 10'' | $ 13.25 |
| Butter dish | 22.00 |
| Cake stand | 17.75 |
| Compote, open, 10'', on standard | 26.50 |
| Goblet | 13.75 |
| Marmalade jar | 15.00 |
| Pitcher | 20.00 |

| | |
|---|---|
| Salt, individual, open | 4.50 |
| Sauce | 5.50 |
| Spooner | 8.25 |
| Sugar bowl, covered | 22.00 |
| Wine | 7.50 |

## BROKEN COLUMN

| | | |
|---|---|---|
| Banana stand | $ | 20.75 |
| Bowl | | |
| a. Berry, various sizes | | 8.25 |
| b. Covered, various sizes | | 12.75 |
| Butter dish | | 20.00 |
| Cake stand | | 20.50 |
| Celery | | 16.00 |
| Compote | | |
| a. Covered, high standard | | 27.00 |
| b. Open, high standard | | 20.50 |
| Cracker jar | | 16.50 |
| Creamer | | 16.00 |
| Cruet | | 11.50 |
| Cup and saucer | | 15.50 |
| Dish, oblong | | 10.00 |
| Finger bowl | | 9.00 |
| *Goblet | | 14.00 |
| Pickle | | 6.50 |
| Pitcher, ½ gallon | | 20.00 |
| Plate | | |
| a. 6'' | | 9.00 |
| b. 7'' (scarce) | | 20.50 |
| c. 8'' | | 12.25 |
| Sauce | | 4.50 |
| Shakers, pair | | 11.00 |
| Spooner | | 7.75 |
| Sugar bowl | | 20.50 |
| Syrup | | 13.75 |
| Tumbler | | 7.50 |
| Water bottle | | 16.00 |
| Wine | | 10.00 |

*Reproduced item

## BRYCE
### (Ribbon Candy)

| | | |
|---|---|---|
| Bowl | | |
| a. Berry, 8'' | $ | 7.75 |
| b. Covered, 5'', 6'' | | 12.25 |
| c. Covered, 7'', 8'' | | 13.75 |
| Butter dish | | 12.75 |
| Cake stand | | 12.25 |
| Celery | | 10.00 |
| Compote | | |
| a. Covered, high standard | | 19.00 |
| b. Covered, low standard | | 16.50 |
| c. Open, high standard | | 12.75 |
| Cordial | | 6.25 |
| Creamer | | 10.00 |
| Cruet | | 8.75 |
| Goblet | | 6.75 |
| Honey dish, covered | | 7.75 |
| Pickle | | 6.00 |
| Pitcher | | |
| a. Milk, quart | | 16.75 |
| b. Syrup | | 12.75 |
| c. Water, ½ gallon | | 16.00 |
| Plate | | |
| a. 6'', 7'', 8'' | | 7.75 |
| b. 9'', 10'' | | 15.50 |
| Spooner | | 7.25 |
| Sugar bowl | | 13.25 |
| Tumbler | | 5.50 |
| Wine | | 9.00 |

## BUCKLE

| | | |
|---|---|---|
| Butter dish | $ | 18.25 |
| Compote | | |
| a. Covered, high standard | | 26.00 |
| b. Covered, low standard | | 22.00 |

| | |
|---|---:|
| Cordial | 9.50 |
| Creamer | 20.00 |
| Dish, oval | 9.00 |
| Egg cup | 9.50 |
| Goblet | 7.75 |
| Pickle | 8.25 |
| Pitcher | 31.00 |
| Salt | |
| a. Footed | 6.00 |
| b. Oval | 5.00 |
| Sauce | 5.00 |
| Spooner | 7.75 |
| Sugar Bowl | 20.00 |
| Tumbler | 10.00 |
| Wine | 8.25 |

## BUCKLE WITH STAR

| | | |
|---|---|---:|
| Bowl, covered | $ | 11.00 |
| Butter dish | | 15.50 |
| Cake stand | | 13.75 |
| Celery | | 11.75 |
| Compote | | |
| a. Covered, large, high standard | | 23.25 |
| b. Covered, small, high standard | | 21.00 |
| c. Covered, low standard | | 22.00 |
| Creamer | | 12.75 |
| Dish | | |
| a. Oval, 7'', 8'' | | 11.75 |
| b. Oval, 9'', 10'' | | 13.25 |
| Goblet | | 9.00 |
| Marmalade jar | | 10.00 |
| Pickle | | 6.75 |
| Pitcher | | |
| a. Syrup | | 13.25 |
| b. Water | | 16.50 |
| Salt, footed | | 5.50 |
| Sauce | | |
| a. Flat, 4'' | | 3.75 |
| b. Footed | | 4.50 |
| Spooner | | 7.25 |
| Sugar bowl | | 16.50 |
| Tumbler | | 8.25 |
| Wine | | 7.75 |

## BUDDED IVY

| | | |
|---|---|---:|
| Butter dish | $ | 18.25 |
| Compote | | |
| a. Covered, high standard | | 24.75 |
| b. Covered, low standard | | 20.50 |

| | |
|---|---:|
| Creamer | 17.75 |
| Goblet | 8.25 |
| Pickle | 6.25 |
| Pitcher | |
| a. Syrup | 14.00 |
| b. Water | 17.75 |
| Salt, footed | 5.75 |
| Sauce, 4'' | 4.50 |
| Spooner | 8.25 |
| Sugar bowl | 18.50 |

## BULL'S EYE

| | | |
|---|---|---:|
| Butter dish | $ | 45.00 |
| Castor bottle | | 9.75 |
| Celery | | 35.50 |
| Champagne | | 27.50 |
| Cologne bottles, pair | | 30.00 |
| Compote | | |
| a. Open, large, high standard | | 44.00 |
| b. Open, low standard | | 39.00 |
| Cordial | | 12.25 |
| Creamer | | 50.00 |
| Cruet | | 20.00 |
| Decanter | | 27.00 |
| Egg cup | | 22.00 |
| Goblet | | 13.75 |
| Jar, covered | | 24.75 |
| Lamp | | 24.00 |
| Lemonade glass | | 18.25 |
| Pickle | | 11.75 |
| Salt | | |
| a. Flat | | 9.00 |
| b. Footed, oblong | | 12.75 |
| Spooner | | 10.00 |
| Sugar bowl | | 53.00 |
| Tumbler | | 26.50 |
| Water bottle | | 31.00 |
| Wine | | 13.25 |

## BULL'S EYE WITH DIAMOND POINT

| | |
|---|---|
| Banana stand _____$ | 50.00 |
| **Bowl** | |
|   a. Flat, 6'' _____ | 22.50 |
|   b. Flat, 7'' _____ | 28.50 |
|   c. Flat, 8'' _____ | 40.00 |
| Butter dish _____ | 48.00 |
| Candlesticks, pair _____ | 39.50 |
| Celery _____ | 50.00 |
| Champagne _____ | 40.00 |
| Cologne bottle _____ | 35.00 |
| **Compote** | |
|   a. High standard, 6'', 7'' _____ | 60.00 |
|   b. High standard, 8'', 9'' _____ | 65.00 |
|   c. Low standard, 6'', 7'' _____ | 45.00 |
|   d. Low standard, 8'', 9'' _____ | 50.00 |
| Cordial _____ | 34.50 |
| Creamer _____ | 85.00 |
| **Decanter** | |
|   a. Bar lip, pint _____ | 40.00 |
|   b. Bar lip, quart _____ | 45.00 |
|   c. With stopper, pint _____ | 48.00 |
|   d. With stopper, quart _____ | 50.00 |
| Egg cup _____ | 30.00 |
| Goblet _____ | 28.50 |
| Honey dish _____ | 14.00 |
| Lemonade glass _____ | 27.50 |
| Mustard jar, Britannia metal cover_ | 25.00 |
| Pitcher, tankard, 10¼'' _____ | 65.00 |
| Sauce _____ | 10.00 |
| Spooner _____ | 21.00 |
| Sugar bowl _____ | 48.00 |
| **Tumbler** | |
|   a. Water _____ | 30.00 |
|   b. Whiskey _____ | 35.00 |
| Water bottle _____ | 65.00 |
| Wine _____ | 16.50 |

| | |
|---|---|
| **Decanter** | |
|   a. Pint _____ | 37.50 |
|   b. Quart _____ | 45.00 |
| Goblet _____ | 27.50 |
| **Lamp** | |
|   a. All glass _____ | 28.50 |
|   b. Marble base _____ | 40.00 |
| Pitcher (scarce) _____ | 95.00 |
| Plate, 10'' _____ | 25.00 |
| Salt, footed _____ | 15.00 |
| Sugar bowl _____ | 45.00 |

## BUTTON BAND

| | |
|---|---|
| Bowl _____$ | 6.50 |
| Butter dish _____ | 11.00 |
| Cake stand _____" | 10.50 |
| Compote, open, small _____ | 13.75 |
| Creamer _____ | 9.50 |
| Goblet _____ | 7.25 |
| Pitcher, water _____ | 13.25 |
| Sugar bowl _____ | 12.75 |
| Tumbler _____ | 5.00 |
| Wine _____ | 5.25 |

## BULL'S EYE WITH FLEUR-DE-LIS

| | |
|---|---|
| Bowl, fruit, flat _____$ | 36.50 |
| Butter dish _____ | 44.50 |
| Celery _____ | 50.00 |
| **Compote** | |
|   a. Open, high standard _____ | 52.50 |
|   b. Open, low standard _____ | 44.50 |
| Cordial _____ | 21.00 |
| Creamer _____ | 60.00 |

## CABBAGE LEAF (CLEAR)

| | |
|---|---|
| Bowl _____$ | 20.00 |
| Butter dish _____ | 26.50 |
| Celery _____ | 33.00 |
| Cheese dish _____ | 27.50 |
| Compote, covered, high standard__ | 34.25 |
| Creamer _____ | 20.50 |
| Pickle dish, leaf-shape _____ | 10.50 |
| Plate, rabbit head in center _____ | 19.00 |

| | |
|---|---|
| Sauce, 3½'' | 5.00 |
| Spooner | 9.00 |
| Sugar bowl | 27.50 |

## CABBAGE LEAF (FROSTED)

| | |
|---|---|
| Bowl, covered | $ 36.00 |
| *Butter dish | 34.25 |
| *Celery | 29.25 |
| Cheese dish | 38.75 |
| Compote, covered, high standard | 56.00 |
| *Creamer | 34.00 |
| Pickle dish, leaf-shape | 16.50 |
| Plate, rabbit head in center | 29.25 |
| Sauce, 3½'' | 7.50 |
| Spooner | 12.25 |
| *Sugar bowl | 36.00 |

NOTE: Goblet is of recent origin and is not listed.

*Reproduced item

## CABBAGE ROSE

| | |
|---|---|
| Bowl, berry, oval | $ 15.50 |
| Butter dish | 26.50 |
| Cake stand, 11'' | 22.00 |
| Celery | 25.75 |
| Compote | |
|   a. Covered, 6'', 7'' | 35.50 |
|   b. Covered, 8'', 9'' | 37.50 |
| Cordial | 12.75 |
| Creamer | 20.00 |
| Egg cup | 11.00 |
| *Goblet | 13.50 |
| Pickle | 8.25 |
| Pitcher | |
|   a. Quart | 38.50 |
|   b. 3 pints (scarce) | 67.50 |
| Plate | |
|   a. 8½'' (scarce) | 41.00 |
|   b. 10½'' (rare) | 84.00 |

| | |
|---|---|
| Salt, footed | 10.50 |
| Sauce | 6.75 |
| Spooner | 9.00 |
| Sugar bowl | 26.75 |
| Tumbler | 15.00 |
| Wine (scarce) | 21.00 |

*Reproduced Item

## CABLE

| | |
|---|---|
| Butter dish | $ 39.50 |
| Celery | 33.00 |
| Compote | |
|   a. High standard | 38.50 |
|   b. Low standard | 33.00 |
|   c. Open, extra large | 30.50 |
| Cordial | 24.75 |
| Creamer | 50.00 |
| Decanter | |
|   a. Pint | 38.50 |
|   b. Quart | 63.75 |
| Egg cup | 16.00 |
| Goblet | 23.75 |
| Honey dish | 7.50 |
| Lamp | |
|   a. All glass | 31.25 |
|   b. Hand lamp | 27.50 |
|   c. Marble base | 35.75 |
| Mug | 31.25 |
| Pitcher | 112.00 |
| Plate, 6'' | 31.00 |
| Salt | |
|   a. Celery dip | 6.50 |
|   b. Footed | 15.50 |
| Sauce | 7.25 |
| Spooner | 13.75 |
| Sugar bowl | 44.50 |
| Tumbler | 35.75 |
| Wine | 25.00 |

## CABLE WITH RING

| | |
|---|---|
| Butter dish _____ $ | 41.00 |
| Compote, open, 8¼'' _____ | 33.00 |
| Creamer _____ | 46.50 |
| Honey dish _____ | 7.25 |
| Sauce _____ | 6.75 |
| Sugar bowl _____ | 39.50 |

## CAMEO
### (Classic Medallion)

| | |
|---|---|
| Butter dish _____ $ | 22.00 |
| Compote, open, low standard ____ | 20.00 |
| Creamer _____ | 13.25 |
| Mug _____ | 9.00 |
| Sugar bowl _____ | 23.25 |

## CANADIAN

| | |
|---|---|
| Butter dish, covered _____ $ | 21.75 |
| Celery _____ | 15.50 |
| Compote | |
| a. Covered, 6'' _____ | 19.00 |
| b. Covered, 7'', 8'' _____ | 22.00 |
| c. Open, high standard _____ | 18.25 |
| d. Open, low standard _____ | 18.00 |
| Cordial _____ | 9.50 |
| Creamer _____ | 16.00 |
| Goblet _____ | 10.75 |
| Marmalade jar _____ | 12.25 |
| Pitcher | |
| a. Large _____ | 30.25 |
| b. Small _____ | 25.75 |
| Plate | |
| a. 6'' _____ | 14.00 |
| b. 8'' _____ | 16.00 |
| c. 10'' _____ | 19.75 |
| Sauce | |
| a. Flat, 4'' _____ | 5.00 |
| b. Footed, 4'' _____ | 6.50 |
| Spooner _____ | 10.00 |

| | |
|---|---|
| Sugar bowl _____ | 22.00 |
| Wine _____ | 8.50 |

## CANDLEWICK

| | |
|---|---|
| Butter dish _____ $ | 16.25 |
| Compote, 7'', covered _____ | 20.00 |
| Creamer _____ | 13.25 |
| Cup and saucer _____ | 11.75 |
| Goblet _____ | 11.00 |
| Pitcher, water _____ | 16.50 |
| Plate, 7½ x 8¾'' _____ | 10.50 |
| Sauce _____ | 4.25 |
| Spooner _____ | 7.25 |
| Sugar bowl _____ | 17.75 |
| Wine _____ | 7.50 |

## CANE
### (See Colored Glass Section)

## CANE AND ROSETTE
### (Flower Panelled Cane)

| | |
|---|---|
| Bowl _____ $ | 9.00 |
| Butter dish _____ | 15.50 |
| Cake stand _____ | 13.75 |
| Compote | |
| a. Covered, 8'', high standard __ | 20.75 |
| b. Open, 9'', high standard ____ | 17.75 |
| Cordial _____ | 6.75 |
| Creamer _____ | 13.25 |
| Egg cup _____ | 7.75 |
| Goblet _____ | 7.50 |
| Pitcher, water _____ | 18.25 |
| Sauce _____ | 3.75 |
| Spooner _____ | 7.25 |
| Sugar bowl _____ | 16.50 |
| Tumbler _____ | 6.75 |
| Wine _____ | 5.00 |

This pattern is occasionally found
in cobalt blue.

## CANNON BALL

**Bowl**
| | |
|---|---|
| a. Berry, large _____ $ | 11.00 |
| b. Berry, small _____ | 8.50 |
| Butter dish _____ | 16.50 |
| Cake stand _____ | 13.75 |

**Celery**
| | |
|---|---|
| a. Flat base _____ | 13.75 |
| b. Footed _____ | 18.25 |
| Cordial _____ | 7.25 |
| Creamer _____ | 15.25 |
| Goblet _____ | 10.75 |
| Pitcher _____ | 19.00 |

**Salt**
| | |
|---|---|
| a. Large _____ | 5.00 |
| b. Small _____ | 3.75 |
| Sauce _____ | 4.50 |
| Spooner _____ | 7.50 |
| Sugar bowl _____ | 18.25 |
| Toothpick holder _____ | 5.50 |
| Tumbler _____ | 8.75 |
| Wine _____ | 11.00 |

## CAPE COD

| | |
|---|---|
| Bowl, 6'', small handle _____ $ | 9.50 |
| Butter dish _____ | 20.75 |
| Celery _____ | 13.75 |

**Compote**
| | |
|---|---|
| a. Covered, 6'' _____ | 22.00 |
| b. Covered, 7'', 8'' _____ | 27.50 |
| c. Open, high standard _____ | 20.75 |
| d. Open, low standard _____ | 18.25 |
| Cordial _____ | 10.00 |
| Creamer _____ | 14.00 |
| Cup and saucer _____ | 16.00 |
| Goblet _____ | 10.50 |
| Marmalade jar _____ | 17.75 |

**Pitcher**
| | |
|---|---|
| a. Large _____ | 20.00 |
| b. Small _____ | 21.50 |

**Plate**
| | |
|---|---|
| a. Small, closed handles _____ | 11.00 |
| b. 6'' _____ | 13.25 |
| c. 8'' _____ | 15.50 |
| d. 10'' _____ | 18.25 |

**Sauce**
| | |
|---|---|
| a. Flat, 4'' _____ | 5.00 |
| b. Footed, 4'' _____ | 6.50 |
| Spooner _____ | 7.75 |
| Sugar bowl _____ | 21.00 |
| Wine _____ | 10.00 |

## CARAMEL SLAG
(See Colored Glass Section)

## CARDINAL BIRD

| | |
|---|---|
| Butter dish _____ $ | 20.75 |
| Cake stand _____ | 16.50 |
| Compote, covered _____ | 23.25 |
| Creamer _____ | 13.25 |
| Goblet _____ | 12.75 |
| Pitcher _____ | 27.50 |
| Plate, 10'', frosted, with girl and bird (scarce) _____ | 32.00 |

**Sauce**
| | |
|---|---|
| a. Flat, round _____ | 5.00 |
| b. Footed, 4'' _____ | 5.75 |
| c. Footed, 5½'' _____ | 6.75 |
| Spooner _____ | 7.25 |
| Sugar bowl _____ | 20.75 |

## CATHEDRAL
(See Colored Glass Section)

## CHAIN

| | |
|---|---|
| Butter dish _____ $ | 13.75 |
| Cake stand _____ | 11.75 |
| Compote, covered _____ | 18.25 |

| | |
|---|---|
| Cordial | 6.75 |
| Creamer | 11.75 |
| Dish, oval | 7.75 |
| Goblet | 7.50 |
| Pickle | 6.75 |
| Pitcher, water | 15.50 |
| Plate | |
| a. 7" | 7.75 |
| b. Bread | 10.50 |
| Platter | 12.25 |
| Sauce | |
| a. Flat | 3.25 |
| b. Footed | 4.50 |
| Shakers, pair | 10.00 |
| Spooner | 7.50 |
| Sugar bowl | 14.50 |
| Wine | 7.25 |

## CHAIN WITH STAR

| | |
|---|---|
| Butter dish | $ 13.75 |
| Cake stand | 13.00 |
| Compote | |
| a. Covered, high standard | 19.00 |
| b. Covered, low standard | 16.00 |
| Cordial | 7.50 |
| Creamer | 11.00 |
| Dish, oval | 7.75 |
| Goblet | 7.25 |
| Pickle | 5.50 |
| Pitcher | 15.50 |
| Plate | |
| a. 7" | 8.25 |
| b. 10" | 10.75 |
| Platter | 11.50 |
| Sauce | |
| a. Flat | 3.25 |
| b. Footed | 4.50 |
| Shakers, pair | 9.00 |
| Spooner | 7.50 |
| Sugar bowl | 15.25 |
| Wine | 6.50 |

## CHECKERBOARD

| | |
|---|---|
| Bowl | |
| a. Small | $ 5.00 |
| b. Large | 9.00 |
| Butter dish, covered | 11.50 |
| Celery tray | 6.75 |
| Celery vase | 9.75 |
| Cheese dish | 6.75 |
| Creamer | 9.75 |
| Cruet | 10.50 |
| Goblet | 7.75 |

| | |
|---|---|
| *Honey dish, square, footed, covered | 8.00 |
| Pickle | 5.50 |
| Pitcher | |
| a. Milk | 13.25 |
| b. Water | 15.50 |
| Plate, 10" | 7.75 |
| Sauce | 3.75 |
| Shakers, pair | 9.50 |
| Sherbet | 5.25 |
| Spooner | 6.50 |
| Sugar bowl, covered | 13.25 |
| Tumbler | |
| a. Iced tea | 4.00 |
| b. Water | 3.50 |
| Wine | 4.25 |

*Reproduced in clear and milk glass

## CHERRY

| | |
|---|---|
| Butter dish | $ 13.75 |
| Compote | |
| a. Covered, high standard | 22.00 |
| b. Open, high standard | 16.00 |
| c. Open, low standard | 13.75 |
| Creamer | 16.00 |
| *Goblet | 11.00 |
| Sauce | 4.00 |
| Spooner | 7.50 |
| Sugar bowl | 15.50 |
| Wine | 6.25 |

*Reproduced Item

## CLASSIC

| | |
|---|---|
| Bowl, footed | $ 24.00 |
| Butter dish | 53.00 |
| Celery | 34.00 |

Compote
a. Covered _____ 41.50
b. On standard, 6'' _____ 33.50
Creamer _____ 39.25
Goblet _____ 41.50
Jar, sweetmeat _____ 31.75
Pitcher
a. Large _____ 62.75
b. Small _____ 50.75
Plate
a. Cleveland, President _____ 41.25
b. Jas. G. Blaine _____ 41.25
c. John A. Logan _____ 45.00
d. Thos. H. Hendricks _____ 39.50
e. Warrior _____ 47.50
Sauce
a. Collared base, 4¼'' _____ 11.75
b. On foot _____ 14.00
Spooner _____ 23.25
Sugar bowl _____ 51.50

## CLEAR DIAGONAL BAND

Butter dish _____ $ 13.25
Celery _____ 10.00
Compote
a. Covered, high standard _____ 20.50
b. Covered, low standard _____ 16.50
Cordial _____ 5.75
Creamer _____ 12.25
Goblet _____ 7.50
Marmalade jar _____ 11.75
Pitcher, water _____ 13.75
Plate _____ 9.50
Platter _____ 11.00
Sauce _____ 4.50
Shakers, pair _____ 8.25
Spooner _____ 6.75
Sugar bowl _____ 14.00

## CLEAR RIBBON

Butter dish _____ $ 15.50
Cake stand _____ 14.00
Celery _____ 11.50
Compote, covered, large _____ 20.00
Creamer _____ 11.00
Dish, covered, oblong, 6'', 7'', 8''_ 10.00
Goblet _____ 9.75
Pickle _____ 6.00
Pitcher _____ 16.50
Platter, oblong _____ 10.00
Sauce _____ 4.00
Spooner _____ 6.75
Sugar bowl _____ 15.50

## CLEMATIS

Butter dish _____ $ 16.00
Creamer _____ 11.50
Goblet _____ 8.50
Lamp, 12'', iron base _____ 10.50
Pickle _____ 5.00
Pitcher _____ 19.25
Sauce _____ 4.25
Spooner _____ 6.75
Sugar bowl _____ 15.75

## COIN (COLUMBIAN)
### (Spanish Coin)

Bowl
a. Berry _____ $ 58.00
b. Finger _____ 35.50
Butter dish _____ 72.50
Cake stand _____ 58.00
Compote
a. Covered, 6'', 7'', 8'' _____ 105.00
b. Open, 7'', 8'', 10'' _____ 82.00
Creamer _____ 55.00
Cruet _____ 62.00

| | |
|---|---|
| Goblet | 47.50 |
| Lamp | 62.00 |
| Pickle | 23.00 |
| Pitcher | 84.00 |
| Sauce | 17.00 |
| Shakers, pair | 54.00 |
| Spooner | 30.50 |
| Sugar bowl | 72.50 |
| Syrup (scarce) | 83.50 |
| Toothpick | 30.75 |
| Tray, water | 52.50 |
| Tumbler | 43.50 |

## COIN (U. S.)

**Bowl**
| | |
|---|---|
| a. Berry, dollar | $ 175.00 |
| b. Berry, half dollar | 150.00 |
| c. Berry, quarters | 140.00 |
| d. Waste, quarters | 95.00 |

**Bread tray**
| | |
|---|---|
| a. Dollar | 175.00 |
| b. Half dollar | 160.00 |

**Butter dish**
| | |
|---|---|
| a. Dollar | 350.00 |
| b. Half dollar | 325.00 |

**Cake stand**
| | |
|---|---|
| a. Dollar | 300.00 |
| b. Half dollar | 275.00 |
| Celery, half dollar | 195.00 |
| Champagne, half dime | 125.00 |
| Claret, half dime | 90.00 |

**Compote**
| | |
|---|---|
| a. High standard, covered | |
|    1. Dollar | 400.00 |
|    2. Half dollar | 350.00 |
|    3. Quarters | 315.00 |
| b. Low standard, covered | |
|    1. Quarters | 225.00 |

| | |
|---|---|
|    2. Twenty cent pieces | 275.00 |
| c. Open | |
|    1. Dollar | 195.00 |
|    2. Half dollar | 180.00 |
|    3. Quarters | 175.00 |
| Creamer, quarters | 210.00 |
| Cruet, quarters. Stopper, dimes | 200.00 |

**Epergne**
| | |
|---|---|
| a. Dollar | 300.00 |
| b. Quarters | 275.00 |

**Goblet**
| | |
|---|---|
| a. Dollar | 225.00 |
| b. Dime | 195.00 |

**Lamp**
| | |
|---|---|
| a. Square bowl, on standard | |
|    1. Dollar | 185.00 |
|    2. Half dollar | 165.00 |
| b. Round bowl, panelled, on standard | |
|    1. Dollar | 175.00 |
|    2. Half dollar | 155.00 |
|    3. Quarter | 135.00 |
| c. Handled, round bowl, panelled, twenty cent pieces | 180.00 |
| d. Flaring bowl, on standard, plain coins | 175.00 |
| Mug, dollar | 125.00 |

**Pickle dish**
| | |
|---|---|
| a. Half dollar | 120.00 |
| b. Quarters | 100.00 |

**Pitcher**
| | |
|---|---|
| a. Milk, half dollar | 300.00 |
| b. Water, dollar | 350.00 |

**Preserve dish**
| | |
|---|---|
| a. Dollar | 135.00 |
| b. Half dollar | 120.00 |
| Salt and pepper shakers, pair, quarters | 195.00 |

**Sauce**
| | |
|---|---|
| a. Flat, quarters | 75.00 |
| b. Footed, quarters | 95.00 |
| Spooner, quarters | 120.00 |

**Sugar bowl**
| | |
|---|---|
| a. Covered, half dollar | 325.00 |
| b. Covered, quarters | 300.00 |
| Syrup jug, quarters | 295.00 |
| *Toothpick holder, dollar | 85.00 |
| Tray, water, dollar | 195.00 |

**Tumbler**
| | |
|---|---|
| a. Dollar on base (scarce) | 125.00 |
| b. Dimes | 115.00 |
| Wine, half dimes (scarce) | 190.00 |

*Reproduced Item

### COLORADO
(See Colored Glass Section)

### COLUMBIA

| | |
|---|---|
| Bowl, 7'', 8'' | $ 6.75 |
| Butter dish, covered | 9.75 |
| Celery tray | 7.25 |
| Creamer | 8.25 |
| Cruet | 7.75 |
| Pickle jar, open | 5.50 |

Pitcher, water _____ 10.75
Plate
  a. Bread _____ 7.25
  b. 8'' _____ 6.75
Relish dish _____ 5.00
Salts, round and square, pair ____ 6.75
Sauce, 4½'' _____ 3.50
Spooner _____ 6.00
Sugar bowl, covered _____ 9.75
Syrup jug _____ 7.75
Toothpick _____ 3.25
Tumbler _____ 4.00
Vase _____ 5.00

## COMET

Butter dish
  a. Plain knob, Covered _____$ 55.00
  b. Washington knob, covered __ 110.00
Creamer _____ 60.00
Goblet _____ 27.50
Mug _____ 45.00
Pitcher _____ 155.00
Spooner _____ 27.50
Tumbler
  a. Water _____ 27.50
  b. Whiskey _____ 31.00

## CONNECTICUT

Bowl
  a. Round, 8'' _____$ 6.75
  b. Round, 4'', 6'' _____ 6.00
Butter dish _____ 9.50
Cake stand, 10'' _____ 9.75
Celery tray _____ 5.50
Creamer _____ 9.00
Pickle _____ 5.50
Pitcher
  a. ½ gallon, tankard _____ 12.25
  b. 1 quart, tankard _____ 11.00
  c. 1 pint, tankard _____ 10.00
Shakers, pair _____ 7.25
Tumbler
  a. Handled _____ 5.25
  b. Plain _____ 4.00

## CORD AND TASSEL

Butter dish _____$ 14.00
Cake stand, 8½'' _____ 15.00
Celery _____ 10.75
Compote
  a. Covered, high standard _____ 18.25
  b. Covered, low standard _____ 16.00
Cordial _____ 7.50
Creamer _____ 10.75
Dish, oval _____ 7.25
Egg cup _____ 8.25
Goblet _____ 8.50
Lamp _____ 13.75
Pitcher
  a. Syrup _____ 13.25
  b. Water _____ 19.00
Sauce _____ 3.75
Spooner _____ 7.25
Sugar bowl _____ 15.00
Wine _____ 5.75

## CORDOVA

Bowl
  a. Covered _____$ 7.75
  b. Finger _____ 6.00
  c. Open _____ 6.50
Butter dish _____ 10.75
Cake stand _____ 10.00
Celery _____ 8.25
Compote
  a. Covered, high standard _____ 12.75
  b. Open, high standard _____ 11.00
Creamer _____ 8.25
Cruet _____ 7.75

Pitcher
  a. Syrup ----------------------- 9.50
  b. Water ----------------------- 13.25
Sauce ----------------------------- 3.00
Spooner --------------------------- 6.00
Sugar bowl ------------------------ 11.75
Toothpick ------------------------- 3.75
Tumbler --------------------------- 5.25

## COSMOS
### (See General Section)

## COTTAGE
### (Dinner Bell)

Bowl, berry ----------------------$ 6.75
Butter dish ----------------------- 12.75
Cake stand ------------------------ 10.00
Celery ---------------------------- 9.00
Compote
  a. Covered, low standard ------ 16.00
  b. Open, low standard -------- 10.50
  c. Open, high standard -------- 11.00
Creamer --------------------------- 9.00
Cruet ----------------------------- 7.75
Cup and saucer -------------------- 9.50
Dish, oval, deep ------------------ 5.50
Fruit bowl, high standard -------- 14.00
Goblet ---------------------------- 6.50
Pickle ---------------------------- 5.00
Pitcher
  a. Pint ------------------------ 10.00
  b. Quart ----------------------- 12.25
  c. ½ gallon -------------------- 13.25
  d. Syrup ----------------------- 9.00
Plate
  a. 6'', 7'' -------------------- 7.25
  b. 8'', 9'' -------------------- 9.00
Shakers, pair --------------------- 7.75
Spooner --------------------------- 6.00
Sugar bowl ------------------------ 12.75
Tray, water ----------------------- 9.50
Tumbler --------------------------- 4.50
Wine ------------------------------ 5.25

(Also found in dark green)

## CROESUS
### (See Colored Glass Section)

## CROW'S FOOT
### (Yale)

Butter dish ----------------------$ 13.75
Cake stand ------------------------ 11.75
Celery ---------------------------- 10.75
Compote --------------------------- 16.50
Cordial --------------------------- 6.75
Creamer --------------------------- 9.00
Goblet ---------------------------- 6.75
Pitcher
  a. Syrup ----------------------- 9.75
  b. Water ----------------------- 16.00
Plate ----------------------------- 9.50
Sauce ----------------------------- 3.75
Shakers, pair --------------------- 9.00
Spooner --------------------------- 6.75
Sugar bowl ------------------------ 13.75
Tumbler --------------------------- 5.25

## CRYSTAL

Ale glass ------------------------$ 11.50
Bowl
  a. 8'' ------------------------- 20.00
  b. 10'' ------------------------ 26.00
Butter dish ----------------------- 18.25
Celery ---------------------------- 15.50
Champagne ------------------------- 12.75
Compote
  a. Covered, 8'', footed -------- 22.00
  b. Covered, 6'', high standard -- 25.50
  c. Open, high standard -------- 16.50
Cordial --------------------------- 10.75
Creamer --------------------------- 20.50
Decanter, quart ------------------- 15.50
Egg cup --------------------------- 9.00

| | |
|---|---|
| Goblet | 7.50 |
| Pitcher | 24.75 |
| Sauce | 3.50 |
| Spooner | 7.50 |
| Sugar bowl | 20.00 |
| Tumbler | |
| a. Bar | 9.50 |
| b. ½ pint | 10.50 |
| c. Gill | 11.75 |
| d. Footed | 13.00 |
| Wine | 10.50 |

## CRYSTAL WEDDING

| | |
|---|---|
| Banana dish | $ 26.50 |
| Bowl, berry | 13.25 |
| Butter dish | 22.00 |
| Cake stand | 20.00 |
| Celery | 15.50 |
| *Compote | |
| a. Open, low standard | 15.00 |
| b. Covered, high standard | 31.00 |
| c. Covered, low standard | 24.75 |
| Creamer | 16.50 |
| *Goblet | 13.25 |
| Lamp | 18.25 |
| Pitcher | 25.75 |
| Sauce | 5.00 |
| Shakers, pair | 11.00 |
| Spooner | 9.75 |
| Sugar bowl | 23.75 |
| Tumbler | 8.25 |

*Reproduced Item

## CUBE WITH FAN

| | |
|---|---|
| Bottle, water | $ 12.75 |
| Bowl | |
| a. Finger | 6.75 |
| b. Rose | 8.25 |

| | |
|---|---|
| Celery | 10.00 |
| Dish, jelly | 6.00 |
| Goblet | 5.50 |
| Jar, covered | 7.25 |
| Plate , | |
| a. 5'' | 6.00 |
| b. 7¾'' | 7.75 |
| Salt dip | 2.00 |
| Sugar bowl, covered | 12.75 |
| Tumbler | 5.00 |

## CUPID AND VENUS
### (Guardian Angel)

| | |
|---|---|
| Bowl, covered, 8¾'', footed | $ 16.00 |
| Butter dish | 20.00 |
| Cake plate, 11'' | 15.50 |
| Celery | 15.00 |
| Champagne | 16.50 |
| Compote | |
| a. Covered, high standard | 25.00 |
| b. Covered, low standard | 20.50 |
| c. Open, high standard | 18.25 |
| Cordial | 13.25 |
| Creamer | 17.75 |
| Cruet, vinegar | 18.00 |
| Dish | |
| a. Oval, large | 9.00 |
| b. Oval, small | 7.75 |
| Goblet | 15.50 |
| Marmalade jar | 13.25 |
| Mug | |
| a. 2'' | 7.25 |
| b. 2½'' | 8.25 |
| c. 3½'' | 10.75 |
| Pickle | 7.75 |
| Pitcher | |
| a. Large | 18.50 |
| b. Small | 15.50 |
| Plate, bread | 16.00 |
| Sauce | |
| a. Flat, round | 4.25 |
| b. Footed | 5.75 |
| Spooner | 7.25 |
| Sugar bowl | 20.50 |
| Wine (scarce) | 22.00 |

## CURRANT

| | |
|---|---|
| Butter dish | $ 21.75 |
| Cake stand | 18.25 |
| Celery | 16.25 |

**Compote**
 a. Covered, 8'', high standard __ 25.00
 b. Covered, 8'', low standard ___ 18.25
 c. Covered, 9'', low standard ___ 20.00
**Cordial** _____ 12.75
**Creamer** _____ 18.25
**Dish**
 a. Oval, 5 x 7'' _____ 7.50
 b. Oval, 6 x 9'' _____ 9.50
**Egg cup** _____ 10.00
**Goblet** _____ 12.25
**Pickle** _____ 6.75
**Pitcher** _____ 23.25
**Sauce**
 a. Flat _____ 4.50
 b. Footed _____ 5.50
**Spooner** _____ 7.50
**Sugar bowl** _____ 22.00
**Tumbler, footed** _____ 10.00
**Wine** _____ 11.00

### CURRIER AND IVES

**Butter dish** _____$ 20.00
**Cordial** _____ 7.75
**Creamer** _____ 13.25
**Cup and saucer** _____ 15.50
**Decanter** _____ 13.25
**Dish, boat shaped, 5½ x 9½''** ____ 12.25
**Goblet** _____ 9.00
**Lamp** _____ 11.00
**Pitcher**
 a. Large _____ 16.50
 b. Small _____ 14.50
**Plate, 10'', dog and rabbit** _____ 12.75
**Sauce** _____ 4.25

**Shakers, pair** _____ 10.50
**Spooner** _____ 7.25
**Sugar bowl** _____ 20.00
**Tray, water** _____ 16.00
**Wine** _____ 7.50

### CURTAIN

**Bowl, waste** _____$ 9.00
**Butter dish** _____ 16.50
**Cake stand** _____ 14.00
**Celery** _____ 11.00
**Compote**
 a. Covered, high standard, small_ 23.25
 b. Covered, high standard, large_ 28.75
 c. Covered, collared base _____ 20.50
**Creamer** _____ 12.25
**Dish, celery boat** _____ 10.50
**Goblet** _____ 12.75
**Mug, large** _____ 8.25
**Pickle** _____ 7.25
**Pitcher**
 a. Quart_____ 20.50
 b. ½ gallon _____ 24.75
**Plate**
 a. Square, 7'' _____ 11.75
 b. Square, bread, large _____ 12.25
**Sauce, 5'', footed** _____ 5.25
**Shakers, pair** _____ 11.00
**Spooner** _____ 8.00
**Sugar bowl** _____ 17.50
**Tray, round** _____ 16.00
**Tumbler** _____ 9.50

### CUT LOG

**Butter dish** _____$ 15.00
**Cake stand** _____ 11.50
**Celery** _____ 10.75
**Compote**
 a. Covered _____ 20.00
 *b. Covered, 6'' _____ 16.50
 c. Open _____ 12.75

Creamer
a. 3" ---------------------------- 9.50
b. 5" ---------------------------- 11.00
Cruet
a. 5½" --------------------------- 9.50
b. 6½" --------------------------- 10.75
Dish, covered, handled ---------- 8.50
Goblet -------------------------- 9.00
Honey dish ---------------------- 11.00
Mug ----------------------------- 7.75
Mustard jar --------------------- 7.25
Olive dish, round, handled ----- 5.25
Pickle -------------------------- 6.75
Pitcher, water ------------------ 20.00
Sauce --------------------------- 3.75
Shakers, pair ------------------- 8.25
Spooner ------------------------- 6.75
Sugar bowl, covered ------------ 16.50
Tumbler ------------------------- 5.25
Wine ---------------------------- 6.50

*Reproduced Item

## DAHLIA

Butter dish ---------------------$ 22.00
Cake stand ---------------------- 16.00
Compote, covered, high standard -- 26.50
Cordial ------------------------- 15.50
Creamer ------------------------- 13.25
Egg cup ------------------------- 11.00
Goblet (scarce) ----------------- 16.50
Mug
a. Large ----------------------- 11.75
b. Small ----------------------- 9.00
Pickle -------------------------- 7.25
Pitcher
a. Milk ------------------------ 20.50
b. Water (common) -------------- 13.75
Plate
a. 7" -------------------------- 15.50
b. 9", cake, closed handles ---- 16.50
Platter, oval, grape handles ----- 20.00
Sauce --------------------------- 5.00
Spooner ------------------------- 7.75
Sugar bowl ---------------------- 22.00
Wine ---------------------------- 16.50

### DAISY AND BUTTON
(See Colored Glass Section)

### DAISY AND BUTTON WITH CROSS BARS
(See Colored Glass Section)

## DAISY AND BUTTON WITH NARCISSUS
(Daisy and Button with Clear Lily)
(Often found "flashed" with gold)

Bowl, round ---------------------$ 6.75
Butter dish --------------------- 13.25
Celery -------------------------- 9.50
Compote, open ------------------- 13.25
Creamer ------------------------- 8.25
Goblet -------------------------- 6.75
Pickle -------------------------- 5.25
Pitcher, water ------------------ 12.75
Sauce, 4" ----------------------- 4.00
Shakers, pair ------------------- 7.75
Spooner ------------------------- 6.75
Sugar bowl ---------------------- 13.75
Tumbler ------------------------- 5.00
*Wine --------------------------- 5.50

*Reproduced Item

### DAISY AND BUTTON WITH V ORNAMENT
(See Colored Glass Section)

## DAKOTA
(Baby Thumbprint, Thumbprint Band)

Bowl, berry ---------------------$ 13.25
Butter dish, covered ------------ 22.00
Cake stand, 10½" ---------------- 18.25
Celery -------------------------- 20.50
Compote
a. Covered, 5", 6" ------------- 23.00
b. Covered, 7", 8" ------------- 22.00
c. Covered, 9", 10" ------------ 25.00
d. Covered, 12" ---------------- 27.50
Creamer ------------------------- 13.75
Dish, oblong -------------------- 10.75
Goblet -------------------------- 13.25
Mug ----------------------------- 9.00
Pitcher, water ------------------ 25.00

| | |
|---|---|
| Plate, round | 11.00 |
| Sauce | |
|   a. Flat | 6.50 |
|   b. Footed | 7.25 |
| Shakers, pair | 13.25 |
| Spooner | 10.00 |
| Sugar bowl | 23.75 |
| Tumbler | 9.50 |
| Wine | 11.75 |

## DEER AND DOG

| | |
|---|---|
| Butter dish | $ 30.25 |
| Celery | 27.00 |
| Compote | |
|   a. Covered | 50.00 |
|   b. Open | 31.00 |
| Creamer | 31.00 |
| Goblet | 26.75 |
| Pitcher, water | 33.00 |
| Sauce | 10.00 |
| Spooner | 13.25 |
| Sugar bowl, covered | 32.75 |

## DEER AND PINE TREE

| | |
|---|---|
| Bowl, waste | $ 11.00 |
| Butter dish | 26.50 |
| Cake stand | 26.75 |
| Celery | 20.00 |
| Compote | |
|   a. Covered, oblong, large | 38.50 |
|   b. Covered, various sizes | 27.50 |
|   c. Open, large, high standard | 22.00 |

| | |
|---|---|
| Creamer | 20.00 |
| Dish | 11.00 |
| Goblet | 17.75 |
| Marmalade jar | 20.00 |
| Mug | |
|   a. Large | 13.75 |
|   b. Small | 11.00 |
| Pickle | 10.75 |
| Pitcher | |
|   a. Large | 27.50 |
|   b. Small | 22.00 |
| Platter | |
|   a. 8x13", clear | 18.25 |
|   b. 8x13", blue | 27.00 |
|   c. 9x15", clear (scarce) | 31.00 |
| Salt, oblong, footed | 7.75 |
| Sauce | |
|   a. Flat | 6.00 |
|   b. Footed, two sides | 8.50 |
| Spooner | 9.75 |
| Sugar bowl | 30.00 |
| Tray, water | 32.00 |

## DELAWARE
(See Colored Glass Section)

## DEW AND RAINDROP

| | |
|---|---|
| Bowl, berry | $ 10.00 |
| Butter dish | 20.00 |
| Cordial | 7.75 |
| Creamer | 13.25 |
| Cup, sherbet | 7.50 |
| *Goblet | 13.25 |
| Pitcher | 18.50 |
| Sauce | 5.25 |
| Shakers, pair | 12.25 |
| Spooner | 7.50 |
| Sugar bowl | 20.50 |
| Tumbler | 10.75 |
| *Wine | 7.50 |

*Reproduced Item

## DEWDROP

| | |
|---|---|
| Bowl | $ 8.25 |
| Butter dish | 15.50 |
| Compote, covered, 9¼", high standard | 26.50 |
| Creamer | 13.25 |
| Goblet | 7.25 |
| Pickle, double | 11.75 |

| Pitcher | 19.00 |
|---|---|
| Salt | 4.50 |
| Sauce | 4.50 |
| Sugar bowl | 16.00 |

## DEWDROP WITH STAR

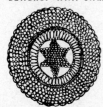

| Butter dish | $ 31.00 |
|---|---|
| Cake stand | |
| a. Large | 20.00 |
| b. Small | 16.50 |
| Celery | 24.75 |
| Compote | |
| a. Covered, high standard | 44.00 |
| b. Covered, low standard | 38.50 |
| c. Covered, footed, 6'', star base | 30.25 |
| d. Covered, footed, 7'', star base | 33.00 |
| Cordial | 8.25 |
| Creamer | 23.25 |
| Goblet | 9.00 |
| Lamp | 20.00 |
| Pickle | 6.25 |
| Pitcher | 38.50 |
| Plate | |
| a. 4½'' | 7.75 |
| b. 5¼'' | 8.25 |
| c. 5½'' | 8.50 |
| d. 6'' | 9.00 |
| e. 6¼'' | 9.00 |
| f. 6½'' | 9.50 |
| g. 7'' | 9.50 |
| *h. 7¼'' | 9.50 |
| i. 7½'' | 9.75 |
| j. 7¾'' | 10.00 |
| k. 8¼'' | 11.00 |
| l. 9'' | 18.25 |
| m. 9½'' | 18.25 |
| n. 11'' | 20.75 |
| o. 11'' honey plate, with large cover | 50.00 |

| p. 11'', with sheaf of wheat | 10.00 |
|---|---|
| q. 10'', with sheaf of wheat | 10.00 |
| *Salt, footed | 7.50 |
| Sauce | |
| a. Flat | 6.75 |
| *b. Footed | 7.75 |
| Spooner | 9.50 |
| Sugar bowl | 32.50 |
| Tumbler | 7.75 |

*Reproduced item

## DEWEY
(See Colored Glass Section)

## DIAGONAL BAND WITH FAN

| Butter dish | $ 13.75 |
|---|---|
| Celery | 10.50 |
| Champagne | 9.00 |
| Compote | |
| a. Covered, high standard | 16.50 |
| b. Covered, low standard | 14.75 |
| Cordial | 6.50 |
| Creamer | 10.00 |
| Goblet | 8.25 |
| Marmalade jar | 8.25 |
| Pickle | 5.50 |
| Pitcher | 12.25 |
| Plate | |
| a. 6'' | 6.00 |
| b. 7'' | 7.75 |
| c. 8'' | 9.00 |
| Sauce, footed | 4.00 |
| Shakers, pair | 7.50 |
| Spooner | 6.75 |
| Sugar bowl | 13.75 |
| Wine | 5.00 |

## DIAMOND MEDALLION

33

| | |
|---|---|
| Butter dish | $ 12.75 |
| Cake stand | 10.00 |
| Celery | 9.50 |
| Compote, covered | 15.50 |
| Creamer | 9.50 |
| Goblet | 6.00 |
| Pitcher, water | 16.00 |
| Plate, 10'' | 8.25 |
| Sauce | 3.25 |
| Spooner | 6.00 |
| Sugar bowl | 13.25 |
| Wine | 4.50 |

## DIAMOND POINT

| | |
|---|---|
| Ale glass | $ 20.00 |
| Bowl | |
| a. Covered, 7'', 8'' | 24.75 |
| b. Open, 7'', 8'' | 20.00 |
| Butter dish | 26.50 |
| Castor bottle | 8.25 |
| Celery | 23.75 |
| Champagne | 18.25 |
| Compote | |
| a. Covered, 6'', high standard | 44.00 |
| b. Covered, 7'', 8'', high standard | 49.50 |
| c. Covered, 6'', 7'', 8'', low standard | 41.00 |
| d. Open, 6'', 7'', 8'', low standard | 22.00 |
| e. Open, 9'', 10'', low standard | 25.75 |
| Cordial | 22.00 |
| Creamer | 41.00 |
| Cruet | 22.00 |
| Decanter | |
| a. Bar lip, pint | 26.50 |
| b. Bar lip, quart | 35.75 |
| c. With stopper, pint | 29.75 |
| d. With stopper, quart | 38.50 |
| Dish | |
| a. Oval, 7'', 8'' | 13.75 |
| b. Oval, 9'', 10'' | 18.50 |
| Egg cup | 15.50 |
| Goblet | 13.25 |
| Honey dish | 6.75 |
| Jug | |
| a. ½ pint | 23.75 |
| b. Pint | 26.50 |
| c. Quart | 33.00 |
| d. 3 pints | 38.50 |
| Lamp, whale oil | 36.50 |
| Lemonade glass | 17.75 |
| Mug | 25.00 |

| | |
|---|---|
| Pitcher | |
| a. ½ pint | 35.25 |
| b. Pint | 39.50 |
| c. Quart | 63.50 |
| d. 3 pints | 50.00 |
| Plate | |
| a. 3'' | 8.25 |
| b. 6'' | 10.00 |
| c. 7'' | 12.25 |
| d. 8'' | 15.50 |
| e. 5½'', star center | 15.75 |
| f. Large, deep, 8'' | 16.50 |
| g. Small, deep, 6'' | 14.75 |
| Salt, covered, footed | 25.75 |
| Sauce | 7.75 |
| Spooner | 12.25 |
| Sugar bowl | 31.00 |
| Syrup jug | 20.50 |
| Tumbler | |
| a. Jelly | 10.50 |
| b. Water | 19.25 |
| c. Whiskey | 21.50 |
| Wine | 15.50 |

## DIAMOND QUILTED
### (See Colored Glass Section)

## DIAMOND SUNBURST

| | |
|---|---|
| Butter dish | $ 13.25 |
| Cake stand | 11.00 |
| Celery | 10.00 |
| Compote, covered, high standard | 17.75 |
| Cordial | 5.50 |
| Creamer | 10.75 |
| Dish, oval | 5.50 |
| Goblet | 6.25 |
| Lamp | 8.75 |
| Pickle | 5.50 |
| Pitcher | 12.25 |
| Salt, footed | 5.50 |
| Sauce | 3.25 |
| Shakers, pair | 7.50 |
| Spooner | 5.50 |
| Sugar bowl | 13.75 |
| Tumbler | 6.75 |
| Wine | 7.25 |

## DIAMOND THUMBPRINT

| | |
|---|---|
| Bowl | $ 38.50 |
| Butter dish | 55.00 |
| Celery | 60.00 |

| | |
|---|---|
| Champagne (scarce) | 95.00 |
| **Compote** | |
| a. Open, low standard | 34.00 |
| b. Open, high standard, medium | 55.00 |
| c. Open, high standard, large | 57.00 |
| Cordial | 62.00 |
| Creamer | 70.00 |
| **Decanter** | |
| a. Pint | 53.00 |
| b. Quart | 67.00 |
| Goblet (rare) | 175.00 |
| Honey dish | 8.50 |
| **Lamp** | |
| a. All glass | 36.00 |
| b. Marble base | 34.00 |
| c. Fluid lamp, 3 burners | 140.00 |
| Mug, handled | 48.00 |
| Pitcher, water (scarce) | 150.00 |
| Sauce | 11.00 |
| Spooner | 22.00 |
| Sugar bowl | 65.00 |
| **Tumbler** | |
| a. Water | 39.00 |
| b. Whiskey | 45.00 |
| Wine (scarce) | 55.00 |

### DOLPHIN

| | |
|---|---|
| Butter dish, covered | $ 33.00 |
| Compote, high standard | 26.50 |
| Creamer | 30.25 |
| Goblet | 27.50 |
| Pitcher, water | 43.50 |
| Spooner | 10.50 |
| Sugar bowl | 33.00 |

### DOUBLE LOOP AND DART

| | |
|---|---|
| Butter dish | $ 15.00 |
| Celery | 11.00 |
| Compote | 20.00 |

| | |
|---|---|
| Cordial | 10.00 |
| Creamer | 13.00 |
| Egg cup | 8.25 |
| Goblet | 7.00 |
| Pitcher | 20.00 |
| Plate, 6'' (scarce) | 15.50 |
| Salt, footed | 7.25 |
| Sauce | 4.00 |
| Spooner | 6.75 |
| Sugar bowl | 16.50 |
| Tumbler, footed | 10.50 |

### DOUBLE RIBBON

| | |
|---|---|
| Butter dish | $ 16.50 |
| Celery | 11.75 |
| Compote, open, high standard | 22.00 |
| Creamer | 13.75 |
| Egg cup | 9.00 |
| Goblet | 11.00 |
| Pickle | 7.25 |
| Pitcher | 22.00 |
| Sauce, footed | 5.00 |
| Spooner | 7.75 |
| Sugar bowl | 17.75 |

### DOUBLE SPEAR

| | |
|---|---|
| Butter dish | $ 11.50 |
| Celery | 9.00 |
| Compote, covered, high standard | 20.00 |
| Creamer | 10.50 |
| Dish, oval, deep | 6.75 |
| Goblet | 7.25 |
| Pickle | 5.00 |
| Pitcher, water | 13.75 |
| Sauce | 3.25 |
| Spooner | 5.00 |
| Sugar bowl | 12.75 |

## DRAPERY

| | |
|---|---|
| Butter dish | $ 16.00 |
| Compote, covered | 20.00 |
| Creamer | 15.50 |
| Dish, oval | 7.25 |
| Goblet | 9.75 |
| Pitcher | 17.75 |
| Plate, 6'' | 10.50 |
| Sauce | 4.50 |
| Spooner | 7.25 |
| Sugar bowl | 17.75 |

## EGG IN SAND

| | |
|---|---|
| Butter dish | $ 18.25 |
| Cake stand | 15.50 |
| Compote | 21.50 |
| Cordial | 7.75 |
| Creamer | 11.50 |
| Goblet | 8.25 |
| Pitcher | |
| a. Milk | 15.50 |
| b. Water | 18.25 |
| Sauce | 3.75 |
| Shakers, pair | 13.25 |
| Spooner | 7.25 |
| Sugar bowl | 18.25 |

| | |
|---|---|
| Tray, bread | 11.00 |
| Tumbler | 7.25 |
| Wine | 7.50 |

## EGYPTIAN
### (Parthenon)

| | |
|---|---|
| Butter dish, covered | $ 18.50 |
| Celery | 13.25 |
| Compote | |
| a. Covered, low standard | 30.25 |
| b. Open, high standard, sphinx on base, large | 23.25 |
| c. Same, small | 20.00 |
| Creamer | 14.00 |
| Goblet | 11.00 |
| Honey dish | 7.25 |
| Pickle, oval | 7.00 |
| Pitcher, water | 23.25 |
| Plate, cake, handled | 15.50 |
| Platter | |
| a. Cleopatra | 16.50 |
| b. Salt Lake Temple | 22.00 |
| Sauce | |
| a. Flat | 4.00 |
| b. Footed, 4½'' | 6.75 |
| Spooner | 7.75 |
| Sugar bowl | 18.75 |

## EIGHTEEN-NINETY

| | |
|---|---|
| Bowl, berry | $ 5.50 |
| Butter dish | 10.50 |
| Celery | 7.75 |
| Creamer | 9.50 |
| Pitcher, water | 11.00 |
| Shakers | |
| a. Salt and pepper, pair | 8.25 |
| b. Sugar | 7.75 |
| Spooner | 5.50 |
| Sugar bowl, covered | 11.00 |

**EMERALD GREEN HERRINGBONE**
(See Colored Glass Section)

**ESTHER**
(See Colored Glass Section)

**ETRUSCAN**

| | |
|---|---|
| Butter dish | $ 16.00 |
| Cake stand | 12.25 |
| Compote | |
| a. Covered, 8'', high standard | 22.00 |
| b. Open, 8'', low standard | 16.50 |
| Creamer | 13.25 |
| Dish, oval | 7.75 |
| Egg cup | 8.25 |
| Goblet | 9.00 |
| Salt, footed | 6.00 |
| Sauce | 5.25 |
| Spooner | 6.75 |
| Sugar bowl | 16.50 |
| Tumbler | 6.75 |

**EUGENIE**

| | |
|---|---|
| Butter dish | $ 33.00 |
| Castor bottle | 10.50 |
| Celery | 38.50 |
| Champagne | 20.50 |
| Compote, covered, on standard | 44.00 |
| Cordial | 13.25 |
| Creamer (scarce) | 55.00 |
| Egg cup | 14.00 |
| Goblet | 13.25 |
| Sauce, flat | 5.25 |
| Spooner | 10.00 |
| Sugar bowl (scarce) | 105.00 |
| Tumbler, footed | 20.00 |
| Wine | 13.75 |

**EUREKA**

| | |
|---|---|
| Butter dish | $ 15.50 |
| Champagne | 10.00 |

| | |
|---|---|
| Compote | |
| a. Covered, 7'', 8'', high standard | 24.75 |
| b. Open, 7'', 8'', low standard | 15.00 |
| Cordial | 10.00 |
| Creamer | 16.50 |
| Dish, oval, shallow | 7.50 |
| Egg cup | 9.00 |
| Goblet | 8.25 |
| Salt, footed | 6.00 |
| Sauce | 4.50 |
| Spooner | 7.50 |
| Sugar bowl | 16.00 |
| Tumbler, footed | 9.50 |
| Wine | 10.00 |

**EXCELSIOR**

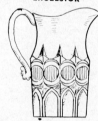

| | |
|---|---|
| Ale glass | $ 25.75 |
| Bitters bottle | 16.50 |
| Bowl | |
| a. Covered, flat | 57.75 |
| b. Open, 10'' | 30.25 |
| Butter dish | 33.00 |
| Candlesticks, pair | 55.00 |
| Celery | 39.50 |
| Champagne | 18.25 |
| Claret | 15.50 |
| Compote | |
| a. Covered, low standard | 53.00 |
| b. Open, 10'', high standard | 38.50 |
| Cordial | 10.00 |
| Creamer | 40.00 |
| Decanter | |
| a. Small, footed | 20.50 |
| b. Pint | 25.75 |
| c. Quart | 27.50 |

| Egg cup | |
|---|---|
| a. Double | 20.00 |
| b. Single | 13.75 |
| Goblet | 16.50 |
| Lamp, whale oil | 47.00 |
| Pitcher | |
| a. Milk (scarce) | 100.00 |
| b. Syrup | 44.00 |
| c. Water (scarce) | 104.00 |
| Salt, footed | 15.50 |
| Spooner | 16.50 |
| Sugar bowl | 35.75 |
| Tumbler | |
| a. Footed | 13.75 |
| b. Jelly | 11.00 |
| c. Water | 12.25 |
| Vase | 16.00 |
| Wine | 14.00 |

| Sauce | 2.75 |
|---|---|
| Sugar bowl, covered | 11.00 |
| Tumbler | 3.25 |

## FAN WITH DIAMOND

| Butter dish | $ 13.75 |
|---|---|
| Compote | |
| a. Covered, high standard | 20.50 |
| b. Covered, low standard | 16.50 |
| Cordial | 6.75 |
| Creamer | 9.50 |
| Dish, oval, 6¾ x 9'' | 6.75 |
| Egg cup | 7.75 |
| Goblet | 6.75 |
| Pickle | 4.50 |
| Pitcher | 12.75 |
| Sauce, flat, 4'' | 3.50 |
| Spooner | 6.00 |
| Sugar bowl | 13.75 |

## EYEWINKER

| Banana dish | $ 22.00 |
|---|---|
| Bowl, berry | 11.00 |
| Butter dish | 18.25 |
| Cake stand | 15.50 |
| Compote | |
| a. Covered | 23.00 |
| b. Open | 16.00 |
| Creamer | 12.75 |
| Cruet | 10.00 |
| Lamp | 17.75 |
| Pitcher | |
| a. Milk | 18.25 |
| b. Syrup | 18.75 |
| c. Water | 22.00 |
| Sauce | 5.00 |
| Sugar bowl | 18.25 |
| Toothpick holder | 6.00 |
| Tumbler | 7.25 |

## FAN WITH ACANTHUS LEAF
### (Bijou)

| Bowl, berry, 9'' | $ 7.50 |
|---|---|
| Butter dish, covered | 11.00 |
| Celery | 7.75 |
| Creamer | 8.50 |
| Dish, jelly, covered | 7.25 |
| Mug | 4.50 |
| Pickle | 5.00 |
| Pitcher, water | 11.00 |
| Plate, cake, flat | 8.50 |

## FEATHER
### (Finecut & Feather, Indiana Swirl)

| Banana dish | $ 17.75 |
|---|---|
| Bowl, 7½'', 8½'' | 7.25 |
| Butter dish | 12.25 |
| Cake stand | |
| a. 8½'' | 11.00 |
| b. 11'' (scarce) | 16.50 |
| Celery | 10.50 |
| Compote, high standard | 20.00 |

| | |
|---|---|
| Cordial | 6.75 |
| Creamer | 9.75 |
| Cruet | 8.25 |
| Dish, oval | 7.25 |
| Goblet | 10.00 |
| Pitcher, water | 13.25 |
| Plate, 10'' | 12.75 |
| Sauce | 3.25 |
| Spooner | 6.75 |
| Sugar bowl | 12.75 |
| Toothpick holder | 5.50 |
| Tumbler | 6.50 |
| Wine | 6.75 |

## FESTOON

**Bowl**
| | |
|---|---|
| a. Berry | $ 8.25 |
| b. Finger | 5.25 |
| Butter dish | 12.25 |
| Cake stand, 9'' | 11.50 |
| Celery | 10.00 |
| Compote, on standard | 19.00 |
| Creamer | 9.75 |
| Pickle dish | 6.50 |
| Pickle jar | 12.25 |
| Pitcher | 14.00 |

**Plate**
| | |
|---|---|
| a. 7½'' (scarce) | 16.50 |
| b. 8½'' (scarce) | 18.25 |
| c. 9¼'' | 13.25 |
| Sauce, 4½'', flat | 4.25 |
| Spooner | 6.00 |
| Sugar bowl | 13.25 |
| Tray, round, 10'' | 11.75 |
| Tumbler | 8.25 |
| Wine | 6.50 |

### FINE CUT
(See Colored Glass Section)

### FINE CUT AND PANEL
(See Colored Glass Section)

### FINE RIB
| | |
|---|---|
| Ale glass | $ 22.00 |
| Bitters bottle | 21.00 |

**Bowl**
| | |
|---|---|
| a. Covered, 7'' | 37.50 |
| b. Shallow | 22.00 |
| Butter dish | 32.50 |
| Castor bottle | 10.00 |
| Celery | 23.75 |
| Champagne | 16.00 |

**Compote**
| | |
|---|---|
| a. Covered, 7'', 8'', high standard | 50.00 |
| b. Covered, 7'', 8'', low standard | 44.00 |
| c. Open, 7'', 8'', low standard | 30.75 |
| d. Open, 9'', 10'', low standard | 33.00 |
| Cordial | 13.75 |
| Creamer | 53.00 |
| Cup, custard | 24.25 |

**Decanter**
| | |
|---|---|
| a. Bar lip, pint | 23.75 |
| b. Bar lip, quart | 27.00 |
| c. With stopper, pint | 39.50 |
| d. With stopper, quart | 44.00 |

**Dish**
| | |
|---|---|
| a. Oval, 7'', 8'' | 22.00 |
| b. Oval, 9'', 10'' | 27.00 |
| Egg cup, double, covered | 26.50 |
| Goblet | 13.75 |
| Honey dish | 6.75 |

**Jug**
| | |
|---|---|
| a. Pint | 35.75 |
| b. Quart | 38.50 |
| c. Three pints | 48.50 |
| Lamp | 30.00 |
| Lemonade glass | 16.50 |
| Mug | 21.50 |
| Pitcher | 66.00 |

**Plate**
| | |
|---|---|
| a. 6'' | 22.00 |
| b. 7'' | 24.75 |

**Salt**
| | |
|---|---|
| a. Celery dip | 5.25 |
| b. Covered, on stem | 27.50 |
| c. Large, open, footed | 12.75 |
| d. Oval | 15.50 |
| Sauce | 5.50 |
| Spooner | 11.00 |
| Sugar bowl | 35.25 |

**Tumbler**
| | |
|---|---|
| a. Jelly | 10.50 |
| b. Water | 15.50 |
| c. Whiskey | 16.50 |
| Water bottle, with tumble-up | 33.00 |
| Wine | 13.75 |

### FISHSCALE
| | |
|---|---|
| Bowl, covered, 7'', 8'', square with round base | $ 13.75 |
| Butter dish | 18.25 |

**Cake stand**
| | |
|---|---|
| a. 9'' | 15.50 |
| b. 10½'' | 18.25 |
| Celery | 11.50 |

**Compote**
- a. Covered, various sizes: 18.00 to 33.00
- b. Open, 4½'', high standard ___ 16.00
- c. Open, 6'', high standard _____ 20.50

Creamer _____ 14.00
Goblet _____ 10.50
Lamp, handled _____ 10.75
Mug, large _____ 9.00
Pickle _____ 8.25

**Pitcher**
- a. Large _____ 20.75
- b. Small _____ 18.25

**Plate**
- a. Round, 7'' _____ 11.75
- b. Square, 8'' _____ 12.75
- c. Square with rounded corners, 9'' _____ 15.50

**Sauce**
- a. Flat _____ 4.25
- b. Footed _____ 6.00

**Shakers**
- a. Salt and pepper (scarce) __ 18.25
- b. Sugar _____ 11.00

Spooner _____ 9.00
Sugar bowl _____ 22.00
Tray, water, round _____ 19.00
Tumbler _____ 10.00

## FLATTENED DIAMOND

Butter dish _____ $ 11.00
Celery _____ 7.75
Creamer _____ 10.50
Goblet _____ 6.75
Sauce _____ 3.00
Spooner _____ 5.50
Sugar bowl _____ 11.50

## FLATTENED HOBNAIL

Bowl, berry _____ $ 9.75
Butter dish _____ 15.00

Cake stand _____ 13.75
Celery _____ 11.75
Cordial _____ 6.75
Creamer _____ 10.00
Cruet _____ 9.75
Goblet _____ 7.50
Pickle _____ 5.25

**Pitcher**
- a. Globular _____ 16.50
- b. Straight sides _____ 13.75

Plate, 4½'' _____ 7.25
Sauce _____ 3.75
Shakers, pair _____ 9.00
Spooner _____ 6.75
Sugar bowl _____ 15.50
Tray _____ 12.25
*Tumbler _____ 7.50
Wine _____ 6.75

**\*Reproduced Item**

## FLATTENED SAWTOOTH

**Bowl**
- a. Finger _____ $ 8.25
- b. Flat, 10'' _____ 11.75

Celery _____ 12.25
Celery tray _____ 7.00
Compote, covered _____ 20.50
Cordial _____ 9.00
Creamer _____ 11.00
Decanter _____ 15.50
Egg cup _____ 9.00
Goblet _____ 8.25
Ice tub _____ 10.00
Pitcher _____ 20.75

**Plate**
- a. 6'' _____ 7.25
- b. 7'' _____ 9.00

**Salt**
- a. Covered _____ 13.75
- b. Footed _____ 6.75
- c. Round, flat _____ 3.75

Sauce _____ 4.25
Spooner _____ 7.25
Sugar bowl _____ 14.00
Tumbler _____ 7.75

## FLOWER POT

| | |
|---|---|
| Butter dish _____ $ | 20.50 |
| Cake stand, 10½'' _____ | 16.00 |
| Compote, open, 7'' _____ | 23.75 |
| Creamer _____ | 12.75 |
| Pitcher | |
| a. Small _____ | 20.75 |
| b. Large _____ | 25.00 |
| Sauce | |
| a. Open, flat _____ | 5.00 |
| b. On standard _____ | 5.75 |
| Spooner _____ | 8.50 |
| Sugar bowl _____ | 20.50 |
| Tray, bread _____ | 16.00 |

| | |
|---|---|
| Celery _____ | 20.50 |
| Compote, footed _____ | 43.50 |
| Creamer _____ | 20.75 |
| *Goblet _____ | 11.00 |
| Lamp _____ | 20.50 |
| Pitcher | |
| a. Syrup _____ | 18.25 |
| b. Water _____ | 41.00 |
| Sauce _____ | 8.25 |
| Spooner _____ | 12.75 |
| Sugar bowl _____ | 35.00 |
| Tray, water _____ | 21.50 |
| Tumbler _____ | 10.75 |

*Reproduced item

## FROSTED CIRCLE

## FLUTE

| | |
|---|---|
| Ale glass _____ $ | 10.00 |
| Bitters bottle _____ | 12.25 |
| Candlesticks, pair _____ | 25.00 |
| Champagne _____ | 11.75 |
| Creamer _____ | 18.50 |
| Cup, footed _____ | 10.75 |
| Decanter _____ | 21.50 |
| Egg cup _____ | 7.50 |
| Goblet _____ | 10.50 |
| Lamp _____ | 13.25 |
| Spooner _____ | 7.75 |
| Tumbler | |
| a. Gill _____ | 6.50 |
| b. ½ pint _____ | 6.75 |
| c. Jelly _____ | 6.75 |
| d. Toy, ½ gill _____ | 5.50 |
| Wine _____ | 7.25 |

FOSTORIA, See Victoria

### FROSTED ARTICHOKE

| | |
|---|---|
| Bowl, 8'' _____ $ | 24.75 |
| Butter dish _____ | 35.50 |
| Cake stand _____ | 25.00 |

| | |
|---|---|
| Bowl | |
| a. Covered, 7'', 8'', flat _____ $ | 16.50 |
| b. Open, 8'', 9'' _____ | 11.00 |
| Butter dish, covered _____ | 22.00 |
| Cake stand, 9'', 10'' _____ | 22.50 |
| Celery _____ | 18.25 |
| Champagne _____ | 13.75 |
| Claret _____ | 12.25 |
| Compote | |
| a. Open, high standard _____ | 21.50 |
| b. Covered, 7'', 8'', high standard | 32.75 |
| Creamer _____ | 16.00 |
| Cruet, oil _____ | 13.25 |
| *Goblet _____ | 13.25 |
| Lamp _____ | 17.25 |
| Pickle jar _____ | 12.75 |
| Pitcher | |
| a. Syrup _____ | 16.50 |
| b. Water _____ | 25.00 |
| Plate | |
| a. 4'' _____ | 9.00 |
| b. 7'' _____ | 12.50 |
| c. 9'' _____ | 15.50 |
| Sauce, 3¼'', 4'' _____ | 5.00 |
| Shakers, pair _____ | 18.25 |
| Spooner _____ | 9.00 |

| | |
|---|---|
| Sugar bowl | 22.00 |
| Tumbler | 10.75 |
| Wine | 11.50 |

*Reproduced item

## FROSTED LEAF

| | | |
|---|---|---|
| Butter dish | $ | 45.00 |
| Celery | | 33.00 |
| Champagne | | 31.00 |
| Compote | | |
| a. Covered | | 72.00 |
| b. Open | | 41.00 |
| Cordial | | 32.75 |
| Creamer | | 69.00 |
| Decanter, quart | | 64.00 |
| Egg cup (scarce) | | 27.00 |
| Goblet | | 27.50 |
| Pitcher, water (very scarce) | | 205.00 |
| Salt, footed | | 16.00 |
| Sauce | | 10.00 |
| Spooner | | 16.50 |
| Sugar bowl | | 45.00 |
| Tumbler | | 29.50 |

### FROSTED LION, See Lion

## FROSTED RIBBON

| | | |
|---|---|---|
| Ale glass | $ | 13.25 |
| Bitters bottle | | 12.25 |
| Butter dish | | 22.00 |
| Celery | | 17.75 |
| Champagne | | 15.50 |
| Compote | | |
| a. Covered, high standard | | 32.50 |
| b. Covered, low standard | | 24.75 |
| c. Open, dolphin standard | | 55.00 |
| Cordial | | 11.00 |
| Creamer | | 18.25 |
| Dish, octagonal, 8'', 9'' | | 15.00 |
| Egg cup | | 10.75 |
| *Goblet | | 13.75 |
| Pitcher, water | | 27.50 |

| | |
|---|---|
| Salt, footed | 7.25 |
| Sauce | 5.25 |
| Spooner | 10.50 |
| Sugar bowl | 23.00 |
| Tray | 18.25 |
| Tumbler | 11.00 |
| Wine | 8.25 |

*Reproduced item

## FROSTED STORK

| | | |
|---|---|---|
| Bowl, waste | $ | 16.25 |
| Butter dish | | 26.50 |
| Creamer | | 22.00 |
| Goblet | | 24.75 |
| Marmalade jar | | 20.50 |
| Pitcher, water | | 40.00 |
| Plate, 9'' | | 19.25 |
| Platter, 9'' | | 18.25 |
| Sauce | | 7.50 |
| Spooner | | 11.00 |
| Sugar bowl | | 27.50 |
| Tray | | 26.50 |

## FUCHSIA

| | | |
|---|---|---|
| Butter dish | $ | 24.75 |
| Cake stand | | 20.50 |
| Celery | | 16.50 |
| Compote, open | | 31.00 |
| Creamer | | 20.00 |
| Goblet | | 10.00 |
| Plate, 10'' | | 20.50 |
| Spooner | | 10.75 |
| Sugar bowl | | 26.50 |

## GARFIELD DRAPE

| | | |
|---|---|---|
| Bowl | $ | 9.00 |
| Butter dish | | 20.50 |
| Cake stand | | 15.50 |
| Compote | | |
| a. Covered, high standard | | 22.00 |
| b. Covered, low standard | | 19.00 |

| | |
|---|---|
| Creamer | 14.75 |
| Egg cup | 10.75 |
| Goblet | 9.50 |
| Honey dish | 5.25 |
| Pickle | 7.75 |
| **Pitcher** | |
| a. Milk | 20.50 |
| b. Water | 17.75 |
| **Plate** | |
| a. Memorial, 11'' | 15.50 |
| b. Edge cut to line of drapery, 10'' | 11.50 |
| **Sauce** | |
| a. Flat | 3.75 |
| b. Footed | 6.00 |
| Spooner | 8.25 |
| Sugar bowl | 21.00 |

### GIBSON GIRL

| | |
|---|---|
| Butter dish | $ 24.00 |
| Creamer | 15.50 |
| Pitcher, water | 27.00 |
| Plate, 10'' | 11.00 |
| Spooner | 10.00 |
| Sugar bowl | 23.75 |
| Tumbler | 10.00 |

### GOOD LUCK, See Horseshoe

### GOOSEBERRY

| | |
|---|---|
| Butter dish | $ 19.25 |
| **Compote** | |
| a. Covered, high standard, large | 27.50 |
| b. Covered, high standard, 6'' | 20.50 |

| | |
|---|---|
| Creamer | 16.50 |
| *Goblet | 10.00 |
| Honey dish | 4.50 |
| Lemonade glass | 15.50 |
| Pickle | 5.50 |
| **Pitcher** | |
| a. Syrup | 17.75 |
| b. Water | 27.00 |
| Sauce | 5.00 |
| Spooner | 7.75 |
| Sugar bowl | 20.50 |
| Tumbler | 11.00 |

*Reproduced item

### GOTHIC

| | |
|---|---|
| Bowl, flat, 8'' | $ 24.75 |
| Butter dish | 32.75 |
| Cake stand | 27.50 |
| Castor bottle | 6.75 |
| Champagne (scarce) | 26.50 |
| **Compote** | |
| a. Covered, on standard | 60.00 |
| b. Open, footed | 26.50 |
| Cordial | 20.50 |
| Creamer | 42.00 |
| Egg cup | 12.25 |
| Goblet | 16.50 |
| Plate | 22.00 |
| Sauce | 5.50 |
| Spooner | 10.50 |
| Sugar bowl | 30.00 |
| Tumbler | 17.75 |
| Wine (scarce) | 20.00 |

### GRAPE AND FESTOON

| | |
|---|---|
| Butter dish | $ 18.50 |
| Celery | 13.75 |
| **Compote** | |
| a. Covered, high standard | 20.50 |
| b. Covered, low standard | 18.25 |

43

| | |
|---|---|
| Cordial | 8.25 |
| Creamer | 15.50 |
| Dish, oval, large | 8.25 |
| Egg cup | 8.25 |
| Goblet | 9.50 |
| Pickle | 5.50 |
| Pitcher | 19.00 |
| Plate, 6'' | 9.75 |
| Salt, footed | 6.75 |
| Sauce | 4.50 |
| Spooner | 9.00 |
| Sugar bowl | 20.00 |
| Wine | 8.25 |

## GRAPE BAND

| | |
|---|---|
| Butter dish | $ 19.00 |
| Compote | |
| a. Covered, high standard | 24.75 |
| b. Covered, low standard | 20.00 |
| Cordial | 7.25 |
| Creamer | 13.25 |
| Goblet | 7.75 |
| Pickle | 6.75 |
| Pitcher | 22.00 |
| Plate, 6'' | 10.00 |
| Salt, footed | 6.25 |
| Sauce | 3.75 |
| Spooner | 8.25 |
| Sugar bowl | 20.25 |
| Tumbler | 7.25 |
| Wine | 10.00 |

## GRAPE WITH THUMBPRINT

| | |
|---|---|
| Bowl | $ 7.75 |
| Butter dish | 13.25 |
| Celery | 9.00 |
| Creamer | 10.50 |
| Goblet | 7.50 |
| Pitcher, water | 15.50 |
| Sauce | 3.00 |
| Spooner | 6.75 |

| | |
|---|---|
| Sugar bowl | 13.25 |
| Syrup | 9.00 |
| Tumbler | 4.25 |

## GRASSHOPPER
### (Locust, Long Spear)

| | |
|---|---|
| Butter dish | $ 22.00 |
| Celery | 13.75 |
| Compote, covered | 26.50 |
| Creamer | 13.75 |
| *Goblet | 10.00 |
| Pickle | 7.75 |
| Pitcher, water | 24.75 |
| Sauce | 5.00 |
| Spooner | 9.00 |
| Sugar bowl | 22.00 |

*Reproduced item

## HAMILTON

| | |
|---|---|
| Butter dish | $ 33.00 |
| Castor set | 66.00 |
| Celery | 27.00 |
| Champagne | 22.00 |
| Compote | |
| a. Open, high standard | 30.75 |
| b. Covered, 6'', high standard | 66.00 |
| c. Open, low standard, deep bowl | 30.00 |
| d. Open, low standard, shallow bowl | 23.75 |
| Cordial | 22.00 |
| Creamer | |
| a. Applied handle | 40.00 |
| b. Pressed handle | 21.00 |
| Decanter | 32.50 |
| Egg cup | 11.50 |
| Goblet | 13.25 |
| Honey dish | 6.25 |

| Pitcher | | | Compote | | |
|---|---|---|---|---|---|
| a. Syrup | 33.00 | | a. Covered, high standard | 35.00 | |
| b. Water | 69.00 | | b. Open | 22.50 | |
| Plate, 6'' | 24.75 | | Creamer | 18.25 | |
| Salt, footed | 13.25 | | Goblet | 13.75 | |
| Sauce | 6.75 | | Honey dish | 7.75 | |
| Spooner | 11.00 | | Marmalade jar | 15.50 | |
| Sugar bowl | 35.00 | | Pickle | 7.75 | |
| Tumbler | | | Pitcher | 30.00 | |
| a. Water | 22.00 | | Platter, 8x10½'' | 16.75 | |
| b. Whiskey | 23.75 | | Sauce | 5.00 | |
| Wine | 13.75 | | Spooner | 9.00 | |
| | | | Sugar bowl | 25.00 | |
| | | | Wine | 12.75 | |

## HAMILTON WITH LEAF

## HARP

| | | |
|---|---|---|
| Butter dish | $ | 36.00 |
| Celery | | 36.00 |
| Compote | | |
| a. Open, high standard | | 30.00 |
| b. Open, low standard | | 27.00 |
| Cordial | | 22.00 |
| Creamer | | 30.00 |
| Egg cup | | 13.75 |
| Goblet | | 15.50 |
| Lamp | | 26.75 |
| Salt, footed | | 13.25 |
| Sauce | | 6.75 |
| Spooner | | 12.25 |
| Sugar bowl | | 36.00 |
| Tumbler | | 24.00 |

| | | |
|---|---|---|
| Butter dish, covered | $ | 49.50 |
| Compote, 6'', covered, low standard | | 80.00 |
| Goblet (rare) | | 175.00 |
| Lamp | | 50.00 |
| Salt, open | | 14.00 |
| Sauce | | 12.00 |
| Spill holder | | 18.50 |

## HAND

## HARTFORD

| | | |
|---|---|---|
| Bowl | | |
| a. 7'', 8'' | $ | 10.50 |
| b. 9'', 10'' | | 13.25 |
| Butter dish | | 25.00 |
| Cake stand | | 20.00 |
| Celery | | 18.75 |

| | | |
|---|---|---|
| Bowl | | |
| a. Berry, 5½'', 6'' | $ | 6.75 |
| b. Berry, 8'' | | 8.25 |
| c. Finger | | 5.50 |
| d. Footed, 4½'', 5½'' | | 5.00 |
| e. Footed, 6'', 7'' | | 7.25 |
| f. Footed, 8'' | | 7.75 |
| g. Oblong, 7'', 8'' | | 8.25 |
| h. Oblong, 9'' | | 9.00 |
| Butter dish, covered | | 12.75 |
| Celery | | 9.00 |
| Creamer | | 9.50 |
| Dish, olive, 5½'' | | 4.50 |
| Nappy, 5½'', handled | | 5.25 |

| | |
|---|---|
| Salt dip | 1.75 |
| Sauce, 4½'' | 3.75 |
| Shakers, pair | 7.75 |
| Spoon basket | 9.00 |
| Spooner | 6.50 |
| Sugar bowl | |
| a. Covered, footed base | 12.75 |
| b. Covered, plain base | 11.00 |
| Syrup jug | 8.25 |
| Tumbler | 4.50 |

## HEART WITH THUMBPRINT
### (Bull's Eye in Heart)

| | |
|---|---|
| Bowl, berry, 9'' | $ 9.50 |
| Butter dish | 20.00 |
| Celery | 11.75 |
| Creamer | |
| a. Regular | 15.50 |
| b. Individual | 8.25 |
| Goblet | 10.00 |
| Pitcher | 20.50 |
| Plate | 18.25 |
| Sauce | 5.25 |
| Spooner | 9.50 |
| Sugar bowl | |
| a. Covered | 20.00 |
| b. Individual | 10.00 |
| Tumbler | 6.50 |
| Vases, 10'', pair | 13.25 |
| Wine, 4'' | 12.00 |

## HERRINGBONE

| | |
|---|---|
| Butter dish | $ 15.00 |
| Compote | 19.00 |
| Creamer | 10.00 |
| Goblet | 6.75 |
| Pickle | 5.50 |
| Pitcher | 13.25 |
| Sauce | 3.00 |
| Shakers, pair | 8.25 |

| | |
|---|---|
| Spooner | 6.75 |
| Sugar bowl | 15.00 |

## HIDALGO

| | |
|---|---|
| Bowl | |
| a. Large | $ 8.25 |
| b. Small | 6.75 |
| Butter dish | 15.50 |
| Celery | 11.00 |
| Compote | |
| a. Open, high standard | 16.50 |
| b. Covered, high standard | 20.75 |
| Cup and saucer | 7.25 |
| Goblet | 7.75 |
| Pickle | 6.25 |
| Pitcher | |
| a. Milk | 16.50 |
| b. Syrup | 11.00 |
| Plate, 10'' | 11.00 |
| Sauce | |
| a. Flat | 3.25 |
| b. Footed | 4.50 |
| Shakers, pair | 7.75 |
| Spooner | 6.75 |
| Sugar bowl | 16.00 |
| Sugar shaker | 7.25 |
| Tray, water | 13.75 |
| Tumbler | 6.75 |

## HOBNAIL, BALL FOOT

| | |
|---|---|
| Bowl, berry | $ 18.50 |
| Butter dish | 24.00 |
| Celery | 18.50 |
| Creamer | 15.50 |
| Sauce | 6.00 |
| Spooner | 9.00 |
| Sugar bowl | 24.50 |

## HOBNAIL BAND

| | |
|---|---|
| Butter dish | $ 16.50 |
| Creamer | 12.00 |
| Goblet | 7.00 |
| Pitcher, water | 22.50 |

| | |
|---|---|
| Spooner | 9.00 |
| Sugar bowl | 17.00 |
| Tumbler | 7.50 |

## HOBNAIL, FAN TOP
(See Colored Glass Section)

## HOBNAIL, FLATTENED
See Flattened Hobnail

## HOBNAIL, OPALESCENT
(See Colored Glass Section)

## HOBNAIL, PANELLED
(See Colored Glass Section)

## HOBNAIL, POINTED
(See Colored Glass Section)

## HOBNAIL, PRINTED
(See Colored Glass Section)

## HOBNAIL, THUMBPRINT BASE
(See Colored Glass Section)

## HOLLY

| | |
|---|---|
| Butter dish | $ 27.50 |
| Compote | |
| a. Covered, high standard | 38.50 |
| b. Covered, low standard | 32.75 |
| Creamer | 33.00 |
| Egg cup | 13.75 |
| Goblet (scarce) | 23.75 |
| Pickle | 7.25 |
| Pitcher | 39.00 |
| Salt, footed | 7.75 |
| Sauce | 6.75 |
| Spooner | 10.50 |
| Sugar bowl | 30.00 |
| Tumbler, footed | 19.00 |
| Wine | 23.50 |

## HOLLY AMBER
(See Colored Glass Section)

## HONEYCOMB

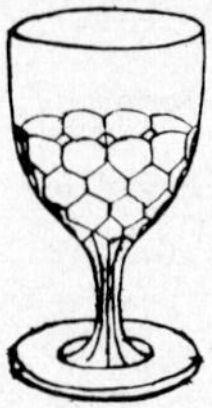

| | |
|---|---|
| Ale glass | $ 9.00 |
| Bitters bottle | 8.25 |
| Bowl | |
| a. Covered, 6", 7" | 9.75 |
| b. Footed, 8", 9" | 15.00 |
| c. Footed, 10" | 21.00 |
| d. Finger | 7.25 |
| Butter dish | 16.00 |
| Castor bottle | 5.50 |
| Celery | 11.50 |
| Champagne | 9.50 |
| Compote | |
| a. Covered, high standard | 22.50 |
| b. Covered, low standard | 18.50 |
| c. Open | 13.75 |
| Cordial | 7.50 |
| Creamer | 12.75 |
| Cup, custard, handled | 9.50 |
| Decanter | |
| a. Pint | 11.50 |
| b. Quart | 17.75 |
| Dish, oval | 7.50 |
| Egg cup | 7.25 |
| Goblet | 7.75 |
| Honey dish | 4.25 |
| Jug | |
| a. ½ pint | 12.75 |
| b. Pint | 15.50 |
| c. Quart | 17.75 |
| d. Three pints | 22.00 |
| Lamp | |
| a. All glass | 13.25 |
| b. Marble base | 16.50 |
| Lemonade glass | 9.50 |
| Mug, ½ pint | 6.75 |
| Pitcher, 9" | 18.25 |
| Plate | |
| a. 6" | 7.50 |
| b. 7" | 9.75 |
| Pomade jar | 7.75 |
| Salt | |
| a. Covered, on standard | 11.75 |
| b. Open, on standard | 6.50 |
| Sauce | 3.75 |
| Shakers, pair | 10.50 |
| Spooner | 6.75 |
| Sugar bowl | 16.50 |
| Tumbler | |
| a. ½ pint | 6.75 |
| b. 1/3 pint | 9.50 |
| c. Footed | 9.00 |

Water bottle _____ 13.75
Wine _____ 6.00

## HORN OF PLENTY

Bowl, flat, 8½" diam. _____$ 32.50
Butter dish
  a. Conventional knob _____ 48.50
  b. Washington's head _____ 325.00
Celery _____ 56.00
Claret, flared top, 5" high _____ 140.00
Compote
  a. Covered, 6", on standard ___ 112.00
  b. Covered, oblong _____ 97.50
  c. Open, extra large, high
    standard _____ 66.50
  d. Open, 7¼", low standard ____ 51.00
  e. Open, low standard _____ 49.50
  f. Oval, on standard _____ 185.00
Cordial _____ 34.00
Creamer _____ 75.00
Decanter
  a. Pint _____ 39.00
  b. Quart _____ 45.00
  c. ½ gallon _____ 56.50
Egg cup _____ 16.75
*Goblet _____ 27.00
Honey dish _____ 11.25
Lamp
  *a. All glass _____ 65.00
  b. Marble base _____ 56.50
Mug _____ 56.50
Pepper sauce bottle _____ 22.25
Pickle _____ 28.00
Pitcher
  a. Milk _____ 163.00
  b. Water _____ 150.00
Plate, 6" _____ 45.00
Salt, oval _____ 11.25
Sauce, 4½", rayed base _____ 15.75
Scent bottle _____ 28.00
Spooner _____ 18.00
Sugar bowl _____ 48.00
*Tumbler
  a. Water _____ 24.00
  b. Whiskey _____ 38.00
Wine _____ 25.00

*Reproduced item

## HORSESHOE
## (Good Luck)

Bowl
  a. Berry, oval _____$ 11.00
  b. Waste _____ 9.00
Butter dish _____ 20.00
Cake stand
  a. 8" _____ 17.75
  b. 9" _____ 20.00
  c. 10" _____ 22.00
Celery _____ 13.25
Cheese dish, covered _____ 44.00
Compote
  a. Covered, 7½", low standard __ 27.00
  b. Open, large, high standard __ 16.50
  c. Covered, large, high standard_ 23.75
Cordial _____ 24.75
Creamer _____ 13.75
Dish
  a. Covered, oblong _____ 24.50
  b. Open 6 x 9", oblong _____ 20.50
Goblet
  a. Knob stem _____ 13.25
  b. Plain round stem _____ 10.50
Marmalade jar _____ 15.50
Pickle _____ 7.25
Pitcher
  a. Large _____ 21.50
  b. Small _____ 18.50
Plate
  a. 7¼" _____ 11.00
  b. 8¼" _____ 15.50
  c. 10" _____ 22.00
Platter
  a. Oval _____ 12.75
  *b. Double horseshoe handles,
    10x14", _____ 27.50
Salt
  a. Celery dip, shape of horseshoe 7.25
  b. Master salt, shape of horse-
    shoe _____ 11.00
Sauce
  a. Flat, 4½" _____ 4.50
  b. Footed, 4" _____ 7.25
Spooner _____ 9.50
Sugar bowl _____ 21.50

*Reproduced item

## HUBER
Ale glass _____$ 9.00

48

| | |
|---|---|
| Bitters bottle | 10.00 |
| Bowl, covered, 6'', 7'' | 13.25 |
| Butter dish | 18.25 |
| Celery | 11.00 |
| Champagne | 10.50 |
| Compote | |
|   a. Covered, 8'', 9'', high standard | 25.75 |
|   b. Covered, 10'', high standard | 27.50 |
|   c. Covered, 7'', 8'', low standard | 22.00 |
| Cordial | 7.50 |
| Creamer | 16.50 |
| Cup, custard | 8.50 |
| Decanter | |
|   a. Bar lip, pint | 20.00 |
|   b. Bar lip, quart | 22.00 |
|   c. With stopper, pint | 23.75 |
|   d. With stopper, quart | 26.75 |
| Dish | 10.50 |
| Egg cup, handled | 9.75 |
| Goblet | 8.50 |
| Honey dish | 5.50 |
| Jug | |
|   a. Quart | 19.00 |
|   b. Three pints | 22.00 |
| Lemonade glass | 8.50 |
| Mug | 8.25 |
| Pitcher | 20.00 |
| Plate | |
|   a. 6'' | 9.00 |
|   b. 7'' | 10.00 |
| Salt | |
|   a. Celery dip | 3.25 |
|   b. Footed | 5.50 |
| Sauce | 5.75 |
| Spooner | 8.25 |
| Sugar bowl | 19.00 |
| Tumbler | |
|   a. Gill | 6.00 |
|   b. ½ pint | 7.25 |
|   c. Jelly | 5.50 |
| Wine | 7.25 |

### HUMMING BIRD
(See Colored Glass Section)

### ICICLE
(See Colored Glass Section)

### ILLINOIS

| | | |
|---|---|---|
| Bowl | | |
|   a. Finger | $ | 5.00 |
|   b. Round, 8'' | | 6.00 |
|   c. Round, 6'' | | 5.50 |

| | |
|---|---|
| Butter dish | 10.50 |
| Candle holder | 6.50 |
| Celery, tall | 8.25 |
| Celery tray, 11'' | 6.75 |
| Cheese dish, covered | 10.75 |
| Creamer | |
|   a. Large | 9.00 |
|   b. Medium | 7.75 |
| Cruet | 7.25 |
| Olive dish | 4.50 |
| Pickle | 5.50 |
| Pitcher | |
|   a. ½ gallon, tankard | 12.25 |
|   b. Water | 11.00 |
| Plate | |
|   a. Round, 7'' | 5.50 |
|   b. Square, 7'' | 6.00 |
| Salt, individual | 2.00 |
| Shakers, pair | 8.25 |
| Spooner | 5.50 |
| Spoon tray | 5.00 |
| Sugar bowl, covered | 11.00 |
| Sugar shaker | 6.75 |
| Toothpick holder | 4.50 |
| Tray, ice cream | 5.25 |
| Tumbler | 4.00 |

### INVERTED FERN

| | | |
|---|---|---|
| Butter dish | $ | 33.00 |
| Champagne (scarce) | | 50.00 |
| Compote, open | | 26.75 |
| Cordial | | 20.00 |
| Creamer | | 44.00 |
| Egg cup | | 11.00 |
| Goblet | | |
|   a. Plain base | | 12.25 |
|   b. Rayed base | | 13.25 |
| Honey dish | | 6.25 |
| Pitcher (rare) | | 125.00 |
| Plate, 6'' (scarce) | | 68.00 |
| Salt, footed | | 11.00 |

| | |
|---|---|
| Sauce ------------------------------------- | 7.25 |
| Spooner ----------------------------------- | 11.00 |
| Sugar bowl -------------------------------- | 36.00 |
| Tumbler | |
| a. Water ------------------------------ | 24.75 |
| b. Whiskey --------------------------- | 26.50 |
| Wine -------------------------------------- | 24.75 |

## IVY IN SNOW

| | | |
|---|---|---|
| Bowl, flat, 8'' diam. --------------$ | | 12.00 |
| *Butter dish ------------------------------ | | 21.00 |
| *Cake stand ------------------------------ | | 15.50 |
| *Celery ----------------------------------- | | 12.25 |
| Compote | | |
| a. Covered, small, high standard_ | | 30.00 |
| b. Covered, medium, high | | |
| standard --------------------------- | | 25.00 |
| c. Covered, large, high standard | | 24.50 |
| Cordial ----------------------------------- | | 10.50 |
| *Creamer --------------------------------- | | 14.50 |
| Cup and saucer -------------------------- | | 9.00 |
| *Goblet ----------------------------------- | | 9.50 |
| Marmalade jar --------------------------- | | 12.75 |
| *Pitcher ---------------------------------- | | 20.50 |
| Plate, 10'' ------------------------------- | | 13.25 |
| Sauce | | |
| a. Flat, round, 4'' ----------------- | | 4.50 |
| b. Deep, 6'' --------------------------- | | 6.75 |
| Spooner ----------------------------------- | | 7.50 |
| *Sugar bowl ------------------------------ | | 21.50 |
| Tumbler ----------------------------------- | | 10.00 |
| Wine -------------------------------------- | | 9.50 |

*Reproduced item

## IVY, RIBBED

| | | |
|---|---|---|
| Bitters bottle ----------------------$ | | 22.00 |
| Bowl, flat, 8½'' diam. ------------- | | 44.00 |
| Butter dish ------------------------------ | | 31.25 |
| Castor bottle ---------------------------- | | 11.00 |
| Celery (rare) ---------------------------- | | -- -- |
| Compote | | |
| a. Covered, small, on standard -- | | 60.00 |

| | |
|---|---|
| b. Open, high standard, scal- | |
| loped edge ------------------------ | 38.50 |
| c. Open, low standard, scalloped | |
| edge ----------------------------- | 30.25 |
| Cordial ----------------------------------- | 27.50 |
| Creamer ---------------------------------- | 53.50 |
| Decanter | |
| a. ½ pint ----------------------------- | 27.50 |
| b. Pint --------------------------------- | 30.25 |
| c. Quart ------------------------------- | 35.75 |
| Egg cup ---------------------------------- | 15.50 |
| Goblet ------------------------------------ | 11.50 |
| Honey dish ------------------------------- | 7.25 |
| Lamp ------------------------------------- | 38.50 |
| Mug -------------------------------------- | 49.50 |
| Pitcher (extremely rare) ---------- | -- -- |
| Salt | |
| a. Covered, footed ---------------- | 52.50 |
| b. Open, beaded edge --------- | 18.25 |
| c. Open, scalloped edge ------ | 15.50 |
| Sauce ------------------------------------- | 7.25 |
| Spooner ----------------------------------- | 10.75 |
| Sugar bowl -------------------------------- | 33.00 |
| Tumbler | |
| a. Water ------------------------------ | 24.25 |
| b. Whiskey --------------------------- | 26.50 |
| Wine -------------------------------------- | 18.25 |

IVY, ROYAL, See Royal Ivy
(See Colored Glass Section)

JACOB'S COAT
(See Colored Glass Section)

### JACOB'S LADDER

| | | |
|---|---|---|
| Bowl, flat, 6'' ----------------------$ | | 10.00 |
| Butter dish ------------------------------ | | 21.50 |
| Cake stand ------------------------------- | | 15.50 |
| Celery ------------------------------------ | | 13.75 |
| Compote | | |
| a. Covered, large, high standard_ | | 30.00 |
| b. Open, large, on standard, | | |
| scalloped edge -------------- | | 22.00 |
| c. Open, Dolphin standard, | | |
| (scarce) --------------------------- | | 115.00 |
| Cordial ----------------------------------- | | 10.75 |
| Creamer ---------------------------------- | | 18.25 |
| Dish, oval, 6'', 7'' ---------------- | | 9.00 |
| Goblet ------------------------------------ | | 16.00 |
| Marmalade jar -------------------------- | | 18.50 |

| | |
|---|---|
| Mug | 9.50 |
| Pickle | 8.25 |
| **Pitcher** | |
| a. Syrup, plain top | 16.00 |
| b. Syrup, knight's head knob | 22.00 |
| c. Water | 33.00 |
| Plate, 6½" | 10.00 |
| **Salt** | |
| a. Master, footed | 10.00 |
| b. Flat, round | 6.50 |
| **Sauce** | |
| a. Flat, 3½", 4" | 5.50 |
| b. Footed, 4½" | 6.75 |
| Spooner | 9.50 |
| Sugar bowl | 22.00 |
| Tumbler | 12.75 |
| Wine | 9.50 |

## JEWEL WITH DEWDROP

| | |
|---|---|
| **Bowl** | |
| a. Berry, 6" | $ 7.25 |
| b. Berry, 7", 8" | 10.00 |
| Butter dish | 13.75 |
| **Cake stand** | |
| a. 8" | 11.00 |
| b. 9" | 12.25 |
| c. 10" | 13.75 |
| Celery | 13.25 |
| **Compote** | |
| a. Covered, high standard, deep bowl | 22.00 |
| b. Open, high standard | 14.00 |
| Cordial | 9.50 |
| Creamer | 12.75 |
| Cup | 7.50 |
| Dish, oblong | 7.75 |
| Goblet (scarce) | 20.50 |
| Mug | 7.25 |
| Pickle | 6.75 |
| **Pitcher** | |
| a. Syrup | 10.50 |
| b. Water | 18.25 |
| Platter, bread | 11.00 |
| Sauce | 4.00 |
| Shakers, pair | 11.00 |
| Spooner | 6.75 |
| Sugar bowl | 15.50 |
| Toothpick holder | 5.50 |
| Tumbler | 9.00 |

## JUMBO

| | |
|---|---|
| **Butter dish** | |
| a. Round | $ 55.00 |
| b. Oblong | 87.50 |
| Castor set, 3 bottles | 80.00 |

| | |
|---|---|
| Compote | 72.50 |
| Creamer | 35.00 |
| Cup and saucer | 21.50 |
| Dish, covered, frosted | 42.50 |
| Goblet (scarce) | 95.00 |
| Spooner | 28.75 |
| Spoon rack (scarce) | 85.00 |
| Sugar bowl | 55.00 |

## KING'S CROWN

Also known as "Ruby Thumbprint" when colored.

| | |
|---|---|
| Banana dish | $ 25.00 |
| **Bowl** | |
| a. Berry | 10.00 |
| b. Punch | 65.00 |
| c. Sawtooth edge | 12.00 |
| Butter dish | 20.00 |
| Cake stand, 10" | 24.00 |
| Castor bottle | 6.75 |
| Castor set, all glass | 33.00 |
| **Compote** | |
| *a. Open, high standard | 22.50 |
| b. Open, large | 26.00 |
| *Cordial | 7.50 |
| **Creamer** | |
| a. Large | 12.75 |
| b. Small | 9.50 |
| Cup and saucer | 14.50 |
| **Dish** | |
| a. Boat shaped, 8" | 11.50 |
| b. Cheese | 20.75 |
| c. Olive | 6.75 |
| d. Oval, 6" | 7.75 |
| e. Oval, 10" | 9.50 |
| *Goblet | 8.00 |
| Mustard jar, covered | 7.75 |
| Pickle | 6.75 |

Pitcher
a. Round, quart _____ 18.50
b. Round, 2 quarts _____ 20.50
c. Tall, slender, large _____ 22.00
d. Tall, slender, small _____ 20.00
Sauce
a. Boat shaped _____ 4.50
b. Round, belled, 4 x 4¼'' _____ 6.00
c. Round, 5'', 6'' _____ 7.50
Shakers, pair _____ 20.00
Spooner _____ 7.50
Sugar bowl _____ 20.00
Toothpick holder _____ 6.25
Tumbler _____ 7.25
*Wine _____ 5.50

**\*Reproduced item**

## LATE BUCKLE

Butter dish _____$ 13.75
Cake stand _____ 13.25
Celery _____ 11.00
Compote
a. Covered, 8'', 9'', high
standard _____ 21.00
b. Open, 10'', 12'', scalloped
edge _____ 18.25
Creamer _____ 11.00
Dish, oval, deep _____ 6.75
Goblet _____ 8.50
Lamp _____ 13.75
Pickle _____ 6.75
Pitcher _____ 16.50
Salt, footed _____ 5.50
Sauce
a. Flat, 4½'' _____ 3.00
b. Large, 5½'' _____ 5.50
Shakers, pair _____ 11.00
Spooner _____ 9.00
Sugar bowl _____ 13.75
Wine _____ 8.25

## LATE PANELLED GRAPE

Bowl, berry _____$ 7.75
Butter dish _____ 15.00
Creamer _____ 12.75
Dish, covered _____ 12.75
*Goblet _____ 7.25
Pitcher
a. Milk _____ 16.50

b. Syrup _____ 13.25
c. Water _____ 18.25

Sauce _____ 3.75
Spooner _____ 8.25
Sugar bowl _____ 15.50
Tumbler _____ 5.50
Wine _____ 5.00

**\*Reproduced item**

## LATTICE

Bowl, waste _____$ 6.75
Butter dish _____ 13.75
Cake stand _____ 11.50
Celery _____ 10.50
Compote, covered, high standard 19.00
Cordial _____ 6.75
Creamer _____ 10.00
Egg cup _____ 7.50
Goblet _____ 6.75
Lamp _____ 11.00
Marmalade jar _____ 9.50
Pickle _____ 4.50
Pitcher
a. Syrup _____ 9.50
b. Water _____ 13.25
Plate
a. 6½'' _____ 6.25
b. 7¼'' _____ 6.75
c. 10'' _____ 11.00
Platter, oblong, inscribed _____ 12.50
Sauce
a. Flat _____ 3.25
b. Footed _____ 5.00
Shakers, pair _____ 9.00
Spooner _____ 8.25
Sugar bowl _____ 15.50
Tray, water _____ 11.00
Wine _____ 6.00

## LEAF AND DART

| | | |
|---|---|---|
| Butter dish | _____$ | 22.50 |
| Celery | _____ | 13.75 |
| Compote, covered, low standard | __ | 27.50 |
| Cordial | _____ | 9.50 |
| Creamer | _____ | 15.50 |
| Egg cup | _____ | 9.00 |
| Goblet | _____ | 8.25 |
| Lamp | _____ | 10.75 |
| Pitcher | _____ | 22.50 |
| Salt | | |
| a. Covered, on standard | _____ | 23.75 |
| b. Open, on standard | _____ | 7.25 |
| Sauce | _____ | 5.50 |
| Spooner | _____ | 7.25 |
| Sugar bowl | _____ | 22.50 |
| Tumbler, footed | _____ | 11.50 |
| Wine | _____ | 8.25 |

## LIBERTY BELL

| | | |
|---|---|---|
| Butter dish | _____$ | 32.50 |
| Celery | _____ | 16.50 |
| Child's Set: Butter dish, creamer, | | |
| spooner and sugar bowl | _____ | 33.50 |
| Compote | | |
| a. Open, 6'' | _____ | 22.50 |
| b. Open, 8'' | _____ | 25.00 |
| Creamer | _____ | 27.50 |
| Goblet | _____ | 16.50 |
| Mug | _____ | 19.00 |
| Pickle | _____ | 10.75 |
| Pitcher | _____ | 39.50 |
| Plate | | |
| a. 6'' | _____ | 13.25 |
| b. 8'' | _____ | 16.00 |
| c. 10'' | _____ | 20.50 |

| | | |
|---|---|---|
| Platter | | |
| a. 7x11½'' | _____ | 24.00 |
| b. 9¼x13'' | _____ | 27.50 |
| Salt | | |
| a. Celery dip | _____ | 6.25 |
| b. Master salt | _____ | 7.75 |
| c. Shaker top, bell-shaped | _____ | 20.00 |
| Sauce | | |
| a. Flat, round | _____ | 4.50 |
| b. Flat, closed handles, 4½'' | ____ | 6.75 |
| c. Footed | _____ | 7.50 |
| Shakers, pair | _____ | 18.50 |
| Spooner | _____ | 16.50 |
| Sugar bowl, covered | _____ | 32.50 |

## LILY OF THE VALLEY

| | | |
|---|---|---|
| Butter dish | _____$ | 25.00 |
| Cake stand | _____ | 20.50 |
| Celery | _____ | 20.00 |
| Compote, covered, high standard | _ | 38.50 |
| Cordial | _____ | 15.50 |
| Creamer | _____ | 22.00 |
| Cruet | _____ | 20.00 |
| Dish, oval | _____ | 11.00 |
| Goblet | _____ | 16.50 |
| Pickle | _____ | 8.25 |
| Pitcher | | |
| a. Water | _____ | 26.50 |
| b. Milk (scarce) | _____ | 50.00 |
| Salt, covered, footed | _____ | 24.75 |
| Sauce | _____ | 5.50 |
| Spooner | _____ | 10.00 |
| Sugar bowl | _____ | 26.00 |
| Wine (scarce) | _____ | 15.50 |

## LINCOLN DRAPE

| | | |
|---|---|---|
| Butter dish | _____$ | 33.50 |
| Celery | _____ | 33.50 |
| Compote, open | _____ | 27.75 |
| Cordial | _____ | 22.75 |

| | |
|---|---|
| Creamer | 46.75 |
| Decanter | 36.00 |
| Egg cup | 12.50 |
| Goblet | 21.00 |
| Lamp | 24.00 |
| Pitcher | |
| a. Syrup | 26.75 |
| b. Water | 79.00 |
| Plate | 20.50 |
| Salt, footed | 12.75 |
| Sauce, flat, 4½'' | 6.75 |
| Spooner | 11.25 |
| Sugar bowl | 35.00 |
| Tumbler | 15.50 |
| Wine | 11.25 |

## LINCOLN DRAPE WITH TASSEL

| | |
|---|---|
| Butter dish | $ 35.00 |
| Compote, open, low standard | 25.75 |
| Egg cup | 12.00 |
| Goblet | 21.00 |
| Spooner | 11.25 |
| Sugar bowl | 36.00 |

## LION

| | |
|---|---|
| *Butter dish | |
| a. Knob, crouched lion | $ 41.00 |
| b. Knob, lion head | 33.50 |
| *Celery | 33.50 |
| Compote | |
| a. Covered, extra large, high standard | 55.00 |
| b. Covered, low standard | 48.50 |
| c. Covered, 5'', on standard | 45.00 |
| d. Covered, collared base | 36.00 |
| e. Oblong, 5½x9'', collared base | 39.25 |
| *Cordial | 44.00 |
| Creamer | 27.50 |
| Dish, cheese (scarce) | 98.50 |

| | |
|---|---|
| *Egg cup | 33.50 |
| *Goblet | 28.50 |
| Lamp | 90.00 |
| Marmalade jar | |
| a. Knob, crouched lion | 27.25 |
| b. Knob, lion head | 25.00 |
| Paperweight | 20.50 |
| Pickle | 16.25 |
| Pitcher | |
| a. Milk | 83.50 |
| b. Syrup | 38.75 |
| *c. Water | 58.00 |
| Plate, bread | 35.75 |
| Platter, oval | 38.25 |
| Salt, master, oval | 52.50 |
| *Sauce | |
| a. Footed, small | 8.25 |
| b. Footed, medium | 10.50 |
| c. Footed, large | 11.00 |
| Spooner | 15.50 |
| *Sugar bowl | |
| a. Knob, crouched lion | 45.00 |
| b. Knob, lion head | 39.00 |
| Tumbler | 15.25 |
| Wine | 50.00 |

*Reproduced item

## LOCKET ON CHAIN
(See Colored Glass Section)

## LOG CABIN

| | |
|---|---|
| Butter dish | $ 32.50 |
| Compote, covered, on standard | 58.00 |
| Creamer | 23.75 |
| Mustard | 11.00 |
| Pitcher | 55.00 |
| Sauce | 8.25 |
| Spooner | 13.50 |
| Sugar bowl (scarce) | 42.50 |

## LOOP AND DART

| | |
|---|---|
| Butter dish | $ 21.50 |
| Celery | 13.75 |
| Compote, 8'', low standard | 21.50 |

| | |
|---|---|
| Cordial | 9.50 |
| Creamer | 20.00 |
| Egg cup | 9.50 |
| Goblet | 7.50 |
| Pickle | 6.25 |
| Pitcher | 23.50 |
| Plate, 6" | 18.25 |
| Salt, footed | 10.00 |
| Sauce | 3.75 |
| Spooner | 7.75 |
| Sugar bowl | 21.50 |
| Tumbler | |
|   a. Footed | 14.00 |
|   b. Water | 11.00 |

## LOOP AND DART
## WITH DIAMOND ORNAMENT

| | |
|---|---|
| Butter dish | $ 20.00 |
| Celery | 13.75 |
| Compote, 8", low standard | 22.00 |
| Cordial | 9.75 |
| Creamer | 16.00 |
| Egg cup | 8.25 |
| Goblet | 8.25 |
| Lamp, iron base | 13.25 |
| Pickle | 5.50 |
| Pitcher | 23.25 |
| Plate, 6" | 17.75 |
| Sauce | 3.75 |
| Spooner | 7.75 |
| Sugar bowl | 20.00 |
| Tumbler | 11.00 |

## LOOP AND DART
## WITH ROUND ORNAMENT

| | |
|---|---|
| Butter dish | $ 21.00 |
| Celery | 13.25 |
| Compote, 8", low standard | 24.75 |
| Cordial | 9.75 |
| Creamer | 16.50 |

| | |
|---|---|
| Dish, $9\frac{1}{4}$" | 8.25 |
| Egg cup | 9.00 |
| Goblet | 8.25 |
| Pickle | 6.50 |
| Pitcher | 26.00 |
| Plate, 6" | 17.75 |
| Salt, footed | 9.00 |
| Sauce | 5.25 |
| Spooner | 8.25 |
| Sugar bowl | 21.50 |
| Tumbler | |
|   a. Footed | 10.00 |
|   b. Water | 10.75 |

## LOOP WITH DEWDROPS

| | |
|---|---|
| Bowl, berry, 7", 8" | $ 9.00 |
| Butter dish | 16.00 |
| Cake stand | 12.25 |
| Celery | 13.75 |
| Compote | |
|   a. Covered, 6", 7", high | |
|     standard | 19.00 |
|   b. Covered, 8", high standard | 22.00 |
|   c. Open, $4\frac{1}{2}$", footed | 12.25 |
| Cordial | 8.25 |
| Creamer | 11.75 |
| Cup and saucer | 10.00 |
| Dish, oval, 8", 9" | 7.25 |
| Goblet | 12.75 |
| Marmalade jar | 11.00 |
| Mug | 7.25 |
| Pickle | 6.25 |
| Pitcher | |
|   a. Syrup | 11.50 |
|   b. Water | 18.00 |
| Plate, bread | 12.25 |
| Sauce | |
|   a. Flat, 4" | 3.75 |
|   b. Footed, 4" | 4.50 |
| Shakers, pair | 11.50 |
| Spooner | 8.00 |
| Sugar bowl | 16.00 |
| Tumbler | 8.50 |
| Wine | 7.25 |

## LOTUS
### (Garden of Eden)

| | |
|---|---|
| Butter dish, covered | $ 22.50 |
| Cake stand | 19.00 |
| Creamer, small | 12.00 |

**Goblet**
| | |
|---|---|
| a. Plain | 10.50 |
| b. Serpent head | 13.75 |
| Mug, handled | 10.50 |
| Pickle, oval | 8.25 |
| Sugar bowl, covered | 21.50 |
| Tray, bread | 12.75 |

## MAGNET AND GRAPE
### (Frosted Leaf)

| | |
|---|---|
| Butter dish | $ 44.50 |
| Celery | 38.50 |
| Champagne | 25.50 |
| Compote, open, large | 46.50 |
| Cordial | 23.25 |
| Creamer | 51.75 |

**Decanter**
| | |
|---|---|
| a. Pint | 40.00 |
| b. Quart | 52.50 |
| Egg cup | 22.25 |

**Goblet**
| | |
|---|---|
| a. Knob stem | 22.50 |
| b. Plain stem | 18.00 |
| Salt, footed | 11.50 |
| Sauce | 7.25 |
| Spooner | 10.50 |
| Sugar bowl | 44.50 |

**Tumbler**
| | |
|---|---|
| a. Water | 20.00 |
| b. Whiskey | 25.00 |
| Wine | 15.75 |

## MAGNET AND GRAPE
### (Stippled Leaf)

| | |
|---|---|
| Butter dish | $ 20.00 |
| Compote, open | 22.00 |
| Cordial | 10.00 |
| Creamer | 19.00 |
| Goblet | 8.25 |
| Pitcher | 22.00 |
| Salt, footed | 7.25 |
| Sauce | 4.50 |
| Spooner | 6.75 |

| | |
|---|---|
| Sugar bowl | 20.50 |
| Tumbler | 11.00 |

## MAIZE
### (See Colored Glass Section)

## MANHATTAN

**Bowl**
| | |
|---|---|
| a. Berry, 12½'' | $ 10.00 |
| b. Berry, 11'', 10'' | 9.00 |
| c. 9½'', 8½'' | 6.75 |
| d. 8'', 7'' | 6.25 |
| e. Fruit, 9½'' | 6.75 |
| f. Punch, large | 56.00 |
| Butter dish | 12.25 |
| Cake stand | 11.00 |
| Celery, tall | 9.50 |

**Compote**
| | |
|---|---|
| a. 10½'' | 15.50 |
| b. 9½'' | 12.25 |

**Creamer**
| | |
|---|---|
| a. Individual | 4.50 |
| b. Large | 9.00 |
| Dish, jelly, 6'' | 4.50 |
| Pickle | 5.00 |

**Pitcher**
| | |
|---|---|
| a. ½ gallon, tankard | 13.75 |
| b. ½ gallon, water | 11.00 |

**Plate**
| | |
|---|---|
| a. 11'', 12'' | 9.50 |
| b. 9½'' | 8.25 |
| c. 5'' | 6.75 |

**Sauce**
| | |
|---|---|
| a. 5'', footed | 3.25 |
| b. 4½'', flat | 2.75 |
| Spooner | 6.75 |

**Sugar bowl**
| | |
|---|---|
| a. Covered | 11.50 |
| b. Open, individual | 4.50 |

**Tumbler**
| | |
|---|---|
| a. Iced tea | 4.50 |
| b. Water | 3.25 |
| Water bottle | 7.25 |

## MAPLE LEAF
(See Colored Glass Section)

## MARQUISETTE

| | |
|---|---|
| Butter dish _____ $ | 16.50 |
| Celery _____ | 11.50 |
| Compote | |
|   a. Covered, low standard _____ | 23.75 |
|   b. Open, high standard _____ | 18.25 |
| Cordial _____ | 10.00 |
| Creamer _____ | 15.50 |
| Dish, oval _____ | 6.75 |
| Goblet _____ | 8.25 |
| Pickle _____ | 6.25 |
| Pitcher _____ | 22.50 |
| Sauce, flat, 4'' _____ | 4.50 |
| Spooner _____ | 7.75 |
| Sugar bowl _____ | 16.75 |
| Wine _____ | 8.25 |

## MASONIC

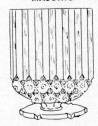

| | |
|---|---|
| Bowl | |
|   a. Berry _____ $ | 7.25 |
|   b. Small _____ | 4.50 |
| Butter dish | |
|   a. Covered, flat _____ | 11.00 |
|   b. Covered, footed _____ | 13.00 |
|   c. Open _____ | 9.00 |
| Cake stand _____ | 10.00 |
| Creamer _____ | 9.00 |
| Honey dish, covered, flat, square__ | 6.75 |
| Pitcher, tankard _____ | 11.00 |
| Sardine box _____ | 4.50 |
| Sauce _____ | 4.00 |
| Spooner _____ | 6.75 |
| Sugar bowl _____ | 11.00 |
| Tumbler _____ | 3.75 |

## MEDALLION
(See Colored Glass Section)

## MELROSE
(See Colored Glass Section)

## MICHIGAN

| | |
|---|---|
| Bowl | |
|   a. Berry, 10'' _____ $ | 7.25 |
|   b. Berry, 8½'', 7½'' _____ | 6.25 |
| Butter dish | |
|   a. Covered, large _____ | 11.00 |
|   b. Covered, small _____ | 9.00 |
| Creamer | |
|   a. Individual _____ | 4.50 |
|   b. Large _____ | 9.00 |
| Cruet _____ | 9.50 |
| Cup _____ | 3.25 |
| Goblet _____ | 5.00 |
| Olive dish _____ | 4.00 |
| Pickle _____ | 5.00 |
| Pitcher | |
|   a. ½ gallon, tankard _____ | 11.00 |
|   b. 3 pints _____ | 12.50 |
| Plate, round, 5½'' _____ | 5.50 |
| Shakers, pair _____ | 6.75 |
| Spooner _____ | 6.50 |
| Sugar bowl _____ | 11.00 |
| Tumbler _____ | 3.75 |
| Water bottle, or Carafe _____ | 8.25 |

## MINERVA

| | |
|---|---|
| Butter dish _____ $ | 20.50 |
| Cake stand | |
|   a. 9'' _____ | 15.50 |
|   b. 13'' _____ | 17.75 |
| Celery _____ | 13.75 |
| Champagne (rare) _____ | 27.00 |
| Compote | |
|   a. Covered, high standard _____ | 33.50 |
|   b. Covered, low standard _____ | 27.75 |
| Cordial _____ | 9.75 |

| | |
|---|---|
| Creamer | 19.25 |
| Dish, oblong, 2½" deep | 10.00 |
| Goblet | 20.75 |
| Marmalade jar | 19.00 |
| Pickle | 11.25 |
| Pitcher | 31.50 |
| Plate | |
| a. Small | 13.75 |
| b. Closed handles, 9" | 15.50 |
| Platter | 20.00 |
| Sauce | |
| a. Flat, round | 6.00 |
| b. Footed, round | 7.25 |
| Spooner | 9.00 |
| Sugar bowl | 21.00 |

## MINNESOTA

| | |
|---|---|
| **Bowl** | |
| a. Berry, round, 6", 7", 8" | $ 6.25 |
| b. Round, flared edge, 9½" | 6.75 |
| c. Round, flared edge, 8½" | 5.75 |
| d. Round, flared edge, 7½" | 6.25 |
| e. Round, flared edge, 4½" | 5.50 |
| f. Square, 6", 7", 8" | 6.75 |
| Butter dish | 11.00 |
| **Celery tray** | |
| a. 13" | 6.75 |
| b. 10" | 5.50 |
| **Compote** | |
| a. Round, 6", 7", 8" | 13.75 |
| b. Square, 6", 7", 8" | 11.50 |
| Creamer | 7.75 |
| **Dish** | |
| a. Candy, 9" | 5.00 |
| b. Jelly, 8" | 4.50 |
| c. Oval, low, 7", 8" | 4.50 |
| d. Preserve, 9" | 5.00 |
| Goblet | 3.75 |
| Pickle, 7½" | 4.00 |
| **Pitcher** | |
| a. ½ gallon, tankard | 11.00 |
| b. ¾ gallon, water | 10.00 |
| Sauce, flat, 4", 4½" | 2.75 |
| Spooner | 6.75 |
| Sugar bowl, covered | 11.00 |
| Tumbler | 3.25 |
| Wine | 3.50 |

## MONKEY
(See Colored Glass Section)

## MOON AND STAR
(Palace)

| | |
|---|---|
| **Bowl** | |
| a. Berry, 6" | $ 10.00 |
| b. Berry, 7" | 11.00 |
| c. Berry, 8" | 12.50 |
| d. Berry, 10" | 15.50 |
| e. Fruit, 12½" | 22.00 |
| f. Waste | 7.75 |
| *Butter dish | 30.00 |
| Cake stand | 25.75 |
| Celery | 20.75 |
| *Champagne, flared top | 18.25 |
| Claret | 20.00 |
| **Compote** | |
| *a. Covered, 8", high standard | 39.00 |
| b. Covered, 10" high standard | 44.50 |
| c. Covered, 7", collared base | 31.50 |
| d. Covered, 10", collared base | 56.00 |
| e. Open, high standard | 26.50 |
| Creamer | 37.00 |
| *Cruet | 31.50 |
| **Dish** | |
| a. Cheese | 32.50 |
| b. Oblong, 8" | 18.25 |
| *Egg cup | 18.75 |
| *Goblet | |
| a. Clear | 18.25 |
| b. Frosted | 20.50 |
| Lamp | 30.50 |
| Pickle | 11.00 |
| **Pitcher** | |
| a. Syrup | 26.50 |
| *b. Water | 56.00 |
| Platter, oblong | 23.25 |
| *Salt, celery dip | 7.75 |
| **Sauce** | |
| a. Flat | 7.75 |
| b. Footed | 9.00 |
| *Shakers, pair | 22.00 |
| *Spooner | 12.25 |
| *Sugar bowl | 33.00 |
| *Toothpick | 10.50 |
| Tray | 20.50 |
| *Tumbler | 18.25 |
| *Wine | 16.00 |
| *Reproduced item | |

## NAILHEAD

| | |
|---|---:|
| Butter dish _____ $ | 14.00 |
| Cake stand _____ | 13.25 |
| Celery _____ | 13.75 |
| Compote | |
|   a. Covered, 8'' _____ | 16.50 |
|   b. Open, high standard _____ | 12.25 |
| Cordial _____ | 7.50 |
| Creamer _____ | 10.50 |
| Goblet _____ | 8.50 |
| Pitcher _____ | 17.75 |
| Plate | |
|   a. Round, 9'' _____ | 11.00 |
|   b. Square, 7'' _____ | 10.00 |
| Sauce _____ | 5.00 |
| Shakers, pair _____ | 9.00 |
| Spooner _____ | 7.75 |
| Sugar bowl _____ | 14.00 |
| Tumbler _____ | 7.25 |
| Wine _____ | 5.25 |

## NEVADA

| | |
|---|---:|
| Bowl, 6'', 7'', 8'' _____ $ | 6.50 |
| Butter dish _____ | 12.25 |
| Cake stand, 10'' _____ | 9.50 |
| Celery, tall _____ | 8.25 |
| Compote | |
|   a. Covered, 6'', 7'', 8'' _____ | 16.00 |
|   b. Open, 6'', 7'', 8'' _____ | 11.00 |
| Cracker jar _____ | 11.00 |
| Creamer _____ | 8.50 |
| Cruet _____ | 7.75 |
| Dish | |
|   a. Oval, 10'', 11'' _____ | 7.25 |
|   b. Oval, 7'', 8'', 9'' _____ | 6.50 |
| Pickle _____ | 4.50 |
| Pitcher | |
|   a. ½ gallon, tankard _____ | 11.50 |
|   b. 3 pints _____ | 10.00 |
|   c. Water _____ | 11.00 |

| | |
|---|---:|
| Salt | |
|   a. Individual _____ | 1.75 |
|   b. Master _____ | 4.00 |
| Sauce _____ | 2.75 |
| Shakers, pair _____ | 7.25 |
| Spooner _____ | 5.50 |
| Sugar bowl, covered _____ | 12.75 |
| Syrup _____ | 8.00 |
| Toothpick holder _____ | 3.50 |
| Tumbler _____ | 4.00 |

## NEW ENGLAND PINEAPPLE

| | |
|---|---:|
| Bowl, fruit _____ $ | 39.50 |
| Butter dish _____ | 55.00 |
| Castor bottle _____ | 13.75 |
| Castor set _____ | 72.50 |
| Celery _____ | 43.50 |
| Champagne _____ | 39.50 |
| Compote | |
|   a. Open, small, high standard __ | 47.50 |
|   b. Open, large, high standard __ | 54.00 |
|   c. Open, small, low standard __ | 43.75 |
|   d. Open, large, low standard __ | 43.75 |
|   e. Open, extra large, high | |
|      standard _____ | 58.50 |
|   f. Covered, 6'', high standard __ | 70.00 |
| Cordial _____ | 29.50 |
| Creamer (scarce) _____ | 60.50 |
| Cruet _____ | 36.00 |
| Decanter | |
|   a. Pint _____ | 30.50 |
|   b. Quart _____ | 45.00 |
| Egg cup _____ | 13.75 |
| *Goblet _____ | 15.75 |
| Honey dish _____ | 8.50 |
| Jug, tall _____ | 54.00 |
| Mug, small _____ | 36.50 |
| Pitcher (scarce) _____ | 125.00 |
| Plate, 6'' _____ | 54.00 |
| Salt, footed _____ | 16.75 |
| Sauce _____ | 10.25 |
| Spooner _____ | 16.75 |
| Sugar bowl _____ | 55.00 |
| Tumbler | |
|   a. Footed (scarce) _____ | 50.00 |
|   b. Water _____ | 28.00 |
|   c. Whiskey _____ | 33.50 |
| *Wine _____ | 31.50 |

*Reproduced item

59

## NEW HAMPSHIRE

| | |
|---|---|
| Biscuit jar, covered _____$ | 8.25 |
| **Bowl** | |
|   a. Flared, 6½'', 7½'', 8½'' _____ | 6.25 |
|   b. Round, 6½'', 7½'', 8½'' _____ | 6.75 |
|   c. Square, 6½'', 7½'', 8½'' _____ | 7.25 |
| Butter dish _____ | 11.00 |
| Celery _____ | 8.25 |
| Champagne _____ | 6.25 |
| **Creamer** | |
|   a. Individual _____ | 4.75 |
|   b. Large _____ | 8.25 |
| Goblet _____ | 4.75 |
| Lemonade cup _____ | 5.00 |
| **Mug** | |
|   a. Large _____ | 6.25 |
|   b. Medium _____ | 5.00 |
| **Pitcher** | |
|   a. ½ gallon, tankard _____ | 11.00 |
|   b. 3 pints, water _____ | 10.00 |
|   c. ¾ gallon, water _____ | 9.50 |
| **Sauce** | |
|   a. Round, deep _____ | 2.75 |
|   b. Round, shallow, 4'' _____ | 2.50 |
|   c. Round, flared _____ | 3.00 |
|   d. Square _____ | 3.00 |
| **Sugar bowl** | |
|   a. Covered _____ | 11.00 |
|   b. Medium, open handles _____ | 5.50 |
| Tumbler _____ | 3.50 |
| Wine _____ | 3.25 |

## NEW JERSEY

| | |
|---|---|
| **Bowl** | |
|   a. Flared, 8'', 9'', 10'' _____$ | 6.50 |
|   b. Oval, 6'', 8'', 10'' _____ | 5.50 |
|   c. Round, high, 6'', 7'', 8'' _____ | 6.25 |
| Butter dish _____ | 10.00 |
| Cake stand, 8'' _____ | 7.75 |
| Celery _____ | 8.25 |
| Celery tray _____ | 5.50 |
| **Compote** | |
|   a. Open, 6'', 7'', 8'' _____ | 11.50 |
|   b. Jelly, covered, 5'' _____ | 13.75 |

| | |
|---|---|
| Creamer _____ | 8.25 |
| Cruet _____ | 7.25 |
| Goblet _____ | 4.25 |
| Molasses jar _____ | 7.75 |
| Pickle _____ | 4.50 |
| **Pitcher** | |
|   a. 1 gallon, applied handle ____ | 13.25 |
|   b. 3 pints, applied handle _____ | 11.00 |
|   c. ½ gallon, pressed handle ____ | 10.00 |
| Plate, round, 8'' _____ | 5.50 |
| Sauce, 4'' _____ | 3.00 |
| Shakers, pair _____ | 7.25 |
| Spooner _____ | 5.50 |
| Sugar bowl, covered _____ | 10.00 |
| Syrup _____ | 7.50 |
| Toothpick holder _____ | 3.25 |
| Tumbler _____ | 3.75 |
| Wine _____ | 4.50 |

## NIAGARA

| | |
|---|---|
| Bowl, berry _____$ | 5.50 |
| Butter dish, covered _____ | 11.00 |
| Celery _____ | 8.50 |
| Creamer _____ | 9.50 |
| Cruet _____ | 8.25 |
| Pitcher, tankard _____ | 10.00 |
| Sauce _____ | 3.00 |
| Shakers, pair _____ | 6.75 |
| Spooner _____ | 6.25 |
| Sugar bowl, covered _____ | 10.00 |
| Syrup jug _____ | 8.25 |
| Tumbler _____ | 4.50 |

### OAK, ROYAL, See Royal Oak
### (See Colored Glass Section)

### ONE HUNDRED ONE

| | |
|---|---|
| Butter dish _____$ | 16.50 |
| Cake stand _____ | 13.75 |
| Celery _____ | 15.25 |
| Compote, covered, low standard __ | 25.00 |
| Creamer _____ | 11.75 |
| Dish, oval, deep _____ | 8.25 |
| Goblet _____ | 9.75 |
| Lamp, hand _____ | 13.75 |
| Pickle _____ | 6.75 |
| Pitcher, water (scarce) _____ | 37.50 |
| Plate | |
|    a. 7" _____ | 9.00 |
|    b. 8" _____ | 10.00 |
|    c. 9" _____ | 11.00 |
|    d. 11" _____ | 15.50 |
|    e. Bread, motto _____ | 16.50 |
| Sauce | |
|    a. Flat _____ | 3.75 |
|    b. Footed _____ | 4.25 |
| Shakers, pair _____ | 9.50 |
| Spooner _____ | 7.75 |
| Sugar bowl _____ | 16.50 |

### OPALESCENT HOBNAIL
### (See Colored Glass Section)

### OPEN ROSE

| | |
|---|---|
| Butter dish _____$ | 21.00 |
| Celery _____ | 13.25 |
| Compote | |
|    a. Covered, low standard _____ | 30.25 |
|    b. Covered, high standard _____ | 35.00 |
| Creamer _____ | 20.75 |
| Dish, oval, 6 x 9½" _____ | 9.00 |
| Egg cup _____ | 10.00 |
| Goblet _____ | 9.75 |
| Pickle _____ | 6.75 |
| Pitcher _____ | 23.75 |
| Salt, footed _____ | 7.25 |
| Sauce _____ | 4.00 |
| Spooner _____ | 7.25 |
| Sugar bowl _____ | 21.50 |
| Tumbler _____ | 6.50 |

### OVAL MITRE

| | |
|---|---|
| Butter dish _____$ | 22.75 |
| Creamer _____ | 25.00 |
| Compote | |
|    a. Covered, 6", high standard __ | 32.00 |
|    b. Open, 6", 8" _____ | 22.00 |
| Dish, oval _____ | 10.50 |

| | |
|---|---|
| Goblet _____ | 10.75 |
| Sauce _____ | 4.00 |
| Spooner _____ | 8.25 |
| Sugar bowl _____ | 23.00 |

### OVAL STAR

| | |
|---|---|
| Bowl | |
|    a. Large _____$ | 7.25 |
|    b. Small _____ | 5.50 |
| Butter dish _____ | 10.50 |
| Compote | |
|    a. Covered _____ | 13.25 |
|    b. Open _____ | 10.00 |
| Creamer _____ | 8.25 |
| Pickle _____ | 4.00 |
| Pitcher, water _____ | 11.00 |
| Sauce _____ | 3.00 |
| Spooner _____ | 6.75 |
| Tumbler _____ | 4.00 |
| Wine _____ | 3.25 |

### PALMETTE

| | |
|---|---|
| Butter dish _____$ | 16.50 |
| Cake stand _____ | 14.00 |
| Castor bottle _____ | 5.50 |
| Celery _____ | 16.00 |
| Compote, covered, low standard __ | 27.50 |
| Cordial _____ | 11.75 |
| Creamer _____ | 22.00 |

| | |
|---|---|
| Egg cup | 10.00 |
| Goblet | 10.00 |
| Lamp | 20.75 |
| Pickle | 7.75 |
| Pitcher | 27.50 |
| Plate, cake, handled | |
| a. Clear | 10.50 |
| b. Amber | 16.50 |
| c. Blue | 20.00 |
| Salt, master, footed | 8.50 |
| Sauce | 4.50 |
| Spooner | 7.50 |
| Sugar bowl | 18.25 |
| Tumbler | |
| a. Footed | 15.50 |
| b. Water | 10.00 |
| Wine | 10.00 |

## PANELLED CHERRY

| | | |
|---|---|---|
| Bowl, berry, covered | $ | 13.25 |
| Butter dish | | 16.50 |
| Compote, covered, low standard | | 22.00 |
| Creamer | | 11.50 |
| Goblet | | 8.25 |
| Pitcher | | |
| a. Syrup | | 15.50 |
| b. Water | | 22.00 |
| Sauce | | |
| a. Flat | | 4.50 |
| b. Footed | | 5.50 |
| Spooner | | 7.50 |
| Sugar bowl | | 16.50 |
| Tumbler | | 9.50 |

## PANELLED DAISY

| | | |
|---|---|---|
| Bowl | | |
| a. Covered, 8'', flat | $ | 11.00 |
| b. Waste | | 7.25 |

| | |
|---|---|
| Butter dish | |
| a. Flat | 16.50 |
| b. Footed | 21.50 |
| Cake stand | |
| a. 8'', 9'' | 17.75 |
| b. 10'', 11'' | 20.00 |
| Celery | 13.75 |
| Compote | |
| a. Covered, 5'', 6'', high standard | 25.00 |
| b. Covered, 7'', 8'', high standard | 32.00 |
| c. Open, 10'', 11'', high standard | 20.75 |
| Creamer (scarce) | 23.00 |
| Dish | |
| a. Oval, 7'', 8'' | 9.00 |
| b. Oval, 9'', 10'' | 12.25 |
| *Goblet | 16.50 |
| Lamp, hand | 11.75 |
| Mug | 10.50 |
| Pickle | 8.25 |
| Pitcher | |
| a. Syrup | 16.50 |
| b. Water | 23.00 |
| Plate | |
| a. Round, $7\frac{1}{4}$'' | 11.75 |
| b. Square, $9\frac{1}{2}$'' | 12.75 |
| Sauce | |
| a. Flat | 4.50 |
| b. Footed, round | 5.50 |
| Shakers | |
| a. Salt and papper | 13.25 |
| b. Sugar | 10.75 |
| Spooner | 9.00 |
| Sugar bowl | 21.00 |
| Tray | 18.25 |
| *Tumbler | 8.25 |

*Reproduced item

## PANELLED DEWDROP

| | | |
|---|---|---|
| Butter dish | $ | 16.50 |
| Celery | | 13.25 |
| Compote | | |
| a. Covered, 8'', on standard | | 25.00 |
| b. Open, high standard | | 18.25 |
| Cordial | | 10.75 |
| Creamer | | 16.00 |
| Dish, oval, collared base | | 7.75 |

| | |
|---|---|
| Goblet | |
|   a. Dewdrops on base | 10.50 |
|   b. Plain base | 8.00 |
| Lemonade glass | 13.25 |
| Liqueur glass | 5.50 |
| Marmalade jar | 13.75 |
| Pickle | 6.75 |
| Pitcher | 23.75 |
| Plate | |
|   a. 7'' | 10.50 |
|   b. 11'' | 13.25 |
|   c. Honey dish, 11'', large, oval | 26.50 |
| Platter | |
|   a. Oblong, handled | 18.25 |
|   b. Oval | 13.25 |
| Sauce | |
|   a. Flat | 5.00 |
|   b. Footed | 6.00 |
| Spooner | 8.50 |
| Sugar bowl | 17.75 |
| Tumbler | 9.00 |
| Wine | 6.50 |

### PANELLED DIAMOND POINT

| | |
|---|---|
| Butter dish | $ 15.00 |
| Celery | 10.50 |
| Creamer | 11.75 |
| Goblet | 7.50 |
| Pitcher | 20.00 |
| Sauce | 4.00 |
| Spooner | 6.75 |
| Sugar bowl | 15.50 |

### PANELLED FORGET-ME-NOT
#### (See Colored Glass Section)

### PANELLED GRAPE

| | |
|---|---|
| Ale glass | $ 9.75 |
| Bowl, deep | 10.00 |

| | |
|---|---|
| *Butter dish | 18.00 |
| Celery | 13.75 |
| Compote | |
|   a. Covered, large | 33.00 |
|   b. Open, 6½'', low standard | 21.50 |
| *Cordial | 8.00 |
| Creamer | 13.75 |
| Cup, sherbet | 6.25 |
| Dish, oval | 8.25 |
| Goblet | 13.25 |
| *Lemonade glass | 10.50 |
| Liqueur glass | 7.25 |
| Pitcher | |
|   *a. Small | 20.50 |
|   b. Syrup | 16.00 |
|   c. Large | 24.50 |
| *Plate, 10'' | 11.75 |
| Salt | 5.50 |
| *Sauce | |
|   a. Oval | 3.75 |
|   b. Round, 4¼'' | 5.25 |
| Spooner | 7.75 |
| *Sugar bowl | 18.50 |
| Toothpick holder | 5.00 |
| *Tumbler | |
|   a. Jelly | 7.75 |
|   b. Water | 9.75 |
| *Wine | 5.50 |

*Reproduced item

### PANELLED THISTLE

| | |
|---|---|
| Bowl | |
|   a. Berry, 7'', 8'', 9'' | $ 9.50 |
|   b. Rose | 6.50 |
| Butter dish | 15.50 |
| Cake stand | |
|   a. Large | 11.75 |
|   b. Small | 9.75 |
| Celery tray | 8.25 |
| Celery vase | 11.00 |
| Compote | |
|   a. Open, small | 10.75 |
|   b. Open, medium | 12.75 |
|   c. Open, large | 16.00 |
|   d. Jelly | 9.50 |
| Cordial | 8.25 |
| Creamer | 12.25 |
| Cruet | 11.00 |
| Cup, sherbet | 6.75 |
| Dish | |
|   a. Honey dish, covered, square, | |
|     footed | 15.50 |

| | |
|---|---|
| b. Oblong | 9.00 |
| c. Oval, curled edges | 9.50 |
| d. Oval, 8¼'' | 8.00 |
| e. Round, handled | 6.50 |
| *Goblet | 12.75 |
| Pickle, 7½'', 8¼'' | 6.75 |
| Pitcher | |
| a. Large | 16.00 |
| b. Small | 13.25 |
| Plate | |
| *a. 7¼'' | 11.00 |
| b. 8¼'' | 12.75 |
| c. 9¼'' | 13.75 |
| d. 10¼'' | 15.50 |
| *Salt | |
| a. Celery dip | 4.00 |
| b. Footed | 5.50 |
| Sauce | 4.50 |
| Shakers, pair | 18.00 |
| Spooner | 6.75 |
| Sugar bowl | 16.50 |
| Toothpick holder | 4.00 |
| Tumbler | |
| a. Lemonade (scarce) | 15.50 |
| b. Water | 9.75 |
| Wine | 9.50 |

## PAVONIA
### (Pineapple Stem)

| | |
|---|---|
| Bowl | $ 9.50 |
| Butter dish | 21.00 |
| Cake stand | |
| a. Small | 19.00 |
| b. Large | 22.00 |
| Celery | 17.75 |
| Compote | |
| a. Covered, high standard | 31.00 |
| b. Open, high standard | 23.25 |
| Creamer | 16.00 |
| Goblet | 13.75 |
| Pitcher, water | 27.50 |
| Salt, individual | 4.00 |
| Sauce, footed | 5.25 |
| Spooner | 13.25 |
| Sugar bowl | 21.00 |
| Tumbler | 10.00 |
| Wine | 11.50 |

## PEACOCK FEATHER

| | |
|---|---|
| Bowl, berry | $ 8.25 |
| Butter dish | 13.25 |

| | |
|---|---|
| Cake stand | |
| a. 9'', 10'' | 11.00 |
| b. 11'' | 13.75 |
| Celery boat | 8.50 |
| Compote | |
| a. Shallow, high standard | 13.75 |
| b. Deep, covered, high standard | 20.50 |
| Creamer | 11.00 |
| Cruet | 9.50 |
| Dish, oval | 6.50 |
| Lamp, hand | 10.50 |
| Pickle | 5.50 |
| Pitcher | |
| a. Syrup | 12.75 |
| b. Water | 15.00 |
| Sauce | 4.50 |
| Shakers, pair | 11.50 |
| Spooner | 6.75 |
| Sugar bowl | 15.50 |
| Tumbler | 7.25 |

## PENNSYLVANIA

| | |
|---|---|
| Bowl | |
| a. Pointed, 6'', 7'', 8'' | $ 7.25 |
| b. Round, 8'' | 7.75 |
| c. Square, 8'' | 8.25 |
| Butter dish | |
| a. Covered, large | 11.00 |
| b. Covered, small | 9.00 |
| Celery | 8.25 |
| Celery tray | 6.75 |
| Cheese dish, covered | 9.75 |
| Creamer | |
| a. Large | 10.00 |
| b. Small | 7.75 |
| Cruet | 7.75 |
| Cup | 3.50 |
| Decanter | 9.50 |
| Goblet | 5.00 |
| Jelly dish | 5.25 |
| Olive dish | 4.75 |
| Pickle dish | 4.50 |

Pitcher
  a. ½ gallon, tankard _____ 11.00
  b. 1½ pints, tankard _____ 10.00
  c. Syrup _____ 7.50
  d. Water _____ 9.50
Plate, round, 7'' _____ 6.75
Punch bowl _____ 25.00
Sauce
  a. Pointed _____ 3.00
  b. Round, 4'' _____ 4.00
  c. Square _____ 3.50
Shakers
  a. Large, pair _____ 7.50
  b. Medium, pair _____ 5.75
  c. Small, pair _____ 5.50
Spooner _____ 5.25
Sugar bowl
  a. Covered, large _____ 11.00
  b. Open, small, handles _____ 5.50
Tumbler
  a. Champagne _____ 5.25
  b. Water _____ 4.50
  c. Whiskey _____ 5.25
Water bottle _____ 8.25

## PICKET

Bowl, waste _____$  9.50
Butter dish _____ 19.00
Celery _____ 13.75
Compote
  a. Covered, 6'', high standard __ 22.00
  b. Covered, 8'', high standard __ 25.75
  c. Covered, oblong, low
     standard _____ 27.00
  d. Open, high standard _____ 16.00
  e. Open, low standard _____ 13.75
Creamer _____ 13.75
Goblet _____ 13.25
Marmalade jar _____ 13.75
Match holder _____ 6.75
Pickle _____ 6.25
Pitcher _____ 26.50
Salt
  a. Celery dip _____ 3.00
  b. Large _____ 9.00
Sauce _____ 6.50
Spooner _____ 9.50
Sugar bowl _____ 20.00
Tray, water _____ 18.25

## PINEAPPLE AND FAN

Bowl
  a. Berry, 8'', 9'' _____$ 10.00
  b. Fruit, with plate, 8'' _____ 11.75
  c. Low, 10'' _____ 9.00
  d. Punch, 12'' _____ 27.50
  e. Salad, 13'' _____ 25.00
Butter dish _____ 16.50
Celery
  a. Medium _____ 11.75
  b. Tall _____ 13.25
Creamer
  a. Individual _____ 8.25
  b. Large _____ 15.00
Custard cup _____ 5.50
Lemonade cup _____ 5.75
Mug _____ 6.00
Pitcher
  a. ½ gallon, tankard _____ 14.00
  b. ¾ gallon, tankard _____ 15.50
  c. ½ gallon, water _____ 13.25
  d. 1 quart, water _____ 10.50
  e. 1 pint, water _____ 9.50
Plate, 6½'' _____ 5.75
Sauce, 4'', 4½'' _____ 3.75
Spooner _____ 7.25
Sugar bowl
  a. Individual, covered _____ 9.00
  b. Large, covered _____ 16.50
Sugar shaker _____ 8.50
Sweetmeat dish, 5'', 6'' _____ 10.50
Tumbler
  a. Water _____ 5.50
  b. Whiskey _____ 6.50

## PLEAT AND PANEL (Darby)

Bowl
  a. 5 x 8'' _____$ 16.00
  b. Waste (scarce) _____ 22.00
Butter chip _____ 3.25

| | |
|---|---|
| Butter dish | 22.00 |
| **Cake stand** | |
| a. 9'' | 15.50 |
| b. 9¾'' | 16.50 |
| Celery | 13.75 |
| **Compote** | |
| a. Covered, 8'', square, high standard | 32.75 |
| b. Open, low standard | 20.00 |
| Creamer | 16.50 |
| **Dish** | |
| a. Covered, oblong | 18.50 |
| b. Covered, square | 22.00 |
| *Goblet | 11.75 |
| Lamp | 11.00 |
| Marmalade jar | 18.25 |
| Pickle | 6.75 |
| Pitcher | 23.75 |
| **Plate** | |
| a. 3½'' (scarce) | 20.00 |
| b. 6'' | 10.50 |
| *c. 7½'', square | 11.50 |
| d. 8½'' (scarce) | 21.00 |
| **Platter** | |
| a. Closed handles | 13.25 |
| b. Open handles | 18.25 |
| **Sauce** | |
| a. Flat, handled | 5.00 |
| b. On standard | 6.00 |
| c. On standard, with cover | 9.50 |
| Shakers, pair | 13.25 |
| Spooner | 9.00 |
| Sugar bowl | 22.00 |
| Tray, water (scarce) | 26.50 |
| Wine (scarce) | 16.50 |

*Reproduced Item

## PLUME

| | |
|---|---|
| **Bowl** | |
| a. Berry | $ 6.75 |
| b. Finger | 5.75 |
| Butter dish | 16.50 |
| Cake stand | 13.75 |
| Celery | 12.25 |
| **Compote** | |
| a. Covered | 22.00 |
| b. Open | 13.75 |
| Creamer | 13.25 |
| Goblet | 11.00 |
| Pickle | 6.25 |
| Pitcher, water | 16.50 |
| Sauce | 4.00 |
| Spooner | 7.75 |
| Sugar bowl | 16.50 |

| | |
|---|---|
| Tumbler | 5.25 |
| Water tray | 13.25 |

## POLAR BEAR

| | |
|---|---|
| Bowl, waste | $ 26.50 |
| Butter dish | 45.00 |
| Creamer | 30.00 |
| **Goblet** | |
| a. Clear | 23.75 |
| b. Frosted | 33.25 |
| Pickle | 12.25 |
| Pitcher | 62.50 |
| Platter, oval, handled, 16½'' | 46.00 |
| Sauce | 11.00 |
| Spooner | 16.50 |
| Sugar bowl | 45.00 |
| Tray, water | 42.50 |

## POPCORN

| | |
|---|---|
| Butter dish | $ 28.50 |
| Cordial | 13.75 |
| Creamer | 22.00 |
| **Goblet** | |
| a. With ear | 19.00 |
| b. Without ear | 13.75 |
| Pitcher | 31.00 |
| Sauce | 7.50 |
| Spooner | 10.00 |
| Sugar bowl | 29.50 |
| Wine | 12.25 |

## POWDER AND SHOT

| | |
|---|---|
| Butter dish | $ 27.00 |
| Castor bottle | 9.75 |
| Celery | 25.00 |

Compote
  a. Covered, high standard _____ 36.00
  b. Covered, low standard _____ 31.00
Creamer _____ 25.00
Egg cup _____ 13.25
Goblet _____ 10.75
Pickle _____ 5.50
Pitcher _____ 33.00
Salt, footed _____ 11.00
Sauce _____ 5.50
Spooner _____ 9.50
Sugar bowl _____ 27.50

## PRESSED LEAF

Bowl
  a. Open _____$  9.50
  b. Covered, 7'', 8'' _____ 13.25
Butter dish _____ 20.50
Cake stand _____ 17.75
Champagne _____ 15.50
Compote
  a. Covered, 6'', high standard __ 22.00
  b. Covered, 7'', 8'', high
     standard _____ 27.50
  c. Covered, 7'', 8'', low standard_ 26.50
Cordial _____ 9.50
Creamer _____ 16.00
Dish
  a. Oval, 5'', 6'' _____ 7.75
  b. 8'', 9'' _____ 10.00
Egg cup _____ 9.00
Goblet _____ 9.50
Lamp, hand _____ 13.25
Pickle _____ 6.50
Pitcher _____ 27.50
Salt, footed _____ 6.75
Sauce _____ 4.50
Spooner _____ 8.25
Sugar bowl _____ 21.50
Wine _____ 10.00

## PRIMROSE
(See Colored Glass Section)

## PRINCESS FEATHER
(Rochelle)

Butter dish _____$ 33.50
Celery _____ 25.00
Compote
  a. Covered, 6'', high standard _ 35.75
  b. Covered, 7'', high standard _ 41.50
  c. Covered, low standard _____ 33.00
  d. Covered, grape vine design
     on flange _____ 47.00
  e. Open, 8'', low standard ____ 23.75
Creamer _____ 32.00
Dish, oval, 8'', 9'' _____ 20.75
Egg cup _____ 16.50
Goblet _____ 11.00
Honey dish _____ 6.75
Pickle _____ 7.25
Pitcher
  a. Quart _____ 56.00
  b. ½ gallon _____ 51.00
Plate
  a. 6'' _____ 12.25
  b. 7'' _____ 13.75
  c. 8'' _____ 15.50
  d. 9'', cake, closed handles ___ 25.00
Salt, footed _____ 11.50
Sauce _____ 5.50
Spooner _____ 10.00
Sugar bowl _____ 34.00

## PRINTED HOBNAIL
(See Colored Glass Section)

## PRISCILLA

| | |
|---|---|
| Banana stand _____ $ | 23.25 |
| Bowl | |
|   a. Square, 8'' _____ | 9.50 |
|   b. Flat, 10½'' _____ | 11.00 |
|   c. Rose _____ | 11.50 |
| Butter dish _____ | 25.00 |
| Cake stand, 10'' _____ | 20.00 |
| Celery _____ | 11.00 |
| Compote | |
|   a. Covered, 7'' _____ | 26.50 |
|   b. Open, 7½'' _____ | 20.50 |
| Creamer _____ | 12.50 |
| Cruet _____ | 11.00 |
| Cup and saucer _____ | 10.50 |
| *Goblet _____ | 10.75 |
| Jelly compote _____ | 10.00 |
| Mug _____ | 7.25 |
| Pickle _____ | 6.75 |
| Pitcher, syrup _____ | 13.75 |
| Sauce, 4½'' _____ | 4.00 |
| Spooner _____ | 7.75 |
| Sugar bowl, covered _____ | 25.50 |
| Toothpick _____ | 6.25 |
| Tumbler _____ | 6.75 |
| Wine _____ | 10.00 |

*Reproduced item

## PRISCILLA, FOSTORIA'S

| | |
|---|---|
| Bowl, berry, 8½'' _____ $ | 6.25 |
| Butter dish, covered _____ | 11.00 |
| Celery _____ | 8.50 |
| Creamer _____ | 9.00 |
| Egg cup _____ | 6.75 |
| Pickle _____ | 5.50 |
| Shakers, pair _____ | 8.50 |
| Spooner _____ | 6.25 |
| Sugar bowl, covered _____ | 11.00 |
| Toothpick holder _____ | 4.25 |

## PRISM AND FLUTE

| | |
|---|---|
| Bowl, covered _____ $ | 13.25 |
| Butter dish _____ | 16.00 |
| Cake stand | |
|   a. 7½'' _____ | 8.50 |
|   b. 9'' _____ | 10.00 |
|   c. 10½'' _____ | 11.00 |
|   d. 12½'' _____ | 11.50 |
| Celery _____ | 13.75 |
| Compote | |
|   a. 8'', 9'', low standard _____ | 18.50 |
|   b. 7'', 8'', high standard _____ | 20.50 |
| Cordial _____ | 8.25 |
| Creamer _____ | 12.25 |
| Egg cup _____ | 7.25 |
| Goblet _____ | 6.75 |
| Pickle _____ | 7.50 |
| Pitcher, water _____ | 21.50 |
| Plate | |
|   a. 6'' _____ | 7.75 |
|   b. 8'' _____ | 9.75 |
| Sauce _____ | 3.25 |
| Tumbler, footed _____ | 7.25 |
| Wine _____ | 6.75 |

## PRISM WITH DIAMOND POINTS

| | |
|---|---|
| Bowl, deep _____ $ | 11.75 |
| Butter dish _____ | 25.00 |
| Compote, 6'', covered _____ | 41.50 |
| Cordial _____ | 10.50 |
| Creamer _____ | 33.00 |
| Egg cup _____ | 11.00 |
| Goblet | |
|   a. Plain stem _____ | 8.50 |
|   b. Knob stem _____ | 18.50 |
| Pickle _____ | 10.50 |
| Pitcher _____ | 42.50 |
| Salt _____ | 10.00 |
| Sauce _____ | 6.00 |
| Spooner _____ | 11.00 |
| Sugar bowl _____ | 25.00 |
| Tumbler _____ | 15.50 |
| Wine _____ | 20.50 |

## PSYCHE AND CUPID

| | |
|---|---|
| Butter dish _____ $ | 22.00 |
| Celery _____ | 15.50 |
| Compote, high standard _____ | 25.00 |
| Creamer _____ | 16.00 |
| Goblet _____ | 11.50 |
| Marmalade jar _____ | 13.25 |
| Pickle _____ | 7.50 |
| Pitcher _____ | 22.00 |
| Sauce _____ | 5.00 |

| | |
|---|---|
| Spooner | 7.75 |
| Sugar bowl | 23.00 |
| Wine | 11.50 |

### PURPLE SLAG
(See Colored Glass Section)

### RAINDROP
(See Colored Glass Section)

### RED BLOCK

| | |
|---|---|
| Bowl, berry | $ 24.00 |
| Butter dish | 34.50 |
| Celery | 28.00 |
| Cordial | 15.50 |
| Creamer | |
|   a. Large | 35.00 |
|   b. Small | 27.50 |
| Cruet | 25.00 |
| Dish | |
|   a. Cheese | 44.50 |
|   b. Oblong, 8'', 9'' | 16.50 |
|   c. Oblong, 10'' | 22.00 |
| *Goblet | 22.50 |
| Mug | 14.00 |
| Pitcher | 45.00 |
| Sauce | 6.25 |
| Shakers, pair | 20.00 |
| Spooner | 15.50 |
| Sugar bowl | 34.50 |
| Tumbler | 13.75 |
| Wine bottle | 25.00 |
| *Wine glass | 14.00 |

*Reproduced item

### RIBBED GRAPE

| | |
|---|---|
| Butter dish | $ 40.00 |
| Celery | 25.00 |

| | |
|---|---|
| Compote | |
|   a. Covered, 6'' | 83.00 |
|   b. Open, low standard | 39.00 |
| Cordial | 33.00 |
| Creamer | 73.00 |
| Goblet | 16.00 |
| Pitcher | 90.00 |
| Plate, 6'' | 23.00 |
| Sauce | 11.00 |
| Spooner | 16.25 |
| Sugar bowl | 41.50 |

RIBBED IVY, See Ivy, Ribbed

### RIBBED PALM

| | |
|---|---|
| Bowl, flat | $ 12.25 |
| Butter dish | 23.75 |
| Castor set, pewter base | 46.75 |
| Celery | 35.75 |
| Compote | |
|   a. Covered, 6'' (scarce) | 68.00 |
|   b. Open, 7'', 8'', high standard | 30.25 |
|   c. Open, 10'', high standard | 35.25 |
|   d. Open, low standard | 26.50 |
| Cordial | 20.50 |
| Creamer | 41.00 |
| Dish, oval, 8'', 9'' | 20.50 |
| Egg cup | 11.00 |
| Goblet | 11.00 |
| Lamp | 27.50 |
| Pickle | 12.75 |
| Pitcher, water (scarce) | 69.00 |
| Plate, 6'' | 16.50 |
| Salt, footed | 11.50 |
| Sauce | 7.75 |
| Spooner | 11.00 |
| Sugar bowl | 26.00 |
| Tumbler | 16.50 |
| Wine | 15.50 |

### RIBBED THUMBPRINT

| | |
|---|---|
| Bowl, berry, 8'' | $ 5.50 |

Butter dish, covered _____ 11.00
Compote, jelly _____ 8.25
Creamer _____ 8.50
Cruet _____ 9.00
Pitcher, water _____ 11.50
Sauce _____ 3.00
Shakers, pair _____ 9.50
Spooner _____ 6.75
Sugar bowl, covered _____ 11.00
Toothpick _____ 5.00
Tumbler _____ 4.75

## RIBBON

Bowl, waste (scarce) _____$ 22.00
Butter dish _____ 30.25
Cake stand _____ 27.00
Celery _____ 23.25
Cheese dish _____ 44.50
Cologne bottle _____ 13.75
Compote
    a. Open, high standard, classic
      figure of woman _____ 56.00
    b. Open, 7'', low standard _____ 22.00
    c. Oblong, on standard, dolphin 81.00
    d. Round, on standard, dolphin 78.50
Cordial _____ 20.50
Creamer _____ 23.25
*Goblet _____ 19.00
Pickle castor, in metal frame ____ 44.50
Pitcher
    a. Large _____ 38.50
    b. Small _____ 31.25
Plate (rare) _____ 53.00
Platter, oblong, cut corners, 9x13'' 35.50
Sauce
    a. Footed _____ 6.75
    b. Round _____ 5.50
    c. Handled _____ 7.25
Spooner _____ 13.75
Sugar bowl _____ 31.00
Tray, water, 15x16½'' _____ 53.00

Wine (very scarce) _____ 57.50
    *Reproduced item

## ROMAN KEY

Bowl, berry _____$ 23.75
Butter dish _____ 26.50
Cake stand, 12'' _____ 21.50
Celery _____ 33.00
Champagne _____ 18.25
Compote, open, high standard ___ 26.50
Cordial _____ 10.00
Creamer _____ 33.50
Egg cup _____ 13.25
Goblet _____ 16.50
Pickle (relish) _____ 12.75
Pitcher, water (scarce) _____ 62.00
Plate (scarce) _____ 48.00
Salt, footed _____ 12.75
Sauce _____ 7.25
Spooner _____ 11.00
Sugar bowl _____ 26.50
Tumbler
    a. Footed _____ 17.75
    b. Water _____ 20.00
Wine _____ 19.00

## ROMAN ROSETTE

Bowl
    a. Berry, 7'', 8'' _____$ 10.50
    b. Berry, covered, 9'' _____ 16.50
Butter dish _____ 20.50
Cake stand, 9'', 10'' (scarce) __ 30.25
Castor set, glass _____ 27.50
Celery _____ 16.50
Compote
    a. Covered, 6'', on standard __ 22.00
    b. Covered, 8'', on standard __ 30.25
    c. Open, 4½'', on standard ____ 18.25
Cordial _____ 11.00
Creamer _____ 13.25
Dish _____ 8.25
*Goblet _____ 11.00

Mug
    a. Large `_____` 10.50
    b. Small `_____` 9.00
Mustard jar `_____` 8.25
Pickle `_____` 9.50
Pitcher
    a. Water, $\frac{1}{2}$ gallon `_____` 23.75
    b. Quart `_____` 26.00
    c. Syrup `_____` 18.25
Plate, $7\frac{1}{4}$'' (scarce) `_____` 21.50
Platter, bread, 9x11'' `_____` 20.00
Sauce
    a. Flat `_____` 4.50
    b. Footed `_____` 6.00
Shakers, pair `_____` 13.75
Spooner `_____` 11.00
Sugar bowl `_____` 22.00
Tumbler `_____` 11.00
Wine `_____` 13.25

*Reproduced item

ROSE IN SNOW
(See Colored Glass Section)

ROSE SPRIG
(See Colored Glass Section)

ROSETTE

Bowl, waste `_____`$ 6.75
Butter dish `_____` 18.00
Cake stand, $8\frac{1}{2}$'' `_____` 12.25
Celery `_____` 11.00
Compote
    a. Covered, 7'', 8'', high
        standard `_____` 23.75
    b. Open, $4\frac{1}{2}$'', footed `_____` 15.50
Cordial `_____` 8.25
Creamer `_____` 11.00
Goblet `_____` 10.75
Pickle `_____` 7.25
Pitcher `_____` 20.00
Plate
    a. 7'' `_____` 11.00
    b. 9'', handled `_____` 13.25
Sauce `_____` 4.00
Shakers, pair `_____` 11.00
Spooner `_____` 8.25
Sugar bowl `_____` 18.25
Tray, water `_____` 10.75
Tumbler `_____` 7.25
Wine `_____` 6.75

ROYAL IVY
(See Colored Glass Section)

ROYAL OAK
(See Colored Glass Section)

RUBY THUMBPRINT
Also known as "King's Crown" when
not colored.

Bowl
    a. Berry `_____`$ 25.00
    b. Punch `_____` 100.00
    c. Sawtooth edge, 7'', $8\frac{1}{2}$'' `____` 28.50
Butter dish `_____` 35.00
Castor bottle `_____` 10.00
Castor set `_____` 75.00
Celery `_____` 27.50
Compote·
    *a. Open, 5'', high standard `___` 40.00
    b. Open, large `_____` 38.00
    c. Covered, 6'', 7'', high
        standard `_____` 60.00
    d. Covered, 8'', 9'', high
        standard `_____` 69.50
Cordial `_____` 14.50
Creamer
    a. Large `_____` 37.50
    b. Small `_____` 20.00
Cup and saucer `_____` 25.00
Dish
    a. Banana `_____` 40.00
    b. Boat shaped, 8'' `_____` 28.50
    c. Cheese dish `_____` 47.50
    d. Olive dish `_____` 12.50
    e. Oval, 6'' `_____` 18.00
    f. Oval, 10'' `_____` 22.50
*Goblet `_____` 20.00
Mustard jar, covered `_____` 16.50
Pickle `_____` 12.50
Pitcher
    a. Round, quart `_____` 44.00
    b. Round, 2 quarts `_____` 49.50
    c. Tall, slender, large `_____` 40.00
    d. Tall, slender, small `_____` 35.00
Sauce
    a. Boat shaped `_____` 18.00
    b. Round, belled, $4x4\frac{1}{2}$'' `_____` 12.50
    c. Round, 5'', 6'' `_____` 9.50
Shakers, pair `_____` 24.00
Spooner `_____` 16.50
Sugar bowl `_____` 35.00
Toothpick holder `_____` 12.50
Tumbler `_____` 16.50
*Wine `_____` 16.75

*Reproduced item

## SAWTOOTH

## SAXON

**Bowl**
| | |
|---|---|
| a. Covered, 7'' | $ 26.50 |
| b. Open, 8'', 9'' | 23.50 |
| c. Open, 10'' | 30.25 |
| Butter dish | 33.00 |
| Cake stand, 9'', 10'' | 27.50 |
| Celery | 23.75 |
| Champagne | 22.00 |

**Compote**
| | |
|---|---|
| a. Covered, 6'', 7'' | 35.00 |
| b. Covered, 8'', 9'' | 39.75 |
| c. Covered, 10'', 11'' | 40.00 |
| d. Covered, 12'' | 61.00 |
| e. Open, 6'', 7'' | 23.25 |
| f. Open, 8'' | 25.00 |
| g. Open, 10'' | 26.00 |
| Cordial | 13.25 |
| Creamer | 35.00 |
| Cruet | 16.50 |
| Decanter | 33.00 |

**Dish**
| | |
|---|---|
| a. Oval | 16.50 |
| b. Covered oval dish with lion knob and handles. Small | 41.00 |
| c. Same. Large | 46.50 |
| Egg cup | 13.25 |
| Goblet | 16.00 |
| Honey dish | 7.25 |
| Lamp | 40.50 |
| Pitcher | 55.00 |
| Pomade jar | 21.50 |

**Salt**
| | |
|---|---|
| a. Covered, footed | 23.75 |
| b. Open, smooth edge | 11.00 |

**Sauce**
| | |
|---|---|
| a. 4'' | 7.25 |
| b. 5'' | 8.00 |
| Spooner | 13.75 |
| Sugar bowl | 35.00 |

**Tray**
| | |
|---|---|
| a. 10'' | 20.00 |
| b. 11'' | 25.00 |
| c. 12'' | 30.50 |
| d. 14'' | 38.00 |

**Tumbler**
| | |
|---|---|
| a. Footed | 12.75 |
| b. Water | 10.50 |
| Water bottle, with tumble-up | 36.00 |
| Wine | 16.50 |

| | |
|---|---|
| Bowl, 8'' | $ 7.25 |
| Butter dish | 12.75 |
| Celery | 10.00 |

**Compote**
| | |
|---|---|
| a. Covered, high standard | 20.75 |
| b. Open, low standard | 13.25 |
| c. Covered, 6'', sweetmeat jar | 20.50 |
| Creamer | 13.25 |
| Dish, oval, 8'', 9'' | 9.75 |
| Egg cup | 8.25 |
| Goblet | 6.75 |
| Pickle | 6.25 |

**Pitcher**
| | |
|---|---|
| a. Quart | 19.00 |
| b. ½ gallon | 15.50 |
| Plate, 6'' | 9.00 |
| Platter, bread, oval, 12'' | 12.75 |
| Salt | 4.50 |
| Sauce | 4.25 |
| Spooner | 8.25 |
| Sugar bowl | 14.00 |
| Tumbler | 7.25 |
| Wine | 6.75 |

## SCROLL

| | |
|---|---|
| Butter dish | $ 13.75 |
| Celery | 10.50 |

**Compote**
| | |
|---|---|
| a. Covered, high standard | 20.00 |
| b. Covered, low standard | 16.50 |
| Cordial | 7.25 |
| Creamer | 10.00 |
| Dish, oval | 7.50 |
| Egg cup | 6.75 |
| Goblet | 7.00 |

| Pickle | 5.50 |
|---|---|
| Pitcher | 16.00 |
| Salt | 5.50 |
| Sauce | 3.50 |
| Spooner | 8.25 |
| Sugar bowl | 15.00 |
| Tumbler | 5.50 |

## SCROLL WITH FLOWERS

| Butter dish | $ 13.75 |
|---|---|
| Cake plate, handled | 10.00 |
| Celery | 10.50 |
| Compote, covered, low standard | 19.00 |
| Cordial | 9.00 |
| Creamer | 10.00 |
| Egg cup | 7.25 |
| Goblet | 6.25 |
| Mustard jar | 7.75 |
| Pickle | 6.25 |
| Pitcher | 13.25 |
| Salt, footed | 5.50 |
| Sauce | 3.75 |
| Shakers, pair | 10.00 |
| Spooner | 7.25 |
| Sugar bowl | 14.50 |
| Wine | 6.25 |

## SHELL AND JEWEL

| Banana stand | $ 18.25 |
|---|---|
| Bowl, 8'' | 7.75 |
| Butter dish | 15.00 |
| Cake stand | 12.75 |
| Compote, open, high standard | 16.00 |
| Creamer | 8.25 |
| Dish, honey, covered | 6.25 |
| Pitcher, water | 13.25 |
| Sauce | 3.75 |
| Spooner | 6.75 |
| Sugar bowl | 15.50 |
| Tray, water | 14.00 |
| Tumbler | 5.00 |

## SHELL AND TASSEL

| Butter dish | | |
|---|---|---|
| a. Round | $ | 26.50 |
| b. Square | | 32.75 |
| Cake stand | | |
| a. Large | | 23.50 |
| b. Small | | 20.00 |
| Celery vase | | |
| a. Round | | 20.00 |
| b. Square | | 26.50 |
| Compote | | |
| a. Covered | | 33.00 |
| b. Open, 4½'' | | 20.00 |
| c. Open, high standard | | 21.50 |
| Creamer | | |
| a. Round | | 16.50 |
| b. Square | | 20.50 |
| Dish, oval | | 16.00 |
| *Goblet | | 23.50 |
| Marmalade jar | | 27.50 |
| Pickle | | 10.00 |
| Pitcher | | |
| a. Round | | 26.00 |
| b. Square | | 32.75 |
| Platter | | |
| a. Oblong, rounded corners | | 26.50 |
| b. Oval, large | | 23.50 |
| c. Oval, small | | 17.75 |
| Salt | | 10.00 |
| Sauce, 4½'' | | 7.50 |
| Shakers (scarce) | | 30.50 |
| Spooner | | |
| a. Round | | 9.75 |
| b. Square | | 11.00 |
| Sugar bowl | | |
| a. Round | | 24.50 |
| b. Square | | 30.50 |
| Tray | | |
| a. Oblong, large | | 33.00 |
| b. Oblong, small | | 27.50 |
| Vases, pair | | 55.00 |

*Reproduced item

## SHERATON
(See Colored Glass Section)

## SINGLE ROSE

| Butter dish | $ 12.75 |
|---|---|
| Creamer | 10.75 |

| | |
|---|---|
| Spooner | 7.75 |
| Sugar bowl | 13.25 |

## SMOCKING

| | |
|---|---|
| Butter dish, covered | $ 40.50 |
| Compote | 72.00 |
| Creamer (scarce) | 56.00 |
| Goblet | 35.50 |
| Lamp, 9'' high | 55.00 |
| Spill holder | 15.75 |
| Sugar bowl | 50.00 |

## SNAIL

| | |
|---|---|
| Bowl, finger | $ 5.50 |
| Butter dish | 16.00 |
| Celery | 9.75 |
| Compote, covered | 21.00 |
| Creamer | |
| a. Individual | 6.50 |
| b. Regular | 10.50 |
| Cruet | 9.50 |
| Goblet | 7.50 |
| Pitcher | |
| a. Syrup | 7.75 |
| b. Water | 13.25 |
| Plate, 7'' | 6.75 |
| Shakers | |
| a. Salt and pepper, pair | 15.50 |

| | |
|---|---|
| b. Sugar | 9.00 |
| Spooner | 8.25 |
| Sugar bowl | |
| a. Individual | 6.75 |
| b. Large, covered | 16.50 |
| Tumbler | 5.50 |
| Wine | 5.25 |

## SOUTHERN IVY

| | |
|---|---|
| Bowl, berry | $ 9.50 |
| Butter dish | 16.50 |
| Creamer | 10.00 |
| Cruet | 10.50 |
| Egg cup | 8.25 |
| Pitcher, water | 17.75 |
| Sauce | 3.75 |
| Spooner | 7.75 |
| Sugar bowl | 17.75 |
| Tumbler | 5.50 |

## SPIRALLED IVY

| | |
|---|---|
| Butter dish | 13.75 |
| Creamer | 9.75 |
| Pitcher | |
| a. Large | 16.50 |
| b. Small | 13.75 |
| Sauce | 3.75 |
| Spooner | 6.75 |
| Sugar bowl | 13.75 |
| Tumbler | 6.50 |

## SPIREA BAND
(See Colored Glass Section)

## SPRIG

| | |
|---|---|
| Bowl, berry | $ 8.25 |
| Butter dish | 20.00 |
| Cake stand | 16.00 |
| Celery | 16.50 |
| Compote | |
| a. Covered, high standard | 23.25 |
| b. Open, high standard | 15.00 |
| c. Open, low standard | 13.25 |

| | |
|---|---|
| Creamer | 14.00 |
| Dish, oval | 8.25 |
| Goblet | 10.50 |
| Pickle | 5.25 |
| Pitcher, water | 22.00 |
| Platter | 14.00 |
| Sauce | |
| a. Flat | 5.00 |
| b. Footed | 5.25 |
| Spooner | 8.25 |
| Sugar bowl | 20.50 |
| Tumbler | 6.00 |
| Wine | 9.75 |

### STAR ROSETTED

| | |
|---|---|
| Butter dish | $ 22.00 |
| Compote | |
| a. Open, high standard | 27.50 |
| b. Open, small, low standard | 20.00 |
| Creamer | 19.00 |
| Goblet | 9.75 |
| Pickle | 6.75 |
| Pitcher | 23.75 |
| Plate, 10'', "A Good Mother" | 16.50 |
| Sauce | 5.00 |
| Spooner | 9.00 |
| Sugar bowl | 22.00 |

### STATES, THE

| | |
|---|---|
| Butter dish, covered | $ 12.75 |
| Celery | 8.25 |
| Compote, open, 7'' | 11.00 |
| Creamer | 8.50 |
| Dish, relish, handled | 6.50 |
| Pitcher, water, gold trim | 12.25 |

| | |
|---|---|
| Plate, large | 7.25 |
| Sugar bowl, covered | 12.75 |
| Toothpick | 3.50 |
| Tumbler | 4.50 |

### STEDMAN

| | |
|---|---|
| Celery | $ 16.50 |
| Champagne | 13.75 |
| Cheese dish, covered | 26.50 |
| Compote | |
| a. Covered, 7'', 8'', high standard | 38.50 |
| b. Open, low standard | 20.00 |
| Creamer | 27.50 |
| Decanter | 25.00 |
| Egg cup | 10.50 |
| Goblet | 10.75 |
| Lamp | 22.00 |
| Pitcher, syrup | 17.75 |
| Plate, 6'' | 13.25 |
| Salt | |
| a. Flat | 5.50 |
| b. Round | 6.50 |
| Sauce | 4.75 |
| Spooner | 8.00 |
| Sugar bowl | 25.00 |
| Tumbler | 13.25 |
| Wine | 12.25 |

### STIPPLED BAND

| | |
|---|---|
| Butter dish | $ 13.25 |
| Celery | 10.50 |
| Compote | |
| a. Covered, high standard | 22.00 |
| b. Covered, low standard | 20.00 |
| c. Open, high standard | 16.50 |
| d. Open, low standard | 13.25 |
| Creamer | 12.75 |
| Goblet | 7.50 |
| Pitcher, water | 21.50 |
| Salt, footed | 6.00 |
| Spooner | 7.25 |
| Sugar bowl | 15.00 |
| Tumbler | 7.75 |

## STIPPLED CHAIN

| | |
|---|---|
| Butter dish, covered | $ 13.25 |
| Creamer | 15.50 |
| Goblet | 7.50 |
| Pickle dish | 6.25 |
| Pitcher, water | 20.00 |
| Salt, footed | 5.50 |
| Sauce | 3.25 |
| Spooner | 6.75 |
| Sugar bowl, covered | 14.00 |

## STIPPLED CHERRY

| | |
|---|---|
| Bowl, berry | $ 7.75 |
| Butter dish | 13.75 |
| Celery | 11.00 |
| Creamer | 10.00 |
| Pitcher | 15.50 |
| Plate | |
| a. 6'' | 9.00 |
| b. 9¼'', bread | 11.00 |
| Sauce | 3.25 |
| Spooner | 8.25 |
| Sugar bowl | 14.00 |
| Tumbler | 8.25 |

## STIPPLED FORGET-ME-NOT

| | |
|---|---|
| Bowl, waste | $ 7.75 |
| Butter dish | 23.00 |
| Cake stand | |
| a. Large | 19.00 |
| b. Small | 16.50 |
| Celery | 17.25 |
| Compote | |
| a. Covered, 6'' | 25.00 |
| b. Covered, 7'', 8'' | 33.00 |
| Cordial | 11.00 |
| Creamer | 17.75 |
| Cup and saucer | 16.00 |
| Goblet | 15.50 |
| Lamp, handled | 16.50 |
| Mug | 7.75 |
| Mustard jar | 8.25 |
| Pickle | 10.00 |
| Pitcher | |
| a. Small | 19.00 |
| b. Syrup | 21.50 |
| c. Large | 23.25 |
| Plate | |
| a. 7'', baby center | 14.00 |
| b. 7'', star center | 13.25 |
| c. 9'', kitten center, handled | 19.00 |
| Salt | 9.75 |
| Sauce | |
| a. Flat | 4.50 |
| b. Footed | 7.00 |
| Spooner | 10.00 |
| Sugar bowl | 23.50 |
| Toothpick holder | 10.00 |
| Tray, water | 20.75 |
| Tumbler | |
| a. Bar | 9.00 |
| b. ½ pint | 10.00 |
| c. Gill | 9.50 |
| d. Footed | 12.75 |
| Wine | 13.75 |

## STIPPLED GRAPE AND FESTOON

| | |
|---|---|
| Butter dish | $ 23.25 |
| Celery | 20.50 |
| Compote, covered, low standard | 30.50 |
| Cordial | 11.00 |
| Creamer | 23.75 |
| Dish, oval | 9.00 |
| Egg cup | 10.00 |
| Goblet | 10.50 |

| | |
|---|---:|
| Pickle | 7.25 |
| Pitcher | 33.00 |
| Plate | 11.50 |
| Sauce | 5.00 |
| Spooner | 10.00 |
| Sugar bowl | 25.00 |
| Wine | 11.00 |

## STIPPLED IVY

| | |
|---|---:|
| Bowl, berry | $ 9.50 |
| Butter dish | 20.75 |
| Compote | |
|   a. Covered, low standard | 33.00 |
|   b. Open, high standard | 20.50 |
| Creamer | 16.50 |
| Egg cup | 10.00 |
| Goblet | 9.75 |
| Pickle | 6.75 |
| Pitcher, syrup | 16.25 |
| Salt, footed | 6.75 |
| Sauce | 4.50 |
| Spooner | 10.00 |
| Sugar bowl | 21.50 |
| Tumbler | 10.00 |
| Wine | 8.25 |

## STIPPLED STAR

| | |
|---|---:|
| Butter dish | $ 21.50 |
| Celery | 20.00 |
| Compote | |
|   a. Open, large, high standard | 27.50 |
|   b. Open, small, high standard | 25.00 |
| Creamer | 27.00 |
| Dish, oval, 8'' | 12.75 |
| Egg cup | 16.00 |
| *Goblet | 16.50 |

| | |
|---|---:|
| Pickle | 8.25 |
| Pitcher | 33.00 |
| Sauce | |
|   a. Flat, 4'' | 6.00 |
|   b. Flat, 6'' | 7.50 |
| Spooner | 11.00 |
| Sugar bowl | 22.00 |
| Tumbler, small | 6.75 |

*Reproduced item

## STRAWBERRY
### (See Colored Glass Section)

## STRAWBERRY AND CURRANT
### (Currants and leaves on reverse)

| | |
|---|---:|
| Butter dish | $ 20.00 |
| Celery | 13.75 |
| Cheese dish | 23.25 |
| Compote | |
|   a. Covered, on standard | 29.50 |
|   b. Open | 20.50 |
| Creamer | 16.50 |
| *Goblet | 11.75 |
| Pitcher | |
|   a. Large | 25.00 |
|   b. Small | 20.50 |
| Sauce | 6.50 |
| Spooner | 10.00 |
| Sugar bowl | 20.50 |
| Tumbler | 10.00 |

*Reproduced in clear, amber,
blue and green

## SUNBURST

| | |
|---|---:|
| Bowl, finger | $ 6.75 |
| Butter dish | 13.25 |
| Cake stand | 10.50 |
| Celery | 10.75 |
| Compote, covered, low standard | 20.00 |
| Cordial | 7.25 |
| Creamer | 10.50 |

| | |
|---|---|
| Cruet | 9.50 |
| Dish, oblong, deep | 7.25 |
| Egg cup | 7.25 |
| Goblet | 7.50 |
| Marmalade jar | 10.50 |
| Pickle | |
|   a. Double, 8'', 10'' | 8.25 |
|   b. Single | 6.75 |
| Pitcher | |
|   a. Large | 16.50 |
|   b. Small | 13.75 |
| Plate | |
|   a. 6'' | 7.25 |
|   b. 7'' | 9.00 |
|   c. 11'' bread, with motto | 11.00 |
| Sauce | 3.75 |
| Spooner | 8.25 |
| Sugar bowl | 13.75 |
| Wine | 5.50 |

### SWAN
#### (See Colored Glass Section)

### SWIRL
#### (See Colored Glass Section)

### TEARDROP AND TASSEL

| | |
|---|---|
| Bowl, berry | $ 8.25 |
| Butter dish | 17.75 |
| Compote | |
|   a. Covered, 6'', 8'', high | |
|     standard | 26.50 |
|   b. Open, 6'', 8'' | 15.50 |
| Creamer | 11.00 |
| Goblet | 16.00 |
| Pickle | 6.00 |
| Pitcher | 18.50 |
| Sauce | 4.00 |
| Shakers, pair | 11.00 |
| Spooner | 9.00 |
| Sugar bowl | 18.25 |

| | |
|---|---|
| Tumbler | 7.75 |
| Wine (scarce) | 16.00 |

### TEXAS
#### (Loop with Stippled Panels)

| | |
|---|---|
| Bowl | |
|   a. Berry, flat, 7½'', 8½'', 9½'' | $ 6.75 |
|   b. Berry, footed, 7½'', 8½'', 9½'' | 7.75 |
|   c. Scalloped, 6'', 7'', 8'' | 7.25 |
| Butter dish | 12.25 |
| Cake stand | |
|   a. Footed, 10'', high standard | 10.00 |
|   b. Footed, 10'', low standard | 9.00 |
| Celery | 8.25 |
| Celery tray | 5.50 |
| Compote | |
|   a. Covered, high standard, | |
|     6'', 7'', 8'' | 19.00 |
|   b. High standard, 5'', jelly | 12.25 |
|   c. Low standard, 4'', jelly | 10.00 |
| Creamer | 9.00 |
| Cruet | 9.00 |
| Goblet | 7.50 |
| Horseradish jar | 5.50 |
| Olive dish | 4.50 |
| Pickle | 5.50 |
| Pitcher, 3 pints | 11.00 |
| Plate, 9'' | 6.75 |
| Preserve dish, 8'' | 6.25 |
| Sauce, 4'' | 2.75 |
| Shakers | |
|   a. Large, pair | 9.50 |
|   b. Small, pair | 8.25 |
| Spooner | 6.50 |
| Sugar bowl | 12.75 |
| Toothpick holder | 3.75 |
| Tumbler | 4.00 |
| Wine | 4.50 |

### THE STATES, See States, The

### THISTLE

| | |
|---|---|
| Bowl, berry, covered | $ 10.00 |
| Butter dish | 16.50 |
| Cake stand | 15.50 |
| Compote | |
|   a. Covered, high standard | 23.75 |
|   b. Covered, low standard | 18.25 |
| Cordial | 10.00 |
| Creamer | 13.75 |
| Dish, oval, deep | 7.75 |
| Egg cup | 9.00 |

| | |
|---|---|
| Goblet | 9.00 |
| Pickle | 5.75 |
| Pitcher | 20.00 |
| Salt, footed | 5.00 |
| Sauce | 4.50 |
| Spooner | 6.75 |
| Sugar bowl | 16.50 |
| Tumbler | |
| a. Footed | 9.75 |
| b. Water | 9.00 |
| Wine | 9.50 |

### THOUSAND EYE
### (See Colored Glass Section)

### THREE FACE

| | |
|---|---|
| *Butter dish | $ 62.50 |
| *Cake stand | |
| a. 8'', 9'' | 50.00 |
| b. 10'', 11'' | 72.50 |
| Celery | 49.50 |
| *Champagne (scarce) | 112.00 |
| Compote | |
| a. Covered, large | 90.00 |
| *b. Covered, 6½'', small | 62.50 |
| c. Open, high standard | 41.50 |
| *Claret | 47.00 |
| Cracker jar (rare) | 245.00 |
| *Creamer | 59.00 |
| *Goblet | 42.00 |
| *Lamp | 78.00 |
| Pitcher, water | 170.00 |
| Salt dip | 15.50 |
| Salt, footed | 40.00 |

| | |
|---|---|
| *Sauce | 16.00 |
| *Shakers, pair | 30.50 |
| Spooner | 24.50 |
| *Sugar bowl | 63.00 |
| Syrup jug | 44.00 |
| *Wine | 47.00 |

*Reproduced item

### THREE-IN-ONE

| | |
|---|---|
| Bowl, berry, fluted | $ 5.50 |
| Butter dish | 9.50 |
| Celery | 6.75 |
| Compote | |
| a. 6'' | 8.25 |
| b. 8'', 9'' | 10.50 |
| c. 10'' | 12.25 |
| d. 10'', fluted | 13.75 |
| Cracker jar | 9.50 |
| Creamer | |
| a. Individual | 5.00 |
| b. Regular | 6.75 |
| Milk jar, covered | 8.25 |
| Pickle jar | 6.00 |
| Pitcher, squatty | 9.00 |
| Spooner | 6.00 |
| Sugar bowl | |
| a. Individual | 5.50 |
| b. Regular | 9.75 |
| Toothpick | 3.00 |

### THREE PANEL
### (See Colored Glass Section)

### THUMBPRINT

| | |
|---|---|
| Ale glass | $ 22.00 |
| Bowl | |
| a. Covered | 30.50 |
| b. Finger | 16.50 |

| | |
|---|---|
| Butter dish | 44.00 |
| Cake stand | |
| a. Regular | 53.00 |
| b. 13'' (scarce) | 102.00 |
| Castor bottle | 11.00 |
| Celery | 69.00 |
| Champagne | 33.00 |
| Compote | |
| a. Covered, 7'', high standard | 55.00 |
| b. Covered, 8'', high standard | 62.50 |
| c. Covered, 10'', high standard | 72.00 |
| d. Covered, 6'', medium high standard | 47.00 |
| e. Open, 6'', low standard | 30.50 |
| f. Open, 8'', 9'', low standard | 36.00 |
| Cordial | 16.50 |
| Creamer | 41.50 |
| Decanter, quart | 53.00 |
| Egg cup | 22.00 |
| Goblet | |
| a. Barrel shape | 17.75 |
| b. Knob stem | 20.50 |
| Honey dish | 6.50 |
| Mug, $\frac{1}{2}$ pint | 15.50 |
| Pickle | 13.25 |
| Pitcher, water (scarce) | 110.00 |
| Plate, 8''. (There are only 6 plates known in the Thumbprint pattern) | — — |
| Punch bowl, $23\frac{1}{2}$x12'' | 300.00 |
| Salt | |
| a. Footed | 16.00 |
| b. Individual | 7.75 |
| Sauce, 4'', $4\frac{1}{2}$'' | 7.25 |
| Spooner | 16.50 |
| Sugar bowl | 47.00 |
| Tumbler | |
| a. Footed | 20.00 |
| b. Water | 15.50 |
| c. Whiskey (scarce) | 30.50 |
| Wine | 18.25 |

## TORPEDO
(Pygmy, Fish-Eye)

| | |
|---|---|
| Banana stand, $9\frac{1}{4}$'' | $ 25.00 |
| Bowl | |
| a. 4'', Rose bowl (scarce) | 16.50 |
| b. 7'', open, flared rim | 9.50 |
| c. 7'', 8'', covered | 15.50 |
| d. 8'', $8\frac{1}{4}$'', open, flared rim | 10.50 |
| e. 9'', $9\frac{1}{2}$'', open, flared rim | 11.75 |
| f. Waste bowl, scalloped top | 8.25 |
| Butter dish, covered | 25.00 |
| Cake stand, 9'', 10'' | 20.00 |
| Celery, scalloped top | 16.50 |
| Compote | |
| a. 4'', covered, jelly | 22.00 |
| b. 5'', open, jelly, flared rim | 16.50 |
| c. 6'', covered, high standard | 31.50 |
| d. 6'', open, flared rim, high standard | 20.00 |
| e. 7'', 8'', covered, high standard | 37.00 |
| f. $8\frac{1}{4}$'', $8\frac{3}{4}$'', open, flared rim, high standard | 22.00 |
| Creamer | |
| a. Flat, collared base, medium | 15.50 |
| b. Footed, large | 18.50 |
| c. Footed, medium | 16.50 |
| Cruet | 16.50 |
| Cup and saucer | 13.75 |
| Decanter | 18.50 |
| Goblet | 13.75 |
| Honey dish, 6'', covered | 10.00 |
| Lamp | |
| a. $3\frac{3}{8}$'', handled, flat base | 13.75 |
| b. $5\frac{1}{4}$'', handled, footed base | 16.50 |
| c. 8'', $8\frac{1}{4}$'', plain bowl, pattern on base | 13.25 |
| d. $8\frac{3}{4}$'', $9\frac{3}{4}$'', pattern on base and bowl | 20.00 |
| Marmalade jar, covered (scarce) | 22.00 |
| Pitcher | |
| a. Milk, $8\frac{3}{4}$'', tankard | 16.00 |
| b. Syrup, brass top | 18.25 |
| c. Water, $10\frac{7}{8}$'', barrel type | 22.00 |
| d. Water, $11\frac{1}{2}$'', 12'', tankard | 25.00 |
| Salt | |
| a. Individual, $1\frac{5}{8}$'' diam. | 5.00 |
| b. Master, 3'' diam. | 7.75 |
| Sauce | |
| a. $3\frac{1}{2}$'', flat, honey | 5.50 |
| b. $3\frac{1}{2}$'', footed, honey | 5.00 |
| c. $4\frac{1}{4}$'', footed | 5.50 |
| d. $4\frac{1}{4}$'', $4\frac{5}{8}$'', flat | 5.25 |
| Shakers | |
| a. S/P, $2\frac{1}{4}$'' high, pair | 13.75 |
| b. S/P, 3'' high, pair | 15.50 |
| Spooner, scalloped top | 9.00 |
| Sugar bowl, covered | 25.00 |
| Tray | |
| a. Water, 10'', round (scarce) | 27.50 |
| b. Water, $11\frac{3}{4}$'', clover-shaped | 25.00 |
| Tumbler | 9.00 |
| Wine | 9.50 |

## TREE OF LIFE
(Portland)

| | |
|---|---|
| Bowl | |
| a. Flat, 8'' | $ 8.25 |
| b. Flat, 10'' | 11.75 |
| c. Finger bowl | 8.25 |
| Butter dish, hand and ball on cover | 27.00 |
| Celery | 15.50 |

Compote
  a. Open, 9'', hand stem _____ 36.00
  b. Open, 10'', hand stem _____ 40.50
  c. Covered, hand holding ball
    on pedestal _____ 52.50
  d. Open, child holding book stem_ 74.50
Creamer _____ 22.50
Goblet _____ 18.50
Pitcher, water _____ 35.25
Plate, 7'' _____ 11.00
Sauce
  a. Round _____ 5.50
  b. Shell-shaped _____ 7.50
Sugar bowl, hand and ball on cover_ 27.50
Tumbler, footed _____ 11.00
Wine _____ 13.75

## TULIP WITH SAWTOOTH

Butter dish _____$ 41.50
Celery _____ 27.50
Champagne _____ 21.50
Compote
  a. Covered, large, high
    standard _____ 69.00
  b. Covered, small, high standard_ 45.00
  c. Open, large _____ 50.00
  d. Covered, low standard _____ 42.50
Cordial _____ 15.50
Creamer _____ 61.00
Cruet _____ 32.50
Decanter
  a. ½ pint _____ 27.50
  b. Pint _____ 31.50
  c. Quart _____ 35.00
Egg cup (scarce) _____ 20.50
Goblet _____ 16.50
Honey dish _____ 7.25
Jug
  a. Pint _____ 52.50
  b. Quart _____ 77.00

Lamp _____ 34.50
Lemonade glass _____ 22.00
Pitcher _____ 72.00
Plate, 6'' _____ 22.00
Pomade jar _____ 21.50
Salt
  a. Footed, smooth top _____ 9.75
  b. Pointed edge _____ 13.75
Sauce _____ 6.75
Spooner _____ 13.75
Sugar bowl _____ 45.00
Tumbler
  a. Footed _____ 16.50
  b. Water _____ 13.75
*Wine _____ 15.50

*Reproduced item

## TWO PANEL
### (See Colored Glass Section)

## UTAH

Bowl
  a. Covered, 6'', 7'', 8'' _____$ 6.50
  b. Open, 6'', 7'', 8'' _____ 5.50
Butter dish
  a. Large _____ 11.00
  b. Small _____ 8.50
Cake plate
  a. 9'', 10'' _____ 9.00
  b. 11'' _____ 10.50
Cake Stand
  a. 7'', 9'' _____ 10.00
  b. 10'' _____ 11.00
Celery _____ 10.00
Compote
  a. Covered, 6'', 7'', 8'' _____ 18.25
  b. Covered, 6'', jelly _____ 12.25
  c. Open, 5'', jelly _____ 7.50
  d. Open, 6'', 7'', 8'' _____ 10.75
Dish
  a. Oval, low standard, 9'' ____ 6.75
  b. Oval, low standard, 7'', 8'' _ 6.25
Goblet _____ 4.50
Pickle _____ 4.75
Pitcher, 3 pints _____ 11.00
Sauce, 4'' _____ 3.00
Shakers
  a. Pair _____ 8.25
  b. Pair in holder· _____ 10.00
Spooner _____ 6.25
Sugar bowl, covered _____ 11.00
Syrup _____ 8.25
Tumbler _____ 4.50

## VICTORIA
### (Fostoria)

| | |
|---|---|
| Bowl, berry _____ $ | 6.75 |
| Butter dish _____ | 12.25 |
| Creamer _____ | 10.50 |
| Cruet _____ | 9.50 |
| Sauce _____ | 3.00 |
| Spooner _____ | 6.75 |
| Sugar bowl, covered _____ | 12.75 |
| Tumbler _____ | 4.50 |

## VIKING
### (Old Man of the Mountain)

| | |
|---|---|
| **Bowl** | |
| a. Covered _____ $ | 15.50 |
| b. Open _____ | 7.75 |
| Butter dish _____ | 16.00 |
| Celery _____ | 10.00 |
| Compote, covered _____ | 20.50 |
| Creamer _____ | 11.00 |
| Goblet _____ | 8.25 |
| Pickle _____ | 5.50 |
| Pitcher, water _____ | 18.25 |
| Platter _____ | 11.00 |
| Salt, large _____ | 6.00 |
| Sauce _____ | 4.00 |
| Spooner _____ | 7.75 |
| Sugar bowl _____ | 16.00 |

## VIRGINIA
### (Galloway)

| | |
|---|---|
| Bon Bon dish, 5½'' _____ $ | 4.00 |
| **Bowl** | |
| a. Flared, 7½'', 8½'', 9½'' _____ | 6.75 |
| b. Straight, 6'', 7'', 8'' _____ | 5.50 |
| Butter dish, covered _____ | 10.50 |
| Celery _____ | 7.75 |

| | |
|---|---|
| **Celery tray** | |
| a. Pointed, oblong _____ | 6.75 |
| b. Straight _____ | 6.25 |
| **Compote** | |
| a. Covered, footed, 6'', 7'', 8'' | 17.75 |
| b. Open, footed, 6'', 7'', 8'' ___ | 9.50 |
| **Creamer** | |
| a. Individual _____ | 5.50 |
| b. Large _____ | 7.75 |
| Cruet _____ | 8.25 |
| Goblet _____ | 6.75 |
| Olive dish _____ | 3.50 |
| **Pitcher** | |
| a. ½ gallon, tankard _____ | 12.25 |
| b. Water _____ | 11.00 |
| Sardine box _____ | 4.25 |
| **Sauce** | |
| a. Flared, 4'' _____ | 3.25 |
| b. Straight, 4'', 4½'' _____ | 3.50 |
| Spooner _____ | 6.75 |
| **Sugar bowl** | |
| a. Covered, large _____ | 11.00 |
| b. Open, small _____ | 6.25 |
| Toothpick _____ | 2.75 |
| Tumbler _____ | 3.00 |
| Water bottle _____ | 8.25 |
| Wine _____ | 3.50 |

## WAFFLE

| | |
|---|---|
| Butter dish _____ $ | 36.00 |
| Celery _____ | 27.50 |
| Champagne _____ | 23.25 |
| **Compote** | |
| a. Covered, high standard _____ | 30.50 |
| b. Open, 8'', high standard ____ | 20.75 |
| Cordial _____ | 16.50 |
| Creamer (scarce) _____ | 50.00 |
| Decanter, with stopper _____ | 27.50 |
| Egg cup _____ | 10.00 |
| Goblet _____ | 13.75 |
| **Lamp** | |
| a. All glass _____ | 44.00 |
| b. Marble base _____ | 33.00 |
| Pitcher _____ | 52.75 |
| Plate, 6'' _____ | 13.50 |
| Salt, footed _____ | 11.00 |

| | |
|---|---|
| Sauce _____ | 5.00 |
| Spooner _____ | 11.00 |
| Sugar bowl _____ | 45.00 |
| Tumbler | |
|   a. Water _____ | 20.00 |
|   b. Whiskey _____ | 17.75 |
| Wine _____ | 13.75 |

## WAFFLE AND THUMBPRINT

| | |
|---|---|
| Butter dish _____$ | 57.50 |
| Celery _____ | 33.00 |
| Champagne _____ | 26.50 |
| Claret _____ | 22.00 |
| Compote | |
|   a. Open, large, high standard __ | 35.50 |
|   b. Open, small, high standard __ | 26.00 |
|   c. Open, small, low standard __ | 27.50 |
| Creamer _____ | 55.00 |
| Decanter | |
|   a. Pint _____ | 22.00 |
|   b. Quart _____ | 27.50 |
| Egg cup _____ | 13.75 |
| Goblet _____ | 16.50 |
| Lamp, hand _____ | 27.50 |
| Pitcher (scarce) _____ | 100.00 |
| Spooner _____ | 13.25 |
| Sugar bowl, covered _____ | 57.50 |
| Tumbler | |
|   a. Water _____ | 21.75 |
|   b. Whiskey _____ | 22.00 |
| Wine _____ | 20.00 |

## WASHINGTON (EARLY)

| | |
|---|---|
| Bitters bottle _____$ | 27.50 |
| Butter dish _____ | 57.50 |
| Celery _____ | 41.50 |

| | |
|---|---|
| Creamer _____ | 69.50 |
| Egg cup _____ | 22.00 |
| Goblet _____ | 27.50 |
| Pickle _____ | 13.75 |
| Pitcher | |
|   a. Syrup _____ | 56.00 |
|   b. Water _____ | 125.00 |
| Spooner _____ | 27.50 |
| Sugar bowl _____ | 57.50 |
| Tumbler _____ | 22.00 |
| Wine _____ | 27.00 |

## WASHINGTON (LATE)

| | |
|---|---|
| Bowl | |
|   a. Covered, 5'', 6'' _____$ | 6.75 |
|   b. Covered, 7'', 8'' _____ | 7.25 |
|   c. Open, 5'', 6'' _____ | 5.50 |
|   d. Open, 7'', 8'' _____ | 5.50 |
| Butter dish _____ | 11.00 |
| Cake stand | |
|   a. 8'', 9'' _____ | 10.75 |
|   b. 10'', 11'' _____ | 11.50 |
| Celery tray _____ | 5.50 |
| Champagne _____ | 7.50 |
| Claret _____ | 7.75 |
| Compote | |
|   a. Covered, 5'', 6'' _____ | 16.50 |
|   b. Covered, 7'', 8'' _____ | 20.00 |
|   c. Fruit, open, $7\frac{1}{2}$'', $8\frac{1}{2}$'', $9\frac{1}{2}$'' __ | 11.75 |
|   d. Open, 5'', 6'' _____ | 8.25 |
|   e. Open, 7'', 8'' _____ | 9.75 |
| Cordial _____ | 6.50 |
| Creamer _____ | 8.25 |
| Cruet _____ | 7.75 |
| Dish | |
|   a. 6'', 8'' _____ | 6.00 |
|   b. 10'' _____ | 7.50 |
| Goblet | |
|   a. 8 ounce _____ | 4.50 |
|   b. 10 ounce _____ | 5.00 |
| Olive dish _____ | 4.25 |
| Pickle _____ | 4.50 |
| Pitcher | |
|   a. $\frac{1}{2}$ gallon, tankard _____ | 12.25 |
|   b. 3 pints, tankard _____ | 11.00 |
|   c. 1 quart, tankard _____ | 10.00 |
|   d. $\frac{1}{2}$ gallon, water _____ | 9.00 |
|   e. 3 pints, water _____ | 9.50 |
|   f. 1 quart, water _____ | 9.00 |
|   g. 1 pint, water _____ | 8.25 |
|   h. $\frac{1}{2}$ pint, water _____ | 7.50 |
| Sauce | |
|   a. 3'', $3\frac{1}{2}$'' _____ | 2.75 |
|   b. 4'' _____ | 3.00 |

| | |
|---|---|
| Spooner | 5.50 |
| Sugar bowl, covered | 11.00 |
| Toothpick holder | 2.75 |
| Tumbler | 3.25 |
| Wine | 3.50 |

## WESTWARD-HO
### (Pioneer)

Goblets were originally produced in clear and frosted only. Reproductions are on the market in amethyst, blue, green, clear and frosted.

| | |
|---|---|
| *Butter dish | $ 60.00 |
| Celery | 48.00 |
| | |
| Compote | |
| *a. Covered, 6", high standard | 80.00 |
| b. Covered, low standard | 85.00 |
| *c. Oval, 9" | 90.00 |
| *Cordial | 44.75 |
| Creamer | 55.00 |
| *Goblet | |
| *a. Clear | 48.50 |
| *b. Frosted | 42.50 |
| Marmalade jar (scarce) | 65.00 |
| Mug (scarce) | 35.00 |
| Pickle | 22.75 |
| Pitcher | |
| a. Milk | 95.00 |
| *b. Water | 85.00 |
| Platter, oval | 42.50 |
| *Sauce | |
| a. 3½" | 12.25 |
| b. 4" | 13.75 |
| c. 4½" | 15.50 |
| Spooner | 30.00 |
| Sugar bowl | 60.00 |
| *Wine | 55.00 |

*Reproduced item

## WHEAT AND BARLEY
### (See Colored Glass Section)

## WILDFLOWER
### (See Colored Glass Section)

## WILD ROSE WITH BOW KNOTS

| | |
|---|---|
| Bowl | $ 9.50 |
| Butter dish | 13.25 |
| Creamer | 11.00 |
| Sauce | 3.75 |
| Spooner | 9.00 |
| Sugar bowl, covered | 13.75 |

## WILLOW OAK
### (See Colored Glass Section)

## WINDFLOWER

| | |
|---|---|
| Butter dish | $ 22.50 |
| Celery | 20.00 |
| Compote | |
| a. Covered, high standard | 37.00 |
| b. Covered, low standard | 30.00 |
| Cordial | 13.75 |
| Creamer | 14.00 |
| Dish, oval, deep | 8.25 |
| Egg cup | 10.75 |
| Goblet | 11.00 |
| Pickle | 8.25 |
| Pitcher | 33.00 |
| Salt, footed | 10.50 |
| Sauce | 5.50 |
| Spooner | 11.00 |
| Sugar bowl | 23.50 |
| Tumbler | 12.75 |
| Wine | 12.50 |

WISCONSIN, See Beaded Dewdrop

## ZIPPER

```
Butter  dish  _____$  12.00
Celery  _____       8.25
Compote,  covered  _____    16.50
Creamer  _____  9.00
Goblet  _____  6.25
Pitcher,  water  _____  12.00
Sugar  bowl  _____   12.25
```

# COLORED GLASS PATTERNS

Quotations listed on Pattern Glass are retail prices for pieces in perfect condition. The Clear Glass Section precedes this group and is designated as "Section One." Items marked with an (*) asterisk have been, or are now being reproduced.

**AMBERETTE**

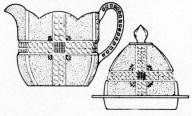

| | |
|---|---|
| Bowl, covered, footed, 8" diam.___$ | 45.00 |
| Butter dish _____ | 67.50 |
| Compote, covered collared base, 8" _____ | 80.00 |
| Creamer _____ | 48.00 |
| Pickle dish, 6 x 9½" _____ | 24.50 |
| Pitcher | |
|    a. Water, square _____ | 70.00 |
|    b. Water, tankard _____ | 62.50 |
| Sauce | |
|    a. Footed _____ | 16.00 |
|    b. Flat, 4½" _____ | 12.00 |
|    c. Flat, scalloped top, 5" _____ | 11.00 |
| Shakers, pair _____ | 35.00 |
| Spooner _____ | 22.50 |
| Sugar bowl | |
|    a. Covered _____ | 67.50 |
|    b. Open _____ | 40.00 |
| Syrup _____ | 55.00 |
| Toothpick _____ | 20.00 |
| Tray, 5½" square _____ | 22.50 |
| Tumbler _____ | 27.50 |

Amberette was first made in 1897-98, by the firm of Dalzell, Gilmore and Leighton Co., Findlay, Ohio. The glass is a combination of satin finished panels and figured bands of flashed or stained old gold (amber). The deep mitres on either side are bright crystal.

Issued during the first period of the great Alaska Gold Rush, the pattern was first called "Klondike." The satin or frosted panels portray suow while the amber bands depict gold.

## BARRED FORGET-ME-NOT

|  | Clear | Amber | Blue | Apple Green |
|---|---|---|---|---|
| Bowl, berry _____ $ | 8.50 | $ 11.50 | $ 13.00 | $ 15.25 |
| Butter dish _____ | 18.00 | 23.50 | 25.25 | 27.25 |
| Cake stand | | | | |
|    a. Large _____ | 17.00 | 19.25 | 21.75 | 25.25 |
|    b. Medium _____ | 14.50 | 19.25 | 20.00 | 23.00 |
| Celery _____ | 18.00 | 21.75 | 22.00 | 27.25 |
| Compote | | | | |
|    a. Covered, low standard ____ | 20.00 | 23.75 | 26.00 | 28.50 |
|    b. Covered, high standard __ | 22.00 | 25.25 | 29.75 | 33.25 |
| Cordial _____ | 8.50 | 11.50 | 13.25 | 15.25 |
| Creamer _____ | 13.25 | 18.00 | 21.75 | 22.00 |
| Goblet _____ | 8.75 | 11.50 | 16.50 | 19.00 |
| Pickle _____ | 7.75 | 12.00 | 14.50 | 17.00 |
| Pitcher _____ | 17.50 | 23.00 | 26.50 | 29.75 |
| Plate, 9'', handled _____ | 10.00 | 15.00 | 17.75 | 18.75 |
| Sauce _____ | 4.25 | 7.00 | 9.75 | 10.75 |
| Spooner _____ | 8.00 | 10.25 | 12.75 | 14.50 |
| Sugar bowl _____ | 18.00 | 21.75 | 25.25 | 29.00 |
| Wine _____ | 8.00 | 12.00 | 14.00 | 17.00 |

## BASKETWEAVE

| Bowl | Clear | Amber | Yellow | Blue | Green |
|---|---|---|---|---|---|
|    a. Berry _____ $ | 8.50 | $ 12.00 | $ 12.00 | $ 13.25 | $ 17.00 |
|    b. Covered, flat _____ | 12.00 | 15.00 | 15.00 | 19.25 | 21.00 |
|    c. Waste _____ | 7.25 | 13.75 | 13.75 | 15.75 | 18.00 |
| Butter dish _____ | 18.00 | 23.50 | 23.50 | 29.00 | 32.50 |
| Compote, covered _____ | 24.00 | 33.00 | 33.00 | 39.00 | 43.50 |
| Cordial _____ | 8.50 | 14.50 | 14.50 | 16.25 | 18.00 |
| Creamer _____ | 13.25 | 21.75 | 21.75 | 25.25 | 29.00 |

| Basketweave, continued | Clear | Amber | Yellow | Blue | Green |
|---|---|---|---|---|---|
| Cup and saucer | 11.50 | 17.50 | 17.50 | 19.75 | 23.00 |
| Egg cup | 7.75 | 14.50 | 14.50 | 16.25 | 18.00 |
| *Goblet | 8.25 | 12.00 | 12.00 | 15.00 | 17.00 |
| Lamp | 12.00 | 17.50 | 17.50 | 19.75 | 22.25 |
| Mug | 7.25 | 12.00 | 12.00 | 14.50 | 17.00 |
| Pickle | 6.00 | 11.50 | 11.50 | 13.25 | 15.00 |
| Pitcher | | | | | |
| a. Milk | 18.00 | 23.50 | 23.50 | 26.50 | 30.00 |
| b. Syurp | 12.00 | 18.00 | 18.00 | 24.00 | 26.50 |
| *c. Water | 19.25 | 24.00 | 24.00 | 27.00 | 31.75 |
| Plate, handled | 11.00 | 15.00 | 15.00 | 17.00 | 19.25 |
| Salt, celery dip | 3.00 | 5.75 | 5.75 | 6.75 | 8.25 |
| Sauce | 4.25 | 7.25 | 7.25 | 8.50 | 9.75 |
| Shakers, pair | 11.00 | 15.25 | 15.25 | 17.00 | 18.00 |
| Spooner | 8.50 | 12.50 | 12.50 | 14.50 | 17.50 |
| Sugar bowl | 18.00 | 23.50 | 23.50 | 29.00 | 31.75 |
| Tray, 12" diameter | 12.00 | 18.00 | 18.00 | 21.75 | 24.00 |
| Tumbler | 7.25 | 11.00 | 11.00 | 12.00 | 13.75 |
| Wine | 6.00 | 10.25 | 10.25 | 12.00 | 14.50 |

*Reproduced item

## BEADED GRAPE

| | Clear | Apple Green |
|---|---|---|
| Butter dish $ | 24.50 | $ 36.50 |
| Cake stand | 24.00 | 35.00 |
| Celery | 21.50 | 30.00 |
| Compote | | |
| a. On high standard | 35.00 | 57.50 |
| b. Open, 4" high | 24.00 | 32.50 |
| c. Shallow, on standard | 23.00 | 34.50 |
| Cordial | 16.00 | 24.00 |
| Creamer | 20.00 | 30.00 |
| Cruet | 18.50 | 35.00 |
| Dish | | |
| a. Oblong, $6\frac{1}{4}$ x $8\frac{1}{4}$" | 16.50 | 29.50 |
| b. Square, $5\frac{3}{4}$", $6\frac{3}{4}$" | 14.50 | 24.00 |
| c. Square, $7\frac{1}{4}$", $8\frac{1}{4}$" | 14.00 | 23.00 |
| *Goblet | 24.00 | 40.00 |
| Pickle | 8.00 | 15.00 |
| Pitcher | | |
| a. Round | 25.00 | 50.00 |
| b. Square | 22.50 | 45.00 |
| Platter | 21.50 | 35.00 |
| *Plate, $8\frac{1}{4}$" square | 12.00 | 21.50 |
| Sauce, 4", $4\frac{1}{2}$" | 5.00 | 10.00 |
| Shakers | | |
| a. Salt and pepper | 20.00 | 32.50 |
| b. Sugar | 14.00 | 20.00 |
| Spooner | 10.00 | 17.50 |
| Sugar bowl | 25.00 | 37.50 |
| Toothpick holder | 11.00 | 16.50 |
| *Tumbler | 16.00 | 24.00 |
| *Wine | 12.00 | 20.00 |

*Reproduced item

## BLACKBERRY

| | Clear | | Milk Glass |
|---|---|---|---|
| Bowl, round, covered _____$ | 13.00 | $ | 28.50 |
| *Butter dish _____ | 30.00 | | 45.00 |
| *Celery _____ | 32.50 | | 87.50 |
| Champagne _____ | 22.50 | | 35.00 |
| Compote | | | |
|    a. Covered, high standard_ _____ | 40.00 | | 89.50 |
|    b. Covered, low standard _____ | 35.00 | | 82.00 |
| *Creamer _____ | 24.00 | | 32.50 |
| Dish, oval, $8\frac{1}{4}$ x $5\frac{1}{2}$'' _____ | 22.50 | | 45.00 |
| Egg cup | | | |
|    a. Double _____ | -- -- | | 25.00 |
|    *b. Single _____ | -- -- | | 20.00 |
| *Goblet _____ | 22.00 | | 40.00 |
| Honey dish _____ | 7.75 | | 12.00 |
| Lamp. Clear bowl, milk | | | |
|    glass base _____ | -- -- | | 45.00 |
| *Pitcher, water (scarce) _____ | 100.00 | | 325.00 |
| Salt, footed _____ | 14.00 | | 22.50 |
| Sauce _____ | 7.00 | | 14.50 |
| Spooner _____ | 15.00 | | 20.00 |
| *Sugar bowl _____ | 30.00 | | 45.00 |
| Tumbler _____ | 10.50 | | 20.00 |

*Reproduced item

## CANE

| | Clear | | Amber | | Vaseline | | Blue | | *Apple Green |
|---|---|---|---|---|---|---|---|---|---|
| Bowl, waste _____$ | 9.00 | $ | 13.75 | $ | 13.75 | $ | 15.00 | $ | 13.75 |
| Butter dish _____ | 18.00 | | 25.75 | | 25.75 | | 28.25 | | 24.00 |
| Compote, open, high | | | | | | | | | |
|   stanadrd _____ | 15.00 | | 24.00 | | 24.00 | | 29.00 | | 21.75 |
| Creamer _____ | 12.00 | | 20.50 | | 20.50 | | 25.25 | | 21.00 |
| Goblet _____ | 9.00 | | 15.00 | | 15.00 | | 19.75 | | 14.50 |
| Marmalade jar _____ | 10.25 | | 18.00 | | 18.00 | | 20.50 | | 17.50 |

## Cane, continued

| | Clear | Amber | Vaseline | Blue | *Apple Green |
|---|---|---|---|---|---|
| Pickle, oval _____ | 7.25 | 13.25 | 13.25 | 14.50 | 12.50 |
| Pitcher _____ | 14.50 | 24.00 | 24.00 | 27.00 | 22.25 |
| Plate, toddy, 4½" _____ | 7.00 | 12.00 | 12.00 | 14.50 | 11.50 |
| Sauce _____ | 4.25 | 9.00 | 9.00 | 9.75 | 8.50 |
| Shakers, pair _____ | 12.00 | 19.25 | 19.25 | 21.00 | 17.00 |
| Spooner _____ | 7.75 | 13.25 | 13.25 | 16.25 | 14.50 |
| Sugar bowl _____ | 18.00 | 27.00 | 27.00 | 30.00 | 25.25 |
| Tray, water _____ | 14.50 | 24.00 | 24.00 | 26.50 | 21.75 |
| Tumbler _____ | 9.00 | 13.75 | 13.75 | 15.50 | 13.25 |

*Apple Green is the most common color in this pattern

## CARAMEL SLAG

Cactus

Bowl
a. 6¼" diam. Cactus _____$ 36.50
b. 7" diam. Cactus _____ 45.00
c. 8" diam. Cactus _____ 55.00
d. Footed, plain _____ 35.00
Butter dish, covered. Cactus ____ 100.00
Candlesticks, pair _____ 75.00
Celery _____ 70.00
Compote
a. Covered, low foot _____ 145.00
b. Open, high standard _____ 110.00
Cracker jar, covered. Cactus ____ 95.00
Creamer
a. Cactus _____ 67.50
b. Fine cut medallion _____ 58.50
Cruet, vinegar
a. Cactus, original stopper ____ 75.00
b. Palm leaf, original stopper__ 70.00
Cup, punch. Hearts of Loch
          Laven _____ 27.50
*Dolphin covered dish _____ 85.00
Goblet _____ 110.00
Mug
a. Hearts of Loch Laven _____ 35.00
b. 4½" high, drinking scenes __ 40.00
c. Beaded rib, handled _____ 42.50
d. Cactus _____ 45.00
Nappy, handled, tri-cornered ____ 42.50
Pitcher
a. Water. Cactus _____ 145.00
b. Water. Panelled. Bellknap 275 120.00

**Caramel Slag, continued**

Plate
    a. 10'', open edge _____ 90.00
    b. Serenade _____ 85.00
Sauce
    a. Cactus _____ 32.00
    b. Shell _____ 35.00
Shakers, pair. Cactus _____ 60.00
Spooner _____ 45.00
Sugar bowl
    a. Covered. Cactus _____ 100.00
    b. Open. Cactus _____ 60.00
    c. Kitten-in-Basket. Basketweave
       bottom, kitten's head on top _ 85.00
    d. Flower Flange _____ 70.00
Syrup. Cord and Drapery _____ 80.00
Toothpick holder
    a. Boot _____ 35.00
    b. Cactus _____ 40.00
    c. Wild rose _____ 35.00
Tray _____ 85.00
Tumbler
    a. Cactus _____ 40.00
    b. Hearts of Loch Laven _____ 45.00
    c. Palm leaf _____ 40.00
    d. Plain _____ 30.00
    e. Shell _____ 40.00
    f. Uneeda Biscuit, tall _____ 35.00
    g. Cord and Drapery _____ 38.50

## CATHEDRAL

| | Clear | Vaseline | Amber | Blue | Amethyst |
|---|---|---|---|---|---|
| Bowl, berry, 7'', 8'' _____$ | 12.00 | $ 18.00 | $ 18.00 | $ 21.75 | $ 33.00 |
| Butter dish _____ | 22.25 | 30.00 | 30.00 | 34.00 | 47.50 |
| Cake stand _____ | 18.00 | 27.00 | 27.00 | 30.00 | 48.00 |
| Compote | | | | | |
|   a. Cov., 11'' high, 8'' diam. | 29.00 | 42.00 | 42.00 | 48.00 | 79.00 |
|   b. Open, on standard ____ | 18.00 | 29.50 | 29.50 | 36.00 | 43.50 |
| Cordial _____ | 9.00 | 14.50 | 14.50 | 17.00 | 18.75 |
| Creamer _____ | 14.50 | 24.00 | 24.00 | 30.00 | 45.00 |
| Egg cup _____ | 9.75 | 18.00 | 18.00 | 21.75 | 25.75 |
| Goblet _____ | 13.75 | 23.00 | 23.00 | 27.00 | 36.00 |
| Pitcher, water _____ | 25.50 | 36.00 | 36.00 | 42.00 | 67.50 |
| Sauce | | | | | |
|   a. Flat, 4'' _____ | 7.00 | 9.75 | 9.75 | 11.00 | 12.00 |
|   b. Footed, 4'' _____ | 7.75 | 11.00 | 11.00 | 12.00 | 13.75 |
|   c. Footed, 4½'' _____ | 8.25 | 12.00 | 12.00 | 13.25 | 15.00 |
| Spooner _____ | 11.00 | 18.00 | 18.00 | 21.75 | 24.00 |

| Cathedral, continued | Clear | Vaseline | Amber | Blue | Amethyst |
|---|---|---|---|---|---|
| Sugar bowl _____ | 22.50 | 30.00 | 30.00 | 33.00 | 54.00 |
| Tumbler _____ | 9.75 | 15.00 | 15.00 | 17.00 | 24.00 |
| Wine _____ | 10.75 | 17.00 | 17.00 | 21.75 | 29.00 |

## COLORADO

| | Clear | Ruby base | Blue | Green |
|---|---|---|---|---|
| Banana dish _____ $ | 27.00 | $ 36.00 | $ 39.50 | $ 45.75 |
| Butter dish _____ | 25.25 | 44.00 | 48.00 | 54.00 |
| Cheese dish, footed, low _____ | 19.25 | 39.00 | 42.00 | 46.00 |
| Creamer | | | | |
| a. Individual _____ | 12.00 | 24.00 | 26.50 | 29.00 |
| b. Large _____ | 15.00 | 33.00 | 36.00 | 39.50 |
| Dish | | | | |
| a. Crimped edge, 4'', 5'' _____ | 8.50 | 18.00 | 19.75 | 21.75 |
| b. Crimped edge, 6'', 7'' ___ | 9.75 | 19.75 | 21.75 | 24.00 |
| c. Crimped edge, 8'' _____ | 11.00 | 22.25 | 24.00 | 26.50 |
| d. Flared edge, 4'', 5'' _____ | 8.50 | 17.00 | 18.00 | 21.75 |
| e. Flared edge, 6'', 7'' _____ | 9.75 | 18.00 | 21.75 | 25.50 |
| f. Flared edge, 8'' _____ | 10.50 | 19.75 | 23.75 | 27.00 |
| g. Footed, round, 5'' _____ | 9.75 | 18.00 | 22.75 | 25.75 |
| Shakers, pair _____ | 9.00 | 18.00 | 21.00 | 24.00 |
| Spooner _____ | 9.75 | 17.00 | 19.25 | 21.75 |
| Sugar bowl | | | | |
| a. Individual _____ | 11.50 | 18.00 | 21.00 | 23.50 |
| b. Large, covered _____ | 25.25 | 45.00 | 50.00 | 54.00 |
| Toothpick holder _____ | 7.00 | 12.00 | 13.75 | 15.00 |
| Tumbler _____ | 7.75 | 15.00 | 17.00 | 19.25 |

## CROESUS

| | Clear | Emerald Green | Amethyst |
|---|---|---|---|
| Bowl, berry _____ $ | 25.00 | $ 55.00 | $ 65.00 |
| Butter dish _____ | 30.00 | 72.50 | 80.00 |
| Celery _____ | 27.50 | 54.50 | 60.00 |
| Creamer _____ | 25.00 | 59.50 | 68.50 |
| Cruet _____ | 20.00 | 60.00 | 70.00 |
| Dish, berry, boat-shaped _____ | 24.00 | 52.50 | 60.00 |
| Pickle _____ | 7.50 | 20.00 | 24.50 |

**Croesus, continued**

| | Clear | Emerald Green | Amethyst |
|---|---|---|---|
| Pitcher, water | 38.50 | 80.00 | 85.00 |
| Sauce | 6.00 | 12.00 | 16.50 |
| Shakers, salt and pepper | 12.00 | 40.00 | 45.00 |
| Spooner | 11.50 | 24.00 | 28.50 |
| Sugar bowl | 30.00 | 72.00 | 80.00 |
| Syrup | 27.50 | 50.00 | 55.00 |
| Toothpick holder | 7.50 | 30.00 | 32.50 |
| Tumbler | 7.75 | 21.50 | 24.50 |

## DAISY AND BUTTON

| | Clear | Vaseline | Amber | Blue | Apple Green |
|---|---|---|---|---|---|
| *Basket $ | 9.00 | $ 15.00 | $ 15.00 | $ 21.00 | $ 23.50 |
| Boat. Canoe | 9.75 | 17.00 | 17.00 | 19.25 | 21.00 |
| Bowl | | | | | |
| a. Finger | 7.75 | 13.25 | 13.25 | 17.00 | 18.00 |
| b. Berry | 9.75 | 17.00 | 17.00 | 21.75 | 24.00 |
| c. Waste | 5.50 | 12.00 | 12.00 | 13.75 | 15.75 |
| *Butter chip | 2.50 | 4.75 | 4.75 | 5.50 | 6.00 |
| Butter dish | 18.00 | 27.00 | 27.00 | 36.00 | 39.50 |
| Castor set | | | | | |
| a. In glass holder | 27.00 | 60.00 | 60.00 | 63.00 | 70.00 |
| b. In metal holder | 36.00 | 54.00 | 54.00 | 60.00 | 67.50 |
| Celery | 12.00 | 22.25 | 22.25 | 24.00 | 27.00 |
| Cheese dish, covered | 14.50 | 24.00 | 24.00 | 33.00 | 36.00 |
| Cologne bottles, pair | 17.00 | 22.25 | 22.25 | 30.00 | 35.50 |
| Compotes, various sizes | 12.00 | 28.00 | 28.00 | 36.00 | 48.00 |
| | To | To | To | To | To |
| | 30.00 | 42.50 | 42.50 | 48.00 | 72.50 |
| Cordial | 5.50 | 12.00 | 12.00 | 14.50 | 17.00 |
| Creamer | 10.25 | 19.75 | 19.75 | 27.00 | 34.00 |
| *Cruet | 12.00 | 27.00 | 27.00 | 30.00 | 36.00 |
| Dishes, various types | 6.75 | 15.00 | 15.00 | 17.00 | 19.75 |
| Egg cup | 7.00 | 11.00 | 11.00 | 12.00 | 13.75 |
| *Goblets, various types | 9.00 | 14.50 | 14.50 | 17.00 | 19.75 |
| Hats | | | | | |
| a. Large, celery holder | 18.00 | 30.00 | 30.00 | 33.00 | 35.50 |
| b. Medium, spooner | 11.50 | 21.00 | 21.00 | 23.50 | 25.75 |
| *c. Small, toothpick holder | 7.25 | 15.00 | 15.00 | 17.00 | 18.00 |
| d. Miniature, salt dip | 4.75 | 8.25 | 8.25 | 10.25 | 12.00 |
| Inkwell | 7.25 | 13.75 | 13.75 | 15.00 | 17.00 |
| Lamp | 14.50 | 30.00 | 30.00 | 33.00 | 36.00 |
| Mug | 6.00 | 13.75 | 13.75 | 15.00 | 17.50 |
| Mustard jar | 7.75 | 17.00 | 17.00 | 18.00 | 19.75 |
| Pickle dish | 6.00 | 12.00 | 12.00 | 13.75 | 15.00 |
| *Plates, various sizes | 7.50 | 14.00 | 14.00 | 17.00 | 19.00 |
| | To | To | To | To | To |
| | 10.50 | 20.00 | 20.00 | 22.50 | 30.00 |

**Daisy and Button, continued**

| | Clear | Vaseline | Amber | Blue | Apple Green |
|---|---|---|---|---|---|
| Platter, oval, handled ____ | 12.00 | 19.75 | 19.75 | 21.75 | 24.00 |
| Salts, various shapes _____ | 1.75 | 4.75 | 4.75 | 5.75 | 6.00 |
| Sauce dishes, various types | 3.75 | 9.50 | 9.50 | 11.00 | 12.00 |
| | To | To | To | To | To |
| | 7.25 | 12.00 | 12.00 | 13.25 | 15.00 |
| *Shakers, pair _____ | 8.25 | 17.00 | 17.00 | 18.00 | 19.75 |
| Sherbet cup _____ | 5.50 | 11.50 | 11.50 | 12.00 | 15.00 |
| Shoes and slippers, various types | 6.00 | 9.50 | 9.50 | 11.50 | 12.00 |
| | To | To | To | To | To |
| | 10.00 | 13.50 | 13.50 | 15.00 | 18.00 |
| Spooner _____ | 7.25 | 15.00 | 15.00 | 17.00 | 18.25 |
| Sugar bowls, various types | 18.00 | 27.00 | 27.00 | 33.00 | 36.00 |
| Syrup pitcher _____ | 12.00 | 21.00 | 21.00 | 24.00 | 30.00 |
| Toothpick holders, various types | 7.00 | 12.00 | 12.00 | 15.00 | 17.50 |
| Trays, various shapes and sizes | 12.00 | 24.00 | 24.00 | 26.00 | 29.00 |
| | To | To | To | To | To |
| | 17.00 | 30.00 | 30.00 | 35.00 | 36.00 |
| *Tumblers, various sizes ___ | 6.00 | 13.50 | 13.50 | 15.00 | 18.00 |
| | To | To | To | To | To |
| | 10.00 | 16.00 | 16.00 | 18.00 | 20.00 |
| Vase. Hand holding cornucopia | 8.50 | 17.00 | 17.00 | 19.75 | 21.50 |
| *Water pitchers | | | | | |
| a. Bulbous _____ | 19.75 | 30.00 | 30.00 | 33.00 | 36.00 |
| b. Cylindrical _____ | 21.00 | 27.00 | 27.00 | 30.00 | 33.75 |
| c. Panelled _____ | 15.00 | 25.50 | 25.50 | 27.00 | 29.50 |
| *Wine _____ | 4.50 | 12.00 | 12.00 | 13.75 | 15.00 |

*Reproduced item

## DAISY AND BUTTON WITH CROSS BARS

| | Clear | Amber | Vaseline | Blue |
|---|---|---|---|---|
| Bowl | | | | |
| a. Open, 6'' _____$ | 9.00 | $ 14.50 | $ 14.50 | $ 18.00 |
| b. Open, 8'' _____ | 11.00 | 18.00 | 18.00 | 24.00 |
| Butter dish | | | | |
| a. Flat _____ | 13.75 | 24.00 | 24.00 | 27.00 |
| b. Footed _____ | 18.00 | 25.75 | 25.75 | 30.00 |
| Compote | | | | |
| a. Covered, 8'' _____ | 22.50 | 34.50 | 34.50 | 39.50 |
| b. Open, 8'' _____ | 14.50 | 22.50 | 22.50 | 25.25 |
| Creamer | | | | |
| a. Individual _____ | 10.25 | 17.00 | 17.00 | 19.75 |
| b. Regular _____ | 13.75 | 21.75 | 21.75 | 27.00 |
| Cruet _____ | 17.00 | 29.50 | 29.50 | 33.00 |
| Goblet _____ | 11.50 | 19.25 | 19.25 | 24.00 |
| Mug | | | | |
| a. Small _____ | 7.25 | 12.00 | 12.00 | 14.50 |
| b. Large _____ | 10.25 | 15.00 | 15.00 | 18.00 |
| Pickle _____ | 7.25 | 12.00 | 12.00 | 15.00 |

**Daisy & Button with Cross Bars, continued**

| | Clear | Amber | Vaseline | Blue |
|---|---|---|---|---|
| **Pitcher** | | | | |
| a. Quart | 13.75 | 24.00 | 24.00 | 29.50 |
| b. ½ gallon | 18.00 | 29.50 | 29.50 | 34.25 |
| **Sauce** | | | | |
| a. Flat | 4.25 | 9.00 | 9.00 | 10.25 |
| b. Footed | 5.50 | 10.25 | 10.25 | 11.00 |
| Shakers, pair | 12.00 | 19.75 | 19.75 | 21.75 |
| Spooner | 7.25 | 12.00 | 12.00 | 15.00 |
| Sugar bowl, covered | 17.00 | 27.00 | 27.00 | 30.00 |
| Syrup jug | 13.75 | 21.75 | 21.75 | 24.00 |
| Toothpick | 6.00 | 12.00 | 12.00 | 14.50 |
| Tray, water | 14.50 | 19.25 | 19.25 | 25.25 |
| Tumbler | 7.25 | 13.25 | 13.25 | 15.00 |
| Wine | 9.00 | 14.50 | 14.50 | 16.25 |

## DAISY AND BUTTON WITH "V" ORNAMENT

| | Clear | Vaseline | Amber | Blue |
|---|---|---|---|---|
| **Bowl** | | | | |
| a. Berry, 8" | $ 10.00 | $ 19.50 | $ 19.50 | $ 23.00 |
| b. Finger | 7.75 | 16.00 | 16.00 | 18.00 |
| Butter dish | 14.00 | 26.50 | 26.50 | 29.50 |
| Celery | 11.00 | 20.00 | 20.00 | 24.50 |
| Creamer | 11.75 | 21.00 | 21.00 | 24.00 |
| Dish, oblong | 8.50 | 13.50 | 13.50 | 16.50 |
| Goblet | 10.00 | 18.00 | 18.00 | 22.50 |
| Mug | 7.50 | 11.50 | 11.50 | 12.75 |
| Pitcher, quart | 18.50 | 29.00 | 29.00 | 32.50 |
| Sauce | 5.50 | 8.50 | 8.50 | 10.00 |
| Spooner | 8.50 | 19.50 | 14.50 | 16.50 |
| Sugar bowl | 14.00 | 26.50 | 26.50 | 29.50 |
| Toothpick | 5.00 | 10.00 | 10.50 | 12.50 |
| Tray, water | 16.00 | 24.00 | 24.00 | 26.50 |
| Tumbler | 7.00 | 14.00 | 14.00 | 16.00 |

## DELAWARE
### (Four-Petal Flower)

| | Clear | Rose with gilt | Green with gilt |
|---|---|---|---|
| **Bowl** | | | |
| a. Round | $ 10.00 | $ 30.00 | $ 35.00 |
| b. Fruit, boat-shaped | 15.00 | 35.00 | 38.50 |
| Butter dish | 18.00 | 50.00 | 55.00 |
| Celery | 10.50 | 30.00 | 35.00 |
| Creamer | 12.00 | 32.00 | 36.00 |

| Delaware, continued | Clear | Rose with gilt | Green with gilt |
|---|---|---|---|
| Cruet | 14.00 | 37.50 | 40.00 |
| Cup, punch | 5.00 | 16.00 | 18.00 |
| Pitcher, water | 16.50 | 50.00 | 55.00 |
| Puff box, covered | 9.00 | 25.00 | 30.00 |
| Sauce | 5.00 | 16.00 | 18.00 |
| Spooner | 9.00 | 24.00 | 27.50 |
| Sugar bowl | 18.00 | 50.00 | 55.00 |
| Toothpick | 4.00 | 18.00 | 24.00 |
| Tumbler | 5.00 | 20.00 | 22.00 |

## DEWEY
### (Flower Flange)

| | Clear | Canary | Green |
|---|---|---|---|
| Butter dish $ | 15.00 | $ 27.50 | $ 35.00 |
| Creamer | 10.00 | 18.50 | 24.50 |
| Cruet | 15.00 | 24.00 | 30.00 |
| Pitcher, water | 16.50 | 30.00 | 37.50 |
| Sauce | 4.00 | 9.00 | 10.00 |
| Shakers, salt and pepper | 12.00 | 18.00 | 22.50 |
| Spooner | 9.50 | 16.50 | 20.00 |
| Sugar bowl | 15.00 | 27.50 | 35.00 |
| Tumbler | 6.00 | 18.00 | 20.00 |

Some items in this pattern were also made in Caramel Slag

## DIAMOND QUILTED

| | Clear | Vaseline | Amber | Blue | Amethyst |
|---|---|---|---|---|---|
| **Bowl** | | | | | |
| a. 7½'' diameter $ | 8.50 | $ 19.75 | $ 19.75 | $ 25.25 | $ 33.00 |
| b. Waste | 7.00 | 17.00 | 17.00 | 19.25 | 21.00 |
| Butter dish | 21.00 | 29.00 | 29.00 | 36.00 | 47.50 |
| Celery | 15.00 | 27.00 | 27.00 | 29.00 | 35.50 |
| Champagne | 11.00 | 19.75 | 19.75 | 22.25 | 27.00 |
| **Compote** | | | | | |
| a. Covered, high standard | 27.00 | 36.00 | 36.00 | 48.00 | 72.50 |
| b. Covered, low standard | 23.50 | 34.25 | 34.25 | 44.00 | 60.00 |
| c. Open, high standard | 17.50 | 24.00 | 24.00 | 33.00 | 39.50 |
| Cordial | 7.75 | 18.00 | 18.00 | 19.75 | 39.50 |
| Creamer | 12.00 | 27.00 | 27.00 | 33.00 | 47.50 |

| Diamond Quilted, continued | Clear | Vaseline | Amber | Blue | Amethyst |
|---|---|---|---|---|---|
| Dish, covered, | | | | | |
| footed, oblong _____ | 13.75 | 33.00 | 33.00 | 36.00 | 42.00 |
| *Goblet _____ | 10.25 | 19.75 | 19.75 | 22.25 | 35.50 |
| Pickle _____ | 7.25 | 13.75 | 13.75 | 17.00 | 22.25 |
| Pitcher | | | | | |
| a. Large _____ | 21.75 | 33.00 | 33.00 | 39.50 | 72.50 |
| b. Small _____ | 24.00 | 36.00 | 36.00 | 42.00 | 75.00 |
| Sauce | | | | | |
| a. Flat, round _____ | 3.75 | 9.00 | 9.00 | 10.25 | 11.50 |
| b. Footed _____ | 4.75 | 9.75 | 9.75 | 11.00 | 14.50 |
| Spooner _____ | 8.50 | 14.50 | 14.50 | 18.00 | 22.25 |
| Sugar bowl _____ | 21.75 | 28.50 | 28.50 | 39.50 | 60.00 |
| Tray, water _____ | 17.00 | 27.00 | 27.00 | 29.50 | 39.50 |
| Tumbler | | | | | |
| * Water _____ | 6.75 | 13.75 | 13.75 | 15.00 | 21.00 |
| b. Whiskey, handled __ | 9.75 | 19.75 | 19.75 | 21.75 | 30.00 |
| Wine _____ | 4.75 | 11.50 | 11.50 | 13.25 | 18.00 |

*Reproduced Item

## EMERALD GREEN HERRINGBONE
### (Panelled Herringbone)

| | Clear | Green |
|---|---|---|
| Bowl, berry, large _____$ | 12.00 | $ 17.50 |
| Butter dish _____ | 15.00 | 29.50 |
| Cake stand (scarce) _____ | 15.00 | 39.50 |
| Celery _____ | 16.50 | 35.00 |
| Compote, open, high standard _____ | 19.50 | 40.00 |
| Cordial _____ | 10.00 | 22.50 |
| Creamer _____ | 12.50 | 20.00 |
| Cruet _____ | 13.50 | 29.00 |
| *Goblet _____ | 8.50 | 25.00 |
| Pickle _____ | 6.00 | 15.00 |
| Pitcher _____ | 22.50 | 40.00 |
| Plate | | |
| a. $7\frac{1}{4}$'' _____ | 10.00 | 25.00 |
| b. $9\frac{1}{4}$'' _____ | 12.00 | 27.50 |
| Sauce _____ | 4.50 | 8.75 |
| Shakers, pair _____ | 14.00 | 24.00 |
| Spooner _____ | 9.00 | 16.00 |
| Sugar bowl _____ | 15.50 | 30.00 |
| Toothpick holder _____ | 5.00 | 12.50 |
| Tumbler _____ | 7.50 | 16.50 |
| Wine _____ | 6.00 | 14.50 |

*Reproduced in Clear, Green, Amber and Blue

## ESTHER

| | Clear | Green |
|---|---|---|
| Bowl, berry, 8'' _____$ | 7.00 | $ 12.50 |

| | Clear | Green |
|---|---|---|
| Butter dish, covered _____ | 14.00 | 24.00 |
| Celery tray, 11'' _____ | 6.00 | 20.00 |
| Compote | | |
| a. Covered, 5'' _____ | 18.00 | 30.00 |
| b. Open, 6'' _____ | 10.00 | 22.50 |
| Creamer _____ | 9.00 | 20.00 |
| Cruet _____ | 12.00 | 28.50 |
| Goblet _____ | 7.00 | 14.00 |
| Pickle _____ | 4.50 | 10.00 |
| Pitcher, water _____ | 12.50 | 30.00 |
| Sauce, footed _____ | 3.25 | 9.50 |
| Spooner _____ | 7.50 | 14.00 |
| Sugar bowl, covered _____ | 14.00 | 24.00 |
| Tumbler _____ | 5.00 | 12.00 |

## FINE CUT

| | Clear | Vaseline | Amber | Blue |
|---|---|---|---|---|
| **Bowl** | | | | |
| a. Finger _____$ | 7.75 | $ 12.00 | $ 12.00 | $ 14.50 |
| b. Waste _____ | 9.00 | 13.25 | 13.25 | ·15.00 |
| Butter dish _____ | 17.50 | 26.50 | 26.50 | 30.00 |
| Compote, covered _____ | 22.50 | 39.00 | 39.00 | 42.00 |
| Creamer _____ | 13.75 | 21.75 | 21.75 | 25.25 |
| Cruet _____ | 9.00 | 19.75 | 19.75 | 24.00 |
| Dish, oblong _____ | 11.00 | 18.00 | 18.00 | 21.75 |
| Goblet _____ | 11.50 | 18.00 | 18.00 | 21.00 |
| Mustard jar _____ | 6.75 | 13.75 | 13.75 | 15.50 |
| **Pitcher** | | | | |
| a. Syrup _____ | 10.25 | 17.50 | 17.50 | 19.75 |
| b. Water _____ | 19.75 | 27.00 | 27.00 | 32.00 |
| **Plate** | | | | |
| a. $6\frac{1}{4}$'' _____ | 9.00 | 13.75 | 13.75 | 16.25 |
| b. $7\frac{1}{4}$'' _____ | 10.25 | 15.00 | 15.00 | 18.00 |
| c. $10\frac{1}{4}$'' _____ | 13.75 | 21.00 | 21.00 | 24.00 |

| Fine Cut, continued | Clear | Vaseline | Amber | Blue |
|---|---|---|---|---|
| Sauce | 4.25 | 8.50 | 8.50 | 9.75 |
| Spooner | 8.50 | 13.25 | 13.25 | 15.00 |
| Sugar bowl | 18.00 | 28.50 | 28.50 | 33.00 |
| Tray | | | | |
|   a. Bread | 10.25 | 18.00 | 18.00 | 19.25 |
|   b. Water | 12.00 | 18.00 | 18.00 | 24.00 |

## FINE CUT AND PANEL

| | Clear | Amber | Yellow | Blue |
|---|---|---|---|---|
| Bowl, waste | $ 6.75 | $ 13.00 | $ 13.00 | $ 15.00 |
| Butter dish | 17.00 | 24.00 | 24.00 | 27.00 |
| Celery | 12.00 | 17.50 | 17.50 | 22.75 |
| Compote, open, high standard | 15.00 | 27.00 | 27.00 | 33.00 |
| Cordial | 7.75 | 13.75 | 13.75 | 17.00 |
| Creamer | 12.00 | 22.75 | 22.75 | 26.00 |
| Dish, oblong | 8.25 | 15.00 | 15.00 | 18.00 |
| Goblet | 7.75 | 16.50 | 16.50 | 22.25 |
| Lamp, 10'', handled | 12.00 | 22.25 | 22.25 | 25.75 |
| Pickle | 6.00 | 12.00 | 12.00 | 15.00 |
| Pitcher | 17.00 | 30.00 | 30.00 | 34.25 |
| Plate | | | | |
|   a. $6\frac{1}{2}$'' | 7.75 | 13.25 | 13.25 | 17.00 |
|   b. $7\frac{1}{4}$'' | 10.25 | 14.50 | 14.50 | 18.00 |
| Platter | 11.50 | 18.00 | 18.00 | 21.00 |
| Sauce | 4.25 | 8.25 | 8.25 | 9.00 |
| Shakers, pair | 11.50 | 21.75 | 21.75 | 23.50 |
| Spooner | 9.00 | 12.00 | 12.00 | 15.00 |
| Sugar bowl | 17.50 | 25.25 | 25.25 | 28.50 |
| Toothpick holder | 4.25 | 10.50 | 10.50 | 11.75 |
| Tray | 12.00 | 18.00 | 18.00 | 21.75 |
| Tumbler | 5.50 | 12.00 | 12.00 | 14.50 |
| Wine | 4.75 | 10.25 | 10.25 | 11.50 |

## HOBNAIL, FAN TOP

Hobnail, Fan Top, continued

| Bowl | Clear | Amber | Blue |
|---|---|---|---|
| a. Large, deep _____$ | 15.00 | $  24.00 | $  29.50 |
| b. 6'' diameter _____ | 11.00 | 15.00 | 17.00 |
| c. Shallow _____ | 12.00 | 17.00 | 19.25 |
| Butter dish _____ | 19.75 | 29.00 | 34.25 |
| Celery _____ | 15.00 | 23.50 | 27.00 |
| Creamer _____ | 15.25 | 21.75 | 25.25 |
| Dish, oblong _____ | 11.00 | 15.00 | 18.00 |
| Goblet _____ | 12.00 | 19.75 | 25.75 |
| Platter, 12'' _____ | 22.50 | 29.00 | 33.00 |
| Salt, individual, small _____ | 4.25 | 7.25 | 8.50 |
| Sauce _____ | 6.00 | 9.75 | 11.00 |
| Sugar bowl _____ | 19.75 | 29.00 | 34.50 |

## HOBNAIL, OPALESCENT

| Bowl | Opalescent | Blue Opalescent | Yellow Opalescent |
|---|---|---|---|
| a. Flat, 9½'' _____$ | 30.00 | $  39.00 | $  42.00 |
| b. Footed, 8'' _____ | 35.50 | 45.00 | 48.00 |
| c. Finger _____ | 19.75 | 29.00 | 34.50 |
| Butter dish _____ | 42.00 | 53.00 | 60.00 |
| Celery _____ | 30.00 | 36.00 | 42.00 |
| Creamer _____ | 29.75 | 34.75 | 39.50 |
| Cup, handled _____ | 14.50 | 24.00 | 29.00 |
| Pickle _____ | 17.00 | 25.25 | 30.00 |
| Platter, 9½ x 14'' _____ | 39.50 | 49.00 | 60.00 |
| Spooner _____ | 15.00 | 24.00 | 27.00 |
| Sugar bowl _____ | 42.00 | 54.00 | 60.00 |
| Tumbler _____ | 18.00 | 25.25 | 35.50 |
| Water bottle (rare) _____ | 47.50 | -- -- | -- -- |

## HOBNAIL, PANELLED

**Hobnail, Panelled, continued**

| | Clear | Vaseline | Amber | Blue |
|---|---|---|---|---|
| Bowl, 8'' _____$ | 8.50 | $ 13.25 | $ 13.25 | $ 15.00 |
| Butter dish _____ | 15.00 | 27.00 | 27.00 | 30.00 |
| Celery _____ | 14.50 | 19.75 | 19.75 | 24.00 |
| Compote, high standard _____ | 18.00 | 27.00 | 27.00 | 30.00 |
| Creamer _____ | 12.00 | 19.75 | 19.75 | 22.25 |
| Goblet _____ | 9.00 | 17.00 | 17.00 | 19.25 |
| Plate | | | | |
| a. 4½'' _____ | 6.00 | 12.00 | 12.00 | 13.75 |
| b. 7'' _____ | 10.25 | 14.50 | 14.50 | 18.00 |
| Sauce _____ | 4.25 | 9.00 | 9.00 | 9.75 |
| Spooner _____ | 8.00 | 14.50 | 14.50 | 17.50 |
| Sugar bowl _____ | 15.00 | 27.00 | 27.00 | 30.00 |
| Wine _____ | 5.50 | 11.00 | 11.00 | 12.00 |

## HOBNAIL, POINTED

| | Clear | Amber | Blue | Light Green |
|---|---|---|---|---|
| Barber bottle_____$ | 12.00 | $ 24.00 | $ 26.50 | $ 28.25 |
| *Bowl, berry _____ | 17.00 | 33.00 | 33.00 | 39.50 |
| Butter dish _____ | 21.75 | 30.00 | 34.25 | 45.00 |
| Cake stand, 10'' _____ | 21.00 | 29.00 | 33.00 | 39.50 |
| Celery _____ | 19.25 | 26.50 | 31.75 | 36.00 |
| Child's set. Butter dish, creamer, | | | | |
| spooner and sugar bowl _____ | 19.75 | 25.75 | 29.50 | 34.25 |
| Compote, 8'' diam., 8'' high__ | 27.00 | 34.25 | 39.50 | 47.50 |
| Cordial _____ | 10.25 | 15.00 | 17.50 | 22.25 |
| Creamer _____ | 13.75 | 18.00 | 21.75 | 24.00 |
| *Cup and saucer _____ | 12.00 | 19.75 | 22.25 | 26.00 |
| Dish | | | | |
| a. Oblong, 8 x 12'' _____ | 13.25 | 23.50 | 25.25 | 28.50 |
| b. Bone dish _____ | 7.00 | 12.00 | 13.25 | 15.50 |
| Egg cup, double _____ | 11.00 | 17.00 | 18.00 | 20.00 |
| Goblet _____ | 15.50 | 22.25 | 24.00 | 27.00 |
| Inkwell _____ | 8.25 | 12.00 | 13.75 | 17.00 |
| Mug _____ | 9.00 | 13.25 | 14.50 | 16.25 |
| Mustard jar _____ | 9.75 | 14.50 | 16.25 | 17.50 |
| Pickle _____ | 7.25 | 11.50 | 13.00 | 15.00 |
| Pitcher | | | | |
| a. Water _____ | 21.75 | 36.00 | 42.00 | 48.00 |
| b. Milk _____ | 19.25 | 31.25 | 34.50 | 36.00 |
| c. Syrup _____ | 14.50 | 24.00 | 26.50 | 30.00 |
| Plate | | | | |
| a. Toddy, 4½'' _____ | 5.50 | 9.00 | 11.00 | 12.00 |
| b. 7½'' _____ | 10.25 | 15.00 | 16.25 | 19.75 |
| Platter, 4½ x 7'' _____ | 13.75 | 19.25 | 21.00 | 23.75 |
| Salt | | | | |
| a. Celery dip _____ | 4.25 | 7.25 | 7.75 | 9.00 |
| b. Round _____ | 4.75 | 7.75 | 8.50 | 10.25 |
| c. Square _____ | 4.75 | 7.75 | 9.00 | 11.00 |
| *Sauce _____ | 5.50 | 8.50 | 9.75 | 11.25 |
| *Shakers, pair _____ | 11.00 | 17.00 | 18.00 | 21.75 |
| Spooner _____ | 8.50 | 14.50 | 16.25 | 17.50 |

**Hobnail, Pointed, continued**

| | Clear | Amber | Blue | Light Green |
|---|---|---|---|---|
| Sugar bowl _____ | 22.25 | 29.50 | 33.00 | 39.50 |
| Toothpick holder _____ | 5.50 | 10.25 | 11.50 | 13.75 |
| Tray | | | | |
| a. Pen _____ | 8.50 | 11.50 | 13.75 | 15.00 |
| b. Water _____ | 14.50 | 21.75 | 24.00 | 25.25 |
| *Tumbler _____ | 8.50 | 12.50 | 14.50 | 17.00 |
| *Vinegar cruet _____ | 12.00 | 25.75 | 28.25 | 30.00 |
| *Wine _____ | 4.75 | 9.75 | 10.25 | 12.50 |

*Reproduced Item

## HOBNAIL, PRINTED

| | Clear | Amber | Canary | Blue | Green |
|---|---|---|---|---|---|
| Butter dish _____$ | 13.75 | $ 21.75 | $ 21.75 | $ 24.00 | $ 27.00 |
| Celery _____ | 12.50 | 19.25 | 19.25 | 21.00 | 23.50 |
| Creamer _____ | 9.75 | 17.50 | 17.50 | 18.00 | 18.75 |
| Goblet _____ | 9.50 | 13.75 | 13.75 | 22.75 | 17.50 |
| Mug _____ | 7.25 | 11.00 | 11.00 | 12.00 | 13.75 |
| Mustard jar _____ | 8.50 | 12.00 | 12.00 | 14.00 | 15.00 |
| Pitcher _____ | 17.50 | 27.00 | 27.00 | 29.00 | 32.50 |
| Sauce _____ | 4.25 | 7.25 | 7.25 | 8.50 | 9.00 |
| Spooner _____ | 7.75 | 12.50 | 12.50 | 13.75 | 15.00 |
| Sugar bowl _____ | 15.00 | 24.00 | 24.00 | 27.00 | 29.00 |
| Tray _____ | 12.00 | 21.00 | 21.00 | 23.00 | 25.25 |
| Tumbler _____ | 7.75 | 12.00 | 12.00 | 13.25 | 14.50 |
| Wine _____ | 5.75 | 11.75 | 11.75 | 12.00 | 13.25 |

## HOBNAIL, THUMBPRINT BASE

| | Clear | Amber | Blue |
|---|---|---|---|
| Bowl | | | |
| a. Berry, 9'', 10'' _____$ | 15.00 | $ 33.00 | $ 39.50 |
| b. Waste _____ | 9.00 | 15.50 | 17.50 |
| Butter dish _____ | 15.00 | 24.00 | 36.00 |
| Celery _____ | 15.00 | 24.00 | 25.75 |

**Hobnail, Thumbprint Base, continued**

| | Clear | Amber | Blue |
|---|---|---|---|
| Child's Set. Butter dish, sugar bowl, creamer and spooner __ | 22.25 | 30.00 | 39.00 |
| Creamer _____ | 13.75 | 21.00 | 23.00 |
| Mustard jar _____ | 9.00 | 14.50 | 17.00 |
| Pitcher, water _____ | 23.50 | 36.00 | 47.00 |
| Salt, celery dip _____ | 3.75 | 7.25 | 8.25 |
| Shakers, pair _____ | 11.50 | 19.75 | 21.75 |
| Spooner _____ | 8.50 | 13.25 | 15.00 |
| Sugar bowl _____ | 18.00 | 33.00 | 36.00 |
| Tray, water _____ | 12.00 | 21.00 | 24.00 |

## HOLLY AMBER

| | |
|---|---|
| Bowl, 7'', 8'' _____ | $ 450.00 |
| Butter dish _____ | 800.00 |
| Cake stand _____ | 900.00 |
| Compotes | |
|   a. Covered _____ | 1250.00 |
|   b. Jelly _____ | 750.00 |
| Cruet _____ | 650.00 |
| Nappy, handled _____ | 400.00 |
| Pickle dish _____ | 350.00 |
| Pitcher, 10'' _____ | 1600.00 |
| Plate, 7½'' _____ | 550.00 |
| Sauce | |
|   a. Flat _____ | 185.00 |
|   b. Footed _____ | 225.00 |
| *Toothpick holder _____ | 175.00 |
| Tray, water, 9¼'' _____ | 650.00 |
| Tumbler _____ | 325.00 |

*Reproduced item

## HUMMING BIRD
### (Flying Robin, Bird and Fern)

| Humming Bird, continued | Clear | Amber | Canary | Blue |
|---|---|---|---|---|
| Bowl, finger _____$ | 7.00 | $ 11.50 | $ 11.50 | $ 13.75 |
| Butter dish _____ | 17.00 | 24.00 | 24.00 | 27.00 |
| Celery _____ | 12.00 | 22.25 | 22.25 | 25.25 |
| Creamer _____ | 13.75 | 19.75 | 19.75 | 24.00 |
| Goblet _____ | 10.75 | 17.00 | 17.00 | 19.25 |
| Pickle _____ | 4.75 | 9.75 | 9.75 | 11.00 |
| Pitcher | | | | |
| a. Milk _____ | 16.25 | 21.75 | 21.75 | 24.00 |
| b. Water _____ | 14.50 | 21.00 | 21.00 | 22.25 |
| Sauce _____ | 3.75 | 7.25 | 7.25 | 8.50 |
| Spooner _____ | 7.75 | 12.00 | 12.00 | 13.50 |
| Sugar bowl _____ | 17.50 | 27.00 | 27.00 | 29.00 |
| Tray, water _____ | 12.00 | 19.75 | 19.75 | 21.75 |

### ICICLE

| | Clear | Milk Glass |
|---|---|---|
| Butter dish _____$ | 17.00 | $ 27.00 |
| Butter pat _____ | 3.00 | 5.50 |
| Compote | | |
| a. Covered, 6'', high standard _____ | 24.00 | 45.00 |
| b. Covered, 8'', high standard _____ | 27.00 | 48.00 |
| c. Open, 8'', low standard _____ | 18.00 | 30.00 |
| Creamer _____ | 13.75 | 25.75 |
| Dish, oval _____ | 9.75 | 12.00 |
| Goblet _____ | 9.75 | 15.00 |
| Pickle _____ | 6.00 | 9.75 |
| Pitcher _____ | 15.50 | 29.00 |
| Salt, large _____ | 4.75 | 7.75 |
| Sauce _____ | 4.75 | 7.25 |
| Spooner _____ | 8.50 | 12.00 |
| Sugar bowl _____ | 17.00 | 29.00 |

### JACOB'S COAT

| | Clear | Amber |
|---|---|---|
| Bowl, berry _____ _____$ | 12.00 | $ 19.75 |
| Butter dish _____ | 15.00 | 24.00 |
| Celery _____ | 12.00 | 21.00 |
| Creamer _____ | 13.00 | 22.75 |
| Goblet _____ | 9.75 | 17.50 |
| Pickle _____ | 7.00 | 13.25 |

| Jacob's Coat, continued | Clear | Amber |
|---|---|---|
| Sauce | 4.75 | 8.50 |
| Spooner | 8.50 | 12.00 |
| Sugar bowl | 15.00 | 24.00 |

## LOCKET ON CHAIN

| | Clear | Green |
|---|---|---|
| Bowl, berry, 8" | $ 7.00 | $ 12.00 |
| Butter dish, covered | 13.25 | 21.75 |
| Cake stand | 11.50 | 18.00 |
| Celery | 9.00 | 14.50 |
| Compote, open, 8" | 13.25 | 17.50 |
| Creamer | 8.50 | 14.50 |
| Cruet | 9.75 | 21.75 |
| Goblet | 7.00 | 12.00 |
| Pickle | 4.50 | 9.00 |
| Pitcher | | |
| a. Milk | 11.50 | 18.00 |
| b. Water | 13.00 | 22.25 |
| Plate, 8" | 7.75 | 14.50 |
| Sauce, 4" | 4.25 | 8.50 |
| Shakers, pair | 10.25 | 18.00 |
| Spooner | 7.25 | 12.00 |
| Sugar bowl | 14.25 | 22.75 |
| Syrup jug | 9.75 | 17.50 |
| Toothpick holder | 4.75 | 9.00 |
| Tumbler | 5.00 | 9.75 |

## MAIZE

| | Milk White |
|---|---|
| Bowl | |
| a. Berry, 9" | $ 35.00 |
| b. Finger, 5" | 21.50 |
| Butter dish | 65.00 |

**Maize, continued**

|  | Milk White |
|---|---|
| Celery | 42.50 |
| Castor set, 3-pieces | 75.00 |
| Creamer | 45.00 |
| Cruet | 47.50 |
| Decanter | |
|   a. Pint | 45.00 |
|   b. Quart | 49.50 |
| Pitcher | |
|   a. Syrup | 45.00 |
|   b. Water | 67.50 |
| Sauce | 14.00 |
| Spooner | 25.00 |
| Sugar bowl | 65.00 |
| Sugar shaker | 32.50 |
| Toothpick holder | 22.50 |
| Tumbler | 25.00 |
| Water bottle (carafe) | 48.50 |

## MAPLE LEAF

|  | Clear | Frosted | Vaseline | Amber | Blue | Green |
|---|---|---|---|---|---|---|
| Bowl, oval, footed $ | 11.00 | $ 15.00 | $ 18.00 | $ 18.00 | $ 21.75 | $ 24.00 |
| Butter dish | 18.75 | 24.00 | 29.00 | 29.00 | 31.75 | 39.00 |
| Celery | 17.00 | 24.00 | 27.00 | 27.00 | 29.00 | 36.00 |
| Compote | | | | | | |
|   a. Covered, high standard | 40.50 | 54.00 | 60.00 | 60.00 | 67.00 | 75.00 |
|   b. Round, footed, open | 24.00 | 34.25 | 39.50 | 48.00 | 54.00 | 58.00 |
| Creamer | 19.25 | 33.75 | 39.50 | 39.50 | 45.00 | 48.00 |
| Dish | | | | | | |
|   a. Covered, oval, on stippled feet | 17.00 | 27.00 | 29.50 | 29.50 | 31.25 | 35.50 |
|   b. Open, oval, not footed | 12.00 | 22.25 | 25.25 | 25.25 | 27.00 | 30.00 |
|   *Goblet | 47.50 | 57.50 | 67.50 | 67.50 | 97.00 | 105.00 |
| Pitcher | | | | | | |
|   a. Large | 21.75 | 27.00 | 33.75 | 33.75 | 39.00 | 45.00 |
|   b. Small | 19.75 | 24.00 | 35.50 | 35.50 | 39.50 | 42.00 |
| Plate | | | | | | |
|   a. 10'' | 13.75 | 19.75 | 27.00 | 27.00 | 29.50 | 33.00 |
|   b. 10½'', Grant Peace | 12.00 | 17.00 | 21.75 | 21.75 | 24.00 | 27.00 |
| Platter, oval | 15.00 | 19.75 | 24.00 | 24.00 | 27.00 | 29.00 |
| Sauce, 5'', 6'', footed | 6.00 | 8.50 | 10.25 | 10.25 | 11.00 | 12.00 |
| Spooner | 9.75 | 14.50 | 16.25 | 16.25 | 17.50 | 19.25 |
| Sugar bowl | 19.25 | 24.00 | 24.00 | 29.50 | 32.00 | 35.50 |
| Tumbler | 8.50 | 12.00 | 15.00 | 15.00 | 16.25 | 18.00 |

*Reproduced item

## MEDALLION

|  | Clear | Vaseline | Amber | Blue | Apple Green |
|---|---|---|---|---|---|
| Bowl, waste $ | 6.75 | $ 14.50 | $ 14.50 | $ 15.75 | $ 18.00 |
| Butter dish | 17.50 | 23.50 | 23.50 | 25.25 | 29.00 |
| Cake stand | 14.50 | 23.50 | 23.50 | 26.50 | 28.50 |

**Medallion, continued**

| | Clear | Vaseline | Amber | Blue | Apple Green |
|---|---|---|---|---|---|
| Celery | 11.00 | 21.00 | 21.00 | 22.25 | 24.00 |
| Compote, covered, high standard | 19.75 | 29.50 | 29.50 | 33.00 | 36.00 |
| Creamer | 12.00 | 22.25 | 22.25 | 24.00 | 26.50 |
| Goblet | 9.00 | 15.00 | 15.00 | 17.00 | 19.25 |
| Pickle | 7.25 | 11.75 | 11.75 | 12.50 | 14.25 |
| Pitcher, water | 18.00 | 25.25 | 25.25 | 28.50 | 30.00 |
| Sauce | | | | | |
| a. Footed | 4.75 | 9.00 | 9.00 | 9.75 | 10.75 |
| b. Flat | 4.00 | 7.25 | 7.25 | 8.50 | 9.00 |
| Spooner | 8.50 | 12.50 | 12.50 | 13.25 | 15.00 |
| Sugar bowl | 18.00 | 24.00 | 24.00 | 25.25 | 29.50 |
| Tray, water | 12.00 | 19.25 | 19.25 | 21.00 | 23.00 |
| Tumbler | 7.75 | 13.25 | 13.25 | 13.75 | 15.00 |
| Wine | 10.75 | 14.50 | 14.50 | 17.20 | 19.25 |

## MELROSE

| | Clear | Etched |
|---|---|---|
| Bowl | | |
| a. Berry | $ 7.00 | $ 11.50 |
| b. Waste | 5.00 | 9.50 |
| c. 6'', footed | 6.00 | 11.50 |
| Butter dish | 12.50 | 15.00 |
| Cake stand | 10.00 | 14.00 |
| Compote | | |
| a. Covered, 6'', high standard | 20.00 | 25.00 |
| b. Covered, 8'', high standard | 22.50 | 27.50 |
| c. Open, 6'' | 12.00 | 12.50 |
| d. Open, 8'' | 14.00 | 15.00 |

**Melrose,** continued

| | Clear | Etched |
|---|---|---|
| Creamer | 7.50 | 12.75 |
| Goblet | 5.50 | 9.00 |
| Mug | 4.00 | 7.00 |
| Pickle | 4.25 | 8.50 |
| Pitcher | | |
| a. Quart | 10.00 | 14.50 |
| b. ½ Gallon | 12.00 | 16.50 |
| Sauce | 3.00 | 4.75 |
| Spooner | 6.00 | 7.50 |
| Sugar bowl, covered | 12.00 | 15.00 |
| Tumbler | 3.50 | 5.50 |
| Water tray | 11.50 | 15.00 |

## MONKEY

| | Clear | Opalescent |
|---|---|---|
| Bowl | | |
| a. Fruit, 8½'' | $ 45.00 | $ 60.00 |
| b. Waste | 35.00 | 45.00 |
| Butter dish | 60.00 | 80.00 |
| Creamer | 35.00 | 58.50 |
| Mug | 27.50 | 40.00 |
| Pitcher | 65.00 | 125.00 |
| Spooner | 30.00 | 45.00 |
| Sugar bowl | 60.00 | 85.00 |
| Toothpick holder | 18.00 | 32.50 |
| Tumbler | 28.50 | 60.00 |

**OPALESCENT HOBNAIL,** See Hobnail, Opalescent

## PANELLED FORGET-ME-NOT

| | Clear | Yellow | Amber | Blue |
|---|---|---|---|---|
| Bowl, covered | $ 12.00 | $ 17.00 | $ 17.00 | $ 17.50 |
| Butter dish | 17.00 | 24.00 | 24.00 | 29.50 |

| Panelled Forget-me-not, continued | Clear | Yellow | Amber | Blue |
|---|---|---|---|---|
| Cake stand | 17.50 | 23.50 | 23.50 | 28.25 |
| Celery | 15.00 | 22.25 | 22.25 | 25.75 |
| Compote | | | | |
| a. Covered, high standard | 24.00 | 36.00 | 36.00 | 42.00 |
| b. Open, large, flaring sides | 17.00 | 27.00 | 27.00 | 31.75 |
| Cordial | 11.00 | 15.00 | 15.00 | 17.50 |
| Creamer | 13.75 | 21.75 | 21.75 | 24.00 |
| Goblet | 11.50 | 17.00 | 17.00 | 21.75 |
| Marmalade jar | 11.50 | 18.00 | 18.00 | 21.00 |
| Pickle | 7.25 | 12.00 | 12.00 | 13.75 |
| Pitcher | 19.25 | 30.00 | 30.00 | 33.75 |
| Platter, oval | 12.50 | 17.00 | 17.00 | 21.75 |
| Sauce | | | | |
| a. Flat | 4.25 | 8.50 | 8.50 | 10.25 |
| b. Footed | 6.00 | 9.75 | 9.75 | 11.00 |
| Shakers, pair | 11.50 | 18.00 | 18.00 | 12.00 |
| Spooner | 7.00 | 11.00 | 11.00 | 12.00 |
| Sugar bowl | 18.00 | 26.50 | 26.50 | 30.00 |
| Wine (scarce) | 15.50 | 21.75 | 21.75 | 24.00 |

## PRIMROSE

| | Clear | Vaseline | Amber | Blue |
|---|---|---|---|---|
| Bowl | | | | |
| a. Berry $ | 12.00 | $ 19.25 | $ 19.25 | $ 22.25 |
| b. Waste | 9.00 | 12.50 | 12.50 | 14.50 |
| Butter dish | 19.25 | 29.00 | 29.00 | 32.50 |
| Cake stand | 17.00 | 24.00 | 24.00 | 27.00 |
| Celery | 13.75 | 19.75 | 19.75 | 23.50 |
| Compote | | | | |
| a. Covered, 6'' | 24.00 | 34.25 | 34.25 | 41.00 |
| b. Covered, 8'' | 23.00 | 36.00 | 36.00 | 46.00 |
| Cordial | 10.25 | 15.00 | 15.00 | 17.00 |
| Creamer | 13.75 | 22.75 | 22.75 | 24.00 |
| Egg cup | 9.00 | 12.00 | 12.00 | 13.75 |
| Goblet | | | | |
| a. Plain stem | 9.75 | 15.00 | 15.00 | 19.75 |
| b. Knob stem | 13.75 | 19.75 | 19.75 | 24.00 |
| Marmalade jar | 11.00 | 17.00 | 17.00 | 19.25 |
| Pickle | 6.00 | 10.75 | 10.75 | 13.75 |
| Pitcher | 22.25 | 35.50 | 35.50 | 43.25 |
| Plate | | | | |
| a. 4½'' | 7.00 | 12.00 | 12.00 | 14.50 |
| b. 6'' | 11.50 | 15.50 | 15.50 | 18.00 |
| c. 7'' | 11.75 | 18.00 | 18.00 | 21.00 |
| d. 8¾'', cake | 13.00 | 17.75 | 17.75 | 19.75 |
| Platter | 13.75 | 22.25 | 22.25 | 24.00 |
| Sauce | 5.50 | 9.00 | 9.00 | 10.50 |
| Spooner | 7.00 | 11.75 | 11.75 | 13.75 |
| Sugar bowl, covered | 16.00 | 29.00 | 29.00 | 33.00 |
| Tray | 12.00 | 21.75 | 21.75 | 24.00 |

## PURPLE SLAG

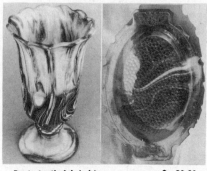

| | |
|---|---|
| Boot, toothpick holder _____$ | 30.00 |
| Bowl, footed _____ | 60.00 |
| Butter dish _____ | 95.00 |
| Cake stand, 11½'' _____ | 85.00 |
| Candlesticks, pair _____ | 70.00 |
| Celery, 8 1/8'' high _____ | 65.00 |
| **Compote** | |
| a. Covered, low standard _____ | 125.00 |
| b. Open, high standard _____ | 90.00 |
| **Creamer** | |
| a. Flower panel _____ | 55.00 |
| b. Scroll with Acanthus, 4½'' ____ | 60.00 |
| c. Sunflower _____ | 65.00 |
| **Dish** | |
| a. Small, round _____ | 35.00 |
| b. Square _____ | 40.00 |
| Goblet _____ | 110.00 |
| Lamp, slag base, clear font _____ | 90.00 |
| **Match holder** | |
| a. 3¾'', 4 small feet. (Millard 232) | 35.00 |
| b. Ring handles. (Millard 233) __ | 35.00 |
| Mug _____ | 36.50 |
| **Pitcher** | |
| a. Milk. 6½'', 3 roses, stippled | |
| background _____ | 125.00 |
| b. Water _____ | 120.00 |
| Plate, 10'', open-edge _____ | 80.00 |
| Sauce _____ | 30.00 |
| **Spooner** | |
| a. Acanthus leaf _____ | 35.00 |
| b. Flower panel _____ | 40.00 |
| c. Footed _____ | 35.00 |
| Sugar bowl, flower panel _____ | 95.00 |
| Tray _____ | 75.00 |
| **Tumbler** | |
| a. Water _____ | 37.50 |
| b. Whiskey _____ | 45.00 |
| Vase. Urn-type with shell and | |
| flower decoration _____ | 50.00 |

# RAINDROP

| | Clear | Amber | Yellow | Blue | Green | Milk Glass |
|---|---|---|---|---|---|---|
| Bowl, finger _____$ | 5.50 $ | 10.25 $ | 10.25 $ | 11.50 $ | 12.50 $ | 13.25 |
| Butter dish _____ | 14.50 | 24.00 | 24.00 | 27.00 | 29.00 | 33.00 |
| **Compote** | | | | | | |
| a. Open, high standard _____ | 14.50 | 19.75 | 19.75 | 22.25 | 24.00 | 26.50 |
| b. Open, low standard _____ | 12.00 | 17.00 | 17.00 | 19.25 | 21.75 | 24.00 |
| Cup and saucer _____ | 10.25 | 14.50 | 14.50 | 16.25 | 17.50 | 18.00 |
| Egg cup _____ | 8.00 | 11.50 | 11.50 | 12.50 | 13.25 | 14.50 |
| Pickle _____ | 7.25 | 10.50 | 10.50 | 11.50 | 12.00 | 13.25 |
| Pitcher, syrup _____ | 12.00 | 18.00 | 18.00 | 23.00 | 24.00 | 28.25 |
| Plate, handled _____ | 11.00 | 13.75 | 13.75 | 16.25 | 18.00 | 19.75 |
| **Sauce** | | | | | | |
| a. Flat _____ | 4.25 | 8.25 | 8.25 | 8.75 | 8.75 | 11.00 |
| b. Footed _____ | 6.00 | 9.75 | 9.75 | 10.50 | 11.00 | 12.00 |
| Tray, water _____ | 11.50 | 18.00 | 18.00 | 22.25 | 26.50 | 29.00 |

## ROSE-IN-SNOW

| | Clear | Amber | Vaseline | Blue |
|---|---|---|---|---|
| **Butter dish** | | | | |
| a. Round _____$ | 29.00 $ | 39.50 $ | 39.50 $ | 46.00 |
| b. Square _____ | 27.00 | 36.00 | 36.00 | 42.00 |
| Cake stand (scarce) _____ | 27.50 | 31.75 | 31.75 | 39.00 |
| **Compote** | | | | |
| a. Covered, high standard ___ | 39.50 | 60.00 | 60.00 | 53.00 |
| b. Covered, low standard ___ | 35.50 | 51.00 | 51.00 | 54.00 |
| **Creamer** | | | | |
| a. Round _____ | 18.00 | 24.00 | 24.00 | 27.00 |
| b. Square _____ | 23.00 | 27.00 | 27.00 | 32.50 |
| **Dish** | | | | |
| a. Oval, large _____ | 25.25 | 36.00 | 36.00 | 39.50 |
| b. Oval, small _____ | 19.75 | 25.75 | 25.75 | 29.00 |
| c. Square, covered _____ | 24.00 | 33.00 | 33.00 | 39.00 |

**Rose-in-Snow, continued**

| | Clear | Amber | Vaseline | Blue |
|---|---|---|---|---|
| *Goblet | 19.25 | 25.25 | 25.25 | 27.00 |
| Lemonade glass | 16.25 | 24.00 | 24.00 | 25.75 |
| Marmalade jar | 54.00 | 65.00 | 65.00 | 70.00 |
| *Mug | 11.50 | 17.50 | 17.50 | 21.75 |
| **Pickle** | | | | |
| a. Double, 8¼ x 7'' (scarce) | 36.00 | 45.00 | 45.00 | 54.00 |
| b. Oval, handles at ends | 11.50 | 18.00 | 18.00 | 21.75 |
| Pitcher | 36.00 | 60.00 | 60.00 | 72.50 |
| **Plate** | | | | |
| a. 5'' (scarce) | 18.00 | 24.00 | 24.00 | 29.50 |
| b. 6'' | 13.25 | 18.00 | 18.00 | 22.25 |
| c. 7½'' | 15.00 | 22.25 | 22.25 | 24.00 |
| *d. 9'' (heavily reproduced) | 13.75 | 19.25 | 19.25 | 21.75 |
| **Sauce** | | | | |
| a. Flat, round | 4.75 | 9.00 | 9.00 | 9.75 |
| b. Square | 7.25 | 11.50 | 11.50 | 12.50 |
| **Spooner** | | | | |
| a. Round | 10.25 | 14.50 | 14.50 | 17.00 |
| b. Square | 12.00 | 17.00 | 17.00 | 19.75 |
| **Sugar bowl** | | | | |
| a. Round | 24.00 | 36.00 | 36.00 | 42.00 |
| b. Square | 29.00 | 40.50 | 40.50 | 45.75 |
| Tumbler | 21.00 | 26.50 | 26.50 | 29.00 |

*Reproduced item

## ROSE SPRIG

| | Clear | Amber | Yellow | Blue |
|---|---|---|---|---|
| Butter dish | $ 18.00 | $ 26.50 | $ 26.50 | $ 29.00 |
| Cake stand | 15.25 | 22.25 | 22.25 | 25.75 |
| Celery | 13.75 | 19.75 | 19.75 | 24.00 |
| **Compote** | | | | |
| a. Covered, high standard | 21.75 | 30.00 | 30.00 | 33.75 |
| b. Open, extra large | 17.00 | 24.00 | 24.00 | 27.00 |
| Cordial | 8.50 | 17.00 | 17.00 | 18.50 |
| Creamer | 12.00 | 19.75 | 19.75 | 21.75 |
| **Dish** | | | | |
| a. Boat-shaped | 11.00 | 15.00 | 15.00 | 19.25 |
| b. Oblong, deep | 9.75 | 13.00 | 13.00 | 16.25 |
| c. Square, handled | 10.25 | 12.50 | 12.50 | 15.75 |
| Goblet | 12.75 | 18.00 | 18.00 | 24.00 |
| Lemonade glass | 12.00 | 18.00 | 18.00 | 22.25 |
| Pickle | 7.75 | 11.50 | 11.50 | 13.00 |
| **Pitcher** | | | | |
| a. Large | 19.25 | 25.25 | 25.25 | 33.00 |
| b. Small | 17.00 | 22.25 | 22.25 | 29.50 |
| **Plate** | | | | |
| a. 6½'' | 9.75 | 13.75 | 13.75 | 15.50 |
| b. 10'' | 13.75 | 20.00 | 20.00 | 24.00 |

**Rose Sprig, continued**

| | Clear | Amber | Yellow | Blue |
|---|---|---|---|---|
| Platter | 11.50 | 17.50 | 17.50 | 22.25 |
| Salt, sleigh | 21.75 | 29.50 | 29.50 | 33.00 |
| Sauce, footed | 5.50 | 9.00 | 9.00 | 10.75 |
| Spooner | 8.50 | 12.00 | 12.00 | 13.25 |
| Sugar bowl | 18.50 | 28.50 | 28.50 | 30.00 |
| Tray, water | 13.25 | 21.00 | 21.00 | 24.00 |
| Tumbler | 10.50 | 15.00 | 15.00 | 18.00 |

## ROYAL IVY

| | |
|---|---|
| Bowl, 7'', open | $ 60.00 |
| Butter dish, covered | 75.00 |
| Creamer | 48.50 |
| Cruet | 55.00 |
| Pitcher | |
|   a. Syrup | 45.00 |
|   b. Water | 80.00 |
| Shakers | |
|   a. Salt and pepper, pair | 40.00 |
|   b. Sugar | 32.50 |
| Sugar bowl, covered | 75.00 |
| Toothpick holder | 25.00 |
| Tumbler | 27.50 |

## ROYAL OAK

| | Frosted to Cranberry |
|---|---|
| Bowl | |
|   a. 8'' | $ 55.00 |
|   b. Finger | 30.00 |
| Butter dish | 70.00 |
| Creamer | 49.50 |
| Cruet | 50.00 |
| Pitcher, water, square mouth | 80.00 |
| Shakers, pair | 40.00 |
| Spooner | 30.00 |
| Sugar bowl | 72.50 |
| Syrup | 48.50 |
| Toothpick holder | 25.00 |
| Tumbler | 28.50 |

## SAWTOOTH AND STAR
### (O'Hara Diamond, Ruby Star "Flashed")

|  | Clear | Red Flashed |
|---|---|---|
| Bowl _____$ | 4.50 | $  11.50 |
| Butter dish, covered _____ | 12.00 | 22.25 |
| Compote, small, open _____ | 9.00 | 15.00 |
| Creamer _____ | 9.25 | 14.50 |
| Cruet _____ | 7.75 | 15.00 |
| Cup and saucer _____ | 9.75 | 17.00 |
| Goblet _____ | 7.50 | 15.00 |
| Pickle _____ | 7.00 | 12.00 |
| Plate _____ | 7.25 | 11.50 |
| Sauce _____ | 3.25 | 6.00 |
| Shakers |  |  |
| a. Salt and pepper _____ | 9.00 | 14.50 |
| b. Sugar _____ | 7.00 | 12.00 |
| Spooner _____ | 6.75 | 11.00 |
| Sugar bowl, covered _____ | 12.50 | 22.25 |
| Wine _____ | 5.50 | 9.75 |

## SHERATON

|  | Clear | Amber | Blue |
|---|---|---|---|
| Bowl, berry _____$ | 8.50 | $  14.50 | $  16.50 |
| Butter dish _____ | 14.00 | 22.50 | 24.50 |
| Compote, covered _____ | 18.00 | 30.00 | 35.00 |
| Creamer _____ | 9.00 | 16.00 | 18.50 |
| Goblet _____ | 8.00 | 12.00 | 15.00 |
| Pitcher, water _____ | 12.50 | 21.50 | 25.00 |
| Plate, bread _____ | 8.25 | 16.50 | 20.00 |
| Sauce, flat_____ | 3.50 | 7.00 | 8.00 |
| Sugar bowl, covered _____ | 14.00 | 22.50 | 24.50 |
| Wine _____ | 5.00 | 8.50 | 9.50 |

## SPIREA BAND
### (Square and Dot)

| | Clear | Amber | Vaseline | Blue | Green |
|---|---|---|---|---|---|
| Bowl, berry _____$ | 9.00 | $ 16.50 | $ 16.50 | $ 18.75 | $ 21.50 |
| Butter dish, covered ___ | 15.25 | 21.75 | 21.75 | 24.00 | 27.00 |
| Cake stand _____ | 11.50 | 18.00 | 18.00 | 21.00 | 23.50 |
| Celery _____ | 9.00 | 15.25 | 15.25 | 18.50 | 21.00 |
| Compote | | | | | |
|   a. Covered _____ | 21.00 | 33.00 | 33.00 | 41.50 | 46.50 |
|   b. Open _____ | 13.75 | 21.75 | 21.75 | 23.50 | 25.75 |
| Cordial _____ | 8.25 | 15.25 | 15.25 | 18.00 | 19.75 |
| Creamer _____ | 9.75 | 20.00 | 20.00 | 21.75 | 23.50 |
| Goblet _____ | 7.25 | 15.25 | 15.25 | 17.00 | 18.00 |
| Pitcher, water _____ | 13.75 | 22.25 | 22.25 | 26.50 | 29.50 |
| Platter, oval _____ | 10.25 | 17.50 | 17.50 | 19.75 | 24.00 |
| Sauce | | | | | |
|   a. Footed _____ | 4.75 | 9.00 | 9.00 | 9.75 | 11.00 |
|   b. Flat _____ | 3.75 | 7.25 | 7.25 | 8.25 | 9.00 |
| Shakers, pair _____ | 11.50 | 18.00 | 18.00 | 19.75 | 21.75 |
| Spooner _____ | 9.00 | 12.00 | 12.00 | 14.50 | 16.25 |
| Sugar bowl, covered ___ | 14.50 | 23.50 | 23.50 | 27.00 | 30.00 |
| Wine _____ | 5.50 | 10.25 | 10.25 | 11.50 | 12.50 |

## STRAWBERRY

| | Milk White |
|---|---|
| Butter dish _____$ | 40.00 |
| Compote | |
|   a. Covered, 8", high standard__ | 75.00 |
|   b. Covered, 8", low stanadrd__ | 70.00 |
| Creamer _____ | 32.50 |
| *Egg cup _____ | 18.50 |
| *Goblet _____ | 25.00 |
| Honey dish _____ | 10.00 |
| Pickle _____ | 12.50 |
| Pitcher | |
|   a. Syrup _____ | 32.50 |
|   b. Water _____ | 80.00 |

**Strawberry, continued**

|  | Milk White |
|---|---|
| Salt _____ | 12.50 |
| Sauce _____ | 10.50 |
| Spooner _____ | 16.00 |
| Sugar bowl _____ | 42.50 |

*Reproduced item

## SWAN

|  | Clear | Amber | Yellow | Blue |
|---|---|---|---|---|
| Butter dish _____$ | 24.00 | $ 33.00 | $ 33.00 | $ 39.50 |
| Creamer _____ | 17.50 | 24.00 | 24.00 | 27.00 |
| Dish, oval, covered _____ | 24.00 | 43.75 | 43.75 | 48.00 |
| Goblet _____ | 30.00 | 42.00 | 42.00 | 50.00 |
| Pitcher, water _____ | 24.00 | 36.00 | 36.00 | 42.00 |
| Sauce |  |  |  |  |
| a. Footed _____ | 6.75 | 9.75 | 9.75 | 11.50 |
| b. Round, flat _____ | 4.75 | 8.00 | 8.00 | 9.00 |
| Spooner _____ | 9.00 | 13.25 | 13.25 | 15.25 |
| Sugar bowl _____ | 25.25 | 33.00 | 33.00 | 42.00 |

## SWIRL
### (Jersey Swirl)

|  | Clear | Amber | Yellow | Blue |
|---|---|---|---|---|
| Bowl, berry _____$ | 10.25 | $ 17.00 | $ 17.00 | $ 18.00 |
| Butter dish _____ | 18.00 | 24.00 | 24.00 | 29.00 |
| Cake stand _____ | 15.25 | 21.75 | 21.75 | 25.25 |
| Candlesticks, pair _____ | 17.00 | 24.00 | 24.00 | 27.00 |
| Celery _____ | 14.50 | 19.75 | 19.75 | 24.00 |
| Compote |  |  |  |  |
| a. Covered, high standard __ | 19.75 | 26.50 | 26.50 | 29.50 |
| b. Covered, collared base ___ | 17.00 | 24.00 | 24.00 | 27.00 |
| Creamer _____ | 14.50 | 19.75 | 19.75 | 22.25 |
| Cup, sherbet _____ | 6.75 | 11.50 | 11.50 | 13.00 |

## Swirl, continued

| | Clear | Amber | Yellow | Blue |
|---|---|---|---|---|
| **Goblet** | | | | |
| *a. Large | 12.00 | -- -- | -- -- | -- -- |
| b. Regular | 14.50 | 21.75 | 21.75 | 24.00 |
| Pitcher, water | 18.00 | 25.75 | 25.75 | 30.00 |
| **Plate** | | | | |
| a. 6¼'' | 10.75 | 15.25 | 15.25 | 17.00 |
| b. 8'' | 12.50 | 17.00 | 17.00 | 19.75 |
| c. 10'' | 15.25 | 19.75 | 19.75 | 21.75 |
| **Salt** | | | | |
| a. Celery dip | 3.75 | 5.75 | 5.75 | 6.75 |
| b. Large | 6.00 | 8.00 | 8.00 | 9.00 |
| Sauce | 4.75 | 7.00 | 7.00 | 8.75 |
| Shakers, pair | 12.00 | 17.00 | 17.00 | 18.00 |
| Spooner | 8.50 | 12.00 | 12.00 | 13.75 |
| Sugar bowl | 18.00 | 25.25 | 25.25 | 29.00 |
| Tray | 13.75 | 19.75 | 19.75 | 22.50 |
| Tumbler | 9.00 | 13.75 | 13.75 | 15.25 |
| Wine | 9.50 | 14.50· | 14.50 | 19.75 |

*Reproduced item

## THOUSAND EYE

| | Clear | Amber | Vaseline | Blue | Green Apple |
|---|---|---|---|---|---|
| **Bowl** | | | | | |
| a. Berry | $ 14.00 | $ 22.50 | $ 22.50 | $ 24.00 | $ 27.00 |
| b. Waste | 11.00 | 17.00 | 17.00 | 19.25 | 22.50 |
| **Butter dish** | | | | | |
| a. Knob stem | 26.00 | 35.50 | 35.50 | 39.50 | 45.00 |
| b. Plain stem | 24.00 | 33.00 | 33.00 | 35.50 | 39.00 |
| **Cake stand** | | | | | |
| a. Knob stem | 21.75 | 36.00 | 36.00 | 39.50 | 47.00 |
| b. Plain stem | 20.00 | 33.00 | 33.00 | 41.50 | 43.75 |
| **Celery** | | | | | |
| a. Knob stem | 20.00 | 27.00 | 27.00 | 31.25 | 34.25 |
| b. Plain stem | 19.25 | 25.25 | 25.25 | 29.00 | 35.50 |
| Cologne bottle | 11.50 | 17.00 | 17.00 | 19.25 | 22.25 |
| **Compote** | | | | | |
| a. Open, plain stem | 25.25 | 33.00 | 33.00 | 42.00 | 48.00 |
| b. Covered, knob stem, high standard | 32.00 | 48.00 | 48.00 | 52.00 | 57.00 |
| c. Covered, 6'' diam., knob stem, high standard | 29.50 | 39.50 | 39.50 | 42.00 | 48.00 |
| Cordial | 12.00 | 19.25 | 19.25 | 23.50 | 27.50 |
| **Creamer** | | | | | |
| a. Knob stem | 25.25 | 29.50 | 29.50 | 35.50 | 39.00 |
| b. Plain stem | 23.50 | 27.00 | 27.00 | 33.00 | 36.00 |

**Thousand Eye, continued**

| | Clear | Amber | Vaseline | Blue | Apple Green |
|---|---|---|---|---|---|
| **Cruet** | | | | | |
| a. Knob stem _____ | 20.00 | 27.00 | 27.00 | 29.00 | 33.00 |
| *b. Plain stem _____ | 18.00 | 24.00 | 24.00 | 26.50 | 29.00 |
| Egg cup (very scarce) _____ | 30.00 | 36.00 | 36.00 | 39.50 | 42.00 |
| *Goblet _____ | 17.50 | 23.50 | 23.50 | 25.75 | 29.50 |
| *Hat, match holder _____ | 8.25 | 12.00 | 12.00 | 13.75 | 15.25 |
| Honey dish _____ | 9.50 | 13.25 | 13.25 | 15.25 | 17.00 |
| **Lamp** | | | | | |
| a. High standard, large __ | 36.00 | 54.00 | 54.00 | 60.00 | 70.00 |
| b. Handled, small _____ | 30.00 | 44.00 | 44.00 | 48.00 | 50.00 |
| *Mug _____ | 8.25 | 12.00 | 12.00 | 13.75 | 15.50 |
| Pickle _____ | 11.00 | 13.25 | 13.25 | 15.25 | 17.00 |
| **Pitcher** | | | | | |
| a. Small, knob stem _____ | 21.75 | 27.00 | 27.00 | 33.00 | 39.50 |
| b. Large, knob stem _____ | 24.00 | 30.00 | 30.00 | 36.00 | 47.00 |
| c. Small, plain stem _____ | 25.25 | 32.50 | 32.50 | 38.50 | 48.00 |
| d. Large, plain stem _____ | 22.50 | 29.00 | 29.00 | 36.00 | 46.50 |
| **Plate** | | | | | |
| a. Round, 6'', alphabet border | 17.00 | 22.25 | 22.25 | 23.50 | 25.25 |
| b. Square, 6'' _____ | 11.00 | 14.50 | 14.50 | 17.00 | 19.25 |
| *c. Square, 8'' _____ | 11.50 | 17.00 | 17.00 | 18.00 | 20.50 |
| d. Square, 10'' _____ | 13.75 | 20.00 | 20.00 | 23.00 | 26.00 |
| Platter, oblong, 8 x 11'' ____ | 17.50 | 23.50 | 23.50 | 25.75 | 28.50 |
| **Sauce** | | | | | |
| a. Flat _____ | 5.50 | 8.25 | 8.25 | 9.75 | 10.25 |
| b. Footed, plain stem _____ | 6.50 | 8.75 | 8.75 | 10.25 | 11.00 |
| c. Footed, knob stem _____ | 7.25 | 8.75 | 8.75 | 10.75 | 11.50 |
| Shakers, pair _____ | 14.50 | 21.75 | 21.75 | 23.50 | 26.00 |
| **Spooner** | | | | | |
| a. Knob stem _____ | 11.00 | 16.25 | 16.25 | 18.00 | 19.75 |
| b. Plain stem _____ | 9.50 | 13.25 | 13.25 | 15.25 | 17.00 |
| **Sugar bowl** | | | | | |
| a. Knob base _____ | 27.25 | 35.50 | 35.50 | 39.00 | 45.00 |
| b. Plain base _____ | 24.00 | 33.00 | 33.00 | 35.00 | 39.50 |
| Syrup jug _____ | 24.00 | 36.00 | 36.00 | 41.00 | 47.00 |
| **Tray** | | | | | |
| a. Oval, water _____ | 27.25 | 35.50 | 35.50 | 41.00 | 45.00 |
| b. Round, water _____ | 23.00 | 30.00 | 30.00 | 33.00 | 36.00 |
| *Tumbler | | | | | |
| a. Jelly _____ | 10.25 | 13.75 | 13.75 | 15.75 | 20.25 |
| b. Water _____ | 11.75 | 16.25 | 16.25 | 19.25 | 22.50 |
| *Twine holder _____ | 12.00 | 21.00 | 21.00 | 23.50 | 27.00 |
| *Wine _____ | 11.00 | 15.25 | 15.25 | 17.50 | 22.25 |

*Reproduced item

### THREE PANEL

| | Clear | Amber | Yellow | Blue |
|---|---|---|---|---|
| Bowl, 9'', footed _____$ | 9.00 | $ 15.25 | $ 15.25 | $ 17.00 |

### Three Panel, continued

| | Clear | Amber | Yellow | Blue |
|---|---|---|---|---|
| Butter dish _____ | 18.00 | 25.25 | 25.25 | 27.25 |
| Celery _____ | 17.00 | 24.00 | 24.00 | 26.00 |
| Compote | | | | |
| a. Open, 7'', low standard __ | 12.00 | 17.75 | 17.75 | 20.00 |
| b. Open, 8½'', 9'', low standard _____ | 12.75 | 18.00 | 18.00 | 21.25 |
| c. Open, 10'', low standard___ | 14.00 | 20.00 | 20.00 | 24.00 |
| Creamer _____ | 13.25 | 17.75 | 17.75 | 20.00 |
| Cruet _____ | 12.00 | 21.25 | 21.25 | 26.00 |
| Goblet _____ | 9.75 | 15.25 | 15.25 | 19.25 |
| Mug _____ | 7.00 | 11.50 | 11.50 | 13.00 |
| Pitcher (water) _____ | 19.25 | 27.25 | 27.25 | 32.50 |
| Sauce _____ | 4.75 | 7.25 | 7.25 | 9.00 |
| Spooner _____ | 9.00 | 12.00 | 12.00 | 14.00 |
| Sugar bowl _____ | 18.00 | 25.25 | 25.25 | 30.00 |
| Tumbler _____ | 9.75 | 14.50 | 14.50 | 18.00 |

## TWO PANEL

| | Clear | Amber | Yellow | Blue | Green |
|---|---|---|---|---|---|
| **Bowl** | | | | | |
| a. Fruit, 10½'' _____$ | 8.50 | $ 12.75 | $ 12.75 | $ 13.25 | $ 15.25 |
| b. Oval, 5½ x 7'' _____ | 7.25 | 11.50 | 11.50 | 12.75 | 15.25 |
| c. Waste _____ | 7.00 | 11.00 | 11.00 | 12.00 | 14.50 |
| Butter dish _____ | 15.25 | 24.00 | 24.00 | 26.50 | 29.50 |
| Celery _____ | 12.00 | 19.25 | 19.25 | 21.25 | 24.00 |
| Compote | | | | | |
| a. Covered, high standard | 21.75 | 29.00 | 29.00 | 32.00 | 35.50 |
| b. Open, high standard ____ | 13.25 | 20.00 | 20.00 | 21.75 | 26.50 |
| c. Open, low standard ____ | 11.50 | 17.00 | 17.00 | 19.25 | 23.75 |
| Cordial _____ | 9.00 | 12.75 | 12.75 | 14.50 | 17.50 |
| Creamer _____ | 12.75 | 17.00 | 17.00 | 18.00 | 21.25 |
| **Dish** | | | | | |
| a. Flat _____ | 9.75 | 14.50 | 14.50 | 16.50 | 17.50 |
| b. Oval, deep _____ | 9.00 | 10.75 | 10.75 | 13.25 | 15.25 |
| *Goblet _____ | 10.25 | 17.00 | 17.00 | 20.00 | 24.00 |
| Lamp _____ | 15.25 | 24.00 | 24.00 | 29.00 | 32.00 |
| Marmalade jar _____ | 11.75 | 18.00 | 18.00 | 21.50 | 26.00 |
| Mug _____ | 8.00 | 11.50 | 11.50 | 13.00 | 13.75 |
| Pickle _____ | 7.25 | 11.00 | 11.00 | 12.75 | 15.25 |
| Pitcher _____ | 20.00 | 25.25 | 25.25 | 30.00 | 36.00 |
| Platter _____ | 11.00 | 15.50 | 15.50 | 17.00 | 20.00 |
| **Salt** | | | | | |
| a. Celery dip _____ | 4.25 | 7.00 | 7.00 | 8.75 | 9.75 |
| b. Large, flat _____ | 5.50 | 9.75 | 9.75 | 11.00 | 12.75 |
| **Sauce** | | | | | |
| a. Flat _____ | 4.75 | 7.25 | 7.25 | 8.25 | 9.00 |
| b. Footed _____ | 6.00 | 9.00 | 9.00 | 9.75 | 11.00 |
| Shakers, pair _____ | 12.00 | 20.00 | 20.00 | 21.25 | 22.50 |
| Spooner _____ | 8.50 | 12.00 | 12.00 | 13.25 | 15.25 |
| Sugar bowl _____ | 15.25 | 24.00 | 24.00 | 27.25 | 30.00 |
| Tray, water _____ | 14.00 | 20.00 | 20.00 | 21.75 | 24.00 |

**Two Panel, continued**

|  | Clear | Amber | Yellow | Blue | Green |
|---|---|---|---|---|---|
| Tumbler _____ | 7.25 | 12.00 | 12.00 | 13.25 | 15.25 |
| *Wine _____ | 9.00 | 13.25 | 13.25 | 14.50 | 18.00 |

*Reproduced Item

## WHEAT AND BARLEY

|  | Clear | Amber | Yellow | Blue |
|---|---|---|---|---|
| Bowl, covered, 8'' _____\$ | 15.25 | $ 21.75 | $ 21.75 | $ 23.75 |
| Butter dish _____ | 18.00 | 22.00 | 24.00 | 27.25 |
| Cake stand |  |  |  |  |
|   a. 8'', 9'' _____ | 14.50 | 21.25 | 21.25 | 26.00 |
|   b. 10'' _____ | 17.00 | 24.00 | 24.00 | 29.00 |
| Compote |  |  |  |  |
|   a. Covered, 7'', 8'', high |  |  |  |  |
|     standard _____ | 24.00 | 33.25 | 33.25 | 39.75 |
|   b. Open, high standard _____ | 14.50 | 22.50 | 22.50 | 24.00 |
| Creamer _____ | 12.00 | 18.00 | 18.00 | 21.25 |
| Goblet _____ | 11.00 | 20.00 | 20.00 | 22.50 |
| Mug _____ | 9.75 | 15.25 | 15.25 | 16.50 |
| Pitcher |  |  |  |  |
|   a. Large _____ | 20.00 | 27.25 | 27.25 | 33.25 |
|   b. Milk _____ | 15.25 | 22.50 | 22.50 | 27.25 |
|   c. Syrup _____ | 14.00 | 22.75 | 22.75 | 28.50 |
| Plate |  |  |  |  |
|   a. 7'' _____ | 13.25 | 17.75 | 17.75 | 19.25 |
|   b. 9'', closed handles _____ | 14.50 | 19.25 | 19.25 | 22.50 |
| Sauce |  |  |  |  |
|   a. Flat _____ | 4.75 | 6.75 | 6.75 | 7.25 |
|   b. Footed, 4'' _____ | 6.75 | 8.50 | 8.50 | 9.00 |
| Shakers, pair _____ | 11.00 | 17.00 | 17.00 | 21.75 |
| Spooner _____ | 7.25 | 12.00 | 12.00 | 12.75 |
| Sugar bowl _____ | 18.00 | 24.00 | 24.00 | 29.00 |
| Tumbler |  |  |  |  |
|   a. Footed _____ | 9.75 | 13.75 | 13.75 | 15.25 |
|   b. Water _____ | 8.50 | 12.00 | 12.00 | 13.25 |

## WILDFLOWER

|  | Clear | Amber | Yellow | Blue | Green |
|---|---|---|---|---|---|
| **Bowl** |  |  |  |  |  |
|   a. 5¾'' square, cut corners\_\_\$ | 8.50 | $ 13.25 | $ 13.25 | $ 14.50 | $ 15.75 |
|   b. 6½'' sq., cut corners, cov. | 11.00 | 15.00 | 15.00 | 16.50 | 18.00 |

**Wildflower, continued**

| | Clear | Amber | Yellow | Blue | Green |
|---|---|---|---|---|---|
| c. 7¾'' sq., cut corners, cov. | 12.00 | 18.00 | 18.00 | 21.25 | 22.50 |
| d. Waste _____ | 12.75 | 19.25 | 19.25 | 22.50 | 23.75 |
| **Butter dish** | | | | | |
| a. Collared base _____ | 17.50 | 25.25 | 25.25 | 27.25 | 30.00 |
| b. Flat _____ | 14.50 | 21.75 | 21.75 | 25.25 | 26.50 |
| **Cake stand** | | | | | |
| a. Large _____ | 18.00 | 24.00 | 24.00 | 26.00 | 28.50 |
| b. Small _____ | 15.00 | 21.75 | 21.75 | 23.75 | 25.25 |
| Celery _____ | 14.50 | 24.00 | 24.00 | 25.75 | 29.00 |
| Champagne (scarce) _____ | 18.00 | 33.75 | 33.75 | 36.00 | 39.75 |
| **Compote** | | | | | |
| a. Covered, 6'', high standard | 21.75 | 30.00 | 30.00 | 34.50 | 39.75 |
| b. Covered, 8'', high standard | 24.00 | 34.50 | 34.50 | 36.00 | 42.00 |
| c. Covered, 8'', low standard | 21.25 | 28.50 | 28.50 | 30.00 | 35.75 |
| d. Open, high standard ____ | 14.50 | 22.75 | 22.75 | 24.00 | 26.50 |
| Cordial _____ | 13.25 | 18.00 | 18.00 | 21.25 | 23.75 |
| Creamer _____ | 12.00 | 20.00 | 20.00 | 23.75 | 25.25 |
| **Dish** | | | | | |
| a. Covered, 7¾'', square ___ | 12.75 | 18.00 | 18.00 | 20.00 | 22.50 |
| b. Open, square _____ | 9.00 | 14.50 | 14.50 | 16.75 | 18.00 |
| *Goblet _____ | 12.00 | 20.00 | 20.00 | 22.50 | 24.00 |
| Pickle _____ | 7.25 | 12.00 | 12.00 | 13.25 | 16.50 |
| **Pitcher** | | | | | |
| a. Syrup _____ | 21.75 | 34.50 | 34.50 | 36.00 | 39.00 |
| b. Water _____ | 18.00 | 24.00 | 24.00 | 27.25 | 32.00 |
| *Plate, 10'' _____ | 12.00 | 17.00 | 17.00 | 21.25 | 23.75 |
| Platter, 10'', oblong _____ | 12.75 | 19.25 | 19.25 | 21.75 | 24.00 |
| Salt, boat on turtle's back __ | 18.00 | 24.00 | 24.00 | 26.00 | 27.25 |
| **Sauce** | | | | | |
| a. Flat, round _____ | 4.25 | 6.75 | 6.75 | 7.25 | 8.00 |
| b. Flat, square _____ | 4.75 | 7.25 | 7.25 | 7.75 | 8.00 |
| *c. Footed, round _____ | 5.50 | 8.50 | 8.50 | 9.75 | 10.75 |
| Shakers, pair _____ | 15.00 | 19.25 | 19.25 | 21.75 | 24.00 |
| Spooner _____ | 8.50 | 12.00 | 12.00 | 13.75 | 15.50 |
| Sugar bowl _____ | 18.00 | 26.50 | 26.50 | 28.50 | 32.00 |
| Tray, water _____ | 18.00 | 24.00 | 24.00 | 29.00 | 32.50 |
| *Tumbler _____ | 11.00 | 15.00 | 15.00 | 16.25 | 18.00 |
| *Wine _____ | 11.75 | 15.25 | 15.25 | 17.50 | 19.25 |

*Reproduced item

## WILLOW OAK

| | Clear | Amber | Blue |
|---|---|---|---|
| **Bowl** | | | |
| a. Berry _____$ | 11.00 | $ 15.25 | $ 20.00 |
| b. Waste _____ | 9.00 | 13.00 | 14.50 |
| Butter dish _____ | 17.00 | 23.75 | 26.00 |
| Cake stand _____ | 14.00 | 22.00 | 27.25 |
| Celery _____ | 12.75 | 23.00 | 26.00 |

**Willow Oak, continued**

| | Clear | Amber | Blue |
|---|---|---|---|
| Compote | | | |
| a. Covered, 7½'', high standard | 20.25 | 27.25 | 34.50 |
| b. Covered, 9'', high standard | 21.25 | 36.00 | 43.00 |
| Creamer | 13.25 | 18.00 | 21.25 |
| Goblet | 11.50 | 21.75 | 23.75 |
| Mug | 12.00 | 18.00 | 21.75 |
| Pitcher | | | |
| a. Large | 14.50 | 23.75 | 29.00 |
| b. Small | 12.00 | 21.75 | 27.25 |
| Plate | | | |
| a. 7'' | 13.25 | 16.50 | 19.25 |
| b. 9'', closed handles | 14.00 | 18.00 | 21.25 |
| Platter, oblong | 14.00 | 17.00 | 18.00 |
| Sauce | | | |
| a. Flat | 4.50 | 8.00 | 8.50 |
| b. Footed, round | 6 00 | 9.75 | 11.00 |
| Shakers, pair | 12.00 | 20.00 | 21.75 |
| Spooner | 9.75 | 13.25 | 16.50 |
| Sugar bowl | 17.00 | 22.00 | 29.75 |
| Tray, water, 10¾'' diam. | 13.25 | 18.00 | 21.25 |
| Tumbler | 9.75 | 13.25 | 14.50 |

## ABC PLATES

Plates made especially for children with the alphabet around the outer rim. Center decorations often consisted of animals, great men, maxims or Aesop's Fables. They were made of various materials including porcelain, pottery, glass, tin and pewter.

Plate. 8" diam. Tin. "I Killed Cock Robin" ---------- $23.50

**China:**

- 8½". Dog with glasses, Staffordshire-type ----------$ 19.50
- 8½". Red Riding Hood. Late Delft ---------- 16.00
- 8½". Red Riding Hood meets the Wolf ---------- 19.50
- 8" . Bible scene. Samuel before Eli ---------- 15.00
- 8" . Elves. 3-Crown. Germany-- 16.00
- 8" . Fishing Elephant, A. Stafofrdshire-type ---------- 17.50
- 8" . Golden crested wrens ---- 15.75
- 8" . Punctuality ---------- 15.00
- 8" . Rabbit center. Hands in sign language ---------- 18.50
- 8" . Whittington and his Cat -- 20.00
- 8" . Young Sergeant ---------- 16.00
- 7¾". Capitol at Washington ---- 16.75
- 7¾". Playing at Lovers -------- 22.50
- 7½". See Saw, Margy Daw. Blue. 14.00
- 7¼". Cat and Four Kittens ----- 18.00
- 7¼". Crusoe Rescues Friday ---- 16.75
- 7¼". Hunters and Dogs -------- 16.00
- 7¼". Little Jack Horner -------- 17.50
- 7¼". Meakin China. Football scene ---------- 20.00
- 7¼". Red Riding Hood meets the Wolf ---------- 18.50
- 7½". The Dancing Master ------ 14.00
- 7½". The New Pony ---------- 16.50
- 7" . Allertons. Comic transfer.-- 15.00
- 7" . Benjamin Franklin -------- 17.50
- 7" . Boatman capturing seal. "England" ---------- 16.50
- 7" . December, old man, holly, goat, turkeys. Green ----- 16.00
- 7" . Early rugby scene -------- 18.00
- 7" . Girl Bathing. With puss-in-boots scene ---------- 16.50
- 7" . Kitten and puppy peeking from pitchers ---------- 15.00
- 7" . Kitten in clothes ---------- 17.50
- 7" . The Guardian. Staffordshire ---------- 16.50
- 7" . Tired of Play ---------- 14.75
- 6¼". The Lord's Prayer. Transfer ---------- 12.00
- 6"¼. Owl center. Hands in sign language around border -- 20.00

Plate. 6¼" diam. Tin. Girl on swing ---------- $12.00

- 6" . Canary, bullfinch and goldfinch ---------- 18.50
- 6" . Cane center ---------- 10.00
- 6" . Little boys at marble play 18.00
- 6" . Our Donkey and Foal with boy and girl decoration -- 16.50
- 6" . Reuben interceding with Brethren for life of Joseph- 15.00
- 6" . "The Gleaners" ---------- 18.50
- 6" . Those Children, etc. ------ 16.00
- 5¼". Robinson Crusoe ---------- 18.00
- 5" . General Grant ---------- 16.50
- 5" . David and Goliath in colored scene ---------- 15.00

**Clear Glass:**

| | | |
|---|---|---|
| 6½". | Dog head center _____ | 12.50 |
| 6" . | Clock center _____ | 21.50 |
| 6" . | Elephant center _____ | 12.75 |
| 6" . | Hen and Chicks _____ | 16.00 |
| 6" . | Rabbit center. Frosted rim_ | 22.50 |
| 6" . | "Sancho Panza and Dapple" | |
| | Frosted rim _____ | 25.00 |
| 6" . | Star center _____ | 11.50 |
| 6" . | Stork center. Frosted rim__ | 22.50 |

**Tin:**

| | | |
|---|---|---|
| 8¾". | Hi Diddle Diddle _____ | 10.00 |
| 8" . | I Killed Cock Robin _____ | 23.50 |
| 8" . | Robin and Sparrow, verse__ | 16.00 |
| 6½". | Jumbo _____ | 15.00 |
| 6" . | Old Into Young _____ | 11.00 |
| 5½". | Victoria-Albert _____ | 12.00 |
| 5½". | Washington center _____ | 15.00 |

## ADAMS ROSE PATTERN

The Chinaware is decorated with brilliant red roses and green leaves on a white background. It was made by Adams & Son, Circa 1820-1840, in the Staffordshire District of England. A variant of the pattern was made later but the colors are not as brilliant and the background is a darker or "dirty" white. This type is known as Late Adams Rose Pattern and commands only about half the price of the early product.

Plate. 10½" diam. Late _____ $40.00

Bowl. 6½". Late _____$ 28.50

**Creamers:**

| | | |
|---|---|---|
| Early | _____ | 67.50 |
| Late | _____ | 39.50 |

**Cups and Saucers:**

| | | |
|---|---|---|
| Early, scalloped edge _____ | | 62.50 |
| Late _____ | | 38.50 |
| Pitcher. Large (about 5-gallon capacity). 16" high _____ | | 500.00 |

Sugar Bowl. Early "Wood" _____ $80.00

**Plates:**

| | | |
|---|---|---|
| 7¼". Early | _____ | 60.00 |
| 7¼". Late | _____ | 32.50 |
| 9¼". Marked "Adams" | _____ | 67.50 |
| 10". Soup. Early | _____ | 55.00 |
| 10½". Early | _____ | 60.00 |
| 10¼". Late | _____ | 40.00 |

**Sugar Bowls:**

| | | |
|---|---|---|
| 6¼" high. Early. Impressed "Wood" | _____ | 80.00 |
| Late | _____ | 45.00 |

**Teapots:**

| | | |
|---|---|---|
| 5". Late | _____ | 70.00 |
| 8". Early | _____ | 100.00 |

## ADVERTISING CARDS

Various firms issued printed and lithographed cards, often in a series of scenes, people, animals, etc., with an advertisement of their products, during the latter part of the 19th century.

### ADAMS AND WESTLAKE NON-EXPLOSIVE STOVES

The Seven Wonders of the World:

| | | |
|---|---|---|
| Colossus of Rhodes | _____$ | 1.10 |
| Egyptian Pyramids | _____ | 1.10 |
| Hanging Garden of Babylon | _____ | 1.10 |
| Olympus | _____ | 1.10 |
| Statue of Jupiter | _____ | 1.10 |

| The Mausoleum | 1.10 |
| The Pharos Watchtower | 1.10 |
| The Temple of Diana | 1.10 |

**PINKERTON'S ORIENTAL COMBINATION COFFEE. John W. Pinkerton & Co. Oriental Coffee & Spice Mills, Zanesville, Ohio** _____ .80

**AYERS CARDS**
"Grandma, See What I Brought You" _____ .75
Hair Vigor. Mermaids and sinking ship _____ .85
Sarsaparilla. Woman with child on shoulder — "Gives health and sunny hours" _____ .85
"The Fight for the Standard" ____ 1.25

**R. W. BELL CO.**
Soapona — Boy and girl leaving church _____ .75
Soapona—Boy chasing girl _____ .80

**CURTIS DAVIS & CO.**
Welcome Soap:
Boy and girl shaking hands _____ .75
Girl and dog _____ .75
Girl on knees caressing mother _____ .75

**DOBBINS ELECTRIC SOAP**
"At first the infant, Mewling and Puking in the nurse's arms" _____ .85

| Judge with hand behind reaching for bar of soap | .85 |
| "Mere oblivion. Sans teeth, sans eyes, sans taste, sans everything" | .85 |
| "The lover sighs like a furnace" | .85 |

**HIGGINS GERMAN LAUNDRY SOAP**
Captain and sailor _____ .75
Captain and two girls _____ .75
Sailor boy and girl _____ .75

**KENDALL MFG. CO.**
Soapine Cards:
Boy climbing rope held by star __ .75
Boy on telephone pole _____ .75
Girl, with mountain in distance __ .75
Sailor in rigging — Dream of home _____ .75
Sailor boy on ship mast _____ .80
Train-man and woman walking tracks _____ .85
Universal Family _____ .60
Woman hanging laundry _____ .75
Woman with bow and arrow ____ .75

**DR. KILMER'S REMEDIES**
Prompt Parilla:
Liver pills — Sick pig with owl, monkey and fox _____ .95

**JAS. S. KIRK & CO.**
Soapmakers, Chicago:
American Family _____ .80
Blue India _____ .70
Columbia _____ .75
Coronet _____ .70
Mottled German _____ .70
Queen of the Laundry _____ .75
Savon Imperial _____ .70
White Celon _____ .70
White Russian _____ .75

**LAZELL'S UNRIVALLED PERFUMES**
Mustached cavalier mounted on horse _____ .70
Two girls on white horse crossing stream _____ .70

**REYNOLDS BROS. SHOES**
Frogs fighting _____ .95

**THE ROYAL PHARMACEUTIC CO.**
Royal Elixir:
Miss Forster, Miss Ulmar, Miss St. Maur "Three Little Maids from School" _____ 2.00
Sallie Williams as "Peep Bo" ___ 1.75
Sallie Williams as "Pitti-Sing" __ 1.75
Vernona Jarbeau as "Yum-Yum" __ 1.75

**UNION CARD CO.**
Side-wheeler boat in rough water "Going into Provincetown Harbor, Cape Cod" _____ 1.50

**WHITE SEWING MACHINES.** "Best in the World" _____ .75

## AGATA GLASS

A glass with spots or blotches of a different shade or color. The mottled effect was produced by applying alcohol to clear or cranberry glass before it was tempered.

Vase. 6'' high. Pinched top,
usual mottled type _____ $995.00

Bowls:
| | |
|---|---|
| 3" high _____ | $ 750.00 |
| 4½" high. Handled _____ | 975.00 |
| 5". Acid finish _____ | 895.00 |
| Celery _____ | 895.00 |
| Cruet. Mottled _____ | 800.00 |
| Finger Bowl. Mottled _____ | 750.00 |
| Milk Pitcher. Rich rose shading to pale pink. Gold and blue mottling, applied hollow-reeded Agata handle _____ | 1200.00 |
| Sugar Bowl. 4½" high _____ | 1000.00 |
| Toothpick Holder. 4-way top ____ | 575.00 |
| Tumbler _____ | 650.00 |
| Vase. 4½" high, 3¼" diam. Pinched sides, frilly top, blue mottling _____ | 700.00 |
| Whiskey Tumbler _____ | 625.00 |

## AKRO AGATE GLASS

The Akro Agate Company was formed in 1911, first as jobbers selling marbles made by the Navarre Glass Marble Specialty Co., to chain stores and wholesalers.

In 1914, the owners moved from near Akron, Ohio, to Clarksburg, W. Va., where cheap labor and a plentiful supply of natural gas were available. They opened a factory known as The Akro Agate Co.

for production of marbles, which continued in profitable operation until 1929.

In 1932, the company diversified and started making bowls, ash trays, flower pots, etc., in green, red and blue onyx. Operations continued successfully until 1948. Finally, because of the lack of profits, the firm was dissolved and the factory and equipment were sold in 1951.

Planter. 4½ x 2¾''. Carved.
White _____ $10.00

| | |
|---|---|
| Bowl. 5" long, 3" wide. Green Slag. Raised flower decor ____$ | 8.50 |
| Cigarette Holder _____ | 6.00 |
| Creamer. Jade Green. Small _____ | 7.50 |
| Cup and Saucer. Orange and white | 10.00 |
| Match Holder. Horn of Plenty. Orange and white _____ | 10.00 |
| Planter. 5¼" long, 3" wide, red and white color. Leaf and blossom decor _____ | 8.75 |
| Tumbler. Green and white _____ | 10.50 |
| Vase. Small, green and white ____ | 7.50 |

## ALMANACS

The almanac was consulted religiously by people of this country in the 18th and 19th century as a guide to daily activities. Crops were planted when the phase of the moon was considered proper. Family activities and outings were planned by using the almanac. Almanacs after 1880 are fairly common and sell for approximately $1.50 each.

| | |
|---|---|
| 1776—North American Almanac, Samuel Stearns _____$ | 20.00 |
| 1783—Bickerstaff's New England Almanac, Norwich _____ | 18.00 |
| 1791—N. Strong, Almanac, Hartford _____ | 15.00 |
| 1794—The New England Almanack by Nathan Daboll, New London _____ | 12.75 |
| 1796—Nehemiah Strong's Almanac, Hartford _____ | 12.75 |
| 1797—Hagerstown Town & Country Almanack, First Edition ____ | 45.00 |

1900—Barker's Illustrated Almanac
with cartoon _____ $3.50

1805—New England Almanac by
Nathan Daboll, New London_ 14.50
1808—New England Almanac by
Nathan Daboll, New London_ 11.75
1808—The Virginia Farmer's Almanac by Benjamin Bates,
Richmond _____ 18.00
1810—New England Almanac by
Nathan Daboll _____ 12.75
1811—New England Almanac by
Nathan Daboll _____ 12.75
1813—New England Almanac by
Nathan Daboll _____ 12.00
1816—New England Almanac by
Nathan Daboll _____ 11.00
1818—New England Almanac by
Nathan Daboll _____ 12.00
1820—New England Almanac by
Nathan Daboll _____ 11.00
1828—The Farmer's Diary or On-
tario Almanac by Oliver
Loud, Canandaigua _____ 10.00
1829—Western Almanac by Oliver
Loud, Rochester, N. Y. ____ 9.75
1834—Poor Richard's Almanac by
Tobias Ostrander, Rochester_ 9.75
1837—American Anti-Slavery Almanac, Boston _____ 10.75
1843—Presbyterian Almanac, Pgh.__ 4.50
1850—Hagerstown Town & Country
Almanack _____ 4.00
1872—Tarrytown Argus Almanac,
Tarrytown, N. Y. _____ 3.75
1874—Hostetter's United States
Almanac, Pgh. Pa. _____ 2.75
1880—Hagerstown Town & Country
Almanac by J. Gruber,
Hagerstown, Md. _____ 2.75

1888—Wright's Pictorial Family
Almanac _____ 2.00
1889—Burdock's Blood Bitters and
Key to Health _____ 2.50
1895—Ayer's American Almanac__ 2.00
1897—Home Almanac _____ 1.75
1900—Barker's Illustrated. Farmer's
Guide and Household Cook
Book. (with cartoons) _____ 3.50
1902—The Ladies' Birthday Almanac _____ 1.50

1899—Burdock's Blood Bitters and
Key to Health _____ $2.50

1867—Pinney's Calendar or Western
Almanac, Geo. R. Perkins __ 9.00
1869—Hagerstown Town & Country
Almanack _____ 2.50

## AMBERINA GLASS

Amberina, or "Rose-amber," ware is a transparent combination of glass shading from ruby to an amber tint. It was first made by the New England Glass Company, Cambridge, Massachusetts, in 1883. The trade name "amberina" was devised by Edward J. Libby, head official of the company.

The product was made by adding gold to the glass batch in the pot. The glass was amber colored upon being blown or molded to shape. The ruby color was developed when the item was reheated to the correct temperature. The practice of the day was to reheat one end of the article and then the other to produce the ruby-red color. The idea was eventually conceived to heat just one end of an item and to market it as a two-tone glass. A wide market developed and amberina was in demand for more than 10 years.

Pitcher. 7''. Inverted Thumbprint,
Clear applied finely ribbed
handle _____$ 185.00

Boat Dish. 14'' long. Daisy and
Button pattern _____$ 175.00
Bottle, Water. Inverted Thumb-
print, 8'' high _____ 110.00
Bowls:
  Daisy and Button, 9'' square,
  2¾'' deep _____ 175.00
  Diamond Quilted, 8'' diam. _____ 150.00
  Finger. Diamond Quilted, with
  plate _____ 180.00
  Plain, large _____ 150.00
  Punch, 11¼'' diam. _____ 450.00
  With applied crystal feet,
  flowers and leaves. 5'' high,
  7'' wide. Inverted Thumbprint__ 135.00
  Round. 2½'' high, 4½'' diam.
  trefoil top _____ 125.00
Butter Dish. Covered, glass
insert _____ 195.00
Celery Vases:
  Diamond Quilted, 4¾'' high,
  blown, scalloped square top __ 180.00
  6¾'' high. Mt. Washington,
  square scalloped top, Diamond
  Quilted _____ 185.00
  7½'' high. Mt. Washington _____ 210.00
  Plain _____ 120.00
Creamers:
  Inverted Thumbprint, clear
  handle _____ 130.00
  Miniature tankard _____ 110.00
  4'' high, 2½'' diam. _____ 150.00
  5½'' high. Melon-shape, amber
  handle _____ 140.00

Cruets:
  Baby Thumbprint, finest color,
  original stopper _____ 180.00
  Inverted Thumbprint, original
  stopper, amberina handle _____ 235.00
  4'' high. Applied clear glass
  handle, amber stopper _____ 220.00
  Plain _____ 170.00
Cups:
  Punch. Inverted Thumbprint ____ 70.00
  Punch. Baby Inverted Thumbprint,
  clear applied handle _____ 60.00
  Punch. Set of 6 _____ 395.00
Decanter, Wine. Ruffled top,
applied white handle, cut
stopper _____ 185.00
Dish, Sauce. Square _____ 50.00
Lamp, Miniature. With shade _____ 250.00
Mug. Handled _____ 75.00
Mustard Pot. Pewter top _____ 95.00
Pitchers:
  Milk. 8''. Inverted Thumbprint__ 190.00
  Syrup. Silver collar and handle,
  deep coloring _____ 210.00
  Water. Blown, ruffled top, clear
  reeded handle _____ 225.00
  Water. Inverted Thumbprint _____ 195.00
  Water. Inverted Thumbprint. Six
  matching tumblers. Set _____ 410.00
  Water. Swirl pattern _____ 225.00
  Water. Rich blue shading into
  amberina _____ 200.00
Plate. 9½'', floral decor _____ 100.00
Salt and Pepper Shakers. Tall and
slender, pewter tops. Pair ____ 100.00
Salt, Master. 1¾'' high, 3½'' diam.,
on pedestal, ruffled edge _____ 65.00
Salt Shaker. ITP, pewter top _____ 55.00
Sauce. Round. 4½'' diam. _____ 45.00
Shade. Flared, ruffled _____ 110.00
Sherbet _____ 75.00
Sugar Bowl _____ 170.00
Sugar Bowl and Creamer. Amber
reeded handles, square tops __ 225.00
Sugar Shaker. ITP, pewter top ___ 135.00
Toothpick Holders:
  Daisy and Button _____ 115.00
  Diamond Quilted _____ 125.00
Tumblers:
  Baby Inverted Thumbprint _____ 60.00
  Diamond Quilted, ground pontil__ 70.00
  Enameled flower decor _____ 60.00
  Inverted Thumbprint _____ 67.50
  Juice. Inverted Thumbprint ____ 85.00
  Lemonade _____ 60.00
  Swirl pattern _____ 65.00
Vases:
  2¾'' high, ITP, bulbous _____ 75.00
  4½'' high, ITP, reeded handles __ 95.00
  4½'' high, Libbey, signed _____ 215.00
  4½'' high, Morning Glory shape__ 97.50
  6¾'' high, D. Q. Blown, square
  top _____ 95.00
  6½'' high, Diamond Quilted,
  bulbous _____ 100.00

| | |
|---|---|
| 7" high, Jack-in-Pulpit _____ | 90.00 |
| 7½" high, ruffled top _____ | 95.00 |
| 11" high, swirled _____ | 115.00 |
| 12" high, Jack-in-Pulpit _____ | 125.00 |
| 12" high, tulip top, bulbous bottom, Inverted Thumbprint _____ | 125.00 |
| 12⅝" high, Lily _____ | 135.00 |
| 15" high, fluted top, pedestal base _____ | 145.00 |
| Whiskey glass _____ | 60.00 |

## AMBERINA GLASS (PLATED)

Plated Amberina has a fiery opalescent (white) lining in addition to the usual amberina characteristics of amber blending cranberry. Another characteristic is the vertical ribbing. It was a product of the New England Glass Company, East Cambridge, Massachusetts.

A cased Wheeling glass of similar nature has an opaque white lining but does not show opalescence when held to light. Neither does it have the vertical ribbing.

| | |
|---|---|
| Syrup Jug. Silver plated top, handle and tray _____ | $4,000.00 |

| | |
|---|---|
| Bowl, 8" diam., 3½" high ____ | $7500.00 |
| Dish. Oblong, with 4 feet _____ | 6000.00 |
| Pitcher. 9" high _____ | 8250.00 |

## ANIMAL DISHES (COVERED)

A variety of covered animal dishes has been made of clear, colored and opal (Milk Glass) glass. Others have been made of pottery—notably Staffordshire types. The bases usually have a slightly depressed inner rim into which the cover fits.

| | |
|---|---|
| Butter Dish. Cow cover. Purple slag _____ | $100.00 |

| | |
|---|---|
| Cat. Blue milk glass, white head. 5" long _____ $ | 60.00 |
| Chicken on sleigh. White milk glass. 4" _____ | 65.00 |
| Chicks and eggs on nest. White milk glass. 3" _____ | 48.50 |
| Cockatoo. Staffordshire. 3½" _____ | 90.00 |
| Cow. Frosted. 6" _____ | 50.00 |
| Dog. White milk glass. 5" _____ | 50.00 |
| Ducks: | |
| Clear glass. 6½" _____ | 29.50 |
| Frosted. 6½" _____ | 40.00 |
| Frosted. 7½" _____ | 45.00 |
| Milk glass, white. 5" _____ | 55.00 |
| Sandwich milk glass. 6½". Pair__ | 175.00 |
| Eagle. White milk glass. "American Hen" _____ | 49.50 |
| Fish, on skiff. White milk glass. 7" _____ | 39.50 |
| Fox. Lacy base. Pat. Date 1889 ____ | 110.00 |
| Hens: | |
| Colored Glass | |
| 5". Dark amber _____ | 50.00 |
| 6½". Honey amber _____ | 52.50 |
| Frosted | |
| 6½" _____ | 25.00 |
| 7" _____ | 29.50 |
| Milk Glass | |
| 5". White _____ | 30.00 |
| 5". White with blue head ____ | 36.50 |
| 6½". White _____ | 32.50 |
| 6½". Blue _____ | 40.00 |
| 6½". White with blue head, on lacy nest _____ | 90.00 |
| 6½". Blue with white head ____ | 48.50 |
| 7". White with lacy nest _____ | 80.00 |
| 7". White with lacy nest and caramel flecked back _____ | 95.00 |
| 7½". White _____ | 59.50 |

7½''. Blue ---------------------- 76.50
Parian. 7'' ---------------------- 110.00
Staffordshire:
2½''. Good coloring ---------- 60.00
3½''. Vivid coloring ---------- 68.50
6½''. Brilliant coloring, on caramel nest ---------------- 140.00
7''. Yellow nest with green exterior ---------------------- 150.00
8''. White, with brown basket base ---------------------- 75.00
Lamb. White, hexagon base ------ 37.50
Lions:
Blue. With white head, on blue picket base ---------------------- 42.00
White. Lacy base. Pat. Date, Aug. 6, 1889 ---------------- 89.50
Man O' War. White milk glass.. . 7'' ---------------------- 35.00
Moses in Bullrushes. White base, grass design ---------------- 64.50
Quail. White milk glass. 5'' ------ 34.50
Rabbits:
White milk glass. 5'' ---------- 30.00
White milk glass. Mule-eared ---- 27.50
Swans:
5''. Blue glass ---------------- 60.00
5''. White milk glass, closed neck- 40.00
6''. Staffordshire -------------- 165.00
6½''. Sandwich clear glass, with frosted head and neck ---------- 55.00
6½''. Sandwich milk glass. Pair -- 175.00
7''. Clear glass. "Pat. Applied For" under top -------------- 40.00
7''. Translucent blue. "Pat. Applied For" under top ------- 60.00
7''. Sandwich milk glass. Pair -- 185.00
7''. White milk glass, open neck, lacy nest ---------------------- 77.50
Turkey. McKee, 5''. White -------- 75.00
Turkey Hen. 9''. Leeds ---------- 150.00
Turkey Hen. 8''. Staffordshire, white with brown nest ---------------- 95.00

## APOTHECARY BOTTLES

Apothecary or Drug Store Bottles were used as storage containers for the various compounds and drugs found in old-time drug establishments.

15" high. Glass, round, slender. Thumbprint base and cover ----$ 20.00
14" high. Bulbous. Fancy T. P. Inverted pedestal and base ---- 18.50
12" high. "Capsicum" ---------- 16.50
12" high. Drug bottle with ground stopper ---------------- 12.00
11" high. 4"½ diam., 2"¼ stopper, wide mouth ------------------ 12.00
9½" high. Clear glass with gold label. "Kino" lettered in black ---------------------- 18.75

TINCT: OPII. 7¾'' to top of stopper. Ribbed. Emerald green-- $22.50

9½" high. Drug bottle with ground pontil ---------------- 11.00
8¾" high. 3½" diam., 1⅞" stopper, wide mouth ---------- 8.00
8½'' high, 3¼" diam., 1¾" stopper, wide mouth ---------- 8.00
7½" high, 2¾" diam., 1½" stopper, wide mouth ---------- 7.50
7½" high, 5½" diam., free blown, clear ---------------------- 15.00
7½" high. Rough pontil ---------- 7.50
Jar. Quart. "Ext. Amygd. A." on side. Clear glass ------------- 6.50

## AURENE GLASS

A type of Art Glass invented by Frederick Carder, an Englishman. The name "Aurene" was bestowed upon the glass by the originator from the Latin "Aurene"—a Roman gold coin. Aurene Glass has a smooth uniform iridescent gold-like surface although some is either silvery or dark blue. It was manufactured by the Steuben Glass Works from about 1904 to 1930. Most items were permanently marked in ink under glaze with the word "Aurene" although some items were marked with paper labels only.

Vase. 5½'' high. Footed, ruffled top. Small white blossoms and green vines on iridescent amber ground $200.00

Vase. 3-stem vase in blue. 6'' ____ $360.00

Atomizers:
  2'' high, 6'' diam., low-footed __$ 68.00
  10'' high. Mint on gold _____ 65.00
Baskets:
  8x8'', flared top, iridescent gold
  and blue, applied handle _____ 225.00
  Miniature, handle _____ 160.00
Biscuit Jar. Signed, straight
  sides, gold, blue & red colors__ 310.00
BonBon Dishes:
  Iridescent peacock blue _____ 110.00
  1¾'' high, 4½'' diam., signed
  Aurene 532 and signed Fred
  Carder _____ 165.00

Bottles:
  6'' high. Ruffled and stretched,
  orange, red, blue, green highlights. _____ 75.00
  6½'' high. Blue color, blossom
  stopper _____ 225.00
Bottle, Cologne. Gold _____ 150.00
Bowls:
  2½'' high, 7'' diam. Signed ____ 165.00
  8'' diam. Signed _____ 275.00
  10'' diam. Signed _____ 295.00
  12'' diam. Signed. Three-footed_ 300.00
Candlesticks:
  Blue, twisted stem. Signed ____ 260.00
  8'' high. Blue twist. Signed. Pair 500.00
  10'' high. Gold. Signed _____ 295.00
Centerpieces:
  12'' diam., gold _____ 200.00
  13'' diam., 3'' high, deep blue
  roll-over rim _____ 265.00
Champagne _____ 95.00
Compote. 8¼'' high, 6'' diam., blue 195.00
Cordial. 5'', stemmed, gold ____ 80.00
Cordial Set. Decanter (10¾'') with
  6 cordials (2¼''). Swirl pattern
  on bottle and neck, flaring lip.
  Gold _____ 400.00
Cup, Sherbet, and Plate. Signed__ 87.50
Cuspidor, Ladies'. Miniature,
  signed, gold _____ 175.00
Finger Bowl with Tray. Signed____ 95.00
Fruit Dish. Clear to blue. Signed
  "Steuben" _____ 135.00

| | |
|---|---|
| Goblet. Gold with blue, twisted stem _____ | 150.00 |
| Lamp Shade. 5'' bell-shaped, green and white leaf, clear outside __ | 48.00 |
| Lamp Shade. 7'', gold, signed __ | 68.00 |
| Liqueur Glass. 5'', blue _____ | 80.00 |
| Plate, Sherbet, Calcite, gold ____ | 75.00 |
| Perfume Bottle. 6'', signed. Melon ribbed, matching stoppers. Pair | 200.00 |
| Salt. 1½'' high, gold color. Signed _____ | 100.00 |
| Tazza. Footed, double twisted stem, scalloped edge. Signed__ | 295.00 |

Vases:

| | |
|---|---|
| Miniature. Jack-in-the-Pulpit. Signed _____ | 195.00 |
| 3'' high. Iridescent silver and gold with green tendrils and lily-pad leaves. Signed _____ | 125.00 |
| 3¼'' high. Flared top, 3 feet____ | 195.00 |
| 4¼'' high. Iridescent blue, scalloped top _____ | 210.00 |
| 4¼'' high. Gold with overtones of blue and purple. Signed _____ | 125.00 |
| 5'' high. Greenish gold. Signed__ | 150.00 |
| 5'' high. Tri-cornered, iridescent | 100.00 |
| 5½'' high. Bell-shaped. Signed ___ | 225.00 |
| 5½'' high. Fluted and flared. Pencil thin base. Signed _____ | 185.00 |
| 6'' high. Jack-in-the-Pulpit. Rose overtones _____ | 235.00 |
| 6'' high. Trumpet-shaped _____ | 240.00 |
| 6½'' high, 5½'' widest diam. Shell shaped body of mottled blue, rose, green and gold glass with iridescent sheen _____ | 215.00 |
| 6¾'' high. Melon shaded tones. Signed _____ | 165.00 |
| 7'' high. Opaque white glass with red, gold and iridescent markings _____ | 275.00 |
| 7'' high. Silvery blue. Signed __ | 285.00 |
| 8'' high. Blue. Signed _____ | 375.00 |
| 8'' high. Deep blue, transparent top, lighter blue swirl. Signed__ | 185.00 |
| 8¼'' high. Gold, leaf design at top _____ | 315.00 |
| 9'' high. Gold, lily-pad decor ____ | 275.00 |
| 10'' high. Brillant blue, scalloped top _____ | 300.00 |
| Wine. 4½'' high. Gold, twisted stem. Signed _____ | 90.00 |

## AUTOGRAPHS

The signatures of famous and sometimes notorious people are in demand by collectors.

Signatures on land grants and other routine papers of presidents and governors were usually affixed by a clerk or secretary and are of little value to serious collectors.

| | |
|---|---|
| Adams, John Quincy. Envelope addressed to Rev. N. Murray with return and J. Q. Adams in very unsteady handwriting. Seal intact on back _____$ | 50.00 |
| Adams, John Quincy. Document signed as President, April 4, 1825. Framed with portrait____ | 85.00 |
| Balfour, Arthur James. Signature and greeting on official Secretary for Scotland stationery __ | 10.00 |
| Banks, Nathaniel P. Governor of Massachusetts. Major General in Civil War. Signature on card__ | 6.75 |
| Beauregard, (P.) G. T. Autograph note signed Aug. 7, 1886, framed with portrait in uniform _____ | 45.00 |
| Bennett, Arnold. Autograph letter signed Jan. 18, 1915. As exlawyer, he claims the law attempts to set up its own rules of composition _____ | 20.00 |
| Browning, Robert. Autographed letter signed June 12, 1880. Framed with colorful portrait__ | 60.00 |
| Calhoun, John C. Excellent engraved portrait, decoratively framed, with large, clear signature _____ | 40.00 |
| Carlyle, Thomas. Scarce and interesting autograph letter signed July 11, 1851. Framed with colored portrait _____ | 150.00 |
| Caruso, Enrico. Important 4-page autograph letter signed Genoa, Aug. 12, 1919. Reluctant to use agents. Insists on favorable terms, and, should his proceeds be taxed, his price will advance. In Italian, with translation ____ | 70.00 |
| Caruso, Enrico. Characteristic photograph signed, London, 1907. Elaborately framed _____ | 75.00 |
| Clay, Henry. Autograph letter signed March 25, 1848. Framed with engraved portrait _____ | 85.00 |
| Clay, Henry. Autographed letter signed, Oct. 31, 1849. Framed with handsome engraved portrait _____ | 85.00 |
| Clinton, George. Governor, New York 1777-95 and governor-to-be DeWitt Clinton. Handwritten Resolution, signed by each, Feb. 6, 1778, that the 4 bills outlined thereupon ''should respectively become Laws of this State.'' Impressively framed with portraits of both Clintons _____ | 135.00 |
| Doyle, A. Conan. Short autograph note signed, Sept. 17, 1897. Framed with photograph _____ | 55.00 |
| Dreyfus, Alfred. Condemned to Devil's Island, later exonerated of treason to France. Auto- | |

graph letter signed. Framed with photograph. With translation __ 110.00

Eliot, T. S. Signature on verso of bank check, Jan. 28, 1963 ____ 7.50

Emerson, Ralph Waldo. Holograph note in third person, framed with excellent engraved portrait ____ 60.00

Fall, Albert B. Bold signature on large Secretary of the Interior card _____ 12.00

Gaugin, Paul. Cordial autograph letter signed Paris, June 24, 1886, to a friend and admirer__ 750.00

de Gaulle, Charles. Letter signed, July 3, 1940, urging all free French to rally to the cause of the resistance _____ 125.00

Gladstone, W. E. Autograph letter, signed by the famous Prime Minister, June 29, 1870 _____ 40.00

Grant, U. S. Document signed as President, Oct. 4, 1869 _____ 125.00

Grant, U. S. Document signed as President, May 28, 1869, suspending the Deputy Postmaster of Newburgh, Orange County, New York. Framed with handsome portrait _____ 95.00

Grieg, Edvard. Manuscript bars of music signed London, March, 1889. Framed, with distinguished portrait _____ 110.00

Guillotin, Joseph Ignace, Dr. After whom beheading instrument was named. Decorative medical diploma signed Paris, June 28, 1785. Strikingly framed _____ 150.00

Hancock, John. Holograph order to pay, signed Boston, April 21, 1774 _____ 500.00

Harrison, William Henry. Order written in his hand, signed July 22, 1795, ordering 17,000 beef and 11 gills of whiskey for the Kickapoo Indians. Framed with full-length engraved portrait__ 50.00

Henry, Patrick. Signature handsomely framed with engraved portrait _____ 60.00

Hunt, W. Holman. Noted Pre-Raphaelite painter. Autograph letter signed Aug. 3, 1874. Framed with large colored portrait _____ 50.00

Huxley, Julian S. Autograph letter signed Feb. 18, 1929 _____ 10.00

Jackson, Andrew. Important autograph letter signed while President, April 22, 1829. Includes suggestion "for the security of the revenue." Framed with portrait. Rare _____ 285.00

Keller, Helen. Inspiring signed typed statement about the importance of women voting,

framed with portrait and addressed envelope, stamped July 4, 1910 _____ 65.00

King George III. Vellum document, seal and revenue stamp intact, signed April 22, 1805. Decorative frame _____ 85.00

Kipling, Rudyard. Signature framed with etched portrait _____ 40.00

Lafayette. Letter signed June 19, 1830, stating that the American government has little influence on science and industry, as private enterprise and public spirit outstrip a government with meager funds at its disposal. Framed, with portrait. Translation _____ 140.00

Lee, Robert E. Rare signed photograph, framed _____ 225.00

Leschetizky, Thedor. Partly printed New Year greeting, with two holograph lines signed in German. Vienna, Dec. 30, 1909 ____ 12.50

Lincoln, Abraham. Impressive document signed August 5, 1861 ___ 600.00

Lincoln, Abraham. Wartime autograph note signed Oct. 10, 1863, in answer to official letter signed by Maj. Gen. J. F. Foster and New York's noted E. D. Morgan. Both letters framed with engraved portrait of Lincoln____ 600.00

Longfellow, Henry Wadsworth. Four manuscript lines from Evangeline, signed. Framed with impressive photograph _____ 95.00

Longfellow, Henry Wadsworth. Signature framed with portrait ___ 57.50

Maeterlinck, Maurice. Nobel Prize for literature, 1911. Autograph letter signed Feb. 11, 1918, to his publisher. Mentions "The Blue Bird" and "The Bee." Translation _____ 50.00

Masefield, John. Poet laureate, novelist and dramatist. Autograph letter signed _____ 12.50

Melba, Nellie. Elaborately framed carte-photo as Marguerite ____ 40.00

Morris, Robert. Signed Declaration of Independence, financial backer Amer. Revolution _____ 135.00

Napoleon I. Early letter signed 6 Pluviose year 4 (Jan. 26 1795). As General-in-Chief with rare and very bold Italian spelling of his family name, Buonaparte _____ 400.00

Nijinsky, Waslaw. Holograph will signed and dated March 25, 1916, witnessed on same day by Berthe Kreps _____ 800.00

Paca, William. Signer from Maryland. Also George Plater, William Carmichael, and John

Henry, members Continental Congress. Letter signed by all 4, Philadelphia, March 9, 1779, on movement of enemy troops from New York to Georgia __ 225.00

Pavlova, Anna. Signed portrait of one of the world's most loved ballerinas in costume _____ 120.00

Pickins, Francis W. Governor of of South Carolina 1860-62. Gave the order to fire upon the "Star of the West." Historically important letter signed Jan. 15, 1862, on official stationery to the Governor of North Carolina (Henry T. Clark) _____ 70.00

Puccini, Giacomo. Unique and musically historic letter to Illica, the librettist of Tosca, Feb. 15-postmarked 1899 _____ 350.00

Queen Victoria. Portrait and large bold signature. Framed _____ 37.50

Rejane. Autograph note on card signed, to Irene Vanbrugh. With envelope _____ 9.50

Rhodes, Cecil John. Prime Minister of Cape Colony, formed De Beers Consolidated Mines Co., and endowed Oxford scholarships. Scarce letter signed, Cape Town, Jan. 5, 1891 _____ 60.00

Robeson, Paul. Serious and significant autograph letter signed, London, Dec. 18, 1928. 4 pages_ 55.00

Roosevelt, Franklin D. Friendly and gracious letter signed as President on White House stationery, March 7, 1935 _____ 150.00

Rutherford, Sir Ernest. Noted British physicist. Nobel Prize for chemistry, 1908. President of the Royal Society 1925-30. Autograph quotation signed. Rare __ 35.00

Schley, Rear Admiral Winfield Scott. Autograph letter signed Nov. 24, 1898 _____ 12.50

Schnitzler, Arthur. Austrian physician, playwright and novelist. 2-page autograph note on correspondence card, Marienbad, July 10, 1895. In German, with translation _____ 25.00

Shaw, G. Bernard. Significant letter signed Dec. 28, 1907. "I have always looked to the Provinces for the harvest which was sown in London under great difficulties" _____ 140.00

Taney, Roger B. Chief Justice. Succeeded John Marshall. Signature with greeting _____ 8.50

Tennyson, Alfred. Poet laureate. Handsome photograph framed with signature _____ 32.50

Tree, Herbert Beerbohm. Holograph quotation signed 1890 __ 7.50

Tunney, Gene. Handsome photograph signed while a young man. In boxing trunks, 7 x 9½" _____ 25.00

Twain, Mark. Excellent cabinet photograph inscribed and signed; once as Mark Twain, again as S. L. Clemens, May 26, 1899___ 120.00

Valentino, Rudolph. Rare photograph in matador costume, signed "with sincere wishes," in Italian _____ 135.00

Verdi, Giuseppe. Holograph music signed and inscribed, Naples, Feb. 22, 1858 _____ 450.00

Verne, Jules. Autograph letter signed July 22, 1899, In French. Translation. Handsomely framed with portrait _____ 85.00

Victoria, Queen. Vellum document signed June 11, 1838, in first year of her reign _____ 110.00

Volta, Allesandro. Noted Italian physicist for whom the volt was named. Autograph signed July 12, (Circa 1782) _____ 525.00

Washington, Booker T. Noted Negro educator. Letter signed Dec. 19, 1912 _____ 20.00

Washington, George. Wartime order signed, Morristown, Jan. 7, 1777, to William Palfrey, Paymaster General to the Army of the U. S. to pay to Col. David Henley, 65 hundred dollars to recruit a regiment. Framed with portrait. Historically important _____ 650.00

Wayne. "Mad Anthony". General. Scarce autographed letter signed Philadelphia. Aug. 2, 1775. Framed with portrait of him standing beside his horse ____ 200.00

Wise, Rabbi Stephen S. Letter signed Dec. 14, 1936, on American Jewish Congress stationery, to E. A. Filene _____ 22.50

## AUTO ITEMS

The motor carriage developed into the automobile between 1900 and 1910. More than 200 different makes were marketed in the past. Most have been consigned to the junk yard but a number of accessories, such as horns, lights, name plates, license plates, etc., remain for the collector of automobiliana.

Audel's Automobile Guide, 1915 __$ 15.00
Auto Blue Book, New England, 1917  10.00
Auto Green Book, A. L. A., Vol. 1, 1922 _____ 8.75
Auto Green Book. New York and New England, 1922 _____ 7.50
Auto Green Book. 1926 _____ 7.25

Auto Horn. 9'' long. Brass, painted
black, without bulb _____ $25.00

Auto and Truck Wiring Manual.
1912-20. Blueprints, 678 pages __ 25.00
Automobile Handbook. Putman's
1918. Brokaw & Starr _____ 8.25
Carbide Tank. For running board.
Newly brass plated _____ 75.00
Clock, Dash. Stevens Duryea. Brass,
bevelled case, 8-day, key wind.
Hoffecker Co., Boston. Running_ 24.00
Dusters:
Linen _____ 12.00
Silk. Man's, large. English _____ 25.00
Emblems:
Buick. Chipped _____ 5.00
Chevrolet. Chipped _____ 5.00
Dodge. Chipped _____ 5.00
Dort. Chipped _____ 5.00
Essex. Very good _____ 10.00
Graham Bros. Chipped _____ 5.00
Hupmobile. Chipped _____ 5.00
Maxwell. Very good _____ 10.00
Nash. Very good _____ 10.00
Studebaker. Discolored _____ 5.00
Glasses, Ladies'. Driving, in orig-
inal tin box _____ 12.50
Headlights. Cadillac, 1915. Pair__ 75.00
Horns:
Brass, English, "King of the Road",
No. 34 _____ 65.00
Brass, flexible tube, no bulb ____ 60.00
Old. Bulb-type _____ 65.00
Old. Plunger-type _____ 15.00
"How to Build Automobiles."
(Steam and Electric). E. T.
Bubler, 1904. Working drawings
and illustrations of many early
cars 49 pages _____ 24.00
Jack. Ford, Model "T" _____ 8.50
Lamps:
"Dietz Eureda". 7½'' high, clear
lens in front, red glass in rear__ 15.00
Driving. Brass _____ 50.00
Ford, 5'' square, 10'' high. Re-
finished and electrified. Brass
and tin combination. Pair _____ 65.00

Ford Model "T". Black. Pair __ 32.50
Hupmobile. "Adlake Balanced
Draft". 8½'' high, original
brackets _____ 22.50

Lamp, Driving. Brass                    $45.00

License Plates. 1910-1912-1914,
enameled. 3 plates for _____ 20.00
Magneto. Ford, Model "N", for 4-
cylinder engine _____ 40.00
Motor Meters:
1916 Boyce _____ 22.50
1916 Dodge _____ 22.50
Midget, Boyce. Works _____ 15.00
Parasol. Touring car accessory.
Silk, yellow with green trim ____ 10.00
Pump, Tire. Marked Ford, new
base _____ 8.00
Radiator Cap Ornaments:
Bird. Large, winged. Fine _____ 15.00
Buick. Blue glass _____ 15.00
Radiator Emblem. Mack Truck,
chrome _____ 9.00
Road Map of New York State in
Soconyland for 1927 _____ 5.00
Robe, Car. Squirrel on branch in
center design. Perfect condition_ 22.50
Spark Coil. For early car _____ 40.00
Steering Wheel. 1925 Durant _____ 25.00

Tail Lights:
Model "T". Not exactly alike.
Brass top on 1915 model. Pair -- 15.00
1928. Red, says "Dodge" _____ 7.00

## AUTOMOBILES

Rolls Royce Convertible Coupe.
Gray colors, 3 horns, electric
lights and starter _____ $8,000.00

Auburn Supercharged 2-Door Con-
vertible, 1936. Complete, 2-speed
rear end, right hand drive, ex-
cellent mechanical condition.
Needs restoration _____$2500.00
Buick Club Sedan, 1934, Model 60.
Original running condition _____ 1400.00
Buick 4-Door Sedan, 1941. 60,000
original miles. Needs restoration_ 450.00
Cadillac 60-S, 1939. Mint _____ 2500.00
Cadillac Opera Coupe, 1938. Good
condition _____ 1450.00
Cadillac Convertible Coupe, 1938.
With rumble seat. Completely re-
stored _____ 3000.00
Cadillac 4-Door Convertible, 1935.
Reconditioned. Includes original
Cadillac radio _____ 2800.00
Cadillac 7-Passenger Touring Car,
1920. 34,000 miles _____ 5000.00
Chevrolet, 1938. Excellent con-
dition _____ 750.00
Chevrolet Coupe, 1931. Chrome
hemi-engine, channeled 8" slicks,
bucket seats, 3-speed stick, vinyl
roof. Good running condition ___ 1200.00
Chevrolet Standard, 2-door Sedan,
1937. Good running condition __ 700.00
Chevrolet Station Wagon, 1930. Re-
stored _____ 1850.00
Chrysler Highlander Convertible,
1947. Excellent condition _____ 1700.00
Chrysler Sedan, 1933. Good condition _____ 1850.00
Ford Deluxe 4-Door Sedan, 1940.
Excellent condition _____ 1250.00
Ford 4-Door Touring, 1913. Low
mileage _____ 2600.00
Ford Touring, 1920. Newly restored _____ 1650.00

Frazer Manhattan Sedan, 1948. 6-
cylinder, overdrive, R&H, excel-
lent condition _____ 950.00
Jaguar SS 100, 1937. Original,
needs restoration _____ 1000.00
Jaguar XK140 Coupe, 1956. Wire
wheels, electric fuel pump and
choke. Good condition _____ 1200.00
Lincoln Continental Mark II, 1956.
Hand-tooled, 50,000 miles. Good
condition _____ 1900.00
Lincoln Continental Mark III, 1956.
Excellent running condition ____ 1800.00
Lincoln Sedan, 1946. 12-cylinder.
Restored and in running condition 950.00
Maxwell Roadster, 1912. Restored__ 4250.00
MG-TC, 1947. Good condition ____ 1475.00
MG-TF Classic, 1954. Excellent
condition _____ 1300.00
Mercedes 300 4-Door Hard Top,
1958. Automatic transmission. Ex-
cellent condition _____ 1800.00
Packard 180 Classic, 1940. 6-wheels,
7-passenger limousine. Dual side-
mounts. Excellent condition ____ 2000.00
Packard 1101 Club Sedan, 1934.
Excellent condition _____ 3500.00
Packard Phaeton, 1931. Restored __ 6000.00
Packard 833 Sedan, 1931. Restored_ 4200.00
Packard Sport Coupe, 1928. Low
mileage, restored _____ 3550.00
Reo Speed Wagon, 1917. Original
leather radiator cover, 16,000
miles. Needs restoration _____ 1300.00
Riley 4-Door Sedan, 1949. Excellent
condition _____ 2300.00
Rolls-Royce Convertible Coupe.
Gray colors, 3 horns, electric
lights and starter _____ 8000.00
Rolls-Royce Henley Roadster, 1931_28000.00
Rolls-Royce PII, 1930. Chassis
116WJ, Eng. FB 55, minibus,
seats 8 _____ 3500.00
Rolls-Royce 'Phantom III', 1937.
40/50 h. p., two seater roadster,
drop-heaa coupe. Built by in-
struction of Gen. Sikorske _____20400.00
Rolls-Royce Silver Ghost, 1912.
Barker Landaulet body, good
condition _____22000.00
Rolls-Royce Silver Ghost, 1919.
PP-Series Tourer _____14400.00
Rover, 1910. Completely restored__ 4500.00
Studebaker Hearse, 1937. Side-
mounts. Running condition _____ 350.00
Studebaker Touring, 1920. Restored,
good condition _____ 2450.00
Stutz Boat-tail Speedster, DV-32,
1929 _____10000.00
Thomas, 1902. Roadster _____24000.00
T-Bird, 1955. Reconditioned _____ 1500.00
T-Bird Classic, 1956. Mint _____ 1875.00
Willis Knight Touring, 1916.
Crimson with black fenders, var-
nished wood spoke wheels. 18,000
miles. Excellent condition _____ 3150.00

## BACCARAT GLASS

Baccarat Glass was made at Baccarat, in Alsace-Lorraine, France. The factory is primarily known for producing beautiful paperweights in the last fifty years of the past century. Many kinds of fine glassware were also made.

| | |
|---|---|
| Cordials. Set of 6 | $120.00 |
| Compote. Etched oak leaves and grapes. Gold trim | 65.00 |
| Cup and Saucer. Blue, lacy | 49.50 |
| Decanters: | |
| 8½" high. Lacy, original stopper | 45.00 |
| 10½" high. Applied Fleur-de-lis and scroll work | 20.00 |
| Pair, with 12 wines | 275.00 |
| Dish. Lacy, rectangular, footed | 35.00 |
| Gas Light Shade. Cranberry with birds in relief | 40.00 |
| Ginger Jar. Brass cover and bail, cranberry on frosted. Signed | 75.00 |
| Goblet. Gold decor, simulated amethyst jewels on crystal glass. 12" high | 95.00 |
| Inkwell. Large clear bowl with 4 deep green leaves, brass top | 80.00 |
| Jam Jar. Covered, amberina swirl. Signed | 45.00 |
| Paperweight. Signed and dated "B 1848," lace background, animal silhouettes | 650.00 |
| Perfume Bottles: | |
| Swirled, clear to amberina. Pair | 35.00 |
| 4" high, including stopper | 12.00 |
| 5"½ high | 32.50 |
| Pharmacy Lamp. Amberina color. Swirl pattern. Signed "Pharmacie L. Miller" | 65.00 |
| Pitcher. 10¼" high. Oval. Taupe and white mottled | 55.00 |
| Relish Dish. 9½", rubina color, signed | 27.50 |
| Tumbler. Blue swirl pattern | 30.00 |
| Vases: | |
| 5" high, lacy Baccarat, circa 1870 | 60.00 |
| 6½" high. Cameo cut, gold washed metal base. Pair | 100.00 |
| 8" high. Etched. Signed | 25.00 |
| 11½" high. Cameo cut, cranberry flowers and leaves, gold trim. Pair | 210.00 |

| | |
|---|---|
| Bottle, Water. 7" high. Light red shading to amber | $ 48.50 |
| Bottle. 6" high. French. Gold stripes, gold star on cut stopper | $ 40.00 |
| Bottle, Cologne. 8" high. Original stopper | 44.50 |
| Bowl. Lacy. Matching 7" diam. Lacy plate | 20.00 |
| Bowl. Cut from ruby to pale rose glass. 10" diam. | 245.00 |
| Candlesticks: | |
| 8" high. Serpents coiling around bamboo shoots, fiery Opalescent color. Pair | 100.00 |
| 9" high. Amberina swirl. Signed | 120.00 |
| Candelabra. 5-branch, with prisms. Pair | 325.00 |
| Carafe with Tumble-up. Amberina swirl pattern. Signed | 75.00 |
| Castor Set. Two-bottle, swirl pattern, silver plated frame. Signed Corwin 1912 | 50.00 |

## BANKS, MECHANICAL

Banks which display some type of action when a coin is inserted are known as mechanical banks. The majority of the approximately 250 different known banks was manufactured between 1870 and 1910. Banks preceded by a numeral are illustrated on another page.

| | |
|---|---|
| Acrobats | $  300.00 |
| Afghanistan | 500.00 |
| Alligator in tin trough | 675.00 |
| #1. Always did 'spise a mule. Darky sitting on bench in front | 85.00 |
| * #2. Always did 'spise a mule. Darky riding mule | 80.00 |
| * #3. Artillery. 4-sided block house | 90.00 |
| Artillery. 8-sided block house | 625.00 |
| Atlas | 465.00 |
| * #4. Bad Accident | 195.00 |
| Bank Teller | 1725.00 |
| Barrel with arms | 225.00 |
| #5. Bear with paws around tree | 115.00 |

**Football Player** _____ **$1,075.00**

| | |
|---|---|
| Bear standing on hind legs | 175.00 |
| Bear—Surly Bruin | 185.00 |
| Bill E. Grin, bust | 215.00 |
| Bird on roof of church | 475.00 |
| Bowery Bank | 675.00 |
| Bowling Alley | 1475.00 |
| Boy on trapeze | 175.00 |
| #6. Boy robbing bird's nest | 200.00 |
| #7. Boy Scout | 180.00 |
| Boys stealing watermelons | 200.00 |
| Breadwinner | 895.00 |
| Buffalo | 250.00 |
| * Buffalo, Bucking | 485.00 |
| Building, circular | 420.00 |

| | |
|---|---|
| Building, small, 8-sided | 115.00 |
| Bull and Bear | 695.00 |
| Bull tossing boy | 995.00 |
| Bull or steer | 145.00 |
| * #8. Cabin | 55.00 |
| #9. Calamity or Football | 450.00 |
| Called Out | 995.00 |
| * Camera or Kodak | 1500.00 |
| Cannon, U. S. | 675.00 |
| Carnival | 465.00 |
| * #10. Cat and Mouse | 200.00 |
| Cat chasing mouse | 315.00 |
| Cat jumps for mouse | 875.00 |
| #11. Chief Big Moon | 145.00 |
| Chimpanzee | 420.00 |
| Chinaman in boat | 1200.00 |
| #12. Chinaman reclining on log | 395.00 |
| Circus | 1400.00 |
| Circus Ticket Collector | 365.00 |
| * #13. Clown on globe | 165.00 |
| Confectionery Store | 895.00 |
| #14. Cow. Milking or kicking | 450.00 |
| * #15. Creedmore | 75.00 |
| Dapper Dan | 185.00 |
| #16. Darktown Battery | 175.00 |
| * #17. Dentist | 595.00 |
| Dinah | 345.00 |
| Dinah and the fairy | 315.00 |
| Ding Dong Bell | 565.00 |
| #18. Dog Barking | 95.00 |
| Dog, Bull. Standing | 125.00 |
| * #19. Dog, Bull. Savings Bank | 380.00 |
| * #20. Dog. On oblong base | 90.00 |
| Dog charges boy | 185.00 |
| #21. Dog. On turntable | 67.50 |
| #22. Dog Speaking | 90.00 |
| Dog with tray | 275.00 |
| #23. Dog, trick | 97.50 |
| Dog, trick. (Modern, with solid base) | 45.00 |
| Doll's Head. (Projects from egg) | 170.00 |
| Donkey, trick | 142.50 |
| #24. Eagle and Eaglets | 98.50 |
| Education and Economy | 425.00 |
| #25. Elephant (Modern) | 37.50 |
| Elephant, Hannibal | 225.00 |
| #26. Elephant, Man in Howdah | 100.00 |
| #27. Elephant, with Locked Howdah | 260.00 |
| Elephant, tiny, Jumbo | 175.00 |
| Elephant, small, Jumbo on wheels | 248.00 |
| Elephant, large, Jumbo | 190.00 |
| #28. Elephant and three clowns | 190.00 |
| Feed the Kitty | 625.00 |
| Ferris Wheel | 2450.00 |
| Football Player | 1075.00 |
| Fortune Teller. Building | 975.00 |
| Fortune Teller. Safe | 450.00 |
| Forty-niner | 240.00 |
| Fowler | 830.00 |
| Freedman | 3950.00 |
| #29. Frogs (2) | 105.00 |
| Frog in den | 295.00 |

Locomotive Savings Bank _____ 635.00
Long May It Wave _____ • 395.00
#44. Magic _____ 95.00
#45. Magician _____ 275.00

**Frogs (2)** _____ **$105.00**

Frog on rock _____ 75.00
#30. Frog on round lattice base__ 62.50
Frog on stump _____ 79.50
Frog and serpent _____ 310.00
Gem _____ 95.00
Germania Exchange Bank _____ 1200.00
Giant _____ 1150.00
Girl in Victorian chair, with dog
on lap _____ 1450.00
#31. Girl skipping rope _____ 1700.00
#32. Globe on arc _____ 42.50
#76. Globe Savings Bank. Semi-
mechanical _____ 110.00
Goat, Butting (Miniature) ____ 565.00
Goat, frog and old man _____ 640.00
Goat—Little Billy _____ 695.00
Guessing Bank _____ 575.00
#33. Hall's Excelsior _____ 42.50
Harlequin, clown and columbine _ 3900.00
#34. Hen, setting _____ 250.00
Hindu with turban _____ 495.00
Hold the fort _____ 498.00
Home Bank _____ 145.00
#35. Home Bank. 6'' high, tin __ 110.00
#36. Humpty Dumpty _____ 100.00
#37. Independence Hall Tower __ 87.50
#38. Indian shooting bear _____ 148.50
Initiating Bank—First Degree __ 1300.00
Jocko, musical _____ 395.00
#39. Jolly Nigger—negro bust __ 75.00
* Jolly Nigger, with high hat ____ 45.00
* Jolly Nigger, with straw hat ____ 200.00
Jolly Nigger, moves ears _____ 515.00
#40. Jonah and the whale _____ 250.00
Jonah and the whale, on pedestal_ 950.00
Katzenjammer Kids _____ 500.00
Keene Registering _____ 185.00
Kick Inn _____ 265.00
#41. Leap Frog _____ 285.00
Liberty Bell _____ 185.00
Lighthouse _____ 300.00
#42. Hall's Lilliput _____ 80.00
#43. Lion and monkeys _____ 100.00
Lion Hunter _____ 380.00
* Little Joe _____ 32.50

**Mammy and Child** _____ **$240.00**

Mammy and Child _____ 240.00
#46. Mason and Hod Carrier __ 295.00
Merry-go-round _____ 2195.00
Merry-go-round. Semi-mechani-
cal _____ 95.00
Mikado _____ 2100.00
#47. Minstrel _____ 85.00
Minstrel. Cross-legged _____ 285.00
#48. Monkey and coconut _____ 265.00
#49. Monkey and Organ Grinder_ 70.00
#50. Monkey and Parrot _____ 240.00
Moody and Sankey, Revivalists__ 1550.00
Moon Face _____ 450.00
Mosque _____ 240.00
#51. Mule entering barn _____ 115.00
Mule, bucking. Miniature _____ 185.00
Multiplying Bank _____ 95.00
Musical Savings Bank _____ 425.00
National Bank _____ 315.00
North Pole _____ 1100.00

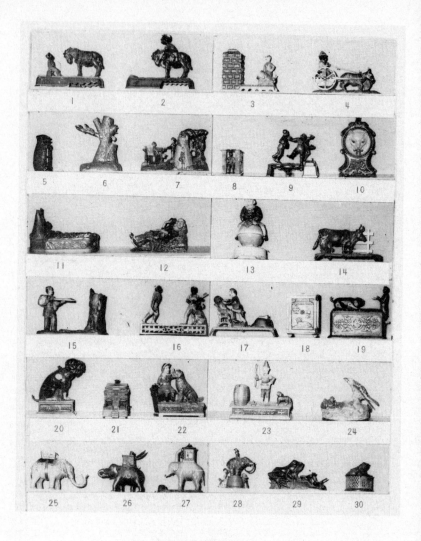

**BANKS, MECHANICAL**
For descriptions, see pages 138-139

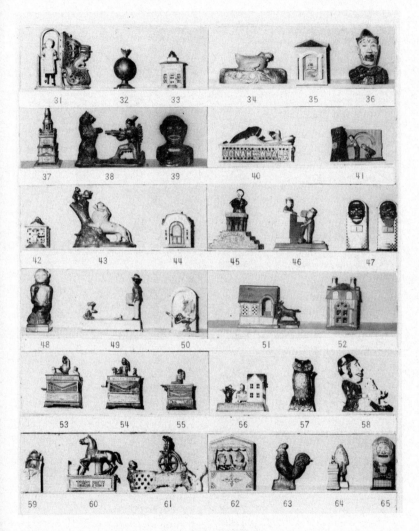

31  32  33  34  35  36

37  38  39  40  41

42  43  44  45  46  47

48  49  50  51  52

53  54  55  56  57  58

59  60  61  62  63  64  65

**BANKS, MECHANICAL**
For descriptions, see pages 139 & 142

| | | |
|---|---|---|
| #52. Novelty | | 75.00 |
| Organ Bank | | 110.00 |
| #53. Organ Bank, cat and dog | | 130.00 |
| #54. Organ Bank, monkey, boy and girl | | 125.00 |
| Organ Bank, with monkey only | | 97.50 |
| #55. Organ Bank. Very small, with monkey on top | | 187.50 |
| #56. Organ grinder and dancing bear | | 480.00 |
| #57. Owl with book. Slot in head | | 70.00 |
| Owl with book. Slot in book | | 80.00 |
| * Owl | | 75.00 |
| * #58. Paddy and His Pig | | 195.00 |
| Panorama Bank | | 595.00 |
| Patronize the Blind Man | | 750.00 |
| Pegleg Beggar | | 475.00 |
| #77. Pelican | | 148.50 |
| Perfection Registering | | 675.00 |
| Piano | | 350.00 |
| Picture Gallery | | 615.00 |
| Pig. Bismark | | 315.00 |
| #59. Pig in High Chair | | 188.50 |
| Pig, trick | | 375.00 |
| #60. Pony, trick | | 95.00 |
| Preacher in Pulpit | | 725.00 |
| Presto. Mouse on roof | | 875.00 |
| Presto. Small building | | 72.50 |
| #61. Professor Pugfrog | | 520.00 |
| Pump and Bucket | | 410.00 |
| * #62. Punch and Judy | | 125.00 |
| Rabbit | | 160.00 |
| Rabbit and Cabbage | | 110.00 |
| Ram, Bucking | | 648.50 |
| Red Riding Hood | | 1600.00 |
| Roller Skating | | 2200.00 |
| #63. Rooster | | 75.00 |
| Sambo | | 175.00 |
| #64. Santa Claus at Chimney | | 148.50 |
| Schley. "Admiral Schley Bottling up Cevera" | | 210.00 |
| #65. Scotchman | | 100.00 |
| Sewing Machine | | 815.00 |
| Shoot and Chute | | 2450.00 |
| Squirrel and Tree Stump | | 310.00 |
| #66. Stump Speaker | | 135.00 |
| #67. Tabby Bank | | 145.00 |
| * #68. Tammany | | 55.00 |
| * #69. Teddy and the Bear | | 115.00 |
| Telephone | | 115.00 |
| Trolley Motor Car | | 1200.00 |
| Turtle | | 1100.00 |
| * Uncle Remus | | 720.00 |
| * Uncle Sam | | 125.00 |
| Uncle Sam bust | | 160.00 |
| #70. Uncle Tom | | 150.00 |
| U. S. Bank | | 975.00 |
| #71. Weedens Plantation | | 195.00 |
| #72. William Tell | | 110.00 |
| Winner Savings Bank | | 200.00 |
| #73. Wireless | | 135.00 |
| Wishbone Bank | | 620.00 |

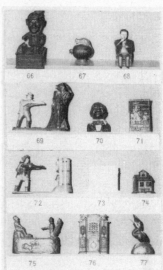

| | | |
|---|---|---|
| Woman in Shoe, Old | | 825.00 |
| Woodpecker | | 490.00 |
| * #75. World's Fair Bank | | 148.50 |
| World's Fair Key Bank | | 120.00 |
| #74. Zoo | | 195.00 |

*Reproduced item
.

## BANKS, STILL
## METAL

Banks, usually cast of metal, in the shape of animals, buildings, men or other figures, in which a slot is provided for inserting coins, are known as "still" banks.

| | | |
|---|---|---|
| Arabian Safe | $ | 18.50 |
| Bank Building. 3½" | | 16.50 |
| Bank Building. 5½" | | 24.00 |
| Baseball Player | | 32.00 |
| Bear, sitting | | 26.50 |
| Bear, standing. 5½" | | 27.50 |
| Bear, Teddy. Small | | 21.00 |
| Billiken | | 24.00 |
| Black Beauty (Horse) | | 28.50 |
| Black Mammy | | 32.50 |
| Blackamoor | | 25.00 |
| Boy Scout | | 35.00 |
| Buffalo. Standing | | 30.00 |
| * Bull Dog, sitting | | 28.50 |
| Bull Dog, standing | | 26.50 |
| Buster Brown and Dog | | 33.50 |
| Camel, standing. Small | | 28.50 |
| Cash Register. 4" | | 29.00 |

| | |
|---|---|
| * Cat, sitting | 27.50 |
| Cat with Ball. Scarce | 45.00 |
| "City Bank" Building. Large | 25.00 |
| Clock | 35.00 |
| * Clown, standing | 30.00 |
| Cocker Spaniel | 27.50 |
| "Coin Deposit Bank" | 20.00 |
| "Columbia" Building. (World's Fair) | 24.00 |
| Cow | 28.50 |
| Decker's Pig | 26.50 |
| Deer, with antlers | 25.00 |
| Dog, on tub | 30.00 |
| Dog, St. Bernard with pack | 27.50 |
| Dog, Shepherd | 24.00 |
| Dog with fly on hip | 25.00 |
| Donkey, standing | 30.00 |
| Donkey, with saddle | 32.00 |
| Duck, large | 28.50 |
| E. River Savings Bank, Rochester | 21.50 |
| * Elephant, on tub | 25.00 |
| Elephant, standing | 22.50 |
| Flat Iron Building, 5½" high | 20.00 |

| | |
|---|---|
| General Eisenhower | $24.50 |
| Frog | 26.00 |
| Gas Stove. "York, Abendroth Bros. N. Y." | 36.00 |

| | |
|---|---|
| General Pershing | 24.50 |
| Globe. Miniature, outlines of continents and oceans | 28.50 |
| "Good Luck" Billiken | 21.50 |
| Goose (Red Goose Shoes) | 22.00 |
| Hansel & Gretel Cigar Box Bank. Tin, 7½x6½x5" deep | 30.00 |
| Heatrola | 28.50 |
| "Home Savings Bank." Dog head finial | 25.00 |
| Horse, prancing | 30.00 |
| * Horse, rearing | 29.50 |
| Horse, standing still | 25.00 |
| Horseshoe. Good luck, encircling horse. Bust of Columbus at top and dog at base. Columbian Exposition item | 40.00 |
| Independence Hall, Enterprize Mfg. Co., Phila., 1875. Bronzed | 35.00 |
| Indian Head | 25.00 |
| Indian Maid, head | 27.50 |
| * Indian, standing | 37.50 |
| Junior Cash Register | 18.00 |
| Junior Safe | 20.00 |
| Kitten, 4¾" | 21.00 |
| Kitten, 5", with neck bow | 21.50 |
| Liberty Bell (Glass) | 12.50 |
| Lion, small | 20.00 |
| Lion, standing | 24.00 |
| Little Daisy | 20.00 |
| Lunch Pail, with handle | 26.50 |
| * Mail Box | 20.00 |
| Mule. 6½x7", saddled | 30.00 |
| Mutt & Jeff | 35.00 |
| Negro | 20.00 |
| Negro, 2-faced | 25.00 |
| Owl | 24.50 |
| Old South Church, 9" high | 35.00 |
| "Pass Around the Hat" | 24.00 |
| Pig. "A Christmas Roast" | 30.00 |
| Pig, sitting | 22.50 |
| Pig. "Thrifty" | 25.00 |
| Polar Bear | 27.00 |
| Policeman, Irish | 32.00 |
| * Policeman, standing | 30.00 |
| Possum | 22.50 |
| Postal Savings Bank. 4½", 1902 | 24.00 |
| Puppy, sitting | 21.50 |
| Puppy, white with black spots | 24.50 |
| * Rabbit, large | 27.50 |
| Radio | 24.50 |
| Radio (Majestic) | 35.00 |
| Refrigerator, G. E. | 24.50 |
| Rival Bank | 23.50 |
| Rooster, standing | 24.00 |
| Roper, Gas Stove | 30.00 |
| Royal Safe Deposit (Safe) | 25.00 |
| Safe, 4", dated 1897 | 22.50 |
| Safe, 6", combination lock | 27.50 |
| Satchel, 6" long, 3" high | 25.00 |
| "Security Safe Deposit." Double combination, dated 1917 | 29.50 |

Elephant _____ $22.50

## BANKS, STILL
## POTTERY

Irish Policeman _____ $32.00

| | |
|---|---|
| * Sheep _____ | 25.00 |
| Soldier, World War 1 _____ | 30.00 |
| "Sport." Safe-type, 3", dated 1-8-82 _____ | 29.00 |
| State Bank _____ | 24.50 |
| Statue of Liberty _____ | 27.00 |
| Steamboat "Arcade" _____ | 39.00 |
| Tank Bank, USA 1918 _____ | 28.00 |
| Teddy Roosevelt _____ | 40.00 |
| Telephone (wall type) _____ | 27.50 |
| The Skyscraper _____ | 24.50 |
| Trader's Bank (Canada). 1891 ___ | 35.00 |
| * Treasury Building _____ | 20.00 |
| Treasury Safe, 5" _____ | 25.00 |
| Turkey, standing _____ | 24.00 |
| Union Bank (Safe) _____ | 23.50 |
| "Washington Mansion, Mt. Vernon." 3" to top of chimney _____ | 20.00 |
| Woolworth Building, 5¾" _____ | 21.00 |
| Woolworth Building, 7" _____ | 25.00 |
| *Reproduced item | |

Pig. 5¼" long, 3⅜" high. Yellow bottom, tan top _____ $12.50

| | |
|---|---|
| Acorn. "Acorn Stoves." 3" high, light brown glaze _____$ | 12.00 |
| Apple. Red _____ | 12.50 |
| Barrel. Gilt hoops _____ | 11.50 |
| Bear. Sitting, 6" _____ | 20.00 |
| Beehive. 4¼" high, brown mottled slipware _____ | 14.00 |
| Bell. 5½" high, heavy unglazed red clay _____ | 12.75 |
| Bennington. Pig _____ | 18.00 |
| Bennington. Scarecrow (Man) _____ | 27.50 |
| Bird _____ | 12.00 |
| Boy's Head. With cap _____ | 14.00 |
| Buffalo _____ | 16.50 |
| Cash Register. White with yellow glaze _____ | 12.75 |
| Cask. "Kentucky Wild Cat—I'm Thirsty." 3¼" high _____ | 15.00 |

| | |
|---|---|
| Cat. Staffordshire, white and yellow, on green and white cushion | 24.00 |
| Chicago World's Fair. 5'' diam., shape of globe | 12.50 |
| Child's Head. With bonnet, brown glaze | 16.00 |
| Cottage | 18.00 |
| Dwarf Head. Brown enameled pottery | 24.50 |
| Elephant. Seated, 3'' high, slipware | 12.50 |
| Frog. 4'' high, coin goes in mouth | 11.00 |
| Jug. 4'' high slot for coins. No handle | 12.50 |
| Jug. 4½'' high, made in Athens, N. Y. | 11.00 |
| Lion. 6'' long | 12.00 |
| Lion's Head | 14.50 |
| Monkey. Mottled yellow and brown | 18.50 |
| Pig in green pocketbook | 18.00 |
| Pig. Fat, mottled slipware | 20.00 |
| Pig. Gray, with splotches | 11.00 |
| Pig. Pennsylvania, red slipware. 10'' long | 75.00 |
| Poodle Head. Staffordshire. 3¾'' tall, 4½'' wide, collar and ears black, gold lock | 20.00 |
| Ram. Rockingham-type | 18.00 |
| Rooster. Standing | 12.00 |
| Round. 4½'' high. Brown | 15.00 |
| Tree Stump. 4½'' high, 3½'' diam. | 8.50 |
| Turnip. Marked "Charity" | 15.00 |

## BARBED WIRE

Barbed wire collecting has recently become a fast growing hobby, especially in the mid-western and southwestern part of the U. S.

It is estimated that there are more than 10,000 active collectors who seek examples of the more than 600 kinds of wire which were patented in the late 1800s. Eighteen inch pieces bring from 50 cents for the common variety to as much as $40.00 for rare examples of the "devils rope" as some people refer to it.

John D. Curtis—1893

Thomas H. Dodge & Chas. G. Washburn— 1882

## BARBER BOTTLES

These bottles were made of clear, colored and milk glass and were used for holding and dispensing hair tonic and shampoo preparations. Many of the colored bottles were imported from Bohemia.

| | |
|---|---|
| Milk Glass. 9'' high. White, hexagon base. "Bay Rum" | $22.50 |

| | |
|---|---|
| Amber | $ 37.50 |
| Amethyst | 40.00 |
| Amethyst. Blown, enamel decor | 42.50 |

Bohemian Glass. 12 ounce capaicty.

| | |
|---|---|
| Enamel floral decor | 52.50 |
| Carnival. Marigold | 38.50 |
| Chartreuse green. Raised enamel decoration | 45.00 |
| Chartreuse green. Raised enamel decoration, old bronze hunting dog with rabbit | 100.00 |
| Clear ribbed, with blue bottom | 32.00 |
| Cobalt blue. Enamel decor. Pair | 72.50 |
| Cranberry, ITP. Pair | 95.00 |
| Cranberry. Overlay portrait of beautiful woman, tall | 68.50 |
| Cranberry and Opaline. Overlay, blown and 3 mold pattern, swirled. 6½" high | 68.50 |
| Cranberry and opaline striped | 60.00 |
| Cut glass. Sterling top | 36.50 |
| End-of-day Glass. Amber and white | 52.50 |

Hobnail:

| | |
|---|---|
| Amber | 50.00 |
| Blue | 55.00 |
| Honey amber | 57.50 |
| Mary Gregory, green | 70.00 |
| Opalescent | 58.00 |
| Vaseline | 62.00 |
| Opalescent, Late | 11.50 |

Milk Glass:

| | |
|---|---|
| Bulbous base | 30.00 |
| Hexagon base | 25.00 |
| Octogan neck, opaque | 15.00 |
| Straight neck | 25.00 |
| Opalescent striped | 57.50 |
| Sapphire blue. Blown, thumbprint | 60.00 |
| Satin glass. Cranberry with white loopings, pewter stopper, 10¾" high | 90.00 |
| Sea Foam. White milk glass, colorful painted flowers and leaves. 11" high | 36.50 |
| Tiffany-type | 125.00 |

## BARBERING

The Barbering trade is ancient. The word is derived from the Latin barba, meaning a beard.

Razors have been found from the Bronze Age. Alexander the Great required his soldiers to shave so an enemy in battle could not grab them by the beard.

In Rome and Athens, the barbershop was a meeting place for men to discuss the problems of the day as well as a spot to discuss philosophy and religion.

In Europe, in the Renaissance period, barbers were also surgeons. In England, Henry VIII, by an act of Parliament, had the professions separated and barbers were only permitted to extract teeth and do bloodletting.

The sign of the barber's profession is a pole with red and white stripes. The stripes represent the bandage with which he wrapped his patient after bloodletting.

## BAROMETERS

The barometer became popular in Victorian England. The barometer is essentially an instrument for measuring the atmospheric pressure which, in turn, aids in the forecasting of weather. For example, low pressure indicates the coming of rain, snow or a storm, while the high pressure means fair weather.

Barometers of the ordinary type run from $85.00 for the simpler kind to $140.00 for ones with more elaborate cases.

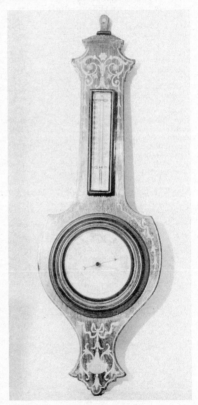

Barometer. 27½" high, 1890. Edwardian carving _____ $95.00

## BASALT

A type of black vitreous pottery originally made in ancient times and rediscovered in the latter part of the 18th century by Josiah Wedgwood. It was later produced by other English potters.

Teapot. 8½" high. Classic design __ $140.00

Atomizer. 6" high, dancing figures.
Black _____$  50.00
Bowl. 12" diam., 5" high, acanthus
decor. Marked "Wedgwood" __   145.00
Bust, Mercury. 18" high, mark on
plinth and bust. Incised "Wedgwood." Black, mint condition___   380.00
Bust, Shakespeare. Half life-size
Ca. 1800. Marked "Wedgwood"_   285.00
Candlesticks. 12" high. Pair _____   125.00
Chalice. 2⅞" deep, beaded pedestal base. Marked "Wedgwood"   130.00
Creamer. Black _____    65.00
Cup and Saucer. Black _____    70.00
Cup and Saucer. Impressed
"Wedgwood" _____    75.00
Inkwell. Impressed "Wedgwood"__    57.50
Medallions. 2¼x2¾", marked "Wedgwood and Bentley." George III
Queen Charlotte. Pair _____   425.00
Pair _____   425.00
Pitcher. 8" high, ribbed top,
scrolled bulbous center _____   135.00
Sugar Bowls:
7" high. Widow finial _____ __   100.00
Covered, black _____    75.00
Teapots:
4½" high, 8½" long. Marked
"Wedgwood, Etruria, England"__   150.00
8½" high. Classic design _____   140.00
Vase. 6" high, Circa 1890, marked
"Wedgwood, England." Pair __   160.00

## BATTERSEA ENAMEL BOXES

A process of fusing enamel onto metal was first used in England at Battersea, circa 1750. However, much of the production was in the Staffordshire district. The name "Battersea" is now a generic or general name for enamel on such items as patch, pill and snuff boxes, candleholders and door knobs.

Box. 3" long, 1¾" wide. Angel
decoration _____ $120.00

Box. Heart-shaped, 3" long, 1⅛"
high. Fresh gathered peas. Multicolored top, blue sides _____$ 375.00
Box. Hexagonal-shaped. 1¾" wide.
Verse in black on white top,
yellow sides _____   300.00
Box. "Make Much of Time When in
Your Prime." Round, 2" diam.
1" high _____   325.00
Box. "Racing and You See the
Race." Cover in colors, robinegg blue sides. 2½" long,
1¼" wide _____   310.00

## BAYREUTH, See ROYAL BAYREUTH

### BELLEEK

A delicate iridescent type of porcelain first made at Fermanagh, Ireland, in 1857. It has a pearly lustre and in keeping with its likeness to the sea, many items were made in the form of shells and similar shapes. It is seldom thicker than a sheet of writing paper, is light in weight, but extremely durable.

Marks of the Irish company include a harp with a crown above; a hound, harp and tower with the name of "Belleek" printed below. Some items have the name "Belleek Co., Fermanagh" with no other identifying mark. China made after 1891 has the words

"Ireland" or "Eire" added. The company continued until World War I. It discontinued operations for a period and then resumed production.

Belleek was made in America by a number of firms. The first producer was Ott & Brewer Co., at Trenton, N. J., in 1884. They used a crown and sword mark, a crescent mark, the mark O. & B., and the firm name in a circle. It was succeeded in 1894 by the Cook Pottery Co., whose mark was three feathers with the word "Etruria."

Another early American manufacturer was The Willets Mfg. Co., which made tea sets, vases, small picture frames and cabinet pieces. The company used two marks—the letter "W" in the form of a serpent and the other with the word "Belleek" above the same mark.

The American Art China Works was established in 1891 and began making Belleek china in 1892. The majority of its output was made for amateurs to decorate. "R.E. Co. /China/ Trenton" within a circle was their mark.

The Ceramic Art Co., started business in 1889 and made a large variety of items —from clock cases and vanity sets to vases and tea and coffee services. Their mark was an artist's palette with the company's initials.

The Columbian Art Co., began operating in 1893 and produced novelties in Belleek, such as Toby Jugs and souvenir items. Their mark was a shield with the letters "M" and "W" inside, "Belleek" above with a ribbon scroll and the word "Trenton" below with the abbreviation "N. J."

Lenox, Inc., was organized in 1906 by Walter Scott Lenox and is still producing fine porcelain tableware. However, Belleek novelties were discontinued about the time of World War I. The company used two marks. Undecorated articles made for amateur painters show an artist's palette with the letter "L" below. Other pieces are marked with a script "L" in a laurel wreath, below is "Lenox" and "Made in U.S.A."

**Bowls:**
| | |
|---|---|
| 3" high, 3" wide _____$ | 25.00 |
| 3½" diam., shellware, marked __ | 27.50 |
| Cake Plate _____ | 32.50 |
| **Cauldrons:** | |
| Shamrock decor, old mark ____ | 30.00 |
| "Witches", 4" high, 4¼" diam., two-handled _____ | 32.50 |
| **Creamers:** | |
| 4½", Bacchus heads, grapes ____ | 35.00 |
| Shape of girl _____ | 40.00 |
| Shell pattern. Green. Harp & Crown mark _____ | 32.50 |
| Shellware, pink handle _____ | 28.50 |

| | |
|---|---|
| 4½", swan, plain, Fermanagh __ | 28.00 |
| Cup and Saucer _____ | 25.00 |
| Cup and Saucer. Alternating green and cream panels, black harp and hound mark (1st mark) ____ | 32.50 |

| | |
|---|---|
| Bouillon Cup and Saucer. White with pink edges. Black harp and crown mark _____ | $20.00 |

**Dishes:**
| | |
|---|---|
| BonBon. 5" diam., 2½" high, applied roses on edge, open work _____ | 36.00 |
| 5½" diam. Clover leaf, open work sides with 3 cream roses and buds, green leaves and Shamrocks applied around edge _____ | 49.50 |
| 6¼" long, 2" high. Heart-shaped, harp and hound mark _____ | 24.00 |
| Finger Bowl. Irish harp and hound Fish. Open shell on back _____ | 29.50 |
| mark _____ | 22.50 |
| Hat Pin Holder. White lustre type. 5" high _____ | 17.50 |
| Jam Jar Holder. Basketweave design with green clover leaves. Lid and plate _____ | 35.00 |
| Mug. 2¾", Shamrock decor, inscribed "Portrush" _____ | 20.00 |
| Mustard. Covered, basketweave design with shamrocks _____ | 20.00 |
| **Plates:** | |
| 6¼", cake _____ | 25.00 |
| 6¾" diam., 3 sprays of shamrocks, basketweave border _____ | 18.50 |
| Dinner. 10" diam., Coxon Belleek _____ | 27.50 |
| Dinner. Open-work edge, purple lustre. Irish hound, harp and castle mark _____ | 29.50 |
| Rose Bowl. 4½" diam. _____ | 25.00 |
| Salt. Individual, pink rose decor __ | 12.50 |
| Sea Horse. 5x3½", black mark____ | 80.00 |
| Sugar Bowl and Creamer. Shell __ | 56.50 |

**Sugar Bowls:**

| | |
|---|---|
| Covered, basketweave and green Shamrocks | 30.00 |
| Open, same decor, 2⅞" high | 24.00 |
| Swan. 6" long, Irish, Fermanagh | 95.00 |
| Teakettle | 68.50 |

**Teapots:**

| | |
|---|---|
| Basketweave, Shamrocks | 55.00 |
| Limpert Cob pattern | 57.50 |

**Tea Sets:**

| | |
|---|---|
| 3-pieces. Teapot, covered sugar bowl, creamer. White, shellware Set | 120.00 |
| 30-pieces. Bacchus pattern, 10 plates, embossed with Bacchus head and grapes, 10 c/s. Set | 275.00 |
| Tea Strainer and Stand | 24.00 |
| Tray. Leaf-shaped, 4¾" long, pink shading | 17.50 |
| Tub. 4½" high. Irish, basketweave and green shamrocks | 35.00 |
| Tumbler. Black hound and harp mark, panelled and ribbed | 27.50 |

**Vases:**

| | |
|---|---|
| Bud. Lenox Belleek, hand-painted apple blossoms | 22.50 |
| 6" high, floral decor | 30.00 |
| 6" high, 7" diam., short fluted neck, pink and yellow roses | 60.00 |
| 7¾" high, painted country scene, three-handled | 65.00 |
| 9" high, pearly lustre on pearl white | 90.00 |
| 13" high, hollyhocks on pale green to lavender background. Willets Mfg. Co. | 68.50 |
| Writing Paper Rack | 30.00 |

## BELLS

Bells have played an important part in the life of man since ancient times. He has had many uses for them—they have called him to worship, tolled at his death, struck the time, summoned him to school, warned him of the approach of enemies, invited him to dinner, bade him to assemble—and the lowly alarm clock has urged him to arise and be about his daily work.

| | |
|---|---|
| Bell. Small, chanticleer handle $ | 18.50 |
| Call Bell. Silverplated, dolphin handle | 14.50 |
| Chinaman with Queque. brass | 10.50 |
| Church Gong. 3-tier, brass | 72.50 |
| Church Gong. 1-tier, brass | 55.00 |
| Clapper. 3", brass | 9.75 |
| Cow Bell. Brass | 12.50 |
| Cow Bell. Iron | 8.75 |
| "Cutter." Nickel, with iron strap. Set of 3 | 21.50 |
| Dogs (2) Spaniels for handle, 4" | 26.50 |
| Dutch Boy and Girl Figural | 8.75 |

| | |
|---|---|
| School Bell. Brass, with wood handle. 6" diam., 10" high | $30.00 |
| El Camino Real Bell, small | 8.50 |
| Elephant Bell | 16.50 |
| Farm Bell. Iron, large, mounted in bracket | 70.00 |
| Goose Bell, small, double clapper, original strap | 9.00 |
| Hame, Swedish. Set of 5 | 45.00 |
| Hand Bell. Brass 12½" high | 40.00 |
| Lady with Hoop Skirt. 4" high | 15.00 |
| Liberty Bell. Bronze, 4¼" high. Marked "Colonial 1832-1925" | 16.50 |
| Mass Bell. Brass | 40.00 |
| School Bell. Small, wood handle | 18.75 |
| School Bell. Large, wood handle | 22.50 |
| Sleigh Bells: | |
| String, 25 bells, graduated sizes, cleaned. good leather strap | 85.00 |
| String, brass, 25 bells, not cleaned | 65.00 |
| String, iron, 30 bells, 1½" diam. | 40.00 |
| Soldier, Roman. 3½" high | 12.75 |

Church Bell. 22'' high without frame. Iron. Made by American Bell Foundry, Northville, Michigan, U.S.A.__$150.00

Temple Bell. 5½'', Japanese, lizard handles, engraved with dragons and flowers _____ 24.00
Town Crier's. Large _____ 60.00
Trolley Bell. Iron, 6'' diam. _____ 45.00
Turtle. Tortoise top, iron legs and head. Wind-up type, bell rings when head or tail is pressed. Germany _____ 29.50

### BELLS, GLASS

Cranberry. 14'' to top of clear glass handle _____ $65.00

Amber, clear glass handle _____$ 55.00
Bristol, glass. 11½'' high _____ 57.50
Bristol. Wedding bell. Red barrel in swirl pattern, clear swirl handle, 4-ball finial. 13¾'' high, with clapper _____ 65.00
Cranberry. swirl pattern. Clear glass handle _____ 60.00
Cut glass _____ 30.00
Green, dark _____ 38.50
Nailsea. Clear glass handle _____ 75.00
Venetian Glass:
  Ruby, enamel decor _____ 45.00
  Latticino, pink, blue, yellow, green, with gold edges, alternating with white stripes. 4½'' high _____ 55.00

### BENNINGTON POTTERY

The first pottery was established in Bennington, Vermont, in 1783. It was first made in Rockingham, England, and is sometimes designated as Bennington-Rockingham Pottery. The original ware was salt glazed crocks and jugs which were unlike the later mottled brown glazed ware now known as Bennington. A full line of kitchen utensils as well as cuspidors and copies of various English "Statuary Ware" was produced.

After 1850, Parian pottery of a dull opaque white was made into figurines, Toby Jugs, pitchers, brooches and pins.

The brown type Bennington was also produced in St. Johnsbury, Middlebury and Dorset, Vermont, at Baltimore, Maryland, and at some potteries in the Ohio Valley. Reproductions of the cow creamer and hound-handled pitchers have been on the market in recent years.

Bed Pan _____$ 18.50
Bottle. Book. Marked _____ 75.00
Bottle. Book. 7½'' long, 5¼'' high, square toe, low heel foot, lace on side _____ 45.00
Bottle. Coachman, 1849 mark _____ 245.00
Bowls:
  7½'' diam. _____ 16.00
  10'' diam. _____ 19.50
  11'' diam. _____ 25.00
  13½'' diam., octagonal _____ 50.00
Bucket. 9½'' diam., wire handle __ 57.50
Cake Mold, 9'' _____ 19.50
Candleholder. 3½'', with handle ____ 36.50
Churn, Butter _____ 65.00
Coffee Pot. 9½'' high _____ 72.50
Cracker Jar. Covered _____ 48.50
Creamer. Cow. Covered _____ 58.50
Creamer. Oval, bulbous _____ 30.00
Cup, Custard. Mottled _____ 9.50

Bennington-type Plate. 11" diam.  $25.00

Cuspidors:
7" diam. _____ 15.00
8" diam. _____ 18.75
Shell pattern, brown glaze _____ 21.00
Stars, lady in flowing robe _____ 26.50
Plain, small _____ 10.00
Dish. 10" diam., deep _____ 28.50
Dish, Vegetable. 10" diam., with
raised hearts in bottom _____ 45.00
Door Knobs. Set _____ 20.00
Flask, Book. "Departed Spirits" ___ 65.00
Flask, Pint. Tavern scene _____ 49.50
Hound. 10" high, sitting on a base
8x4½" _____ 135.00
Inkwell. Reclining girl _____ 32.50
Jar. Covered, handled. 9½" high,
8" diam., brown on yellow _____ 48.50
Jug. 16" high _____ 56.50
Lamp. 7½" high. Scarce _____ 75.00
Mug. 6" high, parrots in relief ___ 18.75
Mug. Large _____ 21.50
Pie Plates:
8¾" diam. _____ 18.00
9¾" diam. _____ 21.50
10½" diam. _____ 24.00
10¼" diam. _____ 25.00
Pitchers:
Boar and stag hunt scene. 2-qt.
Pewter lid _____ 95.00
Castle scene _____ 68.50
"Dead Game" _____ 50.00
Frog in bottom, name on front.
11" _____ 92.50
Hound handle, American Eagle
under spout, birds and animals
on sides _____ 195.00
Hunter, dogs and birds _____ 100.00

Plate, 11½" _____ 37.50
Pudding Cup. Grape pattern _____ 10.00
Pudding Mold _____ 22.50
Salt Box. Hanging-type _____ 49.50
Shoe. High-top _____ 25.00
Soap Dish. 4½" diam. _____ 24.00
Syrup Jug. Signed with U. S. P.
ribbon mark. Rare _____ 225.00
Teapots:
"Rebecca at the Well" _____ 67.50
Tall, plain _____ 34.50
2-quart, Mandarin _____ 75.00
Tiebacks. Pair _____ 30.00
Tobacco Jar. Man smoking, wear-
ing skull cap _____ 52.50
Toby Jug. Pint. Jolly Good Fellow__ 175.00
Toby Jug. Duke of Wellington. Made
by U. S. Pottery Co., Benning-
ton, Vermont. Circa 1850 _____ 265.00
Vase. 7" high _____ 42.50
Wash Board in wood frame _____ 55.00
Wash Bowl Set. 2-piece _____ 145.00

## BISQUE

The term bisque, or biscuit china, is used
to designate ware which has been fired
only once and is not glazed. The body is
soft and porous but will no longer soften
in water as air-dried china will. Some
items are decorated while others are put
on the market in the state in which they
came from the kiln. In recent years, new
items and reproductions have entered the
market. Many collectors have become wary
and the demand has slackened along with
the prices.

Swan. 5". Pink and green decor __  $18.50

Angel. Posed above Holy Water
font. 8" high, 3½" wide _____$ 62.50

Baby kitten with pacifier ________ 36.00
Baby, Piano. Large. On tummy___ 125.00
Boy and Girl. Seated, with musical instruments ____________________ 25.50
Boy and Girl. 7'' high. Holding puppies. Pair _________________ 35.00
Boy teaching poodle to play the horn. 8x8'' ______________________ 65.00
Boy with gun, dog at side. 8'' ____ 28.50
Bust of Girl. $5\frac{1}{2}$" high, blonde hair, blue hat and blouse, gold beads _________________________ 32.50
Darky in nightcap with pig in his arms ___________________________ 18.50
Darky with watermelon. $4\frac{1}{2}$" high__ 20.00
Dog. Orange on lavender cushion. $3\frac{1}{2}$" high ______________________ 14.00
Donkey, Miniature. Nodding, natural color. $2\frac{3}{4}$" long ____________ 18.50
Figurines. 15'' high. Boy and girl dressed as tennis players, colorful. Pair _____________________ 55.00
Figurines. Boy and girl in pastel colors. $9\frac{1}{2}$" high. Pair __________ 25.00
Figurine. $7\frac{3}{4}$" high. Maid in Victorian dress __________________ 16.50
Font, Holy Water. Cross-heart-roses-dove. Hanging type, 5'' high, $2\frac{1}{2}$" wide _________________ 12.00
Girl against stump, blowing horn__ 22.50
Girl and swan on Horn-of-Plenty. Pink and blue. Small __________ 11.50
Girl with basket. 9'' high ________ 18.00
Krazy Kat. $3\frac{1}{2}$" high ____________ 12.00
Lady carrying fan. Glazed. 10'' __ 20.00
Madonna. 9'' high _____________ 21.50
Match Holders:
- $3\frac{1}{2}$" high. Dutch girl holding pitcher ______________________ 15.00
- $5\frac{1}{2}$" high. Girl holding doll ____ 18.00
- 8'' high. ''Happy Hooligan'' __ 17.50

Monkey Horn Player. Blue coat, black hat ____________________ 20.00
Naughty. ''It's A Shame To Take Money'' ______________________ 12.50
Pair in Nightcaps. Seated ________ 24.50
Pig. $3\frac{1}{4}$" high. ''Nodder'' wearing green and gold cut-away suit, holding bouquet of flowers on green pedestal _______________ 22.50
Sheep. $3\frac{1}{4}$" high __________________ 9.00
Shoe. $6\frac{3}{4}$" long, 2 white love birds at top, 3 blue birds on side ____ 26.50
Vases:
- $4\frac{1}{2}$" high. Cone in hand, yellow tint __________________________ 12.50
- $5\frac{1}{2}$" high, 5'' wide _____________ 16.50
- 6'' high. Boy seated under arbor, glazed ________________________ 15.00
- 6'' high. Girls in garden. Yellow and brown, glazed. Pair ______ 24.00

## BITTERS BOTTLES

The bottles originally contained various concoctions of herbs which were mixed with alcohol and sold as tonics from about 1860 to 1900. ''Old Timers'' have stated that many ardent W.C.T.U. members, in the early days of the Phohibition Movement, returned home exhausted after fighting ''demon rum'' at the local meeting house, regained their strength and stability by taking a liberal dose of a favorite bitters tonic which, unknown to her, had an alcoholic content of 75 to 80%.

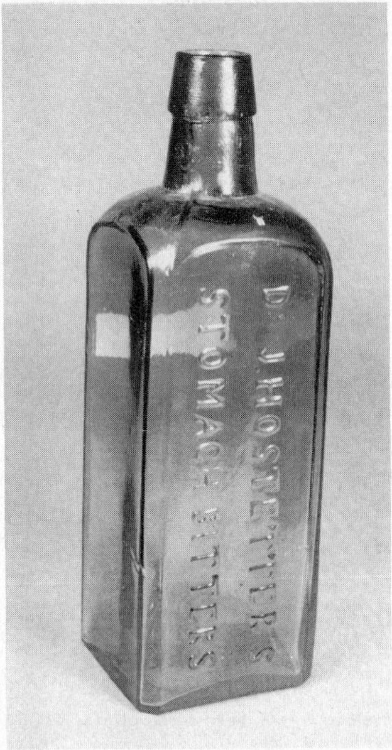

Dr. J. Hostetter's stomach bitters. Amber __________________ $20.00

African Stomach Bitters. Quart, amber, cylindrical ________________$ 24.00
Atwood's Jaundice Bitters. $\frac{1}{2}$ pint, aqua, 12-sided. Moses Atwood, Georgetown, Mass. ____________ 20.00

Augauer Bitters. Light green,
  original label. 8'' tall _____ 28.50
Baker's Orange Grove Bitters.
  Quart, amber, square, rope cor-
  ners _____ 69.50
Baxter's Mandrake Bitters _____ 69.50
Berkshire Bitters. ¾ quart. Shape of
  pig. Reverse, Amann & Co., Cin-
  cinnati, Ohio _____ 48.50
Burdock's Blood Bitters _____ 22.50
Doctor Henley's Wild Grape Root
  Bitters. Quart, cylindrical, aqua,
  "IXL" in oval _____ 27.50
Dr. J. Hostetter's Stomach Bitters__ 12.75
Dr. Jacob's Bitters, thin
  whittle marked bottle _____ 85.00
Dr. Langley's Root & Herb
  Bitters _____ 25.00
Dr. Pierce's Golden Medical Dis-
  covery, Buffalo, N. Y. Aqua ___ 22.50
Dr. C. W. Roback's Stomach
  Bitters. Light amber _____ 70.00
Doctor Shoop's _____ 18.75
Dr. Vonhopf's Curacoa Bitters,
  dark reddish amber _____ 47.50
Doyles Bitters _____ 20.00
Doyle's Hops Bitters. Quart, amber,
  square with bunch of hops and
  leaves _____ 25.00
Drake's S. T. 1860 Plantation Bitters.
  X on roof of log cabin-shaped bot-
  tle. ¾ quart, amber. Patent 1862_ 40.00
Electric Bitters. Amber, square with
  depressed panels. H. E. Bucklew &
  Co. Chicago, Illinois _____ 24.00
Greeley's Bourbon Whiskey Bitters.
  ¾ quart, dark brown _____ 29.50
Hall's Bitters. ¾ quart, amber ____ 72.00
Hartshorn's Bitters _____ 22.50
H. P. Herb Wild Cherry Bitters. ¾
  quart, amber, log cabin-shape,
  rope corners _____ 30.00
Hostetters. Amber _____ 12.50
Indian Queen. Dated 1868, amber__ 85.00
Lash's Kidney & Liver Bitters,
  med. amber _____ 22.75
Myer's American Stomach Bitters,
  paper label only _____ 77.50
National Bitters. 12½'' high, ¾ quart,
  dark amber, shape of ear of
  corn _____ 45.00
Old Dr. Warren's Quaker Bitters__ 55.00
Old Sachem Bitters and Wigwam
  Tonic. ¾ quart, amber, flanged
  mouth _____ 30.00
Paine's Celery Compound. 10'',
  deep amber _____ 25.00
Perrine's Apple & Ginger Bitters,
  ¾ quart, amber, rope corners,
  log cabin-shape _____ 24.00
Pineapple Bitters. Dark honey
  amber, very scarce _____ 135.00
Plain. ¾ quart, amber, barrel-
  shape _____ 11.50
Prickly Ash Bitters. ¾ quart, amber,
  square, bevelled corners _____ 40.00

Richardson's. Green _____ 24.00
Richardson's, S. O. Bitters _____ 24.50
Sarsparilla & Tomato Bitters. Pint,
  aqua. F. Brown, Boston _____ 29.50
Suffolk Bitters. Dark amber pig.
  Scarce _____ 120.00
Tippecanoe Bitters. Deep amber __ 64.50
Travellers Bitters. Amber _____ 35.00
"Warner's Safe Kidney & Liver
  Cure." 9½'' high, dark amber.
  Picture of safe on front. "Roches-
  ter, N. Y." below _____ 14.50
Yerba Buena Bitters _____ 62.50

## BOHEMIAN GLASS

Bohemia was formerly an independent
country but is now part of Czechoslovakia.
It is famed for producing the "flash"
colored glass, overlay, cut and etched
glass. The ruby colored "flashed" or
"stained" glass is one of the better known
products; however, it was also produced
in black, blue, yellow and green colors.
Much of the so-called Bohemian glass was
imitated in Switzerland, England and parts
of Germany to sell at low prices. The glass
was first imported into this country about
1825 and is still being brought in today.
Most of the Bohemian glass desired by collectors today is of the 1875-1900 period.

Basket. Pale pink with applied thorn
  handle, twisted loop _____$  54.50
Beaker. Red, with gold sprays and
  wide gilt rim, 8 facets _____ 47.50
Bell. 4½'' high, deer, castle, clear
  glass handle, clear clapper on
  chain _____ 45.00
Bottles:
  7'' high. Alternating ruby and
  clear panels. Pair _____ 125.00
  7½'' high. White overlay decoration. Pair _____ 185.00
  15'' high. Red. Pair _____ 90.00
Box, Powder. Covered, bird and
  butterfly decor _____ 40.00
Chalice. 10'' high, amber, enameled
  overlay _____ 80.00
Chamber, Bed. Vintage pattern ___ 175.00
Compotes:
  Open, red, 9'' high, 7'' diam.,
  enamel portrait of boy on stem,
  spray and leaf decor in gold,
  gilt trim _____ 185.00
  Open, 8'' high, 9'' diam., colored
  enamel decor, gold scalloped
  edge _____ 200.00
Cordial. Vintage pattern _____ 16.00
Cordial Set. Blown bottle, tray and
  4 glasses in frosted Lily-of-the-
  Valley pattern _____ 80.00
Cruet. Gold and colored "jewels" 60.00
Cuspidor. Open _____ 24.00

153

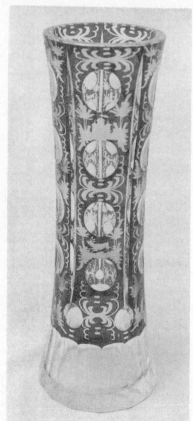

Vase. 12½" high. Castle, leaf and deer decor on red ground, clear base _____ $57.50

**Decanters:**
12" high, Vintage pattern _____ 50.00
12½" high, Vintage pattern, deep red to clear. Pair _____ 80.00
14¼" high, narrow, with original stopper _____ 72.50
Dish, Candy. Covered, 10" high, etched bird and deer decor ____ 49.50
Door Knob Set _____ 24.00

**Finger Bowls:**
4¼" diam. Grape and leaf pattern.
Pair _____ 57.50
Vintage pattern _____ 32.50
Goblet. Knob stem. Vintage _____ 42.50
Lamp. 12" high, cobalt overlay __ 90.00
Mug. 4½" high, clear handle ____ 24.00
Perfume Bottle. Enameled, Vintage decor, original stopper, 5"_____ 18.50
                                    7"_____ 28.50

Wine Decanter. 10½" high. Red decoration _____ $27.50

**Pitchers:**

Quart. Red, Vintage _____ 65.00
Water. Vintage, with 3 rows of
clear rosebuds, applied handle __ 85.00
Powder Jar. Covered, red with
frosted white decor _____ 22.50
Salts. Clear with gold Vintage
decor, on 3 ribbed scrolled feet.
Set of 4 _____ 25.00
Soap Dish. With attached drain__ 18.50
Sugar Bowl. Covered, amber,
etched hunting scene _____ 85.00
Toilet Set. 3-piece; Pair of Cologne
Bottles with original stoppers
and squatty covered Powder Jar.
Blown _____ 75.00

**Tumblers:**

Footed, flowers and birds _____ 21.00
4½'' high. Clear with red flashing, etched _____ 32.50
Vintage Pattern _____ 24.50
Yellow bottom, red top _____ 23.00

**Vases:**

7½'' high. Floral decor, pedestal
base _____ 37.50
10'' high. Red. Pair _____ 72.50
12½'' high. Flowers and birds __ 48.75
12½'' high. Castle, leaf and deer
decor on red ground, clear base_ 57.50
13'' high. Amethyst to clear with
heavy gold overlay _____ 57.50
Water Set. With tumble-up. Vintage
pattern, red _____ 50.00
Wine Glass. Vintage pattern ____ 14.50
Wine Set. Decanter and 6 glasses.
Red deer and castle design ____ 125.00

## BONE

Back Scratcher. Chinese, hand
carved _____$ 7.50
Clothes Pin. Hand carved _____ 5.75
Flour Scoop. Heavy, hand carved 18.50
Letter Opener. Carved figure at
top _____ 5.75
Napkin Ring. Hand carved _____ 4.25
Spoon. 8'' long, not carved with
figures or design _____ 4.50

## BOOT JACKS

Various types of boot jacks were made
to facilitate the removal of boots, the popular footwear of two or three generations
ago. Some were constructed of wood while
others were made of metals such as brass
or iron. Two of the popular designs are
"Beetle" and "Naughty Nellie."

Beetle, Harp-shaped. Iron, 11⅜''
long _____$ 24.00
*Beetle. Iron _____ 12.50
Cast Iron on 8½'' dbl. bbl. cap
pistol. Legend, "American Bull

Dog Boot Jack,'' unfolds into
two sections long way to make
jack _____ 25.00

Variation of the Beetle Pattern.
10¼'' long. Iron _____ $20.00

Double. Ornate, iron. Patent 1869 15.00
Folding or Traveling type. 8'' long 20.00
Lacy Scroll _____ 10.75
Mechanical. Iron, with carpet
covered movable jaws to grip
boot. Pat. 1850 _____ 18.00
Metal. Bowed-type, 7'' long. Name
"C. Hull, Birm.'' on back and
"Regd. Boot Jack'' _____ 8.00
*Naughty Nellie. Iron _____ 10.50
Naughty Nellie. Brass _____ 15.00
Try-It. Iron _____ 10.75
Wood. 16'' long. Adult-type _____ 8.50

## BOTTLES, JIM BEAM

The Beam Distillery was established in
Kentucky by Jacob Beam in 1788. About
1880, Col. James B. Beam (Jim Beam) began work at the family distillery making
Bourbon, which was later to bear his name.

The company got into the novelty bottle-
bourbon business in 1953, when a cocktail
shaker decanter was designed for the
Christmas trade. It was an immediate success. In 1955, the 160th anniversary of the
concern, the first bottle of the present
Executive series was issued, in form of a
decanter with a long pouring lip and a
white stopper. The porcelain bottle was
black with the name and decorations in
gold.

**Centennial:**

1960—Sante Fe _____ 225.00
1961—Civil War North _____ 47.50
1961—Civil War South _____ 47.50
1964—St. Louis Arch _____ 25.00
1966—Alaska Purchase _____ 18.00
1967—Antioch _____ 10.50
1967—Cheyenne, Wyo. _____ 13.50
1967—Nebraska _____ 15.00
1967—St. Louis Arch _____ 21.00
1968—Laramie _____ 12.50

| | |
|---|---|
| 1968—San Diego | 14.50 |
| 1969—Baseball | 16.00 |
| 1969—Lombard Lilac | 10.00 |
| 1969—Reno | 10.50 |
| 1969—Elks Club | 12.50 |

Bowling Pin Bottle. Jim Beam _____ $7.50

**Collector's Bottle:**

| | |
|---|---|
| 1966—Laughing Cavalier | 12.50 |
| 1966—Artist at easel | 12.50 |
| 1966—Aristide Bruant | 12.50 |
| 1966—Mardi Gras | 11.50 |
| 1966—Boy Blue | 18.00 |
| 1966—On the terrace | 20.00 |
| 1949-46—Bowling Pin Bottle: | |
|     Pint | 5.00 |
|     Fifth | 7.50 |
| 1966—Collector's Edition, set | 30.00 |

| | |
|---|---|
| 1967—Collector's Edition, set | 20.00 |
| 1968—Collector's Edition, set | 20.00 |
| 1969—Collector's Edition, set | 25.00 |

**Executive:**

| | |
|---|---|
| 1955—Royal Porcelain | 210.00 |
| 1956—Royal Gold | 165.00 |
| 1957—Royal Di Monte | 85.00 |
| 1958—Cherub, gray | 125.00 |
| 1959—Drinkers or Tavern | 75.00 |
| 1960—Cherub, blue | 80.00 |
| 1961—Chalice, gold | 75.00 |
| 1962—Flower Basket | 50.00 |
| 1963—Royal Rose | 55.00 |
| 1964—Royal Gold Diamond | 45.00 |
| 1965—Marbled Fantasy | 75.00 |
| 1966—Majestic | 35.00 |
| 1967—Prestige | 20.00 |
| 1968—Presidential | 14.00 |
| 1969—Executive | 17.50 |

**Glass Specialties:**

| | |
|---|---|
| 1953—Cocktail Shaker | 7.50 |
| 1953—Royal Reserve | 8.00 |
| 1954—Pyrex Coffee Warmer | 7.00 |
| 1955—Ducks & Geese | 10.00 |
| 1956—Pyrex Coffee Warmer | 9.00 |
| 1957—Royal Opal | 11.50 |
| 1958—Royal Emperor | 9.00 |
| 1959—Royal Crystal | 7.50 |
| 1960—Olympian | 7.00 |
| 1961—Grecian | 5.00 |
| 1962—Cleopatra Yellow | 18.50 |
| 1962—Cleopatra Rust | 7.00 |
| 1962—Mark Antony | 24.50 |
| 1963—Delft Blue | 5.00 |
| 1963—Delft Rose | 7.00 |
| 1963—Dancing Scot, short | 30.00 |
| 1963—Dancing Scot, tall | 12.50 |
| 1964—Smoked Crystal Geni | 7.50 |
| 1965—Cameo Blue | 5.00 |
| 1966—Pressed Crystal Scotch | 5.00 |
| 1967—Pressed Crystal Ruby | 5.00 |
| 1968—Pressed Crystal Emerald | 4.50 |
| 1969—Pressed Crystal Opaline | 5.00 |

**Political:**

| | |
|---|---|
| 1956—Elephant Ash Tray | 18.00 |
| 1956—Donkey Ash Tray | 18.00 |
| 1960—Donkey | 18.00 |
| 1960—Elephant | 18.00 |
| 1964—Donkey Boxer | 18.50 |
| 1964—Elephant Boxer | 18.50 |
| 1968—Donkey | 8.00 |
| 1968—Elephant | 8.00 |

**Regal China (Specialties):**

| | |
|---|---|
| 1955—Ivory Ash Tray | 40.00 |
| 1956—Black Canasta | 35.00 |
| 1962—Seattle World's Fair | 32.50 |
| 1964—Musicians on barrel | 12.50 |
| 1964—N.Y. World's Fair | 30.00 |

| | |
|---|---|
| 1965—Green China Jug | 10.50 |
| 1965—Green Two-Handle Jug | 150.00 |
| 1966—Turquoise Jug | 7.50 |
| 1966—Oatmeal China Jug | 52.50 |
| 1967—Blue Daisy | 11.00 |
| 1967—Blue Fox | 135.00 |
| 1967—Redwood | 12.50 |
| 1967—Yosemite | 11.00 |
| 1968—Antique Trader | 11.00 |
| 1968—Broadmoor Hotel | 8.50 |
| 1968—Cable Car | 6.25 |
| 1968—Grey Slot | 7.50 |
| 1968—Hemisfair | 15.00 |
| 1968—Kentucky Cardinal | 45.00 |
| 1968—Pony Express | 8.50 |
| 1968—Ruidoso Downs | 8.00 |
| 1968—Ruidoso Downs (Pointed Ear) | 30.00 |
| 1968—Yuma Rifle Club | 50.00 |
| 1969—Gold Fox | 68.50 |
| 1969—Grand Canyon, Ariz. | 32.50 |
| 1969—Kentucky Derby | 10.00 |
| 1969—Las Vegas | 10.75 |
| 1969—Mt. Rushmore | 18.00 |
| 1969—Ponderosa | 25.00 |
| 1969—Thailand | 17.50 |
| 1969—White Fox | 38.00 |

Specialties (Customer):

| | |
|---|---|
| 1956—Foremost, white & gold | 125.00 |
| 1956—Foremost, black & gold | 125.00 |
| 1956—Foremost, pink speckled | 300.00 |
| 1957—Harold's Club Silver Opal | 150.00 |
| 1957—Harold's Club — Man in barrel, mustache, black hair | 410.00 |
| 1958—Harold's Club — Man in barrel, no mustache, white hair | 260.00 |
| 1962—Marina City, Chicago | 50.00 |
| 1963—Harold's Club Nevada Grey | 185.00 |
| 1963—Harold's Club Nevada Silver | 185.00 |
| 1963—Harrah's Club Grey | 450.00 |
| 1963—Harrah's Club Silver | 575.00 |
| 1964—First Natl. Bank, Chicago | 1950.00 |
| 1965—Harold's Club Pinwheel | 105.00 |
| 1967—Harold's Club Blue Slot | 20.00 |
| 1967—Harold's Club VIP Exec. | 165.00 |
| 1967—Richard's New Mexico | 10.00 |
| 1967—Yellow Katz | 30.00 |
| 1968—Armanetti Vase | 13.50 |
| 1968—Black Katz | 30.00 |
| 1968—Harold's Club VIP | 165.00 |
| 1968—Zimmerman Cherubs | 10.00 |
| 1969—Churchill Downs Pink Roses | 8.50 |
| 1969—Churchill Downs Red Roses | 19.50 |
| 1969—Harold's Club Covered Wagon | 18.00 |
| 1969—Harry Hoffman Liquors | 15.00 |
| 1969—Harvey's Lake Tahoe | 15.00 |
| 1969—Las Vegas Golden Gate | 145.00 |
| 1969—Las Vegas Golden Nugget | 175.00 |
| 1969—Reno Cal-Neva Club | 17.50 |

| | |
|---|---|
| 1969—Reno Horseshoe Club | 20.00 |
| 1969—Reno Prima Donna Club | 14.50 |

1969 Las Vegas. Jim Beam _____ $10.75

State:

| | |
|---|---|
| 1958—Alaska | 95.00 |
| 1959—Hawaii | 90.00 |
| 1959—Colorado | 50.00 |
| 1959—Oregon | 45.00 |
| 1960—Kansas | 75.00 |
| 1963—Idaho | 80.00 |
| 1963—Montana | 105.00 |
| 1963—W. Virginia | 135.00 |
| 1963—Nevada | 95.00 |
| 1963—New Jersey | 99.50 |
| 1964—No. Dakota | 85.00 |
| 1965—Wyoming | 80.00 |
| 1966—Ohio | 19.50 |
| 1967—Hawaii (Re-issue) | 70.00 |
| 1967—Kentucky | 17.50 |
| 1967—Nebraska | 17.00 |
| 1967—New Hampshire | 13.50 |
| 1967—Pennsylvania | 12.50 |
| 1968—Arizona | 9.50 |
| 1968—Florida | 9.00 |
| 1968—Illinois | 9.50 |

1966 Ohio. Jim Beam _____ $19.50

Pheasant, Ring-neck. 13½''. Jim Beam _$25.00

## MISCELLANEOUS

### ARDOS

| | |
|---|---|
| Clock _____$ | 37.50 |
| Green Duck _____ | 37.50 |
| Rocker _____ | 22.50 |

### AVON

Trophy:

| | |
|---|---|
| 1957—Duck _____ | 50.00 |
| 1957—Fish _____ | 48.50 |
| 1958—Ram _____ | 125.00 |
| 1959—Dog _____ | 75.00 |
| 1961—Pheasant _____ | 19.50 |
| 1962—Brown Horse _____ | 24.00 |
| 1962—Grey Horse _____ | 22.50 |
| 1962—Black Horse _____ | 25.00 |
| 1963—Doe _____ | 35.00 |
| 1965—Fox _____ | 35.00 |
| 1966—Pheasant (Re-issue) _____ | 18.50 |
| 1966—Eagle _____ | 18.50 |
| 1967—Cats _____ | 12.50 |
| 1967—Doe (Re-issue) _____ | 35.00 |
| 1967—Fox (Re-issue) _____ | 35.00 |
| 1969—Bluejay _____ | 14.50 |
| 1969—Robin _____ | 14.50 |
| 1969—Woodpecker _____ | 14.50 |

Sterling Six Car. Avon Bottle ____ $12.00

| | |
|---|---|
| Alpine Flask _____ | 35.00 |
| Bath Seasons _____ | 5.00 |
| Bath Urn, clear _____ | 7.00 |

| | |
|---|---|
| Bath Urn, milk glass | 17.50 |
| Bay Rum Jug | 10.00 |
| Bay Rum Keg | 15.00 |
| Blue Lotus | 3.50 |
| Boot, ceramic | 5.00 |
| Boot, gold top | 6.00 |
| Boot, silver top | 7.50 |

| | |
|---|---|
| Decanter | 8.00 |
| Decanter, Inkwell | 5.00 |
| Decanter, Owl | 3.00 |
| Decisions, Decisions | 30.00 |
| Defender | 20.00 |
| Demi-Cup | 6.00 |
| Dollars and Scents | 25.00 |
| Dolhpin | 7.00 |
| Excalibur | 5.00 |
| First Edition | 10.00 |
| Fragrance Bell | 6.00 |
| Fragrance Belle | 20.00 |
| Gavel | 15.00 |
| Gift Fancy (Sea Shell) | 6.00 |
| Gift Magic (Rocker) | 8.00 |
| Golf Club | 4.00 |
| Greek Warrior | 15.00 |
| Heart, Set of Three | 12.00 |
| Here's My Heart Cologne Mist | 8.00 |
| Island Lime | 4.50 |
| Just Two | 18.00 |
| Key Note | 18.00 |
| Lavender Sachet | 10.00 |

| | |
|---|---|
| Boot. Gold top. Avon Bottle | $6.00 |
| Bud Vase, 1962 | 15.00 |
| Bud Vase, 1966 | 10.00 |
| Bud Vase, 1968 | 6.00 |
| Candleholder, First Christmas | 10.00 |
| Candleholder, Frosted Glass | 6.50 |
| Candleholder, Golden Apple | 8.00 |
| Candleholder, Milk Glass | 12.50 |
| Candlestick | 15.00 |
| Captain's Choice | 12.00 |
| Casey's Lantern, amber | 18.50 |
| Casey's Lantern, green | 16.50 |
| Casey's Lantern, red | 15.00 |
| Christmas Ornaments: | |
|     Angel | 7.50 |
|     Balls | 6.50 |
|     Candle | 10.00 |
|     Icicle | 4.50 |
|     Sparkler | 4.50 |
|     Tree | 4.50 |
| Close Harmony | 30.00 |
| Cologne Mist | 13.00 |
| Crystal Cologne/Beauty Dust Set | 35.00 |
| Crystal Glory | 12.50 |

Pony Post. 8 oz. Avon Bottle _____ $12.50

| | |
|---|---|
| Legendary Hero | 8.00 |
| Mallard Decanter | 8.50 |
| Miss Lollypop Majorette Boot | 4.00 |
| Miss Lollypop Spray Mist | 5.00 |
| Opening Play | 7.00 |
| Pipe Dream | 17.50 |
| Pony Decanter | 6.00 |
| Pony Post, 6 oz. | 9.00 |
| Pony Post, 8 oz. | 12.50 |
| Pretty Peach Spray Mist | 10.00 |
| Renaissance Trio | 5.50 |
| Riviera Decanter | 8.00 |
| Rose Fragrance | 25.00 |
| Royal Orb | 22.50 |
| Scimitar | 10.00 |
| Shaving Time | 10.00 |
| Snail | 12.50 |
| Spicy After Shave | 3.50 |
| Spray Boot | 5.50 |
| Stein, 6 oz. | 6.00 |
| Stein, 8 oz. | 12.50 |
| Sterling Six Car | 12.00 |
| Straight Eight Car | 8.00 |
| To a Wild Rose Cologne | 4.00 |
| Topaze Cologne Mist | 15.00 |
| Town Pump | 8.00 |
| 20 Paces | 25.00 |
| Viking Horn | 15.00 |
| Weather or Not | 7.00 |
| Western Choice | 15.00 |
| Windjammer | 6.50 |

## BARSOTTINI (Italy)

| | |
|---|---|
| Antique Carriage | $ 6.00 |
| Bacchus | 5.00 |
| Cannon | 11.50 |
| Colosseum | 9.50 |
| Donkey | 6.25 |
| Dueling Pistols | 13.00 |
| Elephant | 6.25 |
| Elk | 16.00 |
| Florentine Steeple | 10.00 |
| Fruit Basket | 10.00 |
| Hurricane Lamp | 7.00 |
| Leaning Tower of Pisa | 8.00 |
| Love Birds | 15.00 |
| Monk W/Wine Glass | 13.00 |
| Owl | 15.00 |
| Rabbit Gnawing on Carrot | 14.00 |
| Santa Claus with Bag of Toys | 16.00 |
| Small Cars | 6.50 |
| Wine Cask | 20.00 |

## BISCHOFF

| | |
|---|---|
| Bell Tower | 30.00 |
| Chinese Man | 40.00 |
| Chinese Woman | 40.00 |
| Christmas Tree | 37.50 |
| Church with Bell | 40.00 |
| Clown | 35.00 |
| Cruet, double | 40.00 |
| Egyptian Vase, single | 20.00 |
| Egyptian Vase, double | 30.00 |
| Fish Ash Tray | 20.00 |
| King Vase | 20.00 |

| | |
|---|---|
| Mask | 20.00 |
| Matador | 30.00 |
| Roman Vase | 20.00 |
| Rooster Ash Tray | 20.00 |
| Senorita | 30.00 |
| 3 Dim. Church | 25.00 |
| Vase, plain | 20.00 |

## BOLS

| | |
|---|---|
| Ballerina | 10.75 |
| Blackberry Delft | 12.50 |
| Creme de Menthe Delft | 10.75 |
| Dutch Boy | 20.00 |
| Dutch Girl | 20.00 |

## BORGHINA (Italy)

| | |
|---|---|
| African Bust Alborada | 25.00 |
| Cherubs with Mirror | 11.00 |
| Clown with Mandolin | 25.00 |
| Dog | 25.00 |
| Egyptian Bust Sophia | 25.00 |
| European Bust | 25.00 |
| Horse Head | 25.00 |
| Leaning Tower | 10.00 |
| Mercedes Benz | 8.00 |
| Old Ford | 8.00 |
| Peasant Boy | 10.00 |
| Peasant Girl | 10.00 |

## BROOKS, EZRA

Iron Horse. Ezra Brooks 12 .......... $12.00

| | |
|---|---|
| Antique Cannon | 14.50 |
| Balloon | 11.00 |
| Cabin Still, fifth | 18.50 |
| Cabin Still, orig. pint | 45.00 |
| Cabin Still, 1969 Re-issue | 12.50 |
| Cable Car | 10.50 |
| Chicago Water Tower | 14.50 |
| Clown on Drum, short | 45.00 |
| Clown on Drum, tall | 65.00 |
| Delta Belle (New) | 13.50 |

| | |
|---|---|
| Dice | 12.00 |
| Dueling Pistol | 12.00 |
| Golden Cannon (New) | 13.50 |
| Grizzly Bear | 12.50 |
| Gun Series, set of 4 (New) | 24.00 |
| Harold's Club Dice | 10.50 |
| Indian | 12.00 |
| Iron Horse Train | 12.00 |
| Jack of Diamonds | 13.50 |
| Jayhawk | 14.00 |
| Katz Kats | 14.00 |
| Kentucky Gentleman | 14.00 |
| King of Clubs (New) | 13.50 |
| Kneeling Blue Geisha | 40.00 |
| Mr. Foremost | 14.00 |
| Oil Derrick | 12.00 |
| Pot Belly Stove | 12.00 |
| Queen of Hearts | 12.50 |
| Red Dice | 15.00 |
| Reno Arch | 13.50 |
| Stage Coach | 13.50 |
| Tecumseh | 12.50 |
| Winston Churchill | 11.50 |
| Zimmerman Old Hat | 15.00 |

## BUTON

| | |
|---|---|
| Ceramic Book | 25.00 |
| Ceramic Cherry | 25.00 |

## DANT, J. W.

| | |
|---|---|
| Alamo, black | 4.00 |
| American Legion | 10.00 |
| Bobwhite | 12.50 |
| Boston Tea Party | 4.00 |
| California Quail | 12.50 |
| Chukar Partridge | 12.50 |
| Ft. Sill, Okla. | 10.50 |
| Mountain Quail | 12.50 |
| Prairie Chicken | 12.50 |
| Ringnecked Pheasant | 12.50 |
| Ruffed Grouse | 12.50 |
| Woodcock | 12.50 |
| Wrong Way Charlie | 40.00 |

## DICKEL, GEO.

| | |
|---|---|
| Golf Club | 9.00 |
| Powder Horn | 9.00 |

## GARNIER (France)

| | |
|---|---|
| Alpha Romero, 1913 | $ 12.50 |
| Alpha Romero, 1927 | 12.50 |
| Anses Vase | 22.00 |
| Apollo (Moon) | 18.00 |
| Azteque Vase | 20.00 |
| Baby Foot | 14.50 |
| Bacchus | 17.50 |
| Bellows | 20.00 |
| Birman Vase | 20.00 |
| Black Cat | 18.00 |
| Bullfighters | 22.00 |
| Candlestick | 17.50 |
| Caneton Duck | 20.00 |
| Cardinal | 18.50 |

| | |
|---|---|
| Chinese Dog | 18.50 |
| Clown | 32.50 |
| Coffee Mill | 27.50 |
| Coffee Pot | 25.00 |
| Diamond | 18.00 |
| Drunk on Lamp Post | 22.50 |
| Duck | 27.50 |
| Duo-Liqueur | 10.00 |
| Eifel Tower | 30.00 |
| Elephant | 25.00 |
| Fiat 500, 1913 | 12.50 |
| Fiat Ruevo, 1913 | 12.50 |
| Flower Bouquet | 18.50 |
| Four Compartment (Carafe) | 18.00 |
| Fusee | 14.50 |
| Giraffe | 30.00 |
| Grey Cat | 18.00 |
| Horse Pistol | 22.00 |
| Indian | 17.00 |
| Jockey | 22.50 |
| Landscape | 16.00 |
| Laurel Crown | 22.00 |
| Locomotive | 17.50 |
| Milord | 16.50 |
| Napoleon on Horse | 22.50 |
| Oasis | 22.00 |
| Old Watch | 22.00 |
| Painting w/easel | 22.50 |
| Paris Monument | 23.50 |
| Paris Scene | 17.50 |
| Paris Taxi | 30.00 |
| Parrot | 32.00 |
| Partridge | 20.00 |
| Pheasant | 20.00 |
| Rainbow | 20.00 |
| Renault, 1911 | 12.50 |
| Rooster, black | 24.00 |
| Rooster, maroon | 28.00 |

## GARNIER—Contd.

| | |
|---|---|
| St. Tropez Jug | $ 25.00 |
| Scarecrow | 18.00 |
| Sheriff | 17.00 |
| Soldier, aqua | 65.00 |
| Soldier, green | 70.00 |
| Soldier, red | 65.00 |
| S. S. France | 100.00 |
| Street Scene Jug | 30.00 |
| Tableau | 23.50 |
| Trio | 20.00 |
| Trout | 18.50 |
| Violin | 18.50 |

## GRENADIER

**Colonial Series:**

| | |
|---|---|
| Baylors 3rd Continental (1778) | $ 15.00 |
| Continental Marines (1779) | 15.00 |
| Eighteenth Continental (1778) | 13.00 |
| Second Maryland (1777) | 15.00 |
| Third New York (1775) | 13.00 |

**Napoleon Series:**

| | |
|---|---|
| Eugene | 18.00 |

Grenadier Bottles. LEFT: Napoleon,
$25.00. RIGHT: Baylors 3rd Con-
tinenttal, $18.00

| | |
|---|---|
| Lannes | 18.00 |
| Lassol | 18.00 |
| Murat | 18.50 |
| Napoleon | 25.00 |
| Ney | 20.00 |

## HARPER, I. W.

| | |
|---|---|
| Figurine, blue | 25.00 |
| Figurine, grey | 25.00 |

## HOUSE OF KOSHU

| | |
|---|---|
| Crown | 6.00 |
| Geisha Cherry Blossom | 35.00 |
| Geisha Chrysanthemum | 35.00 |
| Geisha Lily | 35.00 |
| Geisha Plum Blossom | 35.00 |
| Geisha Violet | 35.00 |
| Geisha Wisteria | 35.00 |
| Joan & Darby, set | 25.00 |
| Noh Mask | 18.00 |
| Noh Print | 18.00 |
| Okame | 15.00 |
| Pagoda | 15.00 |
| Red Lion Man | 25.00 |
| Sake God | 12.50 |
| Sedan Chair | 6.50 |
| Stone Lantern | 45.00 |
| Treasure Tower | 14.50 |
| White Lion Man | 27.50 |

## IMPORTS

| | |
|---|---|
| Beameister, 10th | $ 2.00 |
| Beameister, 5th | 3.00 |
| Bronte Yorkshire, miniature | 2.00 |
| Bronte Yorkshire, 12 oz. | 10.00 |
| Bronte Yorkshire, 24 oz. | 12.50 |
| Mundus Rose, 10th | 2.00 |
| Mundus Rose, 5th | 3.75 |

## LUXARDO (Italy)

| | |
|---|---|
| Alabaster Candlestick | $ 32.50 |
| Alabaster Fish | 26.00 |
| Alabaster Goose | 26.00 |
| Amphora | 12.50 |
| Apothecary Jar | 12.50 |
| Barrel | 12.50 |
| Calypso Girl | 12.50 |
| Cellini Vase | 13.50 |
| Coffee Carafe | 12.50 |
| Egyptian Vase | 12.50 |
| Gambia | 12.50 |
| Gold Fish | 26.00 |
| Gold Pheasant | 22.50 |
| Gondola, lge. | 12.00 |
| Green Duck | 27.50 |
| Green Fish | 26.00 |
| Jogan Buddha | 24.00 |
| Leather Cannon | 35.00 |
| Leather Duck | 22.50 |
| Leather Giraffe | 15.00 |
| Modern Pheasant | 26.00 |
| Nubian | 12.50 |
| Penguin | 32.00 |
| Puppy | 35.00 |
| Red Pheasant | 24.00 |
| Ruby Fish | 33.00 |
| Sphinx Head | 12.50 |
| Torre Tinta | 20.00 |
| Tower of Flowers | 12.50 |
| Tower of Fruit | 18.00 |
| Wobble | 12.50 |

## MISCELLANEOUS

### COUGH SYRUP:

| | |
|---|---|
| Dr. A. Boschee's German Syrup | 4.00 |
| Dr. Hess Distemper Fever and Cough Remedy | 3.75 |
| Dr. Hooker's Cough & Croup Syrup | 3.50 |
| Dr. B. J. Kendall's Quick Relief | 4.00 |
| Dr. King's New Discovery to Cough & Colds | 4.25 |
| Indian Vegetable Cough Syrup & Blood Purifiers, S. B. Goffs | 5.00 |

### FIGURAL:

| | |
|---|---|
| Benedictine | 9.00 |
| Castanet Frere. Clear, nude dancing girls on four corners | 12.00 |
| Crane. 14½'' clear glass | 24.00 |
| Danish Kluk | 9.50 |

Dog, brown _____ 10.00
Dog, standing on hind legs, 13",
clear glass _____ 20.00
Guitar, 16", glass, amber, with
cork _____ 15.00
Japanese Gods. Seven, painted
china _____ 18.00
King's Gate. Caernarvon Castle__ 10.00
Leprechaun _____ 11.00
Lucky Jo, Cat & Clown. Banks__ 7.50
Madonna, cobalt, embossed head
of infant at base _____ 15.00
Majolica Rabbit. Head is stopper.
14" high. Colorful decorations__ 65.00
Milk. Baby face top. Quart.
Santa Barbara, Calif. _____ 7.00
Monkey. Wrapped around green
bottle _____ 8.00
Old Hickory. Andrew Jackson __ 17.50
Old Methuselah. Round, amber __ 7.00
Potato shape, 5." long, screw
top. Embossed "World's Fair
1893." _____ 10.00
Riemerschmid Clocks _____ 8.00
Sailor Boy. 13", clear glass ___ 19.75
Taylor's Castle _____ 13.50

### FOOD:

Chase & Sanborn Coffee Im-
posters. Rectangular, amber ___ 4.00
My Wife's Salad Dressing.
Square, sun purple _____ 5.00
S. S. P. Olive Oil. Ball base, long
neck, aqua _____ 4.50
Peppersauce. 8" high. Clear. Tall,
thin, 25 concentric lines _____ 5.00
Peppersauce. Ridgy. Aqua,
green, teal blue _____ 8.75
Snow Crop Syrup. Shape of bear,
bank slot in top _____ 5.00

### FRUIT JARS:

"ABGA Mason Perfect." Quart
gallon, lid and screwband. Aqua_ 6.00
"Atlas Good Luck." Embossed
clover on front. Gallon lid,
½ gallon, quart, pint. Amber____ 4.00
Atlas, Mason's patent, quart __ 3.00
Ball Improved, band, quart, blue_ 2.50
Ball Perfect Mason, purple tint,
screw-on, porcelain liner _____ 3.50
"Ball Standard." Aqua. Quart,
wax seal _____ 3.00
Cross Mason's Improved, dated
'67 on bottom, pint _____ 3.50
"Double Safety." Clear, quart or
pint. Combination gallon lid ___ 2.75
"Electroglas Mason." Quart,
amber _____ 4.75
The "Gem". Quart _____ 5.50
"Glenshaw Mason." Gallon lid;
screwband. Quart or pint, amber_ 3.00
Globe. Quart _____ 12.50

Royal. Fruit Jar _____ $ 5.00

Green Mountain. Quart,
stippled, clear _____ 6.50
Jeannette Mason Home Packer,
pint _____ 2.75
"Lamb Mason." Quart. Amber __ 4.25
Lightning:
Quart. Amber _____ 4.25
Quart. Aqua. Glass lid, wire
ball _____ 2.75
½ Gallon. Amber _____ 4.50
"Milleville Atmospheric." 2-
quart, complete. Aqua _____ 15.00
Narrow mouth, ½ pint, clear,
round _____ 1.00
"Queen." Clear, quart or pint,
Complete, gallon lid _____ 3.00
Queen SKO, side clamps, quart
or pint _____ 3.50
Quick Seal, dated, clear, quart
or pint _____ 2.25
"Safety Valve." Marked on bot-
tom only. ½ gallon with lid and
clamp. Clear _____ 6.50

### GIN:

Blankenheym & Nolet. Case
shape, olive green. Pint _____ 20.00

F. Brown's Jamaica Ginger, Philadelphia _____ 4.00
Dana's Red Sea Jamaica Ginger_ 4.00
Imperial Gin. H. H. S. & Co. I&W in base, case shape. Amber, mint _____ 30.00
Moody's Extract Jamaica Ginger_ 4.00
H. Van Emden, Posthorn Gin. Sun purple, tampered _____ 6.00

## MALTS:

Hoff's whittled, O. G. _____ 7.00
C. A. King. Pure Malt Dept, on bottom. Shape of Hoff, amber__ 4.00
The Old Bushmill's Dist. Co. Pure Malt Dept. _____ 5.00

## MEDICINES:

Dr. Cumming's "Vecetine." Clear__ $ 4.75

"Dr. Abbot's Compound Extract Sarsparilla." Paper label only. Rectangular, aqua. Contents and box _____ 8.50
"Black Gin for the Kidneys." Reverse "Wm. F. Zoeller, Pittsburgh, Pa." 9" square. Full of bubbles. Amber _____ 12.00
Dr. Carter Balsam _____ 10.00
Coe's Dyspepsia Cure _____ 6.00
Conners Blood Remedy _____ 18.50
Cooper's New Discovery. Rectangular. Aqua _____ _____ 6.00
Dr. Crossman's Specific Mixture_ 4.75
Elmer's Great French Remedy___ 5.00
Foley's Pain Relief _____ 5.00
H. D. Fowler, Boston _____ 5.50
"Gooch's Extract of Sarsparilla, Cincinnati, O." Brilliant aqua. Rectangular, quart _____ 10.00
Dr. Hayne's Arabian Balsam ___ 3.50
Hibbard's Rheumatic Syrup. Square, amber _____ 7.00
Hunt's Remedy _____ 5.00
Dr. Jayne's Alterative. Aqua, flask shape, whittle marks, pontil_ 8.50
Dr. H. Kelsey, Lowell, Mass. __ 5.00
Dr. Kennedy's Medical Discovery_ 5.50
Dr. Kilmer's Swamp Root _____ 4.00
Life Plant. Embossed bird. Milk glass. Oval _____ 10.00
Lindsey's Blood plus Searcher. Rectangular, aqua _____ 9.00
Ozomulsion. Amber _____ 7.50
Paine's Celery Compound. Amber _____ 8.00
Wm. Radams Microbe Killer with label _____ 40.00
Reed & Carnick. New York ____ 4.00
Dr. Sanford's Liver Invigorator_ 5.00
Shaker Digestive Cordial, milk. Rectangular, aqua _____ 12.00
M. Stein Spirit Gum _____ 2.50
Jno. Sullivan Phar., milk glass__ 10.00
Van Bell's Rye & Rock. Rectangular, aqua _____ 9.50
Dr. F. C. Wilkinson's Horse Liniment _____ 4.75
"L.Q.C. Wishart's Pine Tree Tar Cordial, Phila. Patent 1859." Embossed pine tree, emerald green, quart _____ 39.50
Wyeth Dose, cobalt. Complete __ 7.00

## MINIATURES:

Ardo Gambia _____ 5.00
Ardo Gondola _____ 5.00
Ardo Nubian _____ 5.00
Ardo Paestum _____ 6.00
Ardo Twist _____ 3.00
Ardo Venus Di Milo _____ 6.00
Bastanoby Forbidden Fruit _____ 7.00
Bralatta (Face) Italy _____ 4.00
Bronte Jug _____ 3.50
Coffee House _____ 2.50

| | |
|---|---|
| Crown Royal | 2.50 |
| Dickel Powder Horn | 4.00 |
| DuBouchett Creme De Menthe | 2.00 |
| El Toro, Mexico | 2.00 |
| Galliano Soldier | 6.00 |
| Gallo Ceramic Jug | 3.50 |
| Giacoma Casanova | 4.00 |
| Glayva (old) | 2.50 |
| Grand Marnier, France | 3.50 |
| Isolabella, Italy | 2.00 |
| Kikubawa Sake, Japan | 5.00 |
| Pasha | 2.50 |
| Pepsi-Cola, old | 2.00 |
| Rafael-Apertif | 1.75 |
| Vandermint | 2.00 |
| Vat, green or clear | 2.50 |
| Velille Cure, France | 7.50 |

## MISCELLANEOUS:

| | |
|---|---|
| Bar bottle. Round, amber. Inset port wine | 12.50 |
| Brown pottery, squatty with Chinese lettering on bottom | 8.00 |
| Canada Dry, carnival | 20.00 |
| Carter, cone inks, aqua | 4.00 |
| Chinese Opium. $2\frac{1}{2}$'' sheared top | 4.50 |
| Cologne. Tall, green | 3.00 |
| Cologne. Monk or Madonna with 6-pointed star, columned corners. Open pontil. Rectangular, aqua | 10.00 |
| Hagan's Magnolia Balm. Milk glass | 12.00 |
| Hazelton's High Pressure Chemical Fire Keg. Barrel, 11''. Amber | 25.00 |
| Hock Wine. Teal blue | 8.50 |
| Hock Wine. Blob seal, amber | 8.50 |
| Buffalo Lithia Water. Light green, fully embossed with lady, etc. Blown | 9.50 |
| Milk, brown. $\frac{1}{2}$ gallon | 6.00 |
| "J. Kennedy Mineral Water, Pittsburgh." Reverse, large "J. K", blue-green blob top, carbon pontil | 18.00 |
| Portugese Wine, blob seal. Deep aqua. $13\frac{1}{2}$x$2\frac{1}{4}$'' | 8.50 |
| Stafford Ink, cobalt, pint | 8.00 |

## PICNIC:

| | |
|---|---|
| $5\frac{1}{4}$x$4\frac{1}{4}$'', clear, bubbles | 6.75 |
| "The Dandy." Clear, ribbed half way down, bottom half plain. 5x$4\frac{1}{2}$'' | 10.00 |
| "Early Morning." Clear, clock with Roman numerals on reverse. Large 5-pointed star, $4\frac{1}{4}$x$3\frac{3}{4}$'' | 25.00 |
| Miniature, clear. $3\frac{1}{4}$x3'' | 8.50 |
| Sunburst, clear. $5\frac{1}{4}$x$4\frac{1}{4}$'' | 8.00 |
| Sunflower, clear. $5\frac{1}{4}$x$4\frac{3}{4}$'' | 11.50 |

## PROHIBITION:

| | |
|---|---|
| Bottoms Up, 15 mo. old | $ 30.00 |
| Brookwood, 1 year old, Pa. | 27.50 |
| Denham's, 1 mo. old | 40.00 |
| Gay Party Gin, 1935 | 30.00 |
| G.O.G. Boston | 25.00 |
| Hill Top, over one month old. Hartford | 37.50 |
| Indian Feathers, chief on bottle, over six months old | 32.50 |
| Kentucky Straight Whiskey, 1 year and 4 mo. old | 27.50 |
| Knock Rummy, 6 mo. old | 35.00 |
| Oak Drum, "You Can't Beat It," drum molded shape | 38.00 |
| Oak Hill Hudson Valley, 3 mo. old | 28.50 |
| Oak Kay, less than one mo. old diamond embossed glass | 48.00 |
| Old Barbee Rye, Spring 1917, for medicinal purposes only | 52.00 |
| Old Quaker Rye, 18 mo. old | 30.00 |
| Old Velvet, 17 yrs. old. Prescription. Rare | 120.00 |
| Picardy, Apple Jack, Md. | 38.00 |
| Shipping Port, 100 proof, Ky | 37.50 |
| Skipper's Favorite | 27.00 |
| Sky Scraper Whiskey, 4 mo. old, glass embossed with stars | 42.00 |
| Snug Harbor, green glass with coat of arms | 40.00 |

## SODA:

| | |
|---|---|
| Coca Cola. Fredericksburg | $ 2.50 |
| Squat, marked C. Burkhardt, Phila., green | 9.00 |
| Coca Cola, "Circa 1903", straight side, embossed Coca Cola, Jacksonville, Fla. | 4.25 |

Squat, marked Twitchell, Phila., green _____ 9.00
Torpedo. blob mouth, "Circa 1870-80," heavy glass _____ 4.25

## WHISKEYS:

Black & White, 3 mold, O. G. __ 7.00
Clarke's Old Cumberland Rye Whiskey, label, embossed Costello & Co., Boston, clear _____ 6.50
H. A. Graef & Son, Brooklyn, N. Y., round, 3 mold, amber __ 6.75
"The Hayner Distilling Co., Dayton, O. & St. Louis, Mo.", clear shot, picture of horseshoe, barrel and stocks of grain, dated 1866 _____ 8.00
"Chas. Huster Wholesale Dealer in Wines & Liquors, 1213 Parade St., Erie, Pa.", clear, quart shoo fly _____ 12.75
"F. R. Jackson Wines and Liquors, #141 Federal St. Allegheny, Pa.", clear, rectangular, quart _____ 12.75
"The Koyner Distilling Co. Distillers, Dayton, St. Louis, Atlanta, St. Paul", clear round quart fluted at base and shoulders _____ 6.00
"Lamdin Thompson & Co., Baltimore." Albion, Maryland Whiskey, amethyst rectangular semiblob top. 6" high _____ 12.75
"John A. McLaren Perth Malt Whiskey, Perth, Ont.", aqua, quart, shoo fly _____ 10.00
Palmer, in script. Cylindrical, deep emerald green _____ 8.50
Shoo fly, clear, ½ pint. Bottom half swirled, marked in circle "Merry Christmas and Happy New Year" _____ 10.00
Pinch, silver overlay _____ 25.00
"P. Welty & Co. Jobbers & Importers Wines & Liquors, Wheeling, W. Va.", oval, quart, turning amethyst _____ 14.00
Wright & Taylor, Louisville ____ 7.50

### OLD FITZGERALD

Flagship Decanter _____ 6.50
Monticello Decanter _____ 6.50
Sons of Erin Crock _____ 11.00

### BRANDING IRONS

Branding Irons were, and still are, used in the western part of the United States to mark animals. The "iron" is heated until hot and then applied to the animal's hide. The print of the iron remains and is used to identify animals belonging to various owners. The designs vary but are usually combinations of letters, numbers or geometric markings.

Wrought iron. Wood handle, letters "LS" _____ $ 10.00

Wrought iron. Letter "O" _____ $ 7.50
Wrought iron. Letter "S" _____ 7.50
Wrought iron. Letter "U" _____ 7.50
Wrought iron. Letter "V" _____ 7.50
Wrought iron. Letters "DR" _____ 10.00
Wrought iron. Letters "LC" _____ 9.75

### BRASS

A yellow alloy consisting mainly of copper and zinc, which is durable, malleable and ductile—or capable of being hammered-out. The list below indicates that the metal was used in the past for a variety of utilitarian purposes.

Candlesticks. 10½". Circa 1840 _____$95.00

Andirons:
7" high. Griffins. Pair _____$ 48.50
9" high. Queen Anne. Pair ____ 60.00

20'' high. Twisted rope columns.
Pair ----------------------------- 45.00
25'' high. Carved decorated posts,
curled feet, 3½'' brass ball finials.
Polished and ]acquered. Pair __ 68.50
Anvil. 5⅛'' long, 2¼'' high _____ 6.50
Basket. Handled, French basket-
weave _____ 18.50
*Bed Warmer. Long pine handle __ 60.00
Bells:
　Cow. Large _____ 12.00
　Dinner. Chinese, with Seahorse on
　a Turtle _____ 14.00
　School. 6'' high, 3'' diam., wood
　handle _____ 18.75
　Slave or Fireplace. 19'' high, with
　striker. Polished and lacquered__ 50.00
　Sleigh. 24'' strap, 2¾'' bells
　graduating to 1⅛'' _____ 85.00
Bible Clips, with connecting brass
chain _____ 6.00
Bird Cage. Small _____ 21.50
Boot Jack. "Naughty Nellie" ____ 15.00
Bowls:
　6'' diam., with collar, etched __ 8.75
　7'' diam., ball foot _____ 10.00
　8'' dian., footed _____ 12.75
　12'' diam., etched dragon de-
　sign, teak wood base stand ____ 21.00
Boxes:
　Tobacco. Coin operated, picture
　of Queen Victoria _____ 95.00
　7x7x2½'', hammered _____ 12.00
Bucket with bail. 11'' high, 12''
diam. Brass band with rivets two-
thirds ot the way up from bottom.
Cleaned and buffed _____ 80.00
Bucket. Large size, 18'' diam., 12''
deep. Burnished and lacquered__ 50.00
　Same as above. Medium size, 12''
　diam _____ 40.00
Bullet Mold. Hinged-end _____ 14.50
Calling Card Holder. Ornate,
woven wire, on easel _____ 10.00
Candelabra:
　11'' high, 3-branch type _____ 52.50
　18'' high, 7 candles, arms turn
　separately _____ 75.00
Candle Holder. Saucer-type _____ 20.00
Candle Holder. With snuffer scis-
sors and cone _____ 45.00
Candlesticks:
　Beehive. 9'', push-up, burnished.
　Pair _____ 55.00
　Beehive. 9¾'', same. Pair _____ 62.50
　Beehive. 11⅞'', same. Pair _____ 62.50
　Saucer-type. Push-up and
　snuffer _____ 24.00
　Winged-dragon type _____ 27.50
Cannons:
　Small, wood frame _____ 15.00
　Large, all brass _____ 65.00
Chafing Dish and Tray _____ 80.00
Chestnut Roaster. 18'' long. Brass

handles ------------------------- 22.50
Cigar Clipper. Desk size _____ 12.50
Clamp, Paper. 3½'' long. In form of
bird, marked "China" _____ 5.75
Coal Box. 12x16x17'' high. Repousse'
decor on slanted front lift-lid.
Fancy brass coal scoop with
holder on outside. Carrying
handle, brass ball feet _____ 95.00
Coal Hod _____ 90.00
Coffee Percolator. With alcohol
burner _____ 30.00
Coffee Pot. Small _____ 20.00
Cuspidors:
　12'' high _____ 27.50
　Mechanical turtle _____ 40.00
Dipper. 6'' diam., old _____ 25.00
Door Knocker. 9'' long, 18th cen-
tury, elongated urn design _____ 27.50
Door Stop. Sleeping Fox _____ 25.00
Ferner. On 3 round legs _____ 18.50
Fire Hose Nozzle _____ 27.50
Fireplace Items:
　Fender. Brass posts and rail,
　iron base. 23'' long, circa 1880__ 70.00
　Foot Warmer. Bail handle _____ 40.00
　Fork. 18'' long, Shakespeare head
　on handle _____ 14.50
　Fork. 20'' long, owl handle ____ 15.00
　Lighter. Cape Cod _____ 20.00
　Trivet. 5¼'' high, 10x6¼'', slender
　legs, pierced leaf design _____ 50.00
Frames:
　6'', oval _____ 18.00
　8x14'', Florentine, with easel___ 40.00
　11x12'', oval, for mirror, Vic-
　torian cherub _____ 24.50
　13½x16'', oval, for mirror, Vic-
　torian cherub _____ 35.00
Ginger Jar. 7½'' high, Chinese,
engraved _____ 29.50
Hand Warmer. 5x7''. French, wood
handle _____ 24.50
Heel Plates. Pennsylvania Dutch,
heart cut-outs _____ 10.00
Horn. 1913 Ford Auto. Complete
with original flex cable and
sounding reed _____ 70.00
Horn, Canal. 24'' high, polished and
lacquered _____ 45.00
Horse Bit _____ 3.50
Ice Tongs _____ 10.50
Inkstand. 7¾'' square, raised well
in center, low feet, elaborate
motif _____ 37.50
Inkwells:
　4¾'' square, hammered, pyramid-
　shape _____ 18.50
　English, with tray _____ 45.00
Jardinieres:
　5x5'', hammered _____ 21.50
　8'' high, 10'' diam., 3 ball feet.
　Polished _____ 27.50
　10'', stag head handles _____ 50.00

Kettles:

| | |
|---|---|
| 6-quart | 25.00 |
| 8-quart | 30.00 |
| 10-quart | 36.00 |
| 11-quart | 42.50 |
| Keys. Each | 3.00 |

Ladles:
3½" bowl, 15" handle _____ 18.50
5½" bowl, 14" iron handle.
Marked "F. B. Co., Canton, Ohio.
Pat. Jan 20, '88 _____ 25.00
Lamp, Hanging. Store-type with
brass shade _____ 75.00
Lock and Key. Old _____ 25.00
Milk Pan. 16" diam. _____ 32.50
Mortar and Pestle. 3½" high.
Polished _____ 24.50
Mortar and Pestle. 4" mortar ____ 25.00
Mortar and Pestle. 5" mortar ____ 27.50

Mortar and Pestle. 5" high _____ $32.50

Mustache Curling Iron. With alcohol burner. Repousse' decor on
handle and stand _____ 20.00
Nutcracker. 7½" long, in form of
alligator _____ 6.75
Oil Can. 11" spout _____ 10.00
Pails:
15" diam. _____ 36.00
18½" diam., 12" high. Iron bail__ 45.00
Pan, Warming. Pierced top _____ 55.00
Pancake Turner. Long fancy iron

handle _____ 10.00
Paperweight. 5". Dragon _____ 12.50
Plaques:
23" diam., Jeanne Seymour ____ 36.50
24" diam., tavern scene in cen-
ter, ornate border _____ 39.50
22x24", William Shakespeare bust
in high relief. 22x24" inlaid and
brass ornamented ebony frame.
29x32" outside frame _____ 69.50
Pot Hanger. With adjustable saw-
tooth ratchet _____ 57.50
Powder Horns:
American Eagle, small _____ 40.00
Fleur-de-lis, embossed _____ 30.00
Petal design _____ 27.50
Roasting Jack. Clockwork _____ 45.00
Samovars:
Russian, with burner, large _____ 100.00
13" high, with burner _____ 89.50
Scale. Fairbanks, #1602, 5½" high,
brass scoop, original paint ____ 32.50
Scoops:
Candy, small _____ 9.00
Scale, small _____ 10.00
Scale, medium _____ 15.00
Scale, large _____ 21.00
5½x3", with 3" handle _____ 11.00
8¾x5¼", with 3¾" handle _____ 14.00
11x7", with 4½" handle _____ 16.00
Sugar _____ 18.50
Scuttle. Hammered, large bail and
ornate handle _____ 90.00
Sewing Bird _____ 12.50
Skimmer. 7¾" diam. _____ 25.00
Slide Bolt. Embossed decor, old __ 9.00
Steamboat Whistle. 10½" high,
small size _____ 40.00
Stove, Hand-warming. Portable,
charcoal burning _____ 28.50
Sundial. 8½" diam., octagonal, old 72.50
Tea Caddy. 5½" high. 6-sided ___ 22.50
Teakettle. Amber handle, button
feet _____ 55.00
Teakettle, Miniature _____ 12.50
Tie Backs:
English Victorian, with white
Bristol morning glories extend-
ing from top. Pair _____ 29.50
French Victorian. Arm-type.
Pair _____ 20.00
Trays:
8¾" diam., for decanter _____ 12.00
12" diam., heavy, round _____ 32.00
14x21", open handles, light ____ 38.50
Trivet. Fox and Tree. Footed ____ 30.00
Umbrella Holder _____ 18.00
Umbrella Stand. Lion Ring handles 25.00
Urns. 16" high, ornate. Pair _____ 80.00
Wall Sconces:
Single candle, dolphin top,
mirror _____ 40.00
Lyre-shaped. 3-branch candle
holders with drip cups. Pair __ 135.00

With mirror, 8x23", 3 candle
holders. Pair _____ 150.00
Weather Vane Arrow. 23" long, filigree brass and cranberry glass
with owner's name in shank_____ 85.00

## BREAD PLATES

A special plate made for the serving
of biscuits, bread or rolls. Most of the
earlier ones are of the Pattern Glass variety, while some are made of china and
metal.

Railroad. Clear glass _____ $29.50

— Clear Glass Patterns —

Actress. "Pinafor." 7x11¼", oval __$ 22.00
Barley _____ 20.00
Beaded Band _____ 9.50
Beehive, Iowa City _____ 50.00
Bunker Hill Monument _____ 28.50
Clear Diagonal Band _____ 11.00
Clear Ribbon _____ 10.00
Coin, U. S. Dollar decoration ____ 175.00
Coin, U. S. ½ Dollar decoration __ 160.00
Constitution Platter _____ 25.00
Coronation. Geo. VI and Elizabeth__ 12.50
Cupid & Venus _____ 16.00
Dog Cart _____ 25.00
Egg-in-Sand _____ 11.00
Egyptian. Cleopatra _____ 16.50
Egyptian. Salt Lake Temple _____ 22.00
Faith, Hope & Charity _____ 22.50
Flower Pot _____ 16.50
Frosted Stork _____ 18.25
Garfield Memorial. 11" _____ 15.50
"Give Us This Day, Etc." Wheat
  center _____ 17.00
Grant, Genl., Patriot & Soldier ___ 20.00
Heroes of Bunker Hill _____ 28.50
*Horseshoe. Single handle _____ 22.50
*Horseshoe. Double handle _____ 27.50
Jewel with Dewdrop _____ 11.00
*Last Supper (common) _____ 9.00

Lattice. Oblong _____ 12.50
Liberty Bell. 7x11½" _____ 24.00
Liberty Bell. 9¼x13" _____ 27.50
Lion _____ 35.75
Little Miss Muffet _____ 22.50
Little Red Riding Hood _____ 24.00
Loop with Dewdrops _____ 12.25
Lotus. "Give Us This Day, Etc." __ 12.75
McCormick Reaper _____ 42.50
McKinley. Clear glass. "It Is God's
  Way. His Will Be Done" _____ 14.50
Minerva _____ 20.00
Mitchell, John. Scarce _____ 42.50
Moon & Star _____ 23.75
Old Statehouse _____ 35.00
Panelled Daisy _____ 18.25
Panelled Dewdrop. Oblong, handled 18.25
Panelled Dewdrop. Oval _____ 13.25
Pleat & Panel _____ 18.25
Polar Bear. Oval, handled, 16½"__ 46.50
Presidents Platter _____ 24.50
Queen Victoria _____ 24.50
Railroad _____ 29.50
Ribbon. Oblong, cut corners _____ 35.50
Roman Rosette _____ 20.00
Saxon. Oval, 12" _____ 12.75
Shell & Tassel. Oblong, small ____ 17.75
Sheraton _____ 8.25
Sprig _____ 14.00
Star Rosetted. "A Good Mother,
  Etc." _____ 16.50
Teddy Bear. (Theo. Roosevelt).
  Frosted _____ 40.00
Three Graces _____ 16.50
Tree of Life _____ 22.50
Viking _____ 11.00
Washington. Frosted center, "First
  in War, Etc." _____ 27.50
Westward-Ho. Oval _____ 42.50

*Reproduced item
— Colored Glass Patterns —

Beaded Grape
  Clear _____ 21.50
  Green _____ 35.00
Caramel Slag _____ 85.00
Centennial
  Clear _____ 20.00
  Blue _____ 30.00
  Green _____ 32.50
  Vaseline _____ 26.50
Daisy & Button. Oval, handled.
  Clear _____ 12.00
  Amber _____ 19.75
  Apple Green _____ 24.00
  Blue _____ 21.75
  Vaseline _____ 19.75
Deer and Pine Tree
  Blue, 8x13" _____ 27.00
  Clear, 8x13" _____ 18.25
  Clear, 9x15" _____ 31.00
Fine Cut
  Clear _____ 10.25
  Blue _____ 19.75
  Vaseline _____ 18.00

**Fine Cut & Panel**
| | |
|---|---|
| Clear | 12.50 |
| Amber | 18.00 |
| Blue | 21.75 |
| Yellow | 18.00 |

**Hobnail, Fan Top**
| | |
|---|---|
| Clear | 22.50 |
| Amber | 29.00 |
| Blue | 33.00 |

**Hobnail, Opalescent**
| | |
|---|---|
| Blue | 38.50 |
| Yellow | 47.00 |
| | 60.00 |

**Hobnail, Pointed**
| | |
|---|---|
| Clear, 7x4½'' | 13.75 |
| Amber | 19.25 |
| Blue | 21.00 |
| Light Green | 23.75 |

**Liberty Bell. Milk Glass, with**
| | |
|---|---|
| John Hancock's signature | 95.00 |
| Without signature | 70.00 |

**Maple Leaf**
| | |
|---|---|
| Clear | 15.00 |
| Amber | 24.00 |
| Blue | 27.00 |
| Frosted | 19.75 |
| Green | 29.00 |
| Vaseline | 24.00 |

**Panelled Forget-Me-Not**
| | |
|---|---|
| Clear | 12.50 |
| Amber | 17.00 |
| Blue | 21.75 |
| Yellow | 17.00 |

**Primrose**
| | |
|---|---|
| Clear | 13.75 |
| Amber | 22.25 |
| Blue | 24.00 |
| Vaseline | 22.25 |

**Purple Slag** | 75.00

**Rose Sprig**
| | |
|---|---|
| Clear | 11.50 |
| Amber | 17.50 |
| Blue | 22.25 |
| Yellow | 17.50 |

**Swirl**
| | |
|---|---|
| Clear | 13.75 |
| Amber | 19.75 |
| Blue | 22.50 |
| Yellow | 19.75 |

**Thousand Eye**
| | |
|---|---|
| Clear. Oblong. 8x11'' | 17.50 |
| Amber | 23.50 |
| Apple Green | 28.50 |
| Blue | 25.75 |
| Vaseline | 23.50 |

**Two Panel**
| | |
|---|---|
| Clear | 11.50 |
| Amber | 17.50 |
| Blue | 20.00 |
| Green | 22.50 |
| Yellow | 17.50 |

**Wildflower**
| | |
|---|---|
| Clear. Oblong. 10'' | 12.75 |
| Amber | 19.25 |
| Blue | 21.75 |
| Green | 24.00 |
| Yellow | 19.25 |

**Willow Oak**
| | |
|---|---|
| Clear. Oblong | 14.00 |
| Amber | 17.00 |
| Blue | 18.00 |

## BRIDE'S BASKETS

"Bride's Baskets" derive their name from the fact that in the period of 1895-1910 many were presented as wedding presents. The majority consisted of ruffled-edge dishes in blue or cranberry colored glass held in a handled silver-plated frame. Occasionally a basket with a glass handle is seen on the market.

White Satin Glass with hobnail pattern. Pale blue rim. Silver plated holder. 11'' to top of frame ____ $145.00

Amber. 6'' high. 4x4¾'', ruffled, oval. No holder _____$ 75.00
Blue. Ruffled Satin Glass bowl in ornate plated holder _____ 125.00
Blue. 7'' high, clear applied ruffled edge. No holder _____ 60.00
Cranberry shading to pink. 13'' diam. Gold enameling. No frame_ 150.00
Cranberry to white. Hobnail pattern. Silver plated frame _____ 175.00
Cranberry. Shading to white with enamel decor and red overlay__ 150.00
Old Rose. 9½'', acorn-type silver holder, marked "Pairpoint" ___ 100.00
Pigeon Blood Satin. 9¾'' diam., white enamel flowers. Frame resilvered _____ 115.00
Pink. Ruffled with white overlay

on outside. In silver plated
holder _____ 115.00
Pink. White lining and ruffled
cranberry edge. In resilvered
footed holder consisting of 3
birds _____ 110.00
Pink. 4½" diam., 7½" high. Tan,
dark red and blue spatter with
white lining and deep ruffled
edge _____ 100.00
Rose. Interior, rose with applied
clear edge, white exterior. Ruffled, in silver plated frame ____ 100.00
Vasa Murrhina. Tan with gold flecks,
oval. In plated holder _____ 125.00
White. 5½" diam., with yellow lining and gold flecks, ruffled
edge. Frame needs resilvering__ 55.00
White. Light tan lining and ruffled
edge. No holder _____ 50.00

### BRISTOL GLASS

Bristol Glass is the product of several
glass houses in Bristol, England, which became a glass center in the middle 1700's.
Much of the so-called Early American
glass ascribed to Amelung Glass Co., and
other glass houses in this country was made
in Bristol. The importation of this glass
hastened the failure of the Amelung and
Stiegel glass houses.
The majority of Bristol glass encountered
in antique shops today is in the form of
vases of the late Victorian period.

Vase. Pink background with floral
decor. Pair _____ $55.00

Bowl, Punch. Covered, enameled
floral and gold decor _____$ 95.00

Carafe with Tumbler _____ 40.00
Cookie Jar. Light blue shading to
white, painted cherries. Resilvered top _____ 54.50
Decanter. 7¾" high. Bird decoration in gold with blue. Orange
flashed top. Pair _____ 55.00
Dish. Large, rectangular _____ 30.00
Dresser Set. Pair of 10" bottles
and covered powder jar _____ 70.00
Hand. Holding vase. Fluted top,
soft green, gilt decor _____ 30.00
Lamp. 6¼" base diam., 8" globe
shade _____ 75.00
Lamp, Fairy. Blue, swirled, enameled flowers _____ 95.00
Mugs:
Ale. Covered, 8¼" high. Blue with
gold decor, star cut bottom,
applied handle _____ 28.50
3¼", flower decor, applied
handle. "Remember Me" _____ 22.50
Patch Box. Hinged cover, enamel
decor _____ 42.50
Pitcher. 5½" high. Smoky gray with
blue handle and gold decoration_ 50.00
Plate. 12" diam., hand-painted____ 40.00
Potpourri. Cream, rose and gold
decor _____ 36.50
Powder Box. 3½" high. Heavy dark
blue glass. Lid decorated with
playing children _____ 49.50
Ring Tree. 3" high. Blue decorated
in bright gold _____ 30.00
Shades. 14" diam., for hanging
lamp:
Red Rose decor _____ 45.00
Spray of purple Morning Glories 39.50
Smoke Bell. 7" high. Applied ruby
ring. Self-ring at top, original
brass chain _____ 12.75
Vases:
English. 8½" high. Opaque with
fired enamel decoration. Pair __ 46.50
Small, blue with enameled flower
decor _____ 26.50
6½" high. Frosted custard with
flying ducks. Pair _____ 60.00
7" high. White with enamel decorations _____ 30.00
8" high. Fire glow-type with stick
neck 1" diam. Hand-painted
flowers, leaves and stems _____ 32.00
Jack-in-the-Pulpit. White with red
fluted top edge _____ 37.50
10½" high. "The Gleaners" transfer on side _____ 22.50
12" high. Opaque white glass,
satin finish, gold colored enamel
decorations _____ 55.00
15" high. White ground, orange
flowers, green leaves outlined in
gold _____ 72.50
24" high. Blue glass with white

casing. Multicolored flowers and
gold leaf decor _____ 70.00
Hand. Pink band of enameled
flowers below fluted top. Pair __ 59.50
Wall Plaque. 9½'' diam. _____ 20.00

## BRONZE FIGURINES

### Animals:

Alligator. Bottle Opener. 6'' long __$ 6.50
Bear. On marble ball, marble base.
6¾'' high _____ 115.00
Bird. Signed Pautrot, 5'' high, 7''
long _____ _____ 175.00
Bird. Holding fish in beak. Signed
DeLabrierre. 5'' high, 6½'' long_ 175.00
Birds. Battling, 12'' high, 9¼'' long_
Signed DeLabrierre _____ 365.00
Birds. Pair on tree stump. 5'' high.
Signed ''L. Carvin'', plus plate
''Le Bengali, 23 Aout 1906''; also
Hallmark of Factory _____ 125.00
Bisons. Battling, 25'' long, signed
Tiffland _____ 475.00
Bisons. Pair, 12'' long, unsigned __ 325.00
Bull. 13''. Signed Rosa B (Rosa
Bonheur) _____ 500.00
Camel. 9'' high, 10'' long _____ 135.00
Camel. Lying with folded legs, 2¾''
long, 1¾'' high ____ _____ 25.00
Cow. 6'' long. Signed I. Bonheur __ 235.00
Dog. 5'' high, 8½'' long, signed
Moigniez _____ 250.00
Dog. 8'' high, 12'' long, signed Mene 300.00
Dog. 9'' high, 10'' long, signed
Pautrot _____ 300.00
Dog. 10'' high, chained to fence.
Sgd. Vallon _____ 325.00
Dog. On figural carpet. Signed
Barye _____ 150.00
Dog. Dachshund, 5¼'' high, 10'' long.
Signed _____ 110.00
Dog. Greyhound, 8'' high, 11'' long
Signed P. J. Mene _____ 210.00
Dog. Manchester, With ball on figur-
al carpet. Signed P. J. Mene ____ 135.00
Dog. Setter. 5¾'' high. Signed.
P. J. Mene _____ 150.00
Dog. Setter, 12'' long, signed Mene 275.00
Duck's Head Paper Clip. Paper-
weight eyes _____ 20.00
Horse. Standing, 10'' long, signed
Vallon _____ 350.00
Leopard. Stalking, 4½'' high, 12''
long _____ 75.00
Lion. Striding, 5¾'' high, 9¼'' long __ 75.00
Panther. 7¾'' long, 4½'' high. Self-
base, signed Barye _____ 150.00
Panther. Crouching, 17'' long, signed
L. Bureau _____ 110.00
Panther. Reclining and looking at 2
bear cubs. Signed ''E. Fremiet''
''F. Barbedienne Founder. Paris,
France.'' 6½'' high, 13'' long ____ 215.00

Partridge. 10'' high, 10½'' long.
Signed Moigniez_____ 350.00
Pheasant. 9'' high, 5½'' long. Signed
Pautrot _____ 185.00
Pheasant. 13'' high, 9¼'' long. Signed
''F. Pautrot.'' _____ 200.00
Rabbit. Vienna, 3'' high, 9¼'' long.
Full figure in running position,
on wood pedestal base. Front feet
have spring to act as letter holder 75.00
Salamander. Paperweight. 3½'' long 10.00
Seal. On rocks, 5'' high. Signed ''E.
Angela 1917'', Gorham & Co.
founder. Hallmark _____ 85.00
Suckling Kid and Goat. 8½'' high,
8'' long, signed Parmentier _____ 250.00
Tiger. On marble base, 5½'' high,
6¾'' long _____ 50.00

### Miscellaneous:

Lamp. Desk, Tiffany. Signs of Zodiac
on shade and base _____$250.00
Panel, Wall. 17½'' long, 4½'' wide.
Raised figure of woman in flowing
robe with pitcher. Ring for hanging. Sgd. ''F. Barbedienne.'' ____ 110.00
Planter, Architectural Round. 6½''
wide, with Roman soldiers mounted. Sgd. ''W. Henning 1817 &
1819.'' _____ 35.00
Plaque, French. 12'' high, 10¾''
wide. Shepherd, shepherdess,
sheep. _____ 75.00
Receptacle, Open. Oval. 8½'' high,
with girl reaching in to feed
kittens. Signed _____ 45.00
Vases:
5¼''. Fully molded cherubs crawl-
ing around shoulder of vase.
Dragonfly on one; 2 butterflies
on other. Pair _____ 45.00
8'' high, 2½'' diam. base. Two
heads of women at rim. Pair ____ 45.00
15'' high. Series of leaves form
fountain with grotesque head with
open mouth pouring water. Plate
reads ''Les Curieuses.'' Sgd. ''C.
Kauba—4890—Geschutz'' _____ 330.00

### Statues:

Arab. On camel, 5'' high, 5'' long_$ 85.00
Arab. On carpet praying, 5'' high,
6'' long _____ 65.00
Arab. Sitting on magic carpet,
partial cover for bronze box. 8''
long _____ 95.00
Arab. Smoking pipe, 3'' high _____ 40.00
Arab. With vending stand, 7'' high,
5½'' long _____ 105.00
Arab. Boy, With cigarette in hand,
standing on carpet, 2¾'' high, 2''
wide, 2½'' long _____ 50.00

Boy. Dutch. Seated with hands in
pockets, looking at ivory button,
3" high, 4" long _____ 50.00
Boy. Page. With plume, buckle shoes,
flowing garments on bronze base.
4½" high _____ 35.00
Boy. Holding dog on log (match-
holder) 5¾" high _____ 45.00
Boy. With jacket, knickers, button
shoes, straw hat, school bag,
picnic basket. 14¼" high. Sgd.
Bouret. Plaque reads: "Recreation
Par Bouret. Mention Au Salon." __ 110.00
Boy. With 2 pigs under arms,
3½" high _____ 35.00
Bust of man on marble column, 10"
high _____ 95.00
Bust of Victorian Lady. Sgd.
"Barthoz", 6¼" high _____ 50.00
Dore and ivory Bachnallian, brown
marble base. French artist
"Somme", 13" _____ 275.00
Four figures. Man, woman, 2 child-
ren; one child on man's back,
other playing tambourine. 10"
high, 12" long. Sgd. "Claudion" 400.00
Girl, Dutch. Bonnet, wooden shoes
on marble base. 5" high. Sgd.
"Keck" _____ 35.00
Girl. With skates. 3¼" high. Marble
cyl. base. Sgd. "H. Keck" _____ 35.00
Lady. Flowing garments, seated on
bench admiring vase in hand while
torch burns beside her. Two-toned
marble base. 12½x9x12". Sgd.
"Moreau" _____ 350.00
Mercury. 41" high. Signed "Barbedienne" _____ 300.00
"The Race". Four race horses with
riders jumping over hurdle. 7"
high, 8" long. By Boyer _____ 850.00
Raphael. 13¼" high. Fine detail,
signed "Duchoieselle" _____ 195.00
Russian Cossack. On horse, 8" high,
6" long _____ 750.00
Statue of Liberty. 4½ feet tall,
outstretched arms hold 2 3-arm
electric torches. Signed _____ 495.00
Venus. Crouching. 21x13". Superb
quality, casting by artist. Sgd. __ 550.00
Woman. Nude with wings, in flowing
garment, seated on marble ball.
4½" high _____ 50.00
Woman. Seated. 2" high. Sgd. CA 10.00
Woman and Child, satyr, 18" high,
Sgd. "Clodion" _____ 450.00

## BUFFALO POTTERY

Information regarding the beginning of
Buffalo Pottery, Buffalo, N. Y., is rather
sketchy. It is believed that the establishment commenced business about 1903 or
1904. The company made a series of quart
jugs in a variety of shapes— some were tall

and graceful, others in quaint Dutch shapes.
The decorations were underglaze in hand-
tinted colors. The subjects were from history
and literature and included John Paul Jones,
Robin Hood, Dutch and Pilgrim Jugs.

In 1908, the company started marketing
Deldare Ware. It has a rich olive-green
body. The underglaze decorations were in
three styles: Old English, Indian Camping
Scenes and Hunting Scenes. The firm also
issued a series of Commemorative plates
depicting various scenes of historic interest.

Placque, Hanging. 12" diam. Pastoral scene _____ $60.00

Bowls:
8" diam. "Dr. Syntax-His Tour."
Deldare _____$140.00
9"diam. "Ye Village Tavern."
Deldare _____ 100.00
Butter Dish. Covered, Deldare ____ 115.00
Butter Pat. Blue willow design _____2.25
Candlesticks. 9" high, Colonial
figures. Deldare. Pair _____ 145.00
Cups and Saucers:
"Fallowfield Hunt." 1909,
Deldare _____ 80.00
"Ye olde Days." 1908, Deldare__ 75.00
Dish, Vegetable. Covered, gold band
decor _____ 17.50
Gravy Boat. LaFrancerose _____ 12.00
Hair Receiver. Covered _____ 65.00
Jardiniere. 6" high, 8" diam. Dated
1908. Deldare _____ 80.00
Mugs:
"Fallowfield Hunt." 1909 2⅜"
high _____ 85.00
"Ye Lion Inn." 4½", open. Del-
dare _____ 75.00

**BUFFALO POTTERY**

TOP, LEFT: Milk Pitcher. Deldare, 6" high. "Return with a Curtsy" __$135.00. TOP, CENTER: Bowl. Deldare, 9½" diam. "Fallowfield Hunt," 1908__$195.00. BOTTOM, LEFT: Mug. Deldare, 1909, 4½" high__$75.00. BOTTOM, CENTER: Tray. Deldare. 13¾x10¼". "Heirlooming"__$175.00. EXTREME RIGHT: Vase. Deldare, 13¼" high. Cylindrical, signed__$150.00.

| | | |
|---|---|---|
| **Pitchers:** | | |
| 7" high. Geo. Washington, blue and gold decor, helmet-shaped, dated 1907 | 77.50 | |
| 8" high. English scene, dated 1908. Deldare | 195.00 | |
| 9" high. Miles Standish.Deldare | 180.00 | |
| 9½" high. John Paul Jones. Dated 1908. Deldare | 210.00 | |
| Milk. Cinderella and Coach. 1909 | 95.00 | |
| **Plates:** | | |
| 6" diam. | 14.00 | |
| Calendar. 1910. Deldare | 80.00 | |
| Child's. Boy bringing candy to girl who has fallen | 16.50 | |
| 7¼" diam. "Dr. Syntax Soliloquising." Deldare | 110.00 | |
| 7¼" diam. "The Fallowfield Hunt." Breaking cover. Deldare | 75.00 | |
| 8½" diam. "Fallowfield Hunt." 1909. Deldare | 67.50 | |
| 8½" diam. "Ye Town Crier" 1908. Deldare | 67.50 | |
| 9½" diam. Tan, brown and red, dated 1912. (Abino Ware) | 21.50 | |
| 10" diam. Commemorative Series with bluish-green decoration: | | |
| Faneuill Hall | 12.75 | |
| Independence Hall | 12.75 | |
| Niagara Falls | 12.00 | |
| The White House | 12.00 | |
| U. S. Capitol | 12.00 | |
| "Ye Lion Inn." 13½" diam. hanging type. Deldare | 165.00 | |
| 14" diam. "Fallowfield Hunt." Deldare | 175.00 | |
| Powder Jar. Covered. Not Deldare | 15.00 | |
| Sugar Bowl. Deldare | 110.00 | |

174

Plate. 10" diam. Deldare Emerald
Ware. "Dr. Syntax Making a Discovery" _____ **$125.00**

Sugar Bowl and Creamer _____  37.50
Tankard. 12½" high. "The great
controversy," and "All you have
to do to teach the Dutchmen
English." Deldare _____  160.00
Tiles:
  "Fallowfield Hunt." 18½x25". Full-
  cry & Death. Oak frames. Pair   75.00
  "Traveling old Days." Deldare __  50.00
Tobacco Humidor. "The Inn." 7"
high. Deldare _____  150.00
Tobacco Jar. Large. (Not Deldare)  42.50
Trivet. Blue and white, willow de-
sign.Dated 1911 _____   7.50
Vase. 13½" high, cylindrical shape.
  Pastoral scene. Deldare _____  120.00

### BURMESE GLASS

Burmese Glass is an Art Glass which
originated and was manufactured by the
Mt. Washington Glass Co., New Bedford,
Mass., for a period of 5 or 6 years. It
was discovered by chance when Fred Shir-
ley, the new manager of the plant, was
making a small pot of Ruby Glass. He
added gold, which gives the coloring, but
the metal sank quickly to the bottom without mixing with the glass. He then added a
quantity of Uranium Oxide, which was used
in making canary yellow glass. (Uranium
Oxide is now the chief source of Uranium
for bombs and atomic power). The reaction
of the gold, when the item was reheated,
produced a soft canary yellow which shaded
to flesh pink. The blending of the colors was
so gradual that it was difficult to determine where one color ended and the other
began.

Although some of the glass has a surface
that is glazed, or glossy, most of it has
a smooth plush (satin) finish. The majority
of items has no pattern, but some have
either a ribbed, hobnail or diamond quilted
design. The pontil mark was often hidden
by a "berry-shaped" piece of glass which
was an added means of identification.

The glass was patented and the only
other factory licensed to make it was Thos.
Webb & Sons in England. It was first known
by the name of "Bermise," but was later
changed to "Burmese." The majority of
items produced was tableware, plates, cups
and saucers, pitchers of various sizes— including creamers and syrup jugs—berry
bowls, salt and pepper shakers, sauces,
cruets and a variety of different sized vases.

Pitcher. Water, acid finish _____ **$795.00**

Bell. 6", glossy-type with pale amber
  reeded loops. Crimped edge ____**$220.00**
Bobeches. 3¼" diam., glossy fin-
  ish. Pair _____  95.00
Bowls:
  Finger. 2¾" high. Salmon pink
  more than one-half way down __ 235.00
  7" diam., applied yellow feet
  and edging _____ 525.00
10" diam., reeded feet, berry
  pontil _____ 750.00
Candlestick. Diamond quilted, on

4 feet _____ 295.00
Condiment Sets:
3-piece. Salt, pepper and mustard
in silver frame _____ 425.00
4-piece. Covered mustard jar,
salt, pepper and cruet in silver
frame _____ 600.00
Creamers:
4¾'' high, reeded handle _____ 300.00
5½'' high, crimped top _____ 350.00
Cruet. Acid finish _____ 500.00
Cups:
Custard _____ 150.00
Punch _____ 135.00
Cup and Saucer _____ 400.00
Cup and Saucer. Demitasse _____ 350.00
Epergne. 26'' high, large ruffled
bottom bowl 15'' diam., center
bowl 10'' diam., third bowl 7''
diam. _____ 950.00
Ewer. 13'' high, salmon-pink shad-
ing to bright yellow, applied
yellow handle _____ 700.00
Finger Bowl. Scalloped _____ 220.00
Lamp, Fairy. Complete, with brass
Clarke holder, 4 bud vases and
large shade. Fine coloring _____ 600.00
Lemonade Glass. Diamond quilted,
glossy finish _____ 200.00
Mustard Pot. 3½'' high, ribbed,
dull finish _____ 195.00
Perfume Bottle _____ 275.00
Pitcher _____ 795.00
Pitcher. Water. Acid finish _____ 795.00
Plates:
5'', slant rim _____ 185.00
6'', glossy finish _____ 215.00
8'', glossy finish _____ 260.00
11⅞'', blue harebells _____ 320.00
Rose Bowls:
2¼'' high. Body decorated with
polychrome acorns and leaves.
Salmon pink half-way down ____ 325.00
6½'' high, 5'' diam., acid finish.
Footed, berry pontil _____ 450.00
Salt and Pepper Shakers. Ribbed
yellow bottom shading to peach
at the top. Pair _____ 215.00
Sauce Dish. 4'' diam. _____ 100.00
Shades:
2'' opening, 6'' flare _____ 210.00
4½'' oening, ruffled _____ 235.00
Sherbet. Footed _____ 300.00
Sugar Bowls:
3½'' high, glossy finish _____ 350.00
5½'' high, crimped top _____ 400.00
Sugar Shaker. Pewter top _____ 310.00
Syrup Jug _____ 475.00
Toothpick Holder. Petal top, tri-
cornered, acid finish _____ 220.00
Tumblers:
D. Q. Salmon pink extending half-
way down _____ 225.00
3¾'', opaque green (See Revi,
P. 59). Agata-type staining.

Scarce _____ 300.00
Lemonade. Diamond quilted, handled, glossy finish _____ 200.00
Lemonade. Diamond quilted, small,
acid finish _____ 220.00
Vases:
4'' high. "Webb" _____ 350.00
6⅛'' high. "Webb", stick-neck,
tapering to 4-sided dimpled-base 400.00
8'' high. Jack-in-pulpit. Glossy,
pink rim at top, yellow below __ 750.00
9½'' high. Scalloped top, bulbous
base. Mt. Washington _____ 475.00
10'' high. Lily, 3½'' base diam.,
4'' top diam. Acid finish _____ 375.00
10¼''high. Lily. 6'' widest diam.,
acid finish. Signed "Webb." Pair 700.00
11¾'' high. Acid finish. Pair _____ 800.00
12'' high. Lily, acid finish. Pair 900.00
12'' high. 6½'' widest diam.
Gourd-shaped with allover decoration of gold leaves _____ 525.00
16'' high. Mt. Washington. Lily
top _____ 500.00
23'' high. Trumpet-shaped, satin
finish _____ 575.00
Whiskey Glass. Mt. Washington,
light salmon to canary _____ 225.00
Wine _____ 320.00

## BUTTER MOLDS

These items are usually made of wood
and are commonly known as butter print-
ers. They are round, square or rectangular
in shape and consist of 2 parts—the frame
and a plunger with a hollowcut pattern,
for impressing a design on the butter.
Their main purpose is to shape the butter
into a form for packaging, as well as to
produce a design which will be appealing
to the buyer.

Wood. Pineapple design. Refinished _____ $15.00

176

Clear Glass. Wood handle ______$ 10.00
Cloverleaf Design. Oblong ________ 8.75
Eagle and Shield. 3¼" diam. Eagle carved handle, maple __________ 50.00
Fern Design. Oblong ____________ 10.50
Fern Leaf Pattern. 4½"diam. ______ 8.50
Leaf Design. Round, large ________ 9.00
Letter "L". Oblong wood frame __ 7.50
Letter "W". Round wood frame __ 7.50
Pineapple Design. Large ________ 7.50
Round. 1 pound size with geometric design. Maple ______________ 15.00
Swan. 1 pound. Plunger-type. Maple 25.00

## CALENDAR PLATES

China Calendar Plates in America cover roughly the period from 1906 to 1929, with the years 1909 through 1912 being the time of greatest popularity. It is believed that they had their origin in England about 1880.

1955. 10" diam. Windmill scene, gold decor on white ground ____ $4.00

1907. Tin, girl's head ___________ 7.50
1907. 9¼" diam. Santa and Holly, calendar center_____________ 9.50
1909. 7½" diam. Calendar border fruit center_________________ 9.00
1909. 8⅜" diam. Calendar in border with small flowers and scenes, spread eagle holding scroll center _______________ 9.50
1909. 9" diam. Pink Rose center Calendar around border____ 9.75
1909. 9⅛" diam. Santa on sleigh. Whip in hand, 4 reindeer. Scarce ____________________ 25.00
1909. 9¼" diam. Gold calendar in center with 3 roses and bud border ____________________ 9.00
1910. 7½" diam. Bright holly with gold trim__________________ 9.50
1910. 8" diam. Lighthouse center, Happy New Year on bottom 9.00
1910. 8½" diam. Betsy Ross making first flag__________________ 12.50
1910. 9" diam. Horseshoe-shaped calendar and fishing scene center ____________________ 9.75
1910. Niagara Falls and Horseshoe 9.00
1911. "Kiss and Make Up"______ 10.00
1911. 9" diam. Red roses and cupid border, fruit center.__ 9.25
1911-12. 8¾" diam. 1911 calendar with rising sun center. 1912 calendar with red flowers in border ____________________ 9.25
1912. 8" diam. Calendar and airplane scene in center________ 11.00
1912. 8¾" diam. Airplane decoration ______________________ 11.00
1912. 9½" diam President Lincoln, Garfield and McKinley______ 12.50
1913. 8¾" diam. Calendar and pink decorations in border; house and rural scene in center__ 9.00
1914. 8" diam. Betsy Ross center 9.50
1914. 9¾" diam. Washington's Tomb 7.50
1915. 7¼" diam. Map of Panama Canal crossed with flags ___ 12.00
1915. 8½" diam. Calendar with map of Panama Canal, U. S. flag, blue and gold trim______ 11.00
1916. 9½" diam. Calendar and birds in center, floral border ______________________ 9.75
1918. 9" diam. Calendar and 4 birds in border, 2 deer, trees and stream in center 10.00
1919. 8¾" diam. Calendar and pink flowers in border with flags of Belgium, France. England and U. S. in border, large U. S. flag in center_______ 11.00
1921. 8½" diam. Calendar with bluebirds and pink flowers in borders, U. S. flag in center ______________________ 9.00
1923. 8½" diam. Calendar with blue, yellow and red flowers at top, trees and stream in center __________________ 8.75

## CAMBRIDGE GLASS

The Cambridge Glass Co., Cambridge, Ohio, started manufacturing colored glass items in the 1920s. Among the wares which are now popular with collectors are such colors as Azurite, Light Blue, Ivory, Helio, Primrose, Violet, Jade, Carmen and Ruby.

The factory, in its earlier years produced pressed tablewares in crystal. In 1958, the plant closed and the molds sold to Imperial Glass Co., Bellaire, Ohio.

Bookends. Black Scottie dogs. 5''
   base. 7'' high. Pair _____$ 55.00
Bowl. Shallow. 13'' diam. Purple
   opaque _____ 45.00
Candy Dish. Three sections. Dianthis
   pink _____ 15.00
Cigarette Box. Crown Tuscan. Dol-
   phin feet. Two trays are tiny
   three-footed shells. Mint _____ 40.00
Compote. 8½''. Nude lady. Base and
lady are clear. 6½'' cupped bowl is
   royal blue. Mint _____ 50.00
Compote. 8½''. Nude lady. Base and
lady are clear. 6½'' cupped bowl
   is etched with gold flowers.
   Mint _____ 45.00
Dish. Covered. 7'' diam. Three-
   footed. Amber _____ 15.00
Opaques:
   Bowl. Rubina Verde' Ram's Head
   with Column Candlesticks _____ 125.00
   Bud Vases. Crown Tuscan. 10''.
   Pair _____ 30.00
   Console Bowl. 11''. Azurite blue_ 45.00
   Mayonnaise Dish with Ladle.
   Footed. Ivory _____ 40.00
   Pin or Powder Box. Covered.
   Primrose _____ 35.00
   Vases. Large Everglades. Violet.
   Pair _____ 60.00
Pitcher. Crystal. Heavy cut glass__ 50.00
Plate. Bread and butter. 6½'' crys-
   tal. Etched rosepoint _____ 25.00
Swans:
   3½'' Signed:
   Apple Green _____ 10.50
   Black Amethyst _____ 45.00
   Crystal _____ 10.00
   Dianthis Pink _____ 10.50
   Mandarin Gold_____ 10.50
   7'' Signed:
   Dianthis Pink _____ 35.00
   3½'' Unsigned:
   Crown Tuscan _____ 17.50
   Crystal _____ 6.50
   Dianthis Pink _____ 8.50
   Emerald Green _____ 8.50
   Mandarin Gold _____ 8.50
   Milk White _____ 15.00
   Ruby Red _____ 15.00

## CAMEO GLASS

A type of Art Glass which originated in
Alexandria, Egypt, Circa 100-200 A. D.
The oldest and most famous example of
this glass is the original Barberini or Portland Vase which was found near Rome in
1582. It contained the ashes of the late
Emperor Alexander Serverus who was as-
sassinated by his own soldiers in A. D.
235. It was made of dark blue glass with
a layer of opaque glass fused onto the
surface—the design then being cut through
the opaque layer. The Wedgwood Portland
vases are made of pottery instead of glass.

The majority of the Cameo Glass found in
antique shops and collections today was
made in the 1884-1900 period. This later
glass was made on the same principle as the
ancient. A thin shell of glass was prepared
and another color blown into it. A design
was later cut through the outer layer leaving
the inner layer exposed. Cameo Glass is also
known as "Cased Glass."

Vase. 8⅜'' high. Bulbous bottom,
   orange background with green
   forest scene _____ 435.00

Atomizers. Scenic, tan, brown and
   blue. Signed Galle'. Pair _____$ 175.00
Bottles:
   5¼'' high, with stopper. Signed
   Galle _____ 125.00
Perfume. Upright-type, carved
   flowers, yellow casing. Daum-
   Nancy _____ 150.00
Perfume. 4'' high, lavender to
   pink. Daum-Nancy _____ 110.00
Scent. White with red, green and
   gold palm leaves. Hallmarked
   silver mountings. Thomas Webb__ 90.00

**Bowls:**

$4\frac{1}{2}$ diam., 2'' high. Floral carvings. Signed Galle' _____ 325.00

$7\frac{1}{2}$'' diam., 3'' high. Cranberry with conventional white carving. Thomas Webb _____ 485.00

8'' wide, 12'' long. Frosted pink at top. Yellow and orange decor. Sgd Ga'le' _____ 500.00

$8\frac{1}{4}$'' diam., $3\frac{1}{2}$'' high. Pink interior, green exterior, crimped scalloped top. Thomas Webb _____ 525.00

Finger Bowl. Cranberry with vine in white. Signed Webb _____ 375.00

Rose. $3\frac{1}{2}$'' diam., blue and white. Webb _____ 375.00

Rose. $3\frac{1}{2}$'' high, yellow, unsigned_ 300.00

Rose. Purple violets carved on wavy frosted background, gold scallops at rim. Signed ''C. Demis'' _____ 225.00

**Boxes:**

Covered, tri-cornered, gray and rose. Galle' _____ 240.00

Round, covered. Daum-Nancy. Cluster of flowers, leaves, butterflies and dragonfly. Carved over matte finish, white and yellow background. $5\frac{1}{2}$'' diam. _____ 300.00

Compote. Footed, $6\frac{1}{4}$'' diam., 6'' high, 4'' deep. In pastel and deep amethyst. Decorated with floral sprays _____ 275.00

**Goblets:**

Engraved and signed by Joseph Locke _____ 185.00

3'' high, amethyst. Barberry pattern _____ 195.00

**Inkwell.** 4'' high, green, yellow, brown and red. Daum-Nancy ___ 195.00

**Jars:**

6'' high, covered. Light rose and blue. Galle' _____ 240.00

Cookie. Cut apricot florals on frosty ground. $6\frac{1}{2}$'' high. Signed ''Muller'' _____ 240.00

Jam. 4'' high, cranberry with white roses, silver cover and bail. Thomas Webb _____ 260.00

**Lamps:**

Complete with chimney and flint globe. 14'' high. Signed Thomas Webb _____ 495.00

Electrified. Dark red to yellow, with black. Daum-Nancy _____ 465.00

Miniature. Electrified. Signed Daum-Nancy _____ 260.00

Night. 4'' high, bronze feet. Galle' _____ 240.00

Lamp Base. Blue satin, white floral carvings. Webb _____ 310.00

**Pitchers:**

8'' high. Yellow with grapes and leaves in tan and red. Galle' __ 315.00

$11\frac{3}{4}$'' high, $8\frac{1}{4}$'' widest diam. Shades from tortoise-shell coloring and mottling at lip to deep orange at base. Cut from orange to brilliant yellow. Carving of dripping grapes and leaves; honeycomb design around base. Signed ''Le Veni Francois.'' (The accomplishment of Francis.) Applied black amethyst snake handle _____ 485.00

Plate. $7\frac{3}{4}$'' diam., blue morning glories and 4 butterflies on a frosted background, blue edge __ 210.00

Punch Bowl. Red and white. Signed ''Thos. Webb & Sons.'' Rare ___ 2500.00

Salt. $1\frac{7}{8}$x$1\frac{1}{4}$'', summer scene. Signed Daum-Nancy _____ 70.00

Toothpick Holder. Daum-Nancy ___ 87.50

**Tumblers:**

$4\frac{1}{2}$'' high. Mint green with frosted base; mistletoe sprigs with white enamel berries _____ 100.00

Frosty chartreuse and gold; mistletoe sprigs with white enamel berries. Daum-Nancy _____ 120.00

**Vases:**

$1\frac{1}{2}$'' high. Scenic, in pastel colors. Signed Daum-Nancy _____$ 215.00

3'' high. Bulbous, green, maroon, red and white. Scenic ''Summer.'' Daum-Nancy _____ 220.00

$3\frac{1}{2}$'' high. Green with violet decor. Daum-Nancy _____ 260.00

$4\frac{1}{2}$'' high, $3\frac{1}{2}$'' top diam. 3 colors. Galle' _____ 250.00

$4\frac{3}{4}$'' high. Bulbous, frosty with yellow jonquils, burnt orange decor. Galle' _____ 300.00

5'' high. White morning glories, silver band at top. Thos. Webb__ 360.00

$5\frac{1}{2}$'' high. Bulbous, brown satin morning glories, white leaves. Signed Webb _____ 400.00

$5\frac{1}{2}$'' high. Bud vase with carved brown leaves and stems, brass collar. Signed ''Richard'' _____ 275.00

6'' high. Delatte Vase. Decorated with fuchsia flowers on pink background _____ 250.00

7'' high. Square overall scenic design. Signed ''Le Gras'' _____ 265.00

$7\frac{1}{2}$'' high. Daum-Nancy, black vines and leaves. Gold buds on frosted white ground _____ 400.00

$7\frac{3}{4}$'' high. Gold background with dark brown scenic design. Signed ''Richard'' _____ 400.00

$8\frac{1}{2}$'' high. Pedestal base, flared top. Florals in deep wine on mottled peach background. Signed ''La Veni Francois'' _____ 425.00

9'' high. Multicolored. Carved insects overall _____ 200.00

$9\frac{1}{4}$'' high, 2'' base diam. Light to dark amber, large flowers with shaded green applied centers. Signed ''Galle'' _____ 425.00

179

10¼'' high, 3½'' square. Amethyst
flowers on frosted background.
Signed "Val St. Lambert" _____ 360.00
11¾'' high. Applied beetles on
frosty green background. Daum-
Nancy _____ 475.00
12½'' high, 4¾'' diam. Floral design. Signed "Honesdale" _____ 325.00
15'' high. Bulbous bottom, slender
neck. Green wisteria design on
frosty background with pink
shading at base, middle and top.
Unsigned _____ 275.00
16'' high. Signed "Le Gras" ____ 365.00
28½'' high. Leaf pattern, tan and
orchid. Daum-Nancy _____ 500.00

## GALLE' GLASS

Emile Galle', son of a French glassmaker,
established a glass factory at Nancy,
France, in 1884. Through experiments he developed and designed many fine articles of
Cameo Glass. Although much of the glass
bears his signature, he merely made the
original design and his many assistants
and students did the actual work—even to
the signing of his name to the various
products of the factory. He died in 1904.

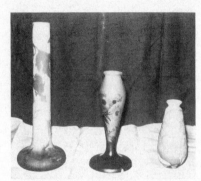

LEFT: Vase. 13½'' high. Bulbous bottom, yellow with red-brown decor.
Signed _____ $275.00
CENTER: Lamp Base. 9¼'' high. Yellow, tri-color. Signed _____ $250.00
RIGHT: Vase. 6¼'' high. Pale shades
of blue, green and beige _____ 265.00

## CAMPAIGN ITEMS

Since the time of the campaign of Wm.
Henry Harrison for President of the United
States in 1840, souvenirs such as buttons,
badges, banners, handkerchiefs, books,
pamphlets and medals have been distrib-
uted during the campaigns to advertise or
win favor for the various candidates.

Vase. 11¾'' high. Signed Galle'.
Frosted yellow ground with
flowers and leaves in red ___ 460.00

Plate. Taft and Sherman. 9½'' diam.
Metal _____ $22.50

Ballot. Republican and Independent ticket for President and Vice-President. Grover Cleveland and Hendricks _____$ 10.00

Bandanna. 23x24''. Roosevelt and Fairbanks. Flags, Eagles and Portraits, framed _____ 75.00

Banner. Harrison and Morton. 22½x24'' _____ 27.50

Buttons:
Cleveland _____ 4.00
Dewey-Warren, 1⅛'' _____ 4.00
Hughes, Chas. E. _____ 9.00
''I Like Ike'' _____ 1.75
McKinley Portrait _____ 9.50
Smith, Al _____ 4.00
Wilkie for President _____ 2.00
Wilkie-McNary _____ 2.00

Buttons, Lapel:
Cleveland _____ 10.00
Stevenson Head. 3 dimension, rubber _____ 11.50

Crock. 10-gallon. Early G. O. P. Elephant underglaze _____ 65.00

Handkerchiefs:
Grover Cleveland & Thurman. Red portraits on silk _____ 20.00
Benjamin Harrison, 1888. Blue cotton, red and white stars and flag _____ 18.50
Thurman. Red portrait on white silk _____ 16.50

Hat. Blaine & Logan, Republican candidates, 1884 _____ 40.00

Lantern, Paper. Abe Lincoln. Red, white and blue with legend, ''Union Forever'' _____ 35.00

Mug. Pottery, Franklin Roosevelt __ 8.00

Music. U. S. Grant is the Man __ 12.00

Plates:
Metal, 9½'' diam. Taft & Sherman in center, ''Standard Bearers of G. O. P. 1856-1908'' on rim ___ 22.50
Milk Glass. Bust of Bryan in center, raised eagle, flags and stars form rim _____ 18.50

Poster. 1894 campaign on wood. Elephant and rooster in color, 9x19'' _____ 40.00

Poster. Portrait of Hoover. 13'' long, diamond-shaped _____ 18.50

Ribbon. Andrew Johnson portrait, for re-election _____ 25.00

Shield. Jefferson Campaign, circa 1802, on canvas. Rare _____ 275.00

Song. Harrison Campaign Song. Large sheet, framed _____ 16.00

Stickpin. McKinley head, metal, gold-colored _____ 20.00

Token. U. S. Grant for Pres. on obverse. For V. Pres. H. Wilson on reverse, hanging from eagle, dated 1872 _____ 29.50

Walking Stick. Silver bust of Cleveland _____ 35.00

## CAMPHOR GLASS

Clear glass, after having been blown or pressed, is treated with Hydrofluoric Acid Vapor. The finished article has a cloudy white appearance similar to gum camphor in lump form.

Bowl, Covered. 4½''. Quilted pattern _____ $5.00

Basket, Glass. Miniature, 4'' high __$ 5.75
Bird Dish. Open _____ 14.50
Bottles:
Perfume. 4'' _____ 7.00
Scotch Whisky _____ 8.50
Boxes:
5¼x5¾x2⅞'' high. Scroll design __ 12.00
Powder. Hinged cover _____ 10.00
Round, hinged, enamel holly spray around bulbous center. 15'' diam. _____ 21.50
Chick and Egg. ''Gillinder'' _____ 27.50
Creamer. Small, wild rose and bowknot decoration _____ 10.00
Dish. 7'' diam., open edge, Fleurde-Lis joined by gold band. Water scene in center _____ 5.00
Duck Dish. Covered (butter) _____ 55.00
Fish Dishes. Covered. Pair _____ 37.50
Hands. Grapes and leaves at wrists 18.50
Hen Dish. Covered. 7'' _____ 24.00
Hen Dish. Covered. 8'' _____ 25.00
Owl. 3½'' high. Standing, with green eyes _____ 9.75
Pin Tray. Blue and silver trim ____ 4.00
Plate. 7¼'', fleur-de-lis pattern____ 10.00
Plate. 7¼'' diam. Owl _____ 11.00
Playing Card Holder. 3¾'' high, on four feet _____ 9.75
Rose Bowl. 4'' diam., hand-painted, blue flowers with gold trim ____ 6.50
Shoe. Marked, made by Libby Glass Co., Toledo, Ohio for 1893 World's Fair _____ 12.50

Tray. 10½x8". Wild rose and bowknot pattern _____ 8.50
Turkey, with removable top. Blue
camphor glass. Possibly Sandwich
glass. Extremely scarce _____ 185.00
Vases:
5" high. Painted with red tulips
and daisies _____ 16.00
8¾" high, on 3 feet, bulbous,
flower motif _____ 18.50

## CANDLE MOLDS, See TOLEWARE

## CANDY CONTAINERS

After the turn of the present century
candy makers resorted to the use of glass
toys shaped as pistols, fire engines, cars,
etc., as containers for their products. These
items are now in demand by collectors.

Glass. Santa and chimney. Original
colors. Tin screw-type lid _____ $20.00
Glass. Donkey with barrel; black-
faced driver. Tin screw-type
lid _____ $18.00

Fire Engine _____ $12.50

Airplane. "Spirit of Good Will."
Small _____$ 15.00
Auto. "Pierce Arrow." No top ____ 16.50
Ball Player _____ 15.00
Battleship _____ 12.50
Boat, Speed _____ 8.75
Boot. Clear glass, with original
candy _____ 8.00
Bull Dog _____ 9.75
Bus, Greyhound _____ 15.00
Carpet Sweeper _____ 11.50
Charlie Chaplin by barrel _____ 18.00
Clock, Alarm _____ 12.50
Clock, Mantel _____ 12.50
Dirigible. "Los Angeles" _____ 17.50
Donkey pulling barrel _____ 14.00
Duck, Sitting _____ 11.00
Electric Coupe _____ 11.00
Elephant (G.O.P.) _____ 11.00
Engine, with original candy _____ 12.50
Fire Engine. Metal wheels _____ 12.50
Horse and Cart. Paper top _____ 10.00
House _____ 12.75
Lantern. Red glass globe _____ 10.00
Lantern. Tin top _____ 12.00
Liberty Bell. Amber glass, tin
base _____ 22.50
Liberty Bell. Blue _____ 22.50

Liberty Bell. Clear glass, tin
base _____ 19.50
Locomotive _____ 12.75
Mailbox _____ 14.00
Motorcycle _____ 12.75
Opera Glasses _____ 17.50
Pistol. Amber glass _____ 14.00
Pistol. Metal cap _____ 12.50
Rabbit. 6", no bottom _____ 10.00
Radio _____ 15.00
Rolling Pin _____ 10.00
Santa. Erect _____ 18.00
Submarine _____ 15.00
Tank _____ 9.00
Telephone _____ 15.00
Top, Spinning _____ 11.50
Trolley, Toonerville _____ 22.75
Trumpet, Milk glass _____ 16.00
Turkey _____ 10.00
Turkey. With tin slide _____ 11.50
Wheelbarrow _____ 13.75
Windmill _____ 15.00

## CANTON CHINA

This was originally a low cost porcelain
chinaware which was brought to Europe
and America from China by clipper ships.
It was usually decorated in blue, but when
done in brown, was known as Canton Bistre.
Most of this ware was not marked. It was
exported from China for about 400 years
until the Chinese "Reds" took over the
country.

Basket. Handled, open lattice-work
on matching tray, with lattice
border _____$ 110.00

Plate. 8⅞" _____ $15.00

Bowl. 9½" diam., with square-cut
  corners _____ 135.00
Butter Dish. 3-piece covered, early,
  blue _____ 79.50
Butter Pat. Early, blue _____ 5.00
Creamer. Helmet-type. Blue _____ 57.50
Cup and Saucer. Demitasse _____ 40.00
Dish. 8½" square, scalloped _____ 58.50
Dish. Leaf. 8x11". Open handles __ 60.00
Ginger Jar. 7" high _____ 50.00
Jardiniere. 10" high, 7" top diam.
  Blue decoration on white ground 80.0U
Pitchers:
  4" high, squat _____ 49.50
  8" high, water, blue and white 90.00
Plates:
  7½" diam. _____ 25.00
  8" diam., open-edge _____' 28.50
  8½" diam., early _____ 3?.00
  8½" diam., soup _____ 21.00
  8½" diam. White ground with
   blue decoration _____ 50.00
  10" diam., scalloped edge, alternating swirls of gold on blue
   flowers on gold background,
   gold design on red _____ 90.00
  10" diam., 100-butterfly pattern 98.50
  10" diam., Wood & Sons, England. Blue (Late) _____ 15.00
  17½ diam., blue, red, green ___ 145.00
Platters:
  10½x7½" _____ 60.00
  10½x8" _____ 72.00
  13½x10½" _____ 80.00
  15½x12½ _____ 90.00
  17½x14½" _____ 95.00
  20½x16½" _____ 100.00
Sugar Bowl. Covered, large, blue
  and white, 2 handles _____ 70.00

Teapots:
  4" high _____ 65.00
  8½" high. Wire handle. Decorative
   Chinese scene _____ 95.00
  9" high. Domed top _____ 80.00
  10½" high. Early, blue, on carved
   wood stand _____ 125.00
Tile. 6" square, blue and white __ 18.00
Tray. Fish-shaped, blue. 10x11" __ 57.50

## CAPO-DI-MONTE CHINA

  This ware was originally made in Italy
from 1743 to 1760 in a soft paste, and
again from 1770 to 1820 in hard paste. It
is estimated that approximately 99% of the
china on the market today bearing the
"Crown" with "N" above is probably fake
china. During the past century factories in
France, Germany, Hungary and Italy have
been using this mark. The original has a
peculiar greyish color as compared with
the fine colored porcelain paste items now
on the market. To be accurate the porcelain
should be designated "Capo-di-Monte-
type."

Demitasse Cup and Saucer. Gold
  ground with classic decor _____ $65.00

Boxes:
  Glove. 11" long, 4½" high, 3½"
   wide. Padded lining _____$ 410.00
  Oval. 2¾" high, hinged lid _____ 110.00
  Trinket. Hinged, 4½x3½", children
   playing instruments in all-over
   relief design _____ 98.50
Busts:
  3¾" high. Balzac _____ 125.00
  3¾" high. Schubert _____ 100.00
Cup and Saucer _____ 90.00
Cup and Saucer. Demitasse _____ 70.00
Figurines. 9¾" high. Child sitting
  on stump holding tambourine.
  Pair _____ 300.00

Group. 8¾" high. 7 dwarfs playing
musical instruments. 3" figures
grouped around stump with one
on top _____ 625.00
Inkwell. Double _____ 140.00
Pitcher. 7" high. Raised mask faces
with female torso handle. Marked
"N" and Crown _____ 200.00
Plaques:
Group of satyrs with bacchus on
mule. "N" marked in blue under
crown. 11x15" _____ 700.00
4x7", framed. Pair _____ 335.00
Plate, Armorial. Rim decorated with
figures, coat-of-arms in center__ 295.00
Tankard. 8½" high, open, elephant
handle _____ 315.00
Tea Set. Late, about 30 years old.
Teapot, sugar, creamer and 4
cups and saucers _____ 95.00
Urn. Marked "N" and crown _____ 300.00
Urns. Covered. 15" high. Pair ____ 725.00
Vases. 15" high, handled, square
bases. Pair _____ 625.00

## CARLSBAD CHINA

This china was made at Carlsbad, Austria,
by a number of factories. Most of the
items found in shops and collections today
were made after 1891.

Bowl. 3¼". Cream ground with
flowers in red, green and gold _ $ 14.00

Cup and Saucer. Pink and yellow
roses on white background. 1"
gold scroll with blue top border_ 24.00
Dessert Set. Serving dish and 12
sauces with portrait centers.
Pink with gold trim _____ 60.00
Fish Set. 23" platter, sauce boat,
12 scalloped 8½" plates with fish
centers and leaf border _____ 140.00

Fish Set. 25x10½" platter, sauce
boat, 12 raised irregular border
9" plates. Fish centers and gold
trim _____ 165.00

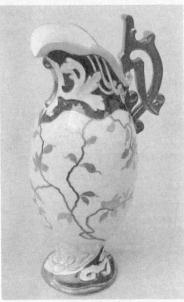

Pitcher. 11½" high. Pink ground
with cobalt blue band at top and
bottom. Gold floral decor, gold
handle _____ $40.00

Oyster Plate. 9" diam. Soft pinks
and golds _____ 28.50
Plate. 8½" diam. Portrait center,
green border with gold decor __ 25.00
Platter. 15¼" long, blue flower
decor _____ 35.00
Tea Caddy. Pink to white background, woman with cupid decor 25.00
Vase, Pitcher. 9¼" high, lavish
gold decoration _____ 49.50

## CARNIVAL GLASS

A glass with many names but most often
referred to as "Carnival" Glass. A cheap
type of iridescent glass made in imitation
of fine Art Glass around the 1900-1925
period, it is often referred to as "Taffeta"
Glass or "Poor Man's Tiffany." The ma-

jority was manufactured in the Wheeling, W. Va., area.

Bowl. 7½'' diam. 3-footed _____ $25.00

Banana Boat. Amethyst. Turned up
sides. 9'' long, 3½'' high _____$ 17.50
Baskets:
  Blue. Northwood. Octagon shape     42.00
  Green. Northwood. Signed _____     45.00
  Marigold. Caroline Bride's
  Basket. Opalescent edge _____     35.00
  Purple. Basketweave. Two handles,
  four feet, flared top _____     38.00
  White. Northwood. Signed _____     45.00
Bells:
  Marigold. Daisy Cut _____   100.00
  White. Hammered _____     40.00
Berry Sets:
  Amethyst. Fruits and Flowers.
  6 pieces _____     90.00
  Blue. Peacock at the Fountain.
  7 pieces _____    150.00
  Marigold. Grape and Cable with
  Thumbprint. 7 pieces _____     70.00
  Purple:
  Grape. Northwood. 7 pieces ___    120.00
  Grape and Cable with Thumb-
  print. "N". 7 pieces _____    150.00
  Singing Birds. Signed. 7 pieces__  150.00
  Springtime. "N". 6 pieces _____    195.00
Bon Bons:
  Blue. Persian Medallion.
  Stemmed _____     16.50
  Green. Ruffled edge. Stemmed.
  "N" _____     20.00
  Marigold Holly Whirl. "Isaac
  Benesch" advertisement _____     40.00
  Lotus and Grape. Three feet ____     14.00
  Purple. Ruffled edge. Stemmed.
  "N" _____     20.00
Bottles:
  Marigold Cologne. Grape and
  Cable. Stopper included _____     60.00
  Purple Cologne. Grape and
  Cable. No stopper _____     50.00
Bowls:
  Amber:
  Diamond Rings. 9''. Fluted ____     18.00

Open Rose. 6''. Serrated edge __     18.50
Amethyst:
  Cherries. 7½''. Flat _____     23.50
  Peacock. Millersburg. 9½x3''
  high _____     65.00
  Peacock at Urn. 8½''. Ruffled __     35.00
Berry:
  Amber. Palm Beach _____     35.00
  Marigold. Grape. 9''. N _____     35.00
  Red. Water Lily and Poinsetta __     65.00
Blue:
  Embroidered Mums. 8'' high. Ruf-
  fled and serrated edge. N ____     40.00
  Double-stemmed Rose. Dome feet.
  Ruffled _____     25.00
  Good Luck. 9'' _____     60.00
  Grape and Cable. 8'' diam., 3½''
  high. Footed _____     35.00
  Grape and Cable outside. Persian
  Medallion inside. 10x5½''. Three
  feet _____    100.00
  Panther Berry. 9''. Footed _____     90.00
  Peacock at Fountain. Orange
  bowl. 11''. Footed _____     90.00
  Persian Medallion. 8'' _____     25.00
  Rose Show _____     95.00
  Stag and Holly. 7-8''x4'' high.
  Three feet _____     50.00
  Stag and Holly. 9''. Three feet __     60.00
Green:
  Concord _____     35.00
  Double Dutch. 9''. Footed _____     38.00
  Fenton's Grape. 7'' _____     28.50
  Good Luck _____     75.00
  Grape and Cable. 8''. Footed __     25.00
  Hattie. 8'' diam., 3½'' high ____     28.00
  Holly and Berry. 9''. Fluted ____     25.00
  Many Fruits. 9''. Ruffled edge __     27.50
  Open Rose. Footed _____     30.00
  Peacock and Grape. 8-9'' _____     30.00
  Peacock at Urn. Millersburg.
  Scalloped _____     70.00
  Primrose. Millersburg. 9½''.
  Fluted _____     30.00
  Primrose. Near-Cut pattern of
  hearts outside. 10'' _____     35.00
  Stippled Rays. 9'' _____     37.50
  Whirling Leaves. Millersburg.
  10'' _____     40.00
Ice Blue:
  Flowering Almond. 9''. N _____     60.00
  Peacock and Grape. Gold irrides-
  cence. 9'' _____     40.00
  Wishbone. 8-9''. Three feet ____     90.00
Marigold:
  Dragon and Strawberry. Footed__     65.00
  Embroidered Mums. 8½'' _____     29.00
  Fenton's Cherry Circles. 8½'' __     25.00
  Fenton's Peacock and Grape. 9''   22.50
  Fleur-de-Lis. 9½'' _____     25.00
  Garland Rose _____     25.00
  Grape. Orange bowl. 10½''.
  Footed _____     48.50
  Grape and Cable. 10'' diam. __     25.00
  Grape and Cable with Basket-

weave. 8'' diam., 2'' high _____ 20.00
Horse's Head. One side turned
up. 7'' diam. Footed _____ 35.00
Little Fishes. 8''. Footed, ser-
rated edge _____ 40.00
Louisa. 8¼''. Footed _____ 16.00
Lustre Rose. 4x7¾''. Three feet __ 14.00
Mums and Sailboat. 8¾''. Fluted 17.50
Northwood Maple Leaf. Master
stemmed _____ 22.00
Orange Tree. 9''. Fluted _____ 18.00
Orange Tree. 10''. Footed _____ 32.50
Pansy Spray. 8½'' _____ 17.00
Panther. Sauce bowl. 6'' _____ 15.00
Peacock on Fence_____ 35.00
Peacock at Fountain. 10¾'' _____ 50.00
Persian Medallion interior.
Grape and Cable exterior. 10¼''_ 37.50
Rose Medallion. Covered _____ 24.50
Rose Show. 8½'' _____ 70.00
Stag and Holly. 10-11''. Three
feet _____ 45.00
Strawberry. 8½''. N _____ 25.00
Strawberry. 9''. Ruffled _____ 25.00
Three Fruits. 8½''. Fluted _____ 18.00
Orange:
Peacock at Fountain. Three
curved feet. 10'' diam., 5½'' high,
ruffled edge _____ 49.50
Peach Opal:
Dragon and Lotus. 9'' _____ 42.00
Purple:
Butterfly. Two handles _____ 27.00
Circled Scrolls. 8½'' _____ 45.00
Grape. Low standard. Scalloped
border. 7'' diam., 2'' high ____ 18.50
Grape and Cable. 8½''. Fluted __ 30.00
Grape and Cable. Three spatula
feet _____ 30.00
Peacock on Fence. N _____ 55.00
Persian Garden. Fruit bowl and
base. 10½'' diam. _____ 140.00
Primrose. Millersburg _____ 55.00
Three Fruits. Satin finish.
Footed _____ 35.00
Whirling Leaves. Millersburg.
9½'' _____ 35.00
Wishbone. 8''. Footed. N _____ 45.00
Turquoise. Two Flowers. Three
feet _____ 42.00
Vaseline. Imperial Jewels. 11½''
diam. _____ 22.50
White:
Fenton's Holly. 8½'' _____ 42.50
Garden Path. 9½'' _____ 58.00
Imperial Jewels. Paneled back.
8'' diam. _____ 22.50
Optic and Buttons. 6'' Ribed.
Signed Im/pe/ri/al _____ 27.50
Persian Garden. 12''. Deep ruf-
fles _____ 30.00
Brooklyn Bridge. Marigold _____ 100.00
Butter Dishes:
Green. Acorn Burr _____ 135.00
Marigold:

Grape and Gothic Arch. Covered 35.00
Northwood Flute. N _____ 35.00
Purple. Grape and Cable. N ___ 100.00
Candlesticks:
Marigold. 6½'' high_____ 15.00
Purple. Grape and Cable. N ____ 40.00
Candy Dishes:
Amethyst. 7'' diam. Footed. N __ 30.00
Blue:
Basketweave. Open edge. 6''
diam. _____ 22.50
Peacock on Fence. Ruffled. 8¾''
diam. _____ 25.00
Blue. Wreath of Roses. Two han-
dles. 8'' diam. Footed _____ 25.00
Cherry Red to Amber. European
Holly. Turned up sides. 7'' diam. 125.00
Green to Amber. Lotus Dragon.
7½'' diam. Footed _____ 30.00
Marigold:
Arabic. Two handles. 7'' diam. __ 10.00
Pansy. One handle. 5½'' diam. __ 8.00
Windflower. One handle. 7¼''
diam. _____ 12.50
Compotes.
Amethyst:
Hearts and Flowers _____ 30.00
Stippled Rays. 7'' high. Fluted__ 12.50
Blue:
Blackberry. Miniature _____ 29.00
Fenton's Birds and Cherries. 5''__ 25.00
Grape. 6'' high, 6¾'' diam.
Ruffled _____ 25.00
Lacy Hearts. 6'' high _____ 37.50
Mikado. 10'' high _____ 95.00
Green:
Iris. 5'' high, 7'' diam. _____ 35.00
Rose Spray _____ 30.00
Marigold:
Coin Spot _____ 14.00
Inverted Strawberry. "Near-Cut" 75.00
Iris. 7¼'' diam. _____ 18.00
Mikado _____ 50.00
Vintage Grape. 7''. Fluted _____ 12.50
Peach. Oval Thumbprint. 4¾''
high, 8¾'' diam. _____ 18.00
Purple. Blackberry interior.
Basketweave exterior. 7¼''.
Fluted _____ 25.00
White:
Constellation. 5½'' diam. Fluted__ 40.00
Peacock at Urn. 5¾'' diam. Fluted 40.00
Cracker Jars:
Green. Inverted Feather _____ 80.00
Purple. Grape and Cable. N ____ 175.00
Creamers:
Marigold:
Pansy Spray _____ 12.50
Shell and Jewel _____ 17.50
Purple. Grape and Cable _____ 50.00
White. Orange Tree _____ 30.00
Cup and Saucer:
Marigold, Kittens _____ 60.00
Decanters:
Marigold. Imperial Grape _____ 25.00

Purple. Grape. N _____ 195.00

**Dishes:**

Amber:
Grape. 6¼" diam. Heavy _____ 15.00
Little Flowers. 5¾" diam. _____ 15.00
Amethyst. Persian Medallion.
7". Fluted _____ 18.00
Blue:
Captive Rose. 9" _____ 32.00
Peacock at Urn. 8" Flat, beaded
berries outside _____ 85.00
Wreath Pine Cone. 6½" diam.
Fluted _____ 15.00
Marigold:
Acorn. 7" diam. Fluted _____ 10.00
Holly. Jelly dish. Stemmed and
fluted _____ 12.00
Miniature kittens _____ 40.00
Opal advertisement. "Miller's
Furniture, Harrisburg, Pa." Lace
edge. Basketweave outside _____ 50.00
Persian Medallion. Two handles.
Flat _____ 16.00
Strawberry. 8" diam., 3" high.
Pinch and serrated edge _____ 27.50
Vintage Grape. 7¼". Fluted ____ 12.50
Purple:
Bellflower. 6¾". Fluted _____ 18.00
Northwood Flute _____ 15.00
Sauces:
Amethyst. Grape and Cable. N__ 13.50
Custard. Grape and Gothic
Arches. Pearlized lustre _____ 20.00
Frosted White. Persian Garden.
6" diam. _____ 27.50

**Dresser Trays.**

Marigold:
Grape and Cable _____ 75.00
Windmill. Flat _____ 50.00
Purple. Grape and Cable _____ 100.00

**Epergne:**

Green. Four Lillies. N _____ 300.00

**Fernery:**

Pastel Blue. Grape and Cable __ 500.00
Purple. Grape and Cable _____ 350.00

**Goblets.**

Marigold:
Flute _____ 12.50
Octagon _____ 20.00
Soda Gold. Footed _____ 10.00
Gravy Boat. Purple _____ 32.50

Hair Receiver. Persian Medallion.
Blue. Square top _____ 50.00

**Hat Pin Holders:**

Blue. Orange Tree _____ 55.00
Green:
Butterfly and Berry. Rare _____ 150.00
Grape and Cable. N _____ 75.00
Purple. Grape. 7" high. N ____ 57.50

**Hats:**

Amethyst. Turned in sides.
Plain outside _____ 12.50
Blue. Blackberry Spray _____ 14.00
Green. Grape and Cable. 4¾"
diam. Fluted _____ 27.50

Turquoise. Blackberry Spray ____ 28.50
Homestead. Nu-Art. Green _____ 400.00

**Ice Cream Bowls:**

Cobalt Blue. Vintage. Flat. 9½"__ 45.00
Marigold. Cherries. 11-12" ____ 28.00
White:
Persian Garden. 6" diam. _____ 20.00
Persian Garden. 11-12" _____ 100.00

Lamp Base. Peacock. Marigold____ 300.00

**Loving Cup. Orange Tree.**

Marigold _____ 60.00

**Mugs.**

Blue:
Beaded Shell _____ 42.50
Orange Tree _____ 22.00
Singing Bird. N _____ 28.50
Green. Singing Bird _____ 25.00
Marigold. Orange Tree _____ 12.00
Purple:
Fisherman _____ 45.00
Heron. Rare _____ 60.00
Singing Birds. "N" _____ 25.00

**Nappies:**

Red. Basketweave _____ 75.00
White _____ 30.00

**Nut Bowls:**

Blue. Fenton's Grape. Three feet 25.00
Green:
Leaves and Beads Straight edge.
N _____ 49.50
Wild Rose. Heart-shaped vertical
edge. N _____ 25.00
Pin Tray. Grape and Cable. Blue __ 95.00

Pitcher and 6 Tumblers. Diamond
Lace pattern. Purple _____ $ 250.00

**Pitchers:**

Green. Diamond. 4" diam. 7"
high _____ 25.00
Marigold:
Field Flower. 10" high _____ 45.00
Octagon. 8" high _____ 25.00
Oriental Poppy. Tankard. N ____ 60.00
Milk:
Green. Windmill _____ 35.00

Marigold:
Raspberry. N _____ 35.00
Windmill. 4½x6½'' _____ 25.00
Water:
Blue. Grape and Gothic Arches__ 125.00
Custard. Fluted Scroll _____ 48.00
Marigold:
Drape. Applied handle _____ 47.50
Floral and Grape _____ 25.00
Purple. Grape _____ 75.00
White. Peacock at Fountain. N __ 200.00
Plates:
Amethyst. Butterfly. "Horlaeher"
advertisement in raised script
on bottom. Two handles. turned
up edge _____ 65.00
Blue. Holly and Berry. 9¾'' diam. 40.00
Frosted Black. Clambroth. 9'' ___ 15.00
Green. Grape and Cable. 9'' __ 30.00
Marigold:
ABC Stork _____ 20.00
Fishscale and Beads. 7'', Flat __ 18.00
Grape and Cable. Spatula feet __ 25.00
Pine Cone _____ 18.00
Rose Show _____ 100.00
Three Fruits _____ 30.00
Peach. Posie and Pods. 10'' ____ 95.00
Purple:
Persian Garden. Chop Plate. 13''.
Rare _____ 250.00
Grape. 9''. N _____ 50.00
Three Fruits. Stippled background.
8-9'' _____ 48.00
Powder Jars:
Green. Grape and Cable. N ____ 22.00
Marigold. Vintage Grape _____ 20.00
Purple. Grape. Covered. N ____ 40.00
Punch Bowls:
Blue:
Orange Tree. Bowl and base ____ 125.00
Orange Tree. Bowl and 6 cups __ 150.00
Marigold:
Grape and Cable. Bowl, Base
and 6 cups _____ 175.00
Orange Tree. Bowl only. 11'' __ 50.00
Orange Tree. Bowl, base and 5
cups _____ 115.00
Rose and Grapes. Bowl, base
and 6 cups _____ 125.00
Purple. Grape. 11'' diam., 11''
high. N. Bowl, base and 5 cups 160.00
Punch Cups:
Amethyst:
Storks and Rushes _____ 10.00
Wreath of Roses _____ 10.00
Marigold. Orange Tree _____ 9.50
Pastel Blue. Peacock at Fountain.
N _____ 20.00
Purple. Grape and Cable _____ 18.00
Rose Bowls:
Amethyst. Drapery. Old circle
mark _____ 45.00
Aqua Opalescent. Drapery Rose__ 59.50
Green:
Leaf and Beads _____ 40.00

Louisa. Three feet _____ 27.50
Marigold:
Fenton's Flowers. Footed _____ 25.00
Garland _____ 25.00
Leaf and Beads. Three twig feet.
N _____ 25.00
Triple layers. Clear handles____ 18.50
Purple:
Grape Delight. Six feet _____ 55.00
Roses. Fine Cut _____ 45.00
Turquoise Opalescent. Leaf and
Beads. Three twig feet. N _____ 60.00
Salts.
Marigold:
Fluted _____ 19.50
Tree of Life _____ 40.00
Shades:
Northwood Drapery. White ____ 29.50
Smoke _____ 11.50
Shaving Mug. Orange Tree. Blue __ 30.00
Sherbet. Orange Tree. Marigold __ 10.00
Shot Glass. Grape and Cable. Mari-
gold _____ 30.00
Spooners:
Amethyst. Maple Leaf. Three
handles _____ 30.00
Blue. Lustre Rose. Two handles__ 27.50
Marigold. Northwood Flute. N __ 20.00
Purple. Peacock at Fountain. N __ 38.50
White Peach. N _____ 40.00
Sugar Bowls:
Green. Lustre Fruit. N _____ 20.00
Marigold:
Basketweave and Cable. Covered 15.00
Butterfly and Berry. Covered __ 25.00
Maple Leaf. Covered _____ 25.00
Sugars and Creamers.
Marigold:
Beaded Shell. Covered sugar __ 35.00
Orange Tree. Open sugar _____ 25.00
Purple:
Singing Bird. Covered sugar ___ 85.00
Struting Peacock. Pedestaled.
Open sugar _____ 48.00
Swans.
Purple:
Nesting. Millersburg _____ 95.00
Salt _____ 95.00
Table Sets:
Green. Acorn Burr and Bark.
4 pieces _____ 250.00
Purple. Peacock at the Foun-
tain. 4 pieces _____ 195.00
Tobacco Jar. Purple. "N" _____ 175.00
Toothpick:
Green _____ 60.00
Marigold _____ 50.00
Purple _____ 50.00
Tumblers:
Amethyst. Maple Leaf _____ 14.75
Blue:
Feather Scroll _____ 25.00
Floral and Grape _____ 14.50
God and Home _____ 165.00
Painted Cherries. "N" _____ 10.50
Peacock at Fountain _____ 16.50

Marigold:

| | |
|---|---|
| Apple Tree _____ | 12.00 |
| Butterfly and Berry _____ | 11.00 |
| Imperial Grape _____ | 7.50 |
| Stork and Rushes _____ | 10.00 |

Purple:

| | |
|---|---|
| Chatelaine. Rare _____ | 175.00 |
| Grape and Cable _____ | 12.50 |
| Singing Bird. "N" _____ | 15.00 |

Vases:

Amethyst. Northwood Drapery.

| | |
|---|---|
| 8¾" high, 4" diam. _____ | 14.00 |

Blue:

| | |
|---|---|
| Holly Hat. Turned edge _____ | 17.00 |
| Pulled Loops. 11" high _____ | 18.00 |
| Ribbed. 10" high. N _____ | 13.00 |
| Stretched Butterfly and Berry __ | 20.00 |
| Custard. Daisy and Drape. 7" __ | 29.50 |
| Frosty White. Corn. N _____ | 100.00 |
| Ice Green. Corn. N _____ | 100.00 |

Marigold:

| | |
|---|---|
| Bud Vase _____ | 13.00 |
| Corn. N _____ | 125.00 |
| Grecian Urn. 9" high _____ | 15.00 |
| Ribbed. 4" diam., 6½" high. N __ | 12.00 |
| Rococo. Miniature _____ | 19.50 |
| Wide Panel. 6" high, 4" diam., signed "N" _____ | 10.00 |

Purple:

| | |
|---|---|
| Colonial Lady. 5¾" tall _____ | 32.50 |
| Imperial Jewels. Old mark _____ | 45.00 |
| Ribbed. 4" diam., 7" high. N __ | 15.00 |
| Smoke. Rococo _____ | 10.00 |

White:

| | |
|---|---|
| Fine Rib. 9". N _____ | 23.50 |
| Lined Lettuce. 9" _____ | 18.50 |
| Wastebasket. Blue. "N" _____ | 30.00 |

Water Sets:

| | |
|---|---|
| Blue. Floral enamel. 7 pieces __ | 90.00 |
| Cherry. Enameled. 7 pieces ____ | 115.00 |
| Custard. Northwood Fan. Gold trim _____ | 200.00 |

Marigold:

| | |
|---|---|
| Butterfly and Berry. 7 pieces __ | 75.00 |
| Crackle finish. Covered pitcher and 4 footed tumblers _____ | 45.00 |
| Imperial Lace. 7 pieces _____ | 60.00 |
| Lattice and Grape. 7 pieces ____ | 60.00 |
| Rose. 7 pieces _____ | 67.50 |
| Spring Flowers. 7 pieces_____ | 100.00 |

Purple:

| | |
|---|---|
| Diamond Lace. 7 pieces _____ | 200.00 |
| Grape and Cable. 7 pieces ____ | 200.00 |
| Grape and Cable. 9 pieces _____ | 210.00 |

Wines:

| | |
|---|---|
| Marigold. Sailboat _____ | 12.50 |
| Orange. Lotus and Grape _____ | 10.00 |

Wine Sets:

Marigold.

| | |
|---|---|
| Golden Harvest. Stopper and 6 wines _____ | 75.00 |
| Star and File _____ | 150.00 |
| Purple. Imperial Grape. 7 pieces | 185.00 |

## CASTOR SETS

| | |
|---|---|
| 5 Clear Glass Bottles. Blue glass base. 11" to top of hanlle ____ | $75.00 |

| | |
|---|---|
| 4-Bottle. English type, square silver plated frame _____ | 60.00 |
| 4-Bottle. Miniature, revolving tin base _____ | 32.50 |
| 5-Bottle. Matching bottles, replated bottle tops and frame _____ | 60.00 |
| 5-Bottle. Matching bottles. Silverplated frame in good condition __ | 65.00 |
| 6-Bottle. 3 bottles with tulip stoppers, also salt, pepper and covered mustard. Resilvered frame__ | 70.00 |

## CATALOGUES AND MAGAZINES

Publications before 1915 are mainly in demand by collectors and libraries.

| | |
|---|---|
| Auto Owners Supply Book. Western Auto, 1929, 128 pp. _____ | 8.50 |
| Chevrolet, 1923. Instructions on three 7x9" sheets _____ | 3.00 |

Chicago Mercantile Co., Wholesale
Millinery. Fall, 1912, 67 pp ____ 5.50
Church Ornaments. Benziger Bros.
of N.Y., 1905. 9x11", 350 pp __ 12.50
Comic Books:
Buster Brown & His Dog Tige,
Cupples & Leon, 1905, complete_ 35.00
Little Orphan Annie, Cupples &
Leon, 1926. 7x9" hard cover,
86 pp _____ 7.50
Mutt & Jeff Cartoon Book, 1910 _ 35.00
Debretts, Peerage, Baronetage &
Knightage, London. 1899, 991 pp_ 14.00
DeLaval Cream Separators, 1916.
8½x11", 72 pp _____ 6.75
Ecclesiastical Statuary, Daprato Co.
of Chicago. 11x14", 128 pp ____ 8.50
Electric Light, Railway, Telephone &
House Supplies, Elec. Appliance
Co., 1924. 7½x11", 472 pp _____ 18.50
Etude Music Magazines. 1910 thru
1930, each _____ 1.00
Flags of the World. National Geo-
graphic Society, McCandless &
Grosvenor, 1917. Hard cover,
420 pp. _____ 17.50
Ford, 1923. 11½x18" salesfolder __ 7.50
Ford Facts, 1920. 6x9", 72 pp ____ 10.00
Fordson Tractor, 1923. 8½x9", 4 pp. 3.50
Franklin Automobile Catalog, 1906.
8x10", 33 pp. _____ 38.50
Furniture & Floor Coverings, Peck &
Hills Furniture, Chicago, 1923.
10½x14" hardbound, 480 pp. ____ 37.50
Godey's Lady's Book. May 1884 __ 5.00
Hamilton Watch. 1909 _____ 2.75
House Supplies, Elec. Appliance
Co., 1924. 7½x11. 472 pp. _____ 18.50
Louden Barn Equipment, 1923.
8x10½", 240 pp. _____ 9.50
Lyon Bros., Chicago. General
Wholesale. Summer 1907 _____ 15.00
McCalls, March 1902, August 1903.
Each _____ 3.00
McKesson & Robbins, 1881 _____ 6.00
Marlin Catalog for Repeating Rifles
and Shotguns. 1918, 24 pp. ____ 12.00
Montgomery Ward. F&W 1918 ____ 20.00
Montgomery Ward. F&W 1926 ____ 15.00
Montgomery Ward. F&W 1929 ____ 13.50
Overland, 1914. 9x11", 18 pp. ____ 25.00
Parke-Davis, 1879. 41 pp. _____ 4.00
Period Ornaments of Furniture,
Woodwork & Interior Decoration.
Decorator Supply Co., 1924. 9
x12", 242 pp. _____ 32.50
St. Nicholas, 1884. 2 bound
volumes _____ 10.00
Scientific American, 1892. 52
weekly issues _____ 15.00
Sears, Roebuck F&W No. 133, 1916 20.00
Sharpe & Dohme, 1899. 183 pp. __ 3.00
Sports Catalogues:
Reach Baseball Guides, 1908-1913,
ea. _____
Spalding Baseball Guide, 1913- 10.00

1915, each _____ 7.50
Weston Electrical Instruments, 1920.
8x10", over 200 pp. _____ 14.50
White Rotary Sewing Machines.
16 pp. _____ 3.50

## CHALKWARE

The term "Chalkware" is a misnomer. The
various ornaments of this type were made
of Plaster-of-Paris and decorated with
water colors. Italian immigrants made and
sold these items around the 1820-1865
period.

In the past many collectors and dealers
were under the impression that the ornaments were folk art of the Pennsylvania
(Dutch) Germans. Investigations have re-
vealed that the figurines and animals were
copied from Staffordshire and other porcelain or pottery models. The demand is now
slack and prices are considerably lower.

Dog. 6¼" high. Red decor on gray
background _____ $75.00

Cat _____ 45.00
Cat Penny Bank. 10" high _____ 40.00
Compote. With fruit and birds ____ 140.00
Dog. 11½" high _____ 42.50
Eagle, Spread. 9½" high, 12½"
wide _____ 40.00
Figurines. 12¼" high. Boy throw-
ing snowballs and girl holding
muff to face, Kate Greenaway-
type costumes. Pair _____ 50.00
Hen. 6⅜" high _____ 60.00
Horse. 8½x9½". Unpainted _____ 41.50

| | |
|---|---|
| Poutier Pigeons. Pair _____ | 45.00 |
| Rabbit. Sitting _____ | 40.00 |
| Rooster. 11" high. Decorated ____ | 55.00 |
| Sheep. Mother and baby sheep. 7" high _____ | 50.00 |
| Squirrel _____ | 49.50 |
| Stag. 15" high, 17" long _____ | 49.50 |

## CHELSEA

A fine English China which was made to compete with Dresden in the home market. The plant began operating in the 1740's. The products can be divided into four periods: 1) Early period (1740's) with incised triangle and the raised anchor mark. 2) The 1750's, red raised anchor mark. 3) The 1760's, the gold anchor period. 4) The Chelsea-Derby period of the 1770's.

Bone ash was introduced to the body in 1758, the glaze was frequently "crazed" showing spots of green. In the Gold Anchor Period 1760, articles showed more sumptuousness decorations of ground colors were in blue, pea-green, and red, along with elaborate guilding which was copied from Sevres Porcelain. Fancy rococo scroll work was also used on figures and vases. A new line of painting representing mythological scenes, birds in polychrome enamels and fruits was introduced.

In 1924 a large number of molds and models of figurines were found at the Spode-Copeland Works and many items were again brought into production.

Figurines. 9" high. Hunter attired in red jacket; milkmaid wearing red skirt. Each _____ $125.00

| | |
|---|---|
| Butter Pat _____ | 3.75 |
| **Creamers:** | |
| Raised lustre flowers _____ | 25.00 |
| Sprig pattern _____ | 17.50 |
| **Cups and Saucers:** | |
| Blue thistle _____ | 18.50 |
| Handled, lustre grapes _____ | 28.50 |
| Handleless, sprig pattern _____ | 18.75 |
| Figure. 8½" high. Woman with tray. White background with rust, red and blue decor _____ | 120.00 |
| Jar. 11" high. Covered, hexagonal, pear-shaped. Iron rust anchor mark on bottom _____ | 200.00 |
| Parrots. Group of 2 _____ | 175.00 |

| | |
|---|---|
| Bowl. 10" diam. Grape and leaf decor in gold lustre _____ | $18.50 |
| **Plates:** | |
| Cake. 9½" diam. _____ | 35.00 |
| Cup Plate _____ | 8.00 |
| 7½" diam. Purple decor _____ | 12.50 |
| 10" diam. Peafowl in brilliant colors. Circa 1825 _____ | 95.00 |
| Poodle, French. 2¾x1" base, bird in dog's mouth _____ | 60.00 |
| Sauce Dish. Lustre grapes _____ | 12.75 |
| Sugar Bowl. Lustre grapes _____ | 65.00 |
| Teapot. 9" high. Squat type, blue lustre-type decor _____ | 87.50 |

## CHINA MUGS

| | |
|---|---|
| "A Brother's Gift." Green decorations. "Josiah" on reverse. Staffordshire _____ | 30.00 |
| "A Present for a Good Boy." Canary Lustre. Yellow with brown decor. 2¼" high _____ | 115.00 |
| "A Trifle for Fanny." Canary yellow, red transfer name and border _____ | 37.50 |
| Bryan and McKinley portraits in sepia on white background. 5" | |

high, 2 handles. Marked "Compliments of Raphael & Zeugschmidt, Wholesale Liquor Dealers, Pittsburgh, Pa." _____ 15.00

Staffordshire-type. 2¾" high. With scene of blacksmith working. Green, blue and brown, pink lustre rim _____ $28.00

Child's Mug. Canary lustre, red, churchyard scene decor. Circa 1820 _____ 60.00
"Chit Chat." 2½" high. Pink decor 18.50
"Eliza." Fruit and flowers _____ 25.00
"For Eliza." Black transfer on blue background _____ 22.00
History of House that Jack Built. Franklin Maxim _____ 30.00
"Martha." 2½" high, children and pink see-saw _____ 25.00
"Mary." 2½" high, blue and white 24.00
"The Seasons." 2½" high. Franklin Maxim _____ 30.00
The Seasons. August, with verse __ 28.50
"The Way to Wealth" or "Dr. Franklin's Poor Richard." 2½" high _____ 31.50
Washington, George. Centennial, eagles and flags. Copeland China _____ 33.50

### CHINESE, See ORIENTAL

### CIGAR STORE FIGURES, ETC.

Fifty to seventy-five years ago Cigar Store Indians, Squaws or Turks, were familiar sights in front of the cigar stores and tobacco shops. The figures are now scarce and command a good price when offered for sale.

Cigar Store Indian. Over 7' high ..$4,800.00

Cigar Store Indian Chief. Tall ___ 4500.00
Cigar Store Indian Chief. Small __ 3500.00
Cigar Store Squaw. Tall _____ 3000.00
Cigar Store Squaw. Small _____ 2400.00
Cigar Store Turk _____ 4000.00
Harness Maker's Horse. No equipment _____ 1200.00

Indian. 6 feet high, original
paint. "Frank" _____ 3750.00
Indian Maiden. Half life-size.
On base with wheels. 5'8" high.
Painted _____ 3000.00
Standing Figure. Cap, ruffled
collar, red and blue costume.
Holding box of cigars in left
hand. On square base. 5'9"
high _____ 3250.00
Statue of Lincoln. Life-size
carved wood _____ 4000.00

## CIVIL WAR AND RELATED ITEMS

Civil War Items consist mainly of military items used in the War between the States (1861-65) in the United States.

Sword, Confederate. 34½" long    165.00

Bayonet, Socket. Tower Enfield,
blockade marked _____ 10.00
Bayonet, Socket. Tower Enfield,
without scabbards _____ 12.00
Blinker Bridle. Marked with a
faint Richmond, Va. maker's
name, w/bit _____ 45.00
Bowie Knife. Ivory handle, no
maker or scabbard _____ 65.00
Bowie Knife. "IXL". 1860s stage
handle, Wostenholme address.
Fine etchings of eagles, flags,
leather scabbard _____ 310.00
Bowie Knife. W/out scabbard, wood
handle, brass guard, marked
Weiss London. Massive blade
with classic lines _____ 60.00
Buckle, Brass. 1851 pattern with
wrong Federal motto, w/eagle
and wreath _____ 10.00
Buckle, Bronze. 1851 pattern with
wrong Federal motto, w/eagle
and wreath _____ 10.00
Buckle. Oblong. Bannerman, copper
colored. Remake of the famous

Atlanta CSA. Hook back fittings_ 5.00
Buttons. India Wars. On old cards,
6 to set) unused 1870s enlisted
type _____ 3.00
Buttons. Old Horstmann Navy type.
Gilt finished, 24 per card _____ 3.00
Canteen. Wooden with iron supports believed to be Confederate _____ 40.00
Carbine. Enfield Cavalry. Same
type sent to aid the South _____ 100.00
Carbine. Starr with Yonkers NY
address. Replaced saddle ring
and forend _____ 210.00
Cross Belt Plates. CW Battlefield__ 10.00
Cross Sabers. Brass. 7th Cavalry,
with letters "A" and "7" _____ 3.00
Enlistment Papers. Civil War from
all over the Union, all fully
signed _____ 11.00
Helmet Badge. New York. Shield
and eagle with Co. number in
center _____ 7.00
Helmet. Dress. 1870s Cavalry.
Brass trim with eagle badge
w/spike _____ 50.00
Holster Cover. 1851 Navy Colt
silver flap over. Made of pure
silver with cannons and harp on
face. On reverse is South Carolina State Crest and "From
fellow officers of the S. Carolina
Reserve Force. To a fine man
Brigadier General James Chestnut CSA January 3rd, 1875."
Mint _____ 350.00
Mail Service Waybills. Confederate
States. Signed and Government
heading _____ 10.00
Musket. Enfield 2 band. CW circa.
Restocked and blued _____ 135.00
Musket. Enfield 2 band. Original
with CW markings _____ 190.00
Musket. Enfield 3 band. Original
with CW markings _____ 190.00
Musket. Tower Percussion. Converted to from Flintlock. CW
circa _____ 125.00
Plume, Shako. Cavalry and Artillery. Genuine horse hair _____ 4.00
Poster. Garnett's Brigade, in black
and white _____ 30.00
Pouch, Ammo. McKeever. Marked
with Custer's famous "7th Cav." 10.00
Pouch. Hagnor. Marked 7th Cavalry. With original contents _____ 10.00
Revolver. LeMat No. 171. Marked
Col. A. LeMat Brte. and Paxton
ANV. All original except for replaced side ejector _____ 800.00
Revolver. Relic Colt pattern. Copy
of the 1850s _____ 35.00
Saddle, Cavalry. Civil War Relic.
Mixed, McCullems and Militia
types _____ 50.00

Saddle Bag. Leather. Marked with a small VA. address. CW circa _ 80.00

Saddle Bag. Maker's name inscribed in the leather. Set of two _____ 85.00

Sling Musket. Tower Blockade Enfield. CW period _____ 5.00

Spurs, Tear Drop. Civil War. 1" rowels with chins _____ 20.00

Sword Belt Plates. Union NCO's 1851 _____ 12.00

Tarpot, Cavalry. Civil War, old and original _____ 40.00

## CLOCKS

Clock. Visible mechanism. 14" high. Circa 1850 _____ $125.00

Acorn Clock. Made by Forestville Mfg. Co., Bristol, Conn. View of Merchants Exchange, Phila., Pa. All original _____ 3000.00

Alarm Clock. "Gilbert Nine." Circa 1900 _____ 12.50

Animated Face Iron Clock. With 3 presidents, man beating drum on minute _____ 100.00

Anniversary Clock. German, 8" to top of dome. Winds once a year_ 140.00

Ansonia Alarm Clock, 1880-1885. Strikes hour and half hour, alarm 55.00

Ansonia Alarm Clock Bank. Coin must be inserted to wind. Combination dial under movement opens bank. Mint condition ____ 125.00

Ansonia Clock. 18" high. In French style but with metal case. 15-minute chimes, brass works _____ 60.00

Banjo Clock. Brewster & Ingraham. One of first spring-wound made in America. 8-day movement, walnut drum, brass bezel and side rails _____ 325.00

Banjo Clock. Gilbert, 8-day. Mahogany case with eagle top, brass on sides with picture of schooner on stormy sea _____ 115.00

Banjo Clock. Howard & Davis. Large _____ 175.00

Banjo Clock. Ingraham #209 _____ 110.00

Banjo Clock. Reverse wooden side arms, brass finial, wood bezel, 8-day weight driven brass movement. Circa 1825 _____ 215.00

Bartholomew Clock. 30-hour weight driven movement. Carved eagle on top, carved columns. Original picture _____ 165.00

Black Forest "Whistler." Hand carved man, 12" high, whistles "The Bear Went Over the Mountain." Holds 30-hour clock under his arm. Both movements in excellent condition. Circa 1890 ____ 195.00

Boardman & Wells, Bristol. 30-hour weight driven wooden movement. Stenciled gold leaf decor on top and columns _____ 95.00

Calendar Clock, Seth Thomas. 8-day weight driven. Refinished Rosewood case with original picture in the door _____ 95.00

China Case Clock. 12½" high. White ground, dark blue decor, roses in panels. #93 on base _____ 95.00

China Clock. Ansonia works, green with pink tulips, 12x10x5" _____ 95.00

China Clock. Ansonia works, Royal Bonn. Blue with rose decor. 11½x8x5" _____ 90.00

Clepsydra, or English Water Clock. Brass 24-hour dial, all brass parts. Dated 1690 _____ 600.00

Cottage Clock. Shelf-type with half round gold leaf columns, finial on top. 8-day spring movement. Made by Waterbury Clock Co. _____ 49.50

Cow Clock. Iron, 13" long, 9" high. Base incised "St. Charles Evaporated Cream" _____ 42.50

Cuckoo Clock. Carved Black Forest scene:

With cuckoo and Whip-poor-will
and weights _____ 120.00
With one bird and weights _____ 80.00
Cuckoo Clock. English, shelf-type,
with 8-day fusee brass movement 90.00
Cuckoo Clock. Stag head, 14x18"
body with applied carving _____ 79.50
Curtis Girandole Clock. Similar to
Plate #16 in Wallace Nutting's
Clock Book. Mahogany case with
gilded front, gilded eagle, carved
bracket, eagle on top _____ 2750.00
Cut Glass. Boudoir or desk type.
Small. 4x5½", 30-hour movement.
New Haven Clock Co. _____ 60.00
Daisy and Button Glass Clocks:
Amber _____ 65.00
Blue _____ 70.00
Double Steeple Clock. Birge &
Fuller. 8-day wagon spring _____ 390.00
Double Steeple Clock. Terry & An-
drews. 8-day spring _____ 160.00

Mantel-type. Edwardian. Circa 1900__$75.00

English. 8-day brass movement, in
refinished case, with 11" dial.
Fusee spring-wound works. Surrounded by circle of carving,
all resting on platform _____ 125.00
English "Homing Pigeon" Clock.
With "Turner's Patent" on dial
and "Hateley's Patent No. 14307-
07" on case. In excellent condition, in carrying case _____ 200.00
French Bronze Clock. 10" high, 10"
wide. Under dome _____ 120.00
French Clock. Mercury pendulum,
oval brass frame _____ 65.00
French Gold Wall Clock. 4½" circular porcelain dial decorated
with rose garlands, gold filigree hands, gilt metal motif on
case in form of ribbons and
bows. 8-day movement _____ 100.00
French Gothic Clock. Mahogany
case with satin wood inlay. 15-
day movement, strikes _____ 90.00

Jasperware Clock Case. 4½ x 7".
Green and white _____ $35.00

French Haviland China Case. Deep
green with gold trim. American
works _____ 115.00
French Majolica Mantel Clock.
Wine colored with gold decor.
Fretted brass dial under beveled
glass door. 12" high, 7" wide,
8-day striking movement _____ 100.00
French-style Clock. In washed gold
with painted pictures in inserts__ 250.00
German. Brass "Sauce Pan" Kitchen
Clock. 30-hour movement, spring
is wound by pulling down a cord.
Excellent condition _____ 75.00
Gilbert Kitchen Clock. Carved oak
case. Has alarm _____ 38.00
Grandfather's Clocks:
B. Whitling, Winchester. Pine
case. 7'9" high, sweep second
hand _____ 400.00
Silas Hoadley, 1808-1849, 7'3"
natural finish pine case _____ 360.00
J. Kent, Monmouth (1820). With
second, minute, hour hand, calendar and painted seascape. 7'
6" mahogany case with satin
wood inlay _____ 400.00
Kenneth Maclennan, London
(1776). Watteau-type painting,
brass dial phases of moon, calendar. 7'7" gold lacquered
case _____ 900.00
John Murray, Aberdeen. Painted
seascape and thistles, inlaid
brass, calendar. Mahogany case___400.00
Ithaca. 7' oak case. Late _____ 110.00

A. Rusted, Littleton (1690). Brass dial, rare single hand, original ornament, 6'6" high. Polished oak case _____ 375.00

Hanging Ceramic Clock. Made about 1825, with removable top. Grooved in various geometrical designs, highly colored with bright glaze finish. French or Viennese 8-day movement _____ 95.00

Hepplewhite Tall Case Clock. Cherry with maple inlay. So-called "Moon Face" type. 3 ball finials on hood. 6'11" high, 20" wide _____ 2000.00

Ingraham Kitchen Clock. Carved oak case _____ 37.50

Lantern Clock. 17th century. 10" square dail, unsigned, with single hour hand indicator. Silvered chapter ring fitted to usual lantern clock pillared case, verge escapement and side doors. 30-hour movement with Ting Tang quarter striking. Circa 1698 ____ 165.00

Octogan Doric, New Haven. Rosewood case, 15½x9", 8-day movement, strikes _____ 115.00

Painting, 15x20" of Big Ben in London. Clock movement near top of tower _____ 120.00

Paperweight Watch, or Bull's Eye Clock. 10" diam., 8-day French movement with second hand and porcelain dial _____ 85.00

Rosewood Clock. 17½x14x4" deep, with hand carving _____ 125.00

Royal Bonn "LaCannes" China Clock. 12x11x5½", Ansonia works, porcelain dial, 8-day movement, floral decor _____ 100.00

Royal Bonn. 9x12", green with purple and yellow orchids _____ 95.00

Seth Thomas. Brass Ship's Clock, for wall or table. 7" diam., 4" deep. Silvered dial, strikes ship's bells every half hour _____ 125.00

Seth Thomas. Circassian Walnut Clock. 8-day spring movement. Door fits flush against case and locks with winding key _____ 85.00

Seth Thomas. "Round Band Style". 1-day clock with rabbit picture in base _____ 60.00

Seth Thomas. Chime Clock. Gothic, Westminster chimes. 15x9" mahogany case _____ 95.00

Seth Thomas "Plymouth Hollow." 33" high, 8-day brass movement. Reverse painting on glass decor__ 200.00

Ship's Clock. 7" diam., brass, engraved steel face with numerals and Maryland Steel Co. Marine Dept. _____ 100.00

Skeleton Clock. 15" high. Single train works, under glass dome __ 225.00

Seth Thomas Clock. Empire style, wood case, spring drive. 8-day brass works _____ $85.00

Steeple Clock. In 19½x9½" Rosewood case. 8-day movement. Strikes and alarms. Waterbury Clock Co. _____ 120.00

Steeple Clock. 21" mahogany case, 8-day movement _____ 110.00

Steeple Clock. 21" mahogany case, 36-hour movement, strikes _____ 89.50

Sun Dial. Pewter, unmarked _____ 58.50

Sun Dial. Pocket. By Charles Blond, 18th century. Ivory _____ 120.00

Sun Dial, Pocket. By Johann Schrettegger, circa 1700, in original case _____ 110.00

Sun Dial, Pocket. By E. B. Meyrowitz, Paris. Made for U. S. Market, with silver dials, nickle case _____ 50.00

Tall Case Clock. Late 18th century style. Mahogany, 7'8" long, 21" wide _____ 850.00

Tall Case Clock. With wag-on-wall works, cherry case. Made in Pennsylvania _____ 650.00

Terry, Eli. Pillar and Scroll. 31" to top of center finial. Wood face with painted black numerals. 30-hour wood movement. Bottom has reverse painting on glass with eye to show movement of pendulum _ 650.00

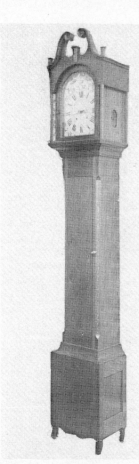

dial encircling cannon post under
hands _____ 280.00
Terry Clock Co. 1-day spring movement in rosewood case with pilas-
ters on either side, original gold
leaf picture on door _____ 90.00

Eli Terry & Son. Pillar & Scroll
type. Painted glass panes at bottom. Brass finials, 3-hour wooden
works _____ 650.00

Tiffany Desk Clock. Blue jewels
around border _____ 250.00
Wag-on-Wall Clock. German or
Dutch origin, circa 1800. Dial has
brass bezel and convex crystal
surrounded by octagonal carved
wood frame. Weight driven, 39"
pendulum, 30-hour, strikes on bell,
"Wags" strike on gongs _____ 95.00
Waterbury Clock Co. Ship's Bell
Striking Clock. In brass drum
on mahogany platform, with large
balance wheel escapement and
porcelain dial _____ 90.00
Westminster Chime Clock. For
mantel, mahogany case, 8-day,
strikes and chimes every 15 min-
utes. Made in Black Forest of
Germany _____ 140.00

Tall Case Clock. With wag-on-wall
works, cherry case. Made in Pennsylvania _____ $650.00

Terry, Eli, Jr. 8-day brass weight-
driven, empire case. Brass movements are rare under the Terry
name _____ 200.00
Terry, E. & Son. 8-day weight-
driven wood movement Shelf and
Mantel Clock. Stenciled top and
columns, alarm set by small brass

Williams, Orton and Preston, Farmington, Conn. 30-hour wooden movement with carved basket of flowers at top, carved columns on sides _____ 125.00

Williams, Orton and Preston, Farmington, Conn. Empire-type case, 8-day brass movement weight-driven. Cut steel pinions and machine-cut wheels. Mirror and original picture in door _____ 135.00

Willard, Simon. Lighthouse Clock __ 6000.00

## 30-HOUR WOODEN MOVEMENT WEIGHT-DRIVEN CLOCKS

Jonathan Frost, Reading, Mass. Mahogany columns and top _____ 100.00

Chauncey Ives, Bristol, Conn. Stenciled columns on door frame, stenciled top _____ 95.00

Jerome & Darrow. Carved eagle top, columns and claw feet, Winding hole at bottom of dial. Refinished _____ 165.00

Daniel Pratt, Jr., Reading, Mass., 1838. Mahogany columns and top board _____ 135.00

Seymour, Hall & Co., Unionville, Conn. Labeled "Invented by Eli Terry" _____ 110.00

Seymour, Williams & Porter, Farmington, Conn. Mahogany columns and top _____ 118.50

Terry, Eli, Jr., Plymouth, Conn. Stenciled columns and top, original picture _____ 170.00

## CLOISONNE

This name applies to enamel work on a metallic background. It originated in the Orient in ancient times. The bulk of the items found today was made in Europe and was exported to this country in the latter part of the Victorian Era (1870-1900).

Tea Set. Individual. Typical decoration on dark blue ground _____ $56.50

Bird. $5\frac{1}{2}$" high. _____$ 45.00
Bowls:
  Nut 3x3½" _____ 22.50
  Rice. 4½" diam., 2½" high. Red and yellow flowers over green, green lining _____ 7.75
  Rose. Red ground _____ 42.75
Boxes:
  1" high, 2¼" diam., 6-sided____ 24.50
  Covered, on legs, 5x6" _____ 26.50
  Floral decor. 3½x4" _____ 21.50
  Round. Covered. 7½" high, Colorful floral decor, Fu dog finial__ 52.50
  Stamp.1x1½". Pink and white flowers on blue ground. Marked "China" _____ 10.00
  Tobacco. Large, brightly colored. Fu dog finial _____ 57.50
Cup and Saucer _____ 27.50
Dish. Rectangular, on wood base __ 32.50
Incense Burner. 9½", ball-shaped __ 24.00
Inkwell. Covered, white background 33.50
Jars:
  3", with lid, footed _____ 20.00
  Ginger. 7½" high. Rusty red ground, floral decor _____ 42.50
Jardiniere and Stand. Black with dragon motif _____ 140.00
Napkin Ring. Floral and butterfly decor _____ 10.00
Pipe, Opium _____ 50.00
Plates:
  7" diam. Blue background _____ 28.50
  7¼" diam. Landscape _____ 30.00
  11" diam. Birds and flowers ___ 55.00
  11¾" diam. Hanging-type. Elaborately decorated with flowers and birds on light blue backers and birds on light blue background. Pair _____145.00
  12" diam. White and yellow background _____ 80.00
  14" diam. Butterfly and flowers 95.00
Tea Set. Individual. Typical decoration on dark blue background 56.50
Teapot. Individual _____ 21.50
Toothpick Holder. Varicolored ____ 10.50
Vases:
  4" high. Chinese design _____ 35.00
  5" high. Green, brown and blue with touches of red and cream. Pair _____ 32.50
  5½" high. Dark blue background, white dragon decorated in red and green _____ 35.00
  6" high. Bulbous bottom, narrow neck, floral decor of blue and white blossoms on green and yellow _____ 40.00
  6" high. Enamel bird and cherry blossoms on blue background. Pair _____ 47.50
  7¼" high. Dark brown with tan, green and orange decor _____ 32.50

9" high. Royal blue with butterflies and gold decor _____ 57.50
9½" high. On teakwood stand, cut-
out design in top part. Pair ____ 85.00
11" high. Moss green ground with
elaborate decorations of flowers,
butterflies and birds. Circa 1850.
Pair _____ 150.00

## CLOTHING

Styles of the past sometimes amuse and fascinate members of the present generation. Old clothing is often used for advertising and exhibition purposes. It is worn to balls and parties and, occasionally, a woman's club will have members who act as hostesses dress in old costumes.

Black mourning hat with feather ____ $8.50

Cap. Black and white, fur ears and
neck flaps _____$ 7.00
Dress. Black, 2-piece, fancy lace.
Circa 1880 _____ 12.00
Gown. Black silk, antique lace.
Puffed sleeves, separate skirt
over gray taffeta with basque
blouse. Size 14 _____ 22.00
Hat, Top. Black silk, in original
hat box _____ 18.00
Hat. Plug-type. Black. Circa 1825__ 24.50
Neck Piece. Fox, reddish gray__ 15.00
Night Gown, Woman's. Long, white_ 5.00
Robe. Buffalo fur. Felt lined,
64 x 54" _____ 40.00
Skirt, Hoop _____ 10.00
Suit. Size 40. Swallowtail-type with
vest, stiff bosomed shirt _____ 45.00

## COFFEE MILLS

IRON:
1-wheel and crank _____$ 40.00
Small, dated 1873, 7½" wheels, 9"
high. Excellent condition _____ 55.00

Coffee Mill. 7½ x 7½ x 5" high. Wood
with iron handle _____ $18.50

Squat. urn-shaped cup and cap
dome, iron lift-lid side door ___ 21.50
2-wheel, 17" high, repainted ____ 100.00
2-wheel, with crank. Eagle finial
on dome. Original paint in good
condition _____ 125.00
Same. Original paint in poor con-
dition _____ 50.00
Wall-type. with glass jar _____ 10.50
Wall-type. Original red scroll with
gold decor made by National
Specialty Co., Phila., Pa. _____ 28.50
Wall-type. Universal. Metal container above _____ 12.75
White iron, white china jar, blue
Delft-type scene. German _____ 54.50
WOOD:
Dovetailed. iron cup with lid.
Hinged door on base. Refinished 21.00
Dovetailed. 6" square, embossed
iron top _____ 22.50
Dovetailed. 6" square, early pew-
ter cup, iron crank, drawer.
Refinished _____ 30.00
7x7x8". Urn-shaped iron cup, sliding
doors, dovetailed drawer. Good
original finish _____ 21.00
2½x2½x3". Iron cup and crank.
Drawer _____ 20.00
Wall-type. 4½x7x10" high, glass
dome, round top _____ 16.00

## COIN SPOT GLASS

The glass derives its name from the opalescent spots appearing like coins in the glass. The usual glass colors are clear, light blue and cranberry in which the "spots" appear.

Bride's Basket. Cranberry with
opalescent spots, in plated
silver frame _____ 135.00

Pitcher and 6 glasses. Red and white.
Set _____ $165.00

Cruet. Cranberry with opalescent spots _____ 65.00
Pitcher. Large, light blue with
  spots _____ 60.00
Pitcher. Tankard size, cranberry with opalescent spots ____ 85.00
Sugar Shaker. Cranberry with
  opalescent spots _____ 27.50
Sugar Shaker. Light blue with
  opalescent spots _____ 23.50
Syrup. Clear glass with opalescent spots _____ 24.50
Syrup. Light blue, with tin lid,
  opalescent spots _____ 45.00
Tumbler. Blue with opalescent
  spots _____ 19.50
Tumbler. Clear glass with opalescent spots _____ 15.00
Tumbler. Cranberry with opalescent spots _____ 22.50

### COLLECTORS PLATES, ETC.

Bavarian Bareuther:
  1967—Xmas Plate. First issue ___ 50.00
  1968—Xmas Plate _____ 20.00
  1969—August 1st _____ 10.00
  1969—Father's Day _____ 25.00
  1969—Mother's Day _____ 25.00
  1969—Xmas Plate _____ 10.00

Bing and Grondahl:

| | | | |
|---|---|---|---|
| 1904 | 55.00 | 1937 | 47.50 |
| 1906 | 58.00 | 1938 | 68.00 |
| 1907 | 58.00 | 1939 | 79.00 |
| 1908 | 49.50 | 1940 | 79.00 |
| 1909 | 55.00 | 1942 | 72.00 |
| 1910 | 52.50 | 1943 | 72.00 |
| 1911 | 52.50 | 1944 | 47.50 |
| 1916 | 45.00 | 1945 | 70.00 |
| 1917 | 45.00 | 1946 | 47.50 |
| 1918 | 45.00 | 1947 | 59.50 |

Bing & Grondahl. 1909 _____ $85.00

| | | | |
|---|---|---|---|
| 1919 | 45.00 | 1953 | 52.00 |
| 1920 | 45.00 | 1959 | 67.00 |
| 1921 | 45.00 | 1960 | 67.00 |
| 1922 | 45.00 | 1961 | 50.00 |
| 1923 | 45.00 | 1962 | 32.50 |
| 1924 | 45.00 | 1963 | 45.00 |
| 1925 | 45.00 | 1964 | 25.00 |
| 1926 | 45.00 | 1965 | 25.00 |
| 1927 | 45.00 | 1966 | 22.00 |
| 1928 | 45.00 | 1967 | 20.00 |
| 1929 | 45.00 | 1968 | 18.00 |
| 1931 | 41.50 | 1969 | 10.00 |

Bing and Grondahl:
  1969—Mother's Day Plate _____ 75.00
Danish Roskilde:
  1969—Xmas Plate _____ 15.00
  1969—Xmas Plate _____ 10.00
Delft:
  1969—First Men Around The Moon 28.50
  1969—First Men On The Moon __ 28.50
Donaldo:
  1968—Annual Plate. Portraying
    John F. Kennedy _____ 20.00
Frankoma:
  1965 _____ 150.00
  1966 _____ 65.00
  1967 _____ 45.00
  1968 _____ 10.00
  1968—Mug. First Issue _____ 10.00
  1969 _____ 5.00
  1969—Mug. Red _____ 3.00
  1969—VIP Bottle Vase _____ 30.00
  Cherokee Alphabet Plate _____ 3.00
  Kansas State Plate _____ 3.00
  Oklahoma Plate _____ 3.00
Haviland:
  Abhaham Lincoln _____ 100.00
  Martha Washington _____ 100.00

**Israeli:**

| | | |
|---|---|---|
| 1967—Tower of David | ---------- | 10.00 |
| 1967—Wailing Wall | ----------- | 10.00 |
| 1968—Masada | ----------------- | 7.50 |
| 1969—Rachel's Tomb | ----------- | 6.50 |

**Lalique:**

| | | |
|---|---|---|
| 1965 | ------------------------------ | 1200.00 |
| 1966 | ------------------------------ | 250.00 |
| 1967 | ------------------------------ | 150.00 |
| 1968 | ------------------------------ | 100.00 |
| 1969 | ------------------------------ | 85.00 |

**Norway Prorsgrad:**

| | | |
|---|---|---|
| 1968—First Edition | ------------- | 25.00 |
| 1969 | -------------------------- | 10.00 |

**Rosenthal:**

| | | |
|---|---|---|
| 1967 | -------------------------- | 25.00 |
| 1968 | -------------------------- | 25.00 |

**Royale:**

| | | |
|---|---|---|
| 1969—First Man On The Moon | -- | 30.00 |
| 1969—Xmas Plate. First issue | -- | 12.00 |

**Spode:**

| | | |
|---|---|---|
| Prince Charles Investiture | ----- | 70.00 |
| Winston Churchill | -------------- | 100.00 |
| Winston Churchill Bust | --------- | 75.00 |

**Sweden Rorstrand:**

| | | |
|---|---|---|
| 1968 | ------------------------- | 85.00 |

**Val St. Lambert:**

| | | |
|---|---|---|
| 1968—Rembrandt and Rubens. Pair | ------------------------- | 100.00 |
| 1969—Van Dyck and Van Gogh. Pair | ------------------------- | 75.00 |
| 1969—Heritage or Pilgrims Plate | | 200.00 |

**Wedgwood:**

| | | |
|---|---|---|
| 1969—Xmas Plate | ------------- | 40.00 |

### COMMEMORATIVE PLATES
#### See SOUVENIR PLATES

### COMMEMORATIVE SPOONS
#### See SPOONS, SOUVENIR

### COPELAND    SPODE  CHINA

The firm was founded by Josiah Spode in 1770 in the Staffordshire section of England. Later, W. T. Copeland & Sons succeeded him using the designation "Late Spode" on their wares. The firm made various types of ware including Salt Glaze, Jasperware, Delft, porcelain figurines and fine dinner services. Still later the firm became known as Copeland and Garrett.

German Ed. 1917. Royal Copenhagen..$88.00

**Royal Copenhagen:**

| | | | |
|---|---|---|---|
| 1916 | 55.00 | 1931 | 65.00 |
| 1917 | 55.00 | 1933 | 66.50 |
| 1918 | 55.00 | 1954 | 75.00 |
| 1919 | 55.00 | 1960 | 50.00 |
| 1922 | 45.00 | 1961 | 50.00 |
| 1923 | 45.00 | 1962 | 65.00 |
| 1924 | 45.00 | 1963 | 35.00 |
| 1925 | 45.00 | 1964 | 30.00 |
| 1926 | 49.00 | 1965 | 25.00 |
| 1927 | 55.00 | 1966 | 22.50 |
| 1929 | 55.00 | 1967 | 20.00 |
| 1930 | 55.00 | 1968 | 20.00 |

**Royal Copenhagen:**

| | | |
|---|---|---|
| 1967—Large Mug | ------------- | 40.00 |
| 1967—Small Mug | ------------- | 15.00 |
| 1968—Large Mug | ------------- | 30.00 |
| 1968—Small Mug | ------------- | 12.50 |
| 1969—Large Mug | ------------- | 25.00 |
| 1969—Small Mug | ------------- | 10.00 |
| 1969—Xmas Plate | ------------- | 12.50 |
| Virgin Islands | ----------------- | 29.50 |

Biscuit and Candy Dish. 7½" ------- $42.50

Bowl. 9" diam., footed, scalloped rim, blue and white colors. Marked Copeland Spode's Tower, England ------------------------$ 25.00

Cracker Jar. White classical figures on blue ground ----------- 55.00

Cup and Saucer. Orange and gold
color. About 100 years old ____ 50.00
Jug. Large, blue Jasper ground,
applied grape vine, drinking
scenes in cream. Applied cream
band around rim, vine handle __ 68.50
Pitchers:
Blue and white, men on horses
on fox chase _____ 80.00
8¼" high. White with orange peel
decor. Signed _____ 45.00
Plates:
8¼" diam., cream with green and
brown leaf decor _____ 16.00
9" diam., Greek key design with
Classic figures on blue ground__ 16.50
Platter. 15x19" Leaf and acorn
border _____ 72.50
Soup Plate. Brown border, English
scene in center _____ 11.50
Soup Tureen. Matching ladle and
platter. Brown and white _____ 135.00

Miniature Sugar Bowl, Creamer and
Teapot. Decor of pink roses and
green leaves. Set _____ $35.00

Sugar and Creamer. Blue ground,
raised white hunting scene. Set__ 60.00
Tea Kettle. All china. Rare _____ 250.00
Teapots:
Dark blue and rust colored floral
decor _____ 100.00
9½" high, clear blue, gilded
handles. Fu dog finial on lid. Imported from England by Tiffany
Co. in late 19th century _____ 115.00
Wash Set. Pitcher 12" high, bowl
15" across, blue and white color 85.00

## COPENHAGEN, See ROYAL COPENHAGEN

## COPPER

Apothecary's Still. Bulbous body,
pointed snout _____$ 65.00
Bed Warmer. Pierced, wood handle 72.50
Boilers:
Wash _____ 24.00
Wash. Made into seat, brass and
copper _____ 40.00

Chafing Dish. Covered, 9½" to top
of finial, wood handle on burn-
er, brass lobster-type legs        $55.00

Wash. Cut down to height of 6½"
and made into a planter _____ 35.00
Chafing Dish. Covered. 9¼" dish
with fancy handles, wood grips
and knob. Wood handle on burn-
er. 14" copper tray with perforated rim. Perfection. Manning-
Bowman Co., 1901 _____ 49.50
Coal Hod. Large helmet-type. 16"
to top of handle. Polished and
lacquered _____ 95.00
Coffee Pots:
Pewter trim, burnished and
lacquered _____ 25.00
Rough condition _____ 12.00
10" high. Burnished and lacquered _____ 32.50
Compote. Openwork _____ 33.50
Dippers:
One-gallon capacity. Burnished
and lacquered _____ 35.00
Well. Polished and lacquered ___ 22.50
Dow Pot. Dutch. Large _____ 135.00
Eagle, American. Large, with cop-
per ball, from old weathervane__ 235.00
Funnel. Handled _____ 10.00
Hot Water Bottle. Oval, with screw
top _____ 24.50
Jug, Water. 7½" high, plus a stand-
ing 12" handle, hinged cover__ 29.50
Kettles:
22" diam. _____ 55.00
24" diam. Apple butter, good
condition, not cleaned _____ 65.00

Water. English, burnished and
  lacquered _____ 45.00
Ladles:
  Heavy, decorative with hook
    handle _____ 24.50
  Iron handle _____ 26.50
Megaphone, Ship's. 35'' high, flared
  mouthpiece _____ 50.00
Milk Bucket with spout, lid and
  handle. Bound with brass bands.
  15'' high. Cleaned and buffed__ 65.00
Milk Tank. 10 gal., with spigot___ 35.00
Mold $2\frac{1}{2}$x$2\frac{3}{4}$'' _____ 15.00
Pails:
  16'' diam. _____ 49.50
  24'' diam. _____ 17.50
Pans:
  7 ''diam., 5'' deep _____ 35.00
  10'' diam., $7\frac{1}{2}$'' deep, iron handle 50.00
  13'' diam., 9'' deep _____ 60.00
Pitcher. $1\frac{1}{2}$'' high. Small _____ 5.00
Saucepan. Covered. 10'' diam., 5''
  deep. 12'' iron handle pierced
  for hanging. Burnished and lacquered _____ 40.00
Skillet. $9\frac{1}{2}$'' diam., 10'' iron handle_ 37.50
Tea Set. Medium size. Teapot,
  sugar, creamer and tray _____ 48.50

Square _____ 49.50
Swedish _____ 48.00
Teapots:
  Burnished and lacquered _____ 35.00
  $1\frac{1}{2}$ pint. Copper and wood handle.
  hinged lid on spout, 3 hand-
  forged legs _____ 33.50
Toast Rack _____ 11.00
Tray. 18x15'' _____ 32.50
Umbrella Stand. Brass lion handles 25.00
Vase. $15\frac{1}{2}$'' high. Sterling silver
  inlay of ivy foliage _____ 35.00
Weather Vane. Cow. 15x25'' _____ 275.00


## COPPER LUSTRE

Copper Lustre was first made in England
by the Staffordshire district potters between
1800 and 1805. The use of a copper compound in the glaze resulted in a metallic
copper-like surface. The bulk of the ware
imported into the United States was between
1840 and 1890.

A number of reproductions have come
onto the market recently—small creamers
and a so-called "Polka Jug" or pitcher. The
new ware is usually thicker and heavier
than the old.

Teakettle. French origin. Opaline
handle. $8\frac{1}{2}$'' high ____ _____ $45.00

Teakettles:
  American, early _____ 55.00
  Early. Iron handle and 3-legged
  iron trivet. Hinged cover on
  spout _____ 58.50
  Goose-neck spout:
    Footed _____ 48.50
    Metal handle _____ 50.00
    Norwegian _____ 47.50

Cream Jug. $6\frac{1}{2}$''. Brown and blue __ $100.00

Bowls:
  $5\frac{3}{4}$'' diam., covered _____$ 65.00
  $5\frac{3}{4}$'' diam., light brown band __ 48.50
  Waste. Blue with lustre band __ 50.00
Chalice. 4'' high, $1\frac{1}{4}$'' green band
  with raised fruit and beads ____ 57.50

203

**Cups and Saucers:**
Hand painted design _____ 52.50
Scalloped edge _____ 48.00
Dog. 8'' high _____ 65.00
Flower Pots. Tub-shaped with stands, 4'' high. Mock shell handles. Pair _____ 135.00
**Goblets:**
Colored flowers, light blue band 65.00
Colored flowers, buff bands ____ 60.00
Girl and dog decor, blue band__ 58.50
**Mugs:**
$2\frac{1}{2}$'' high, plain _____ 32.50
$3\frac{1}{2}$'' high, plain _____ 35.00
4'' high, 4'' diam., pink lustre on rim, tan band _____ 40.00
Name, ''Samuel'', pink lustre inside _____ 35.00
Shaving. Floral sprays on blue band, decorated handle _____ 45.00

Pitcher. 5'' high. Leaf decor at top. Masonic symbol at bottom _____ $75.00

**Pitchers;**
3'', sanded band _____ 35.00
$3\frac{1}{2}$'', blue band with figure of girl and cat on either side ____ 38.50
4'', lustre schoolhouse design on tan band _____ 75.00
$4\frac{1}{2}$'', white band with red decor_ 55.00
5'', blue bands with lustre design 65.00
$5\frac{1}{2}$'', rough sand finish around middle _____ 60.00
$5\frac{3}{4}$'', red flower band with purple leaves _____ 89.50
6'', Man-of-the-Woods spout, dolphin handle _____ 75.00
7'', white band with floral decor 95.00
7'', dancing figures, blue trim. Late _____ 38.50

$7\frac{1}{2}$'', decorated bands on yellow ground _____ 175.00
8'', green, white and purple decor _____ 90.00
Salt. Footed, open _____ 30.00
Sugar Bowl. Open, raised floral and leaf design on 2'' blue border _____$ 65.00
**Teapots:**
$6\frac{1}{2}$'' high, pink, green and white decor on copper, 4 feet _____ 150.00
Multicolored band _____ 125.00
Toby Jug _____ 115.00
Toothpick Holder. Sanded band___ 29.50
Urn. $8\frac{1}{2}$'' high, 8'' across handles, $3\frac{1}{2}$'' green band with lustre decoration _____ 115.00

## CORALENE

A type of ''so-called'' Art Glass made by the New England Glass Co., in the late 1880's and early 1890's. It is Satin Glass with applied glass beading in a design similar to natural coral. A wheat and Fleur-de-lis design was also used for decorating this glass.

Vase. $8\frac{1}{2}$'' high. Heavily decorated. Scarce-type _____ 600.00

Bowls, various types _____$ 325.00
Cup, Punch. Scarce _____ 335.00
Toilet Bottle. Blue, with beaded decorations _____ 350.00

Tumbler. Greenish-blue to pale blue
  with beading _____ 400.00

Vases:
  4¼" high. Rose colored spherical
  body covered with coral branch
  beading. Smooth 2¼" opening at
  top, off-white casing _____ 350.00
  5" high. Dusky rose to light
  pink with yellow coral trim ____ 375.00
  5" high. Cranberry to pink with
  all over beading _____ 385.00
  5¾" high. Bulbous, yellow with
  gold rim at top _____ 375.00
  6¼" high. 6 panels with beaded
  fleur-de-lis decoration _____ 395.00
  7" high. Dusky pink at top, white
  at bottom. Deep yellow beaded
  decor in seaweed pattern _____ 420.00
  8" high. Red top blending to
  yellow at base _____ 425.00
  9½" high. Yellow on blue overlay
  Satin Glass. Bulbous base, round
  mouth _____ 450.00
  11" high. Chartreuse with gold
  beading _____ 500.00

## CORONATION ITEMS

Interest in Coronation Items has been
shown by a small group of collectors. The
ruling heads of England, from the time
of Queen Victoria to the present, are
among the most desirable. They are usually
made of chinaware or glass.

Plate. 9" diam. Queen Elizabeth II,
  Duke of Edinburgh—June 1953.
  Gold trim, white ground, deep
  red _____ $ 4.00

Beaker. King George V, 1902 _____ 22.00
Glass, Liqueur. Clear. Coronation
  of Elizabeth II _____ 6.00
Medallions. Blue Jasper, Elizabeth
  and Philip, 1953. 3¾x4¼", pair___ 60.00
Mug. King Edward VIII. 3¼" high__ 12.50
Paperweight. St. Louis-type. Eliza-
  beth II. Modern, but collectible__ 150.00
Plaque. Ivory-colored. George &
  Elizabeth _____ 18.00

Plate. 9" diam. Queen Elizabeth.
  White with deep red _____ $ 4.00

Plates:
  Elizabeth II, 1953. Chinese de-
  sign _____ 9.50
  King Edward. 1937, 10" diam. __ 9.00
  King Edward VII. 1902. Scalloped
  edges, 8" diam. _____ 10.00
  King George V and Queen Mary.
  9" diam. _____ 10.50
  King. Geo. VI and Queen
  Elizabeth. _____ 9.00
  Queen Victoria. 60th Anniversary
  Plate, small _____ 6.50
  Queen Victoria Jubilee, 1887. 9½"
  diam., with Reg. #63164 _____ 15.00
  Sterling Spoon. Queen Victoria.
  4¾" long. Cut-out on handle
  end. 1837-97 pressed in bowl.
  Gold wash _____ 8.50

## COSMOS GLASS

A type of Milk Glass with a design of
Cosmos flowers in various color combinations of blue, red and yellow. The decorations are the "stained" or "flashed"
type and colors are usually worn or faded
on pieces which received considerable use.

Pitcher, Water ------------------ $ 150.00

| | |
|---|---|
| Butter Dish ---------------------- | 140.00 |
| Castor, Pickle. With tongs ------- | 120.00 |
| Castor Set. Salt, pepper, mustard_ | 135.00 |
| Creamer ------------------------- | 85.00 |
| Lamps: | |
|   Large ------------------------- | 140.00 |
|   Miniature --------------------- | 90.00 |
|   Miniature. Base only ---------- | 38.50 |
| Lemonade Set. Bulbous pitcher with lid. 6 mugs with cobalt blue handles ------------------------- | 250.00 |
| Pitcher, Water. 8¾'' high --------- | 150.00 |
| Salt Shaker. From castor set ---- | 25.00 |
| Salt Shakers. Matching pair ------ | 55.00 |
| Spooner ------------------------- | 49.50 |
| Sugar Bowl. Covered ------------ | 140.00 |
| Syrup --------------------------- | 95.00 |
| Tumbler ------------------------- | 40.00 |

## CRACKER JARS

The cracker jar was, more or less, a companion to the old cookie jar. The types vary from crude pottery to fine satin glass with silver-plated lids and bails. Many of the finer types were produced by Silver Plating Companies from 1880 to 1900.

| | |
|---|---|
| Bristol. Turquoise, enamel cranes and floral decor. Strawberry finial on cover -------------------- | 65.00 |

| | |
|---|---|
| Cracker Jar. Light green cased glass. 9'' to top of silver plated handle, with plated cover --------------- | $32.50 |
| China. Blue and gold with floral decor, straight sides. Metal cover and bail ---------------------- | 32.50 |
| China. 10'' high, bulbous. Transfer flower design ------------------ | 27.50 |
| Limoges. 4¾'' high. Yellow with handles, edges and finial in gold | 30.00 |
| Satin Glass. Pink, blue and gold decor. Shell design around base. Top and handle resilvered. Finest type --------------------------- | 160.00 |
| Satin Glass. White to green with pink wild roses. Top and handle resilvered --------------------- | 75.00 |
| Staffordshire. White salt glaze. Allover design of leaves and poppies, with silver band and lid_ | 65.00 |

## CRANBERRY GLASS

Cranberry, or Ruby Glass, was made by adding a small quantity of gold to a pot of glass. Objects were blown or molded and were amber in color. When reheated at a low temperature the ruby or cranberry shade having a blue-violet tint was developed.

Copper was used at times to produce a cheaper grade of cranberry glass. The finished product is amber-red in color and does not have the blue-violet tint of glass made with gold.

Prices have dropped on cranberry glass. Importers have recently been flooding the market with English glass, most of which is of recent manufacture. Prices on good old glass have decreased because of the slack demand among collectors who have lost interest because of the deluge of imported glass.

Pitcher. English. 7½" high. Flared ribbed top, clear applied handle __$75.00

Barber Bottles. See "Barber Bottles."
Basket. 7½" diam., applied lily-of-the-valley and forget-me-not decor. Gilded metal frame and handle _____$ 72.50
Bell. 10¼" diam. English Bristol, clear handle (Late) _____ 52.50
Bobeches. Opalescent ruffled edges. Pair _____ 24.50
Bottles. 8". Thumbprint design, crystal stopper _____ 42.50
Bowl. 5½"x6¼", footed, applied flowers, ribbed sides _____ 50.00
Boxes:
    Covered, on metal feet. Gold-leaf type decor _____ 75.00
    Patch. Gold filigree design, with cover _____ 35.00

White enamel portrait on hinged cover _____ 40.00
Bucket, Ice. Enamel lily-of-the-valley decor. 5¼" high _____ 72.50
Butter Dish. Crystal finial on Inverted Thumbprint cover. Clear Daisy & Button pattern base ____ 87.50
Castor. See "Pickle Castors"
Celery, ITP. Scalloped top, enamel decor _____ 50.00
Compote. 8" diam., 5½" clear standard _____ 75.00
Compote. 5" diam. Clear blown stem _____ 42.50
Cordial Set. Tray, decanter, 8 cordials _____ 95.00
Creamers:
    3" high. Fluted cloverleaf top__ 42.50
    4½" high. Panelled, bulbous, with clear handle _____ 40.00
Cruets. See "Cruet" section
Decanters. See "Decanters, Glass"
Finger Bowl _____ 32.50
Gas Shades:
    7½" diam. Swirled fluted rim __ 21.50
    Hobnail _____ 30.00
Goblet, Footed _____ 29.50
Lamps. See "Lamps, Glass"
Milk Bowl. English. 9" diam. 5½" high _____ 79.50
Mustard Jar. Silver plated top and spoon _____ 25.00
Pickle Castors. See "Pickle Castors"

Vase. English. 6½" high. Crimped top, applied white decorations ___$40.00

Pitchers:
    5½" high _____ 50.00
    7½" high. ITP, 5 neck rings ____ 68.50
    7½" high. English. Flared ribbed top, clear applied handle _____ 75.00

11" high. Clear handle, possibly
English ---------------------------- 65.00
Lemonade. White enamel trim -- 65.00
See also, "Pitchers, Glass"
Salt, Master. Sterling holder with
spoon. 2 pieces ------------------ 60.00
Sauce Boat. 4½" high, early, free
blown ---------------------------- 98.50
Sugar Bowl and Creamer. Applied
clear handles. Set -------------- 75.00
Sugar Shakers:
Plain ---------------------------- 28.50
4¾" high, lattice overlay ------- 35.00
Syrup -------------------------------- 62.50
Toothpick Holder. English. Applied
ruffled clear glass band around
middle, applied clear feet ------ 40.00
Tray. 13" diam., 2" deep -------- 69.50
Tumblers:
ITP -------------------------------- 27.50
Lemonade. Handled ------------ 30.00
Opalescent coin-spot ---------- 22.50
Ribbed swirl ------------------- 25.00

Vase. 9½" high. Circa 1860. Gold
decor --------------------------------- $45.00

Vases:
4" high. Applied handles ------ 30.00
6½" high. Bud ------------------ 45.00
6½" high. English. Crimped top,
applied white decorations ------ 40.00
8" high. Footed, good color --- 35.00
8" high. Jack-in-Pulpit -------- 42.50
8¼" high. Shell pattern,
flared neck. Pair -------------- 80.00
11" high. Opalescent, fluted ---- 65.00
16½" high ---------------------- 120.00
Water Set. Deep Cranberry.
Pitcher, 9" high, and 6
tumblers -------------------------- 140.00
Wine Glass. Clear foot and stem-- 15.00

### CROWN DERBY,
### See ROYAL CROWN DERBY

### CROWN MILANO

A fine type of glass made at the Mt.
Washington Glass Co., New Bedford, Mass.,
in the latter part of the 19th century. It
is often decorated with flowers and leaves
encrusted with gold and silver. Many pieces
are signed with the letters "C. M." in the
pontil.

Pitcher ------------------------------ $785.00

Bowl. 4½" diam. Petal top, melon
ribbed ---------------------------- 275.00
Cookie Jar. Silver top and bail.
Yellow body with gold and red
decorations --------------------- 425.00
Creamer. Signed ---------------- 400.00
Cruet. Signed ------------------- 600.00

Cup and Saucer. Demitasse _____ 435.00
Humidor, Cigar. 5" high. Cream
  ground with varicolored pansies__ 325.00
Jardiniere. 13" high, 16" wide.
  Pastel tans, pinks, greens and
  yellows. Enamel leaf decoration
  with gold and silver. "C.M."
  in pontil _____ 550.00
Pitcher. Water. Signed _____ 785.00
Rose Jar. Deep colored roses on
  white background _____ 325.00
Sugar Bowl, Covered. Signed ____ 450.00
Sugar Bowl and Creamer. Ivory
  background, blue, pink and green
  handpainted flowers. Original
  tops and handles _____ 700.00
Sweet Meat Jar, Covered. 4¾"
  diam. Jewelled. Metal lid with
  turtle finial _____ 460.00
Syrup. Metal spout and top. White
  satin glass _____ 600.00
Syrup. Signed _____ 600.00
Vases:
  8½", gold embossed in oak leaf
  and acorn design. Signed "C.M."
  and numbered _____ 650.00
  8¾", square, oak leaf and acorn
  decoration, 2 handles at neck.
  Unsigned _____ 585.00

Amber:
  Blown, with applied blue handle
  and stopper _____ 42.50
  Daisy and Cube _____ 36.00
  Inverted Thumbprint, original
  matching stopper _____ 52.50
Amberina _____ 180.00
Amethyst:
  Deep, with brown oval panels
  and clear stopper _____ 60.00
  Light, with amber handle and
  stopper, melon-shaped _____ 60.00
Baccarat. 10", original amber-
  swirl stopper _____ 75.00
Blue:
  Cobalt, clear stopper and
  handle _____ 40.00
  Inverted Thumbprint, blown, with
  clear reeded handle and stopper 48.50
  Milk Glass, with flower panels__ 49.50
  Nailsea. 6" high, blue with white
  Satin Glass loopings, frosted base
  and handles _____ 100.00

## CRUETS

Cranberry Glass. Applied clear
glass handle and stopper. Small__ $60.00

Clear Glass. Blown, with etched fern
and flower design _____ $18.00

**Clear:**

| | |
|---|---|
| Bull's Eye | 23.50 |
| Cut Glass. Small | 40.00 |
| Cut Glass. 9¾'' high | 49.50 |
| Hobnail. Miniature | 19.00 |
| Interlocking Hearts | 22.50 |
| Maize | 45.00 |
| Peacock Eye | 16.00 |
| Threaded | 30.00 |

**Cranberry:**

| | |
|---|---|
| 8'' high, orinigal stopper | 89.50 |
| 11½'' high, wine, melon-shaped | 100.00 |
| Hobnail | 95.00 |
| Opalescent coin-spot, clear handles and stopper | 65.00 |

**Custard Glass:**

| | |
|---|---|
| Plain | 60.00 |
| Chrysanthemum Sprig | 125.00 |
| Winged Scroll | 175.00 |

Flowing Blue Centennial. 1815-1915. Lord Kitchner portrait on one side, another Lord on reverse. English Rd. #625614 _____ 75.00

Mary Gregory Glass. Blue with white enamel decor of girl. Matching blue stopper. 7'' high__ 67.50

Opalescent Spanish Lace. Ribbed__ 55.00

Rubina. Hobnail pattern. Clear top and handle _____ 72.50

Ruby top, block design. Flint ____ 49.50

Vaseline opalescent threaded glass. Lion Leg trim, enamel flowers__ 60.00

White. Milk Glass. Royal Oak pattern. 4¾'' high. Made by Northwood Co., Wheeling, W. Va., about 1900 _____ 55.00

## CUPS AND SAUCERS

So-called "Farmer's" Cup. Large, light blue. Marked Staffordshire, England _____ $18.00

**Adams:**

| | |
|---|---|
| Columbus. Blue | 19.50 |
| Gazelle. Pink | 21.00 |
| Seasons. Sepia | 21.50 |

Arabian Pattern. Purple, handle less _____ 16.00

Bride of Lammermoor. Dark blue Staffordshire _____ 28.50

**Canton:**

| | |
|---|---|
| Demitasse | 21.50 |
| Early, handleless | 34.50 |

Chelsea. Green sprig _____ 16.75

Farmers. Large, with German inscription _____ 18.00

Farmers. Staffordshire. Large, with motto "Take Ye A Cuppe O' Kindness" etc. _____ 24.50

French China. Large, violets _____ 10.50

Hand Painted. Currant spray ____ 12.50

Hand Painted. Holly and berries __ 12.50

Maastricht. Lavender _____ 13.75

Mustache. Haviland china. Painted violets _____ 18.50

Mustache. Ivory ground, wide cerise edge _____ 16.00

Newhall. Oriental flower pot design _____ 32.50

Pink Lustre. House pattern _____ 35.00

Pink Lustre. Red flower _____ 31.50

"Remember Me." Large c/s ____ 10.75

"Remember Me." Standard size __ 9.75

**Rose Medallion:**

| | |
|---|---|
| Bouillon, covered | 15.00 |
| Demitasse | 11.00 |
| Handleless | 14.50 |
| Standard size | 12.00 |

Staffordshire. Light blue, beehive__ 18.75

Tea Cup and Saucer. German, porcelain. Circa 1820-1840. Raised border, hand painted multicolor floral decor _____ 48.00

Note: See Staffordshire China for Other Cups

## CUSTARD GLASS

A cream or custard colored opaque glass which was a product of the Northwood Glass Co., Wheeling, W. Va., about 1898. Two popular patterns were the Argonaut Shell and Chrysanthemum Sprig.

**Banana Boats:**

| | |
|---|---|
| Chrysanthemum Sprig | 200.00 |
| Louis XV. Signed Northwood | 190.00 |

Berry Bowl. Argonaut Shell. Footed_ 250.00

Berry Set. Grape and Gothic Arch. Signed Northwood. Bowl and 4 small berry dishes _____ 240.00

Bowl. Argonaut Shell. Northwood. 8½x11½'' _____ 250.00

Bowl. Beaded Circle. Large, enamel decor _____ 130.00

Bowl, Punch. Panelled. Sunburst Cane. 14½'' diam. _____ 300.00

Bowl, Punch. 13'' diam., 8½'' high. Pink scrolls, gold decorated scalloped edge _____ 185.00

**Sugar Bowl. Crysanthemum Sprig** . . . **$75.00**

**Butter Dishes:**

| | |
|---|---:|
| Argonaut Shell _____ | 175.00 |
| Covered. Chrysanthemum Sprig__ | 195.00 |
| Covered. Inverted Fern _____ | 160.00 |
| Covered. Panelled Flower _____ | 150.00 |
| Covered. Winged Scroll _____ | 165.00 |
| Louis XV _____ | 125.00 |
| **Cake Stand. High standard. 10''** | |
| diam. _____ | 90.00 |
| **Celery. Chrysanthemum Sprig** ____ | 140.00 |

**Compotes:**

| | |
|---|---:|
| Candy. Tall, stemmed. Signed | |
| Northwood _____ | 69.50 |
| Chrysanthemum Sprig. Signed | |
| Northwood _____ | 75.00 |
| Jelly. Argonaut Shell _____ | 85.00 |
| **Creamer and Sugar Bowl. Argonaut** | |
| Shell. Northwood _____ | 125.00 |

**Creamers:**

| | |
|---|---:|
| Chrysanthemum Sprig _____ | 75.00 |
| Inverted Fan and Feather _____ | 145.00 |
| Nautilus. Signed Northwood ____ | 80.00 |
| Winged Scroll _____ | 100.00 |

**Cruets:**

| | |
|---|---:|
| Chrysanthemum Sprig _____ | 125.00 |
| Plain _____ | 60.00 |

| | |
|---|---:|
| Winged Scroll _____ | 175.00 |
| **Goblet. Grape** _____ | 35.00 |

**Pitchers:**

| | |
|---|---:|
| Argonaut Shell. Water _____ | 245.00 |
| Chrysanthemum Sprig. High gold | |
| feet _____ | 160.00 |
| Plain _____ | 67.50 |

**Plates:**

| | |
|---|---:|
| 7'' diam. Three Fruits. Northwood | 48.50 |
| 8'' diam. Grape. Signed | |
| Northwood _____ | 39.50 |
| 9'' diam. Lion. Fenton _____ | 50.00 |
| **Rose Bowl. Square top. Persian** | |
| medallions. Signed Northwood __ | 72.50 |

**Sauce Dishes:**

| | |
|---|---:|
| Chrysanthemum Sprig. Signed | |
| Northwood _____ | 50.00 |
| Geneva. Footed _____ | 18.00 |

**Spooners:**

| | |
|---|---:|
| Argonaut Shell. Signed North- | |
| wood _____ | 80.00 |
| Chrysanthemum Sprig _____ | 70.00 |
| Geneva _____ | 50.00 |
| Louis XV. Signed Northwood ____ | 65.00 |
| Nautilus. Signed Northwood ____ | 65.00 |

**Sugar Bowls:**

| | |
|---|---:|
| Covered. Beaded Circle _____ | 95.00 |
| Covered. Chrysanthemum Sprig__ | 95.00 |
| Covered. Grape and Gothic | |
| Arch _____ | 70.00 |
| Covered. Louis XV. Signed | |
| Northwood _____ | 90.00 |
| Covered. Panelled Flower _____ | 75.00 |
| **Table Set. Chrysanthemum Sprig,** | |
| Butter, covered sugar, creamer, | |
| spooner. Signed Northwood ____ | 325.00 |
| **Table Set. Louis XV. Covered but-** | |
| ter, sugar, creamer and spooner_ | 245.00 |
| **Toothpick. Chrysanthemum Sprig.** | |
| Signed Northwood _____ | 125.00 |

**Tumblers:**

| | |
|---|---:|
| Argonaut Shell _____ | 55.00 |
| Chrysanthemum Sprig _____ | 40.00 |
| Inverted Fan and Feather _____ | 50.00 |
| Winged Scroll _____ | 55.00 |
| **Water Set. Chrysanthemum Sprig.** | |
| Signed Northwood. Pitcher and 6 | |
| tumblers _____ | 340.00 |

## CUT GLASS

Any incisory form of ornamenting glass with diamond or hard metal point by a lapidary's wheel is known as ''cutting'' glass.

Cut Glass is reputed to have first been made by the ancient Romans. In the 1700's the art spread to Europe, England and Ireland.

The popularity of the glass reached its peak in the early 1900's in the United States.

| | |
|---|---:|
| Atomizer. $5\frac{1}{2}$'' high _____ | 18.50 |
| Basket. $8\frac{1}{4}$'' across _____ | 77.50 |

Plate. 9½'' diam. Tuthill _____ $75.00

Bell. 5½'' high _____ 25.00
Bobeches. Pair _____ 22.50
Bottle. Dresser, with stopper. Hobstar and fan pattern, 8½'' high,
  2⅜'' diam. _____ 30.00
Bowls:
  7⅞'' diam., 4¼'' high, footed,
    signed ''Fry'' _____ 75.00
  8'' diam., ''Starling'' pattern __ 50.00
  8'' diam., hobstar _____ 48.50
  8'' diam., pinwheel pattern ____ 49.50
  8'' diam., 2 handles, signed
    ''Clark'' _____ 65.00
  8'' diam., 4'' high, signed
    ''Libbey'' _____ 72.50
  8'' diam., strawberry pattern,
    star bottom. Signed ''Gravic
    Glass Hawkes'' _____ 82.50
  9'' diam., ordinary cut pattern__ 35.00
Box, Glove. 10½'' long, intaglio
  basket on top _____ 185.00
Box, Round. 8'' diam., 4'' high.
  Beveled mirror inside. Rim and
  hinges sterling. Completely cut__ 175.00
Bread Tray _____ 60.00
Butter Dish. Covered, cane border__ 67.50
Butter Pat _____ 5.00
Butter Tub _____ 48.50
Candlesticks. Curtain Drape, five
  panel, hollow stems. 4'' base,
  8'' tall. Pair _____ 90.00
Canoe. Harvard pattern. Notched
  edge. 11½'' long, 5'' wide, 3''
  high _____ 75.00
Carafe. Hobstar, fan, bull's eye__ 39.50
Celery Dish. 11'' long _____ 28.50
Champagne Glass. Russian pattern.
  Honeycomb stems, rayed base __ 29.50

Cheese Dish. Covered, diamond and
  fan pattern _____ 95.00
Compotes:
  7½'' high, 7'' diam. _____ 65.00
  8'' high, 6'' diam. Pair _____ 125.00
  8'' high, 7'' diam. Pinwheel
    pattern, signed ''Clark'' _____ 95.00
  11½'' high, 7'' diam. _____ 125.00
Creamer. Pineapple and fan. Small. 25.00

Pitcher. 10½'' high _____ $55.00

Cruets:
  Small _____ 40.00
  9¾'' _____ 49.50
Decanter. Signed ''Hawkes'' _____ 50.00
Dishes:
  6'' square _____ 37.50
  8'' round, flat _____ 45.00
  8½'' oval _____ 45.00
  15½'', panel cut sides _____ 49.50
Ferner. 7¼'' diam., 4'' high, 3 feet_ 38.50
Finger Bowl. Diamond and fan pat-
  tern _____ 30.00
Goblets:
  Diamond Cut _____ 30.00
  Pinwheel _____ 25.00
  Strawberry and fan _____ 34.00
Hair Receiver. Sterling top _____ 32.50
Ice Bucket. 7'' diam. _____ 72.50
Knife Rests:
  3¾'' long _____ 12.00
  5½'' long _____ 14.00
Lamp. Boudoir, small, domed shade

212

cut with daisies and leaves.
Prisms _____ 75.00
Lamp. Shade, 13'' diam., and
prisms _____ 500.00
Lamp. Strawberry type, 17'' high __ 275.00
Mayonnaise Dish. Two piece _____ 45.00
Muffineer. Fine cut and panel,
swirled, sterling top _____ 21.50
Mustard. Covered, serrated prisms_ 29.50
Nappie. 6'' diam., handled _____ 18.00
Perfume Bottles:
Purse-size. Sterling top _____ 15.00
4'' long, dresser-type. Signed
"Hawkes" _____ 25.00
5½'' high. With stopper. Nailhead
design _____ 16.00
Pin Tray. Oval type _____ 40.00
Pitchers:
10½'' high _____ 55.00
Milk. 7½'', Pinwheel design,
tankard shape, small _____ 48.50
"Meteor" pattern. 3 pints _____ 60.00
Water. Bulbous-type _____ 57.50
Water. Ordinary-type _____ 62.50
Water. "Rambler" pattern _____ 58.00
Water. Tankard-type _____ 75.00

Punch Bowl. 14½'' high, 12'' top diam.
Pinwheel pattern. Signed "Fry" __$600.00

Plates:
5½'' ice cream plate. Sunburst
pattern _____ 16.50
10'', deep cutting, scalloped edge 42.50
12'' diam. Harvard cut _____ 54.50
Powder Jar. Sterling top _____ 32.50
Platter. 21½'' long, 8½'' wide. Boat

shape, hobstar with small dia-
monds _____ 80.00
Punch Bowls:
14'' diam. _____ 300.00
14'' diam. Separate base _____ 360.00
14½'' high, 12'' top diam. Pin-
wheel pattern. Signed "Fry" __ 600.00
16'' diam. Signed "Hoare" ____ 395.00
Relish · Dish _____ 20.00
Rose Bowl. Heavy cut, notched rim.
Hobstar base, strawberry, fan
and diamond point _____ 75.00
Salt and Pepper Shakers. 6'' high,
glass caps. Pair _____ 29.50
Salts:
Individual _____ 5.50
Master _____ 12.50
Sugar Bowls and Creamers:
Marked "Libbey" _____ 60.00
Pinwheel _____ 54.50
Sugar Shaker. 5'' high _____ 36.00
Tobacco Jar. 5½x4¼''. Panel cut
sides with flowers and leaves.
Rayed star base _____ 48.50
Toothpick _____ 18.75
Tray. Heart-shaped _____ 20.00
Tray. Ice Cream _____ 60.00
Tumblers:
Marked "Fry" _____ 15.00
Ordinary _____ 10.00
Whiskey. Pinwheel and fan. 16-
rayed star at bottom _____ 18.00
Vases:
3'', Strawberry and fan _____ 20.00
10'', footed _____ 52.50
12'', bulbous, flared top. Fine
cut. Pair _____ 295.00
21'', silver holder _____ 150.00
Water Set. Pitcher and 6 matching
tumblers _____ 165.00
Wine. 4'' high. Flaring top, hobstar
with diamond and fan _____ 20.00

**DELDARE WARE, See BUFFALO POTTERY**

### CUT VELVET GLASS

Cut Velvet is Satin Glass which shows the
design in a high relief with the white lining
showing where the pattern has been cut.
It is usually ribbed, but is sometimes found
with diamond quilting—the diamond shapes
in high relief with the centers of the diamonds showing 'the white lining of the item.

Bowl. 5'' diam. Rose color. D. Q.
pattern, crimped flared top ____ 125.00
Ewer. 10¼'' high, 3-pour top with
ruffled rim, bulbous body. 5½''
diam. Green quilting over white,
applied opaque white handle __ 180.00
Vases:
7'', square top _____ 149.50
7'' high. Pink _____ 160.00

Vase. 7'' high. Pink color _____$160.00

7½'', apple green, diamond
quilted _____ 165.00
8½x5'', blue, fluted edge _____ 175.00
10''. Lavender over white ground 175.00
11¼''. Raspberry color, D. Q.,
gourd shape _____ 195.00
12''. Deep rose on white ground 190.00

## DAGUERREOTYPES

Daguerreotypes were the first photo-
graphic pictures ever made. The process
consists of a bright copper plate being
covered with silver salts; then placed between glass to protect the surface. The
action of light in the silver compound produces the picture. The method was discovered by Daguerre, a Frenchman, in 1839.

Case. American Eagle design ____ 11.50
Case. Black, embossed locomotive and girl on cover _____ 12.00

5 x 6''. Picture of man with surly
expression _____ $15.00

Case. Girl at piano with musi-
cians _____ 9.00
Case. 3½x4'', eagle atop shield
with draped flags. Banner,
"The Union and Constitution."
Man in Confederate uniform ____ 21.50
Collection in frame _____ 20.00
4x6'' with statue of war hero im-
pressed on cover _____ 24.00
Round. 2½'' diam. _____ 10.75

### DANISH CHRISTMAS PLATES, see
### COLLECTOR'S PLATES, ETC.

### DAVENPORT CHINA

The ware was made by John Davenport
who opened a pottery at Longport in the
Staffordshire district of England in 1793.
Items made at the pottery are light weight,
cream colored and have a soft velvety
texture. The mark consisted of an impressed anchor with the name Davenport
above. Ironstone chinaware was produced
at a later date. One pattern, "Cypress,"
was produced with mulberry colored decorations. Davenport died in 1848, but his
heirs continued the factory until 1886, at
which time it closed.

Bowl. 13'' diam. 4½'' high. Impressed Davenport and anchor
mark. Man, woman, child and
dog in English scenic view. Floral
border inside and out _____ 75.00
Compote. 9½'' diam., 3'' high.
Grape and Leaf design_____ 49.50
Creamer. Bulbous, white, with deep
blue decor _____ 42.50
Cup and Saucer. Dark blue, with
flower border _____ 44.00

Tureen. Early. 12" long. Castle
scene .in blue, shell handles _____ $85.00

Dish. 12½x8x6½". Covered. In Corn
  pattern, corn shaped handles __    50.00
Ewer. C. 1820. White with blue
  marbling _____    49.50
Jug. Brilliant blue decoration.
  Circa 1800 _____     92.50
Plate. 8½" diam. Milkmaid and cow,
  floral border. Impressed Daven-
  port and anchor _____    54.50
Plate, Warm. 9½" diam. Circa 1820.
  Blue transfer of figures in ro-
  mantic scene. Deep blue handles    52.50
Platter. 9½x12¼". Cypress pattern__   42.50
Teapot. Tall, pink lustre decor ____  165.00
Tea Set. Spring pattern in red and
  green. Teapot, covered sugar,
  creamer, cup and saucer _____    69.50
Tureen. Early. 12" long. Castle
  scene in blue, shell handles ____   85.00

## DECANTERS

The primary use of the decanter was to
hold wine or liquor. Many old-time tap-
rooms used the bottles to store and dis-
pense these beverages. The first decanters
were simple in form and style but later became .more globular and were decorated
with scrolls and festoons. The use of emblems, initials and names followed. Occasionally the container was decorated to represent the owner's occupation. Later, they
were adapted to home use.

(Illustrated on following page)

1. Raised block, original stoppers _____  36.50
2. Waffle & Thumbprint. Early. __      34.50
3. Deep star and channel cut.
   Pair _____  65.00
4. Early blown, with 3 hand-run
   rigarees around neck. Mushroom stopper, wheel-cut base.
   Etched floral design above __        46.50
5. Cut Glass. Late _____        45.00

6. Long cut and faceted necks
   with cutting about bulbous
   lower sections. Pair _____        52.50
7. Vertically ribbed bottle, cut
   stopper, iridescent hue _____         28.50
8. Early flint Sawtooth, hand-
   shaped neck _____          50.00
9. Bohemian, frosted vintage design, clear panels _____        57.50
10. Bohemian red. Similar to # 9__       58.00
11. Bohemian red, plume stopper.
    Bold cut and etched Roman
    Key design, clear cut panels __       57.50
12. Bohemian red, pointed stop-
    per. Vintage pattern and clear
    panels on both _____        62.50
13. Similar to # 12 _____        58.50
14. Bellflower, stopper _____        67.50
15. Bohemian red with traces of
    gold decorations. Matched pair        64.00
16. Tall, heavy flint, with plume
    stopper _____         49.50
17. Wheel cut panels, heavy flint        40.00
18. Heavy ribbed petticoat, or
    "River Boat" bottle _____         33.50
19. Early cut and etched with
    mushroom stopper _____          45.00
20. Heavy ribbed petticoat-type__        30.00
21. Deep amethyst, panelled early
    flint. Rare _____        100.00
22. Petticoat, or "Ohio River
    Boat" type _____         34.50
23. Early, heavy cutting. Cut
    hollow steeple stopper _____         52.50
24. Heavy early Sawtooth with
    original hollow Sawtooth
    stopper _____         62.50
25. English, heavy cutting, with
    flattened pear-shape stoppers.
    Pair _____         105.00
26. Heavy flint, panelled cutting,
    blown stopper _____         40.00
27. Early, Irish flint with fila-
    ment-like crackle inside glass.
    Geometrical cutting, rigarees
    on neck, sunburst stopper ____        44.50
28. Sawtooth, footed _____        40.00
29. Cranberry, with 2 matching
    whiskey glasses. Set _____         72.50
30. Small, footed, prism whiskey
    bottles with hand shaped necks.
    Pair _____         55.00
31. Fine cut flint whiskey. Cut,
    faceted, bulbous stopper ____         38.50
32. 4-part Spirits bottle - four
    bottles blown into one ____          57.50
33. Early cut flint glass _____       29.50
34. Plain thin early blown bottle
    with Sunburst stopper _____          35.00
35. Heavy flint glass with rigaree.
    Colonial group pattern _____         38.50
36. Heavy flint glass with Loop
    design _____         33.50

**GLASS DECANTERS**
For descriptions, see preceding page.

## DECOYS

These are wood-turned models of water fowl, painted to the likeness, and used in groups to lure live ducks into gun or net range.

| | |
|---|---|
| Cork. Red head duck | $12.00 |

| | |
|---|---|
| 16'' long. Black, red and white decor. Early | 16.75 |
| Black Breasted Plover. Pair | 40.00 |
| Golden Plover: | |
| Single | 17.50 |
| Pair | 37.50 |

| | |
|---|---|
| 14'' long. Gray back, black body | 16.50 |

| | |
|---|---|
| Yellow Legs: | |
| Shallow. Single | 16.75 |
| Winter: | |
| Single | 18.75 |
| Pair | 36.00 |

## DEDHAM POTTERY

The business was originally established as Chelsea Pottery, in Chelsea, Mass., in 1860, by Alexander W. Robertson. In 1872, if was known as the Chelsea Keramic Art Works. In 1875, the Pottery moved to Dedham, Mass., and the name was changed to Dedham Pottery. The famous Crackleware, or Dedham Pottery, has an unusual spiderweb effect of blue in the glaze. The rabbit pattern was their most popular design. Other patterns include: apple, azalea, bird-orange tree, butterfly, chicken, clover, crab, dolphin, duck, elephant, grape, horse chestnut, iris, lion, lobster, magnolia, owl, polar bear, snow tree, swan, turtle and water lily.

The following marks can be used to determine the approximate age of items made by the company. 1) Chelsea Keramic Art Works, name Robertson impressed—1876-1889. 2) C. P. US impressed in a clover leaf—1891-1895. 3) Fore-shortened rabbit—1895-1896. 4) Conventional rabbit with Dedham Pottery stamped in blue—1897. 5) Word "Registered" added to rabbit mark—1929-1943.

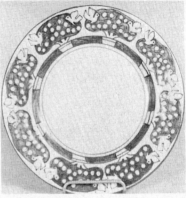

| | |
|---|---|
| Plate. 6'' diam. Dove pattern | $25.00 |

| | |
|---|---|
| Bowl. 7½'' diam. | 45.00 |
| Candlesticks: | |
| Azalea. Pair | 65.00 |
| Rabbit. Pair | 55.00 |
| Celery Dishes: | |
| Elephant | 50.00 |
| Rabbit | 45.00 |
| Chocolate Pot. Rabbit | 60.00 |
| Coaster. Elephant | 24.00 |
| Creamer. 4'', rabbit | 30.00 |
| Cups and Saucers: | |
| Demitasse. Rabbit | 36.50 |
| Elephant | 37.50 |
| Polar Bear | 40.00 |
| Rabbit | 40.00 |
| Cup Plate. Rabbit | 22.50 |
| Dish, 6-sided. Elephant | 49.50 |
| Egg Cup, Double. 4'' high. Rabbit | 27.50 |
| Mayonnaise Bowl. 6¼'' diam. | |
| Rabbit | 36.50 |
| Mug. Handled, large | 24.00 |
| Plates: | |
| Chop plate. Crab | 55.00 |

| | |
|---|---|
| 6'' diam. Dove _____ | 25.00 |
| 6'' diam. Horse chestnut _____ | 25.00 |
| 6'' diam. Mushroom _____ | 25.00 |
| 6'' diam. Rabbit _____ | 25.00 |
| 8½'' diam. Butterfly _____ | 29.50 |
| 8½'' diam. Duck _____ | 29.50 |
| 8½'' diam. Pond Lily _____ | 29.50 |
| 8½'' diam. Rabbit _____ | 29.50 |
| 10'' diam. Butterfly _____ | 35.00 |
| 10'' diam. Dove _____ | 35.00 |
| 10'' diam. Iris border _____ | 30.00 |
| 10'' diam. Rabbit _____ | 35.00 |
| 10¼'' diam. Mushroom _____ | 32.50 |
| 10¼'' diam. Rabbit _____ | 35.00 |

Platters:

| | |
|---|---|
| Rabbit border _____ | 70.00 |
| 10x6'', dated, signed _____ | 70.00 |

Salt and Pepper Shakers. Rabbit.

| | |
|---|---|
| Pair _____ | 40.00 |
| Saucer. Rabbit, medium blue _____ | 11.50 |
| Sugar Bowl. Covered. Rabbit ____ | 45.00 |
| Tile. 6'' square. Horse chestnut ___ | 21.50 |

## DELDARE WARE, See BUFFALO POTTERY

### DELFT

Delft is usually referred to today as earthenware with a blue decoration on a white background. The glaze is produced with the use of a tin compound. A number of potteries produced the ware at Delft, Holland, near the beginning of the 17th century. It was made in England at Lambeth, Bristol and Liverpool. The majority of Delft found in the antique market today is from the late Victorian period to the World War 1 period.

Plaque, Hanging. 8½ x 10¾''. Typical windmill scene in blue on white ground _____$ 25.00

Bottle. 8½''. Dutch boy astride beer keg, holding two bottles, farm

| | |
|---|---|
| and windmill scene, hat stopper__ | 35.00 |
| Bottle, Perfume. German, with original stopper _____ | 21.00 |
| Box. 7x2x1'', covered _____ | 27.50 |
| Cat, Sitting. 6'' high, black and white _____ | 33.00 |
| Clock, Boudoir. Windmill scene, running _____ | 89.50 |
| Condiment Set. Delft-type, 15-piece set with windmill decor. Hanging salt box, 6 large covered jars, 6 small covered jars, 2 tall vinegar cruets _____ | 64.00 |
| Cow. 6½'' long, blue and white. Marked ''Delft'' _____ | 50.00 |
| Cracker Jar. Covered _____ | 39.50 |

Vinegar Jugs. Blue decor. 8¾'' high.
Pair ---------------------------$ 60.00

Creamers:

| | |
|---|---|
| 3'' high _____ | 18.50 |
| 4½'' high _____ | 20.00 |
| 5½'' high, man standing _____ | 22.50 |
| Reclining cow _____ | 50.00 |
| Cup and Saucer. Flared top _____ | 22.00 |
| Decanter, Wine. 11'' high _____ | 45.00 |
| Ewer. 6½'' high. Blue and white applied flowers _____ | 15.00 |

Inkwells:

| | |
|---|---|
| Small, with insert _____ | 20.00 |
| Large, lion and shield with thistle _____ | 55.00 |
| Kitchen Utensil Holder. 14'' long, 8'' high _____ | 50.00 |

Lamps:

| | |
|---|---|
| 12'' high, applied flowers, high stem, ornate bowl and base ____ | 100.00 |
| 22'' high, with matching parchment shade. Electrified _____ | 110.00 |
| Lemon Squeezer, on pitcher base __ | 16.50 |
| Liqueur Set. 9½'' bottle, 8½'' tray, four 2'' handled mugs. Set _____ | 100.00 |
| Molds, Melon. 5x7'' _____ | 20.00 |
| Piano. Upright type, 4'' long, 2'' wide, crossed swords mark ____ | 28.50 |

Plaques:
8'' diam., hanging-type, crossed

swords mark _____ 24.00
8½x10¾''. Typical windmill scene
in blue on white ground _____ 25.00
15½'' diam., fancy scrolled border, colorful ship decor _____ 50.00
Plates:
8'' diam. Boats _____ 22.00
8'' diam. Windmill scene _____ 22.00
Puzzle Mug _____ 45.00
Shoes:
4½'' long _____ 20.00
6½'' long _____ 25.00
Tea Caddy _____ 27.50
Tiles:
Children playing _____ 9.00
Soldiers and civilians in ancient
costumes, birds, animals and
flowers _____ 9.00
Tulip design. Mulberry on white__ 9.00
Tobacco Jar. 5'', fisherman's head_ 32.50
Toothpick Holder _____ 14.00
Trays:
6x9'', dresser _____ 30.00
10¼''x8½'', windmill scene, scalloped edge _____ 30.00
18x14'', oval, 2 handles, windmill
scene and ships, 4 round feet,
nickel plated edge _____ 55.00
Urn. 17'' high, with cover. Blue
windmill decoration _____ 72.50
Vases:
4½'' high. Sailboat scene in blue
and white _____ 25.00
5½'' high, marked. Pair _____ 41.50
10'' high, canal scenes _____ 30.00
Vinegar Jugs. Blue decor. 8¾'' high.
Pair _____ 60.00

### DOLL FURNITURE

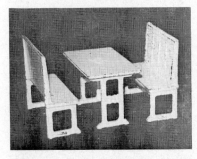

Booth Table. 3'' high, 4¾'' long,
seat height 4''. 3-piece, metal.
Made by "Arcade," Freeport, Ill._$15.00

Bed, Brass. 21x14'', with springs,
pad, bolster, crocheted spread __ 65.00
Bedroom Set. 6 pieces. 1'' scale,

2 metal beds, tin wash stand
with mirror, table and 2 chairs__ 35.00
Bed, Tester. With canopy. Small __ 12.00
Bureau, Victorian. 16'' high, old
mirror _____ 60.00

Wardrobe. Two doors with drawer beneath. 8¾'' wide, 13'' to top of
finials. Oak _____ _____ $27.50

Chairs:
Ladder-back. Pair _____ 10.50
Oval back _____ 9.00
Wicker Rocker. 17'' high, silk
seat _____ 15.00
Chests of Drawers:
Oak, 4 drawers, brass pulls ____ 12.00
Period style. 5 drawers _____ 15.00
Cradle. Walnut. Cut-out hearts
each end _____ 25.00
Dishes. Pewter-type. Plates, cups
and saucers with chafing dish,
napkin rings, cutlery, etc. 30-
piece set _____ 24.50
House. Wood with applied paper
design. 13½'' high, 10'' wide.
Over 75 years old _____ 22.50
Parlor Set. 7 pieces, 1'' scale,
sofa, 4 side chairs, table with
drawer, roll-arm chair. Velvet
upholstery _____ 47.50
Piano. Upright _____ 14.00

Sideboard, table and 2 chairs.
Oak. Set _____ $15.00

Trunk _____ 20.00

## DOLLS
### (Not Illustrated)

Alphabet. 8" long _____ $ 45.00
Bisque Head. Ash-blonde hair, light blue painted eyes, cloth body. 15" _____ 115.00
Bisque Head. Open mouth, sleeping eyes, leather body, cloth legs. Marked"Made in Germany." 22" _ 48.00
Bisque Boy Baby. Tongue shows. 19" _____ 65.00
Bye-Lo. Grace Storey Putnam Doll. Composition head, not dressed __ 125.00
Celluloid Boy. Old, 19" _____ 60.00
China. All original, black hair, blue eyes, deep shoulders, dressed in yellow calico. 23" __ 120.00
China Head. Black molded hair, china hands and feet, cloth body. 24" _____ 135.00
Dionne Quints. Made by Alexander. Composition heads, arms and legs. Cloth bodies, dressed. 16". Set of 5 dolls for _____ 70.00
Dolly Madison, Parian. Blonde hair, blue eyes, dressed in pink velvet. 21" _____ 200.00
Eden Bebe, Paris. Open mouth, brown wig. pierced ears, blue jeweled eyes, jointed body. 14". Marked _____ 100.00
French Fashion Doll. Bisque head, brown hair wig, blown blue-gray eyes, kid body, arms and legs. Not dressed. 14" _____ 260.00
French Fashion Doll. Marie Antoinette. Snow white wig, beauty spot, deep blue eyes, white kid body. All original. 18" _____ 300.00
Gibson Girl Doll. High neck, closed mouth, high blonde hairdo, kid body. Underclothing only. 20"___ 160.00

Heubach. Brown eyes, open mouth, kid body, bisque hands, wig, dressed. 21" _____ 49.50
Jenny Lind. China head, black hair, 17" _____ 215.00
Jumeau. Mechanical doll, vari-colored eyes, head turns, hands move up and down, music box in base plays 2 tunes. 20" _____ 325.00
Jumeau. Bisque with rigid inset eyes, real hair wig, tightly packed kid body, 28" Circa 1860-80 _____ 315.00
Parian Quality, French. Pink kid arms and legs. Fully dressed. 14" _____ 265.00
Parian. Curly blonde hair, pierced ears, painted blue eyes, cloth body, legs, leather arms. 23"__ 125.00
Schoenhut Baby. Curved legs, orig-inal wig, dressed. 11" _____ 45.00
Schoenhut Baby. Painted eyes, hair wig, jointed. 16". Dated 1913___ 50.00
Schoenhut. Walking, original wig, not dressed. 14" _____ 95.00
Simon & Halbig. Brown eyes, pierced ears, body marked "Hein-rich-Handwarch." 24". Not dressed _____ 50.00
Steiner. Closed mouth, pierced ears, signed. 24" _____ 260.00
Wax. Lady doll, pierced ears, painted high button shoes, orig-inal dress. $28\frac{1}{2}$" _____ 75.00
Wax. Glass eyes, blonde curly wig. All original. 12" _____ 80.00
Wood. Queen Anne Miniature. All wood, jointed arms and legs, original clothes. $4\frac{1}{2}$" _____ 90.00

### EARLY WOOD DOLLS

Early prints of children holding what appear to be wooden dolls are to be seen as early as 1540. It is reported that Sir Walter Raleigh's expedition in 1583 brought wooden dolls to America and presented them to Indian children.

A wooden doll of the 1664 to 1714 period is called "Queen Anne" by collectors. A painting by John Singleton Copley, done in 1776 of his own family, shows a replica of this doll pictured in the lefthand corner of the canvas. The painting is located in the National Gallery of Art in Washington, D. C.

Dolls of this type had their heads and necks covered with a coat of plaster and then enameled flesh color. Each eye is made of three pieces of glass. A wig of human hair is nailed to the head. Arms nailed to the shoulders are of rolled linen to the elbow and then become ivory painted wood with fork-like fingers. The legs are slotted into the hips and are freely movable.

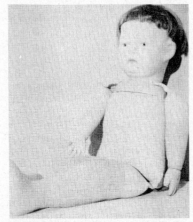

Late Schoenhut doll with pink cloth body. Head rests on wooden breast plate. Has wooden hands, a wig, painted features and a voice box _____$85.00

**COUNTESS ANGEL.** Blonde Parian. In cocoa taffeta and pale cocoa lace. Ivory velvet bow. Blue eyes and blue heart-shaped earrings in pierced ears _____$375.00

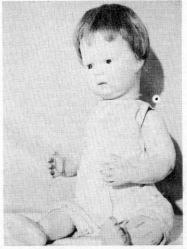

**BABY JEAN.** Bisque, Solid dome head, glass eyes, open mouth, two upper teeth. Composition baby body _____$85.00

Infant with Schoenhut's copyrighted head. Doll has wire-strung natural limbs, 14'' high _____$85.00

LEFT: Blonde china head. 16" high.
Kid leather body, china hands.
Circa 1900 _____ $125.00
RIGHT: German. Bisque head and hands.
15" high. Hair wig. Dressed in
blue with gold stripes _____ $85.00

## DOLL FACTS

Dolls have been made for several centuries, not only as playthings but for the purpose of telling a story, illustrating fashions or presenting an image of a living person.

Over the years, they have been made of a variety of materials which include clay, china, porcelain, wax, wood, rags and other materials.

About 200 years ago ladies in the Colonies eagerly awaited the arrival of ships from abroad, carrying "fashion dolls," dressed in miniature in the latest styles—even to underclothes. Once obtaining them, they "flew" to their dressmakers to be the first to wear the new fashion from Paris. Rivalry was high to get the dolls off the ships first and it is reported many of the women were battered and bruised.

## DOOR KNOCKERS

Centuries or more before the advent of the electric doorbell, metal door knockers announced the arrival of visitors at the front door of a home. The majority was made of brass, however, occasionally one was of iron. One popular style of the period was a lion's head.

Iron. Glove-in-hand _____ $16.50

| | |
|---|---|
| Brass. Hand holding ball _____ | 42.50 |
| Charles Dickens. Bronze _____ | 20.00 |
| Elephant and Castle. Bronze _____ | 18.50 |
| Grecian Head and Bust. Bronze __ | 15.00 |
| Iron. Made of horseshoe and hammer _____ | 12.00 |
| Iron. Shape of spur with metal block below. Mounted on small wood plaque _____ | 17.50 |
| Lion. Ring in mouth, medium size. Brass _____ | 15.00 |

## DOOR STOPS

As the name indicates, door stops were used to hold doors at a desired place. Almost every home has a door or two which will not stay open.

They were made of brass or iron, with iron predominating. Production of those ordinarily encountered in antique shops today was from the mid-Victorian period to about 1920.

| | |
|---|---|
| Airedale, Iron _____ | 18.75 |
| Aunt Jemima. Black dress, brownish gray apron and scarf, red and white polka dot kerchief. Iron __ | 19.75 |

## DRESDEN

The first fine porcelain in Europe was discovered or invented by Johann Frederick Bottger at the Royal Saxon Porcelain Works at Meissen, Germany, about 1710. The ware is finely modeled and decorated, often having applied raised flowers. The famous marks of the company are a variety of crossed swords in blue color under glaze.

The factory is still in existence although it is now behind the "iron curtain." It has been reported that a new mark has been instituted since the Russian occupation—that of a hammer and sickle. Much of the ware in America today was brought in by importers in the latter part of the 19th century (1875-1900).

Door Stop. 11" high. Cornucopia
with flowers _____ $10.00

| | |
|---|---|
| Bull. Iron _____ | 17.50 |
| Bulldog. 10½" high, 9" long. Iron _____ | 18.75 |
| Cat. 4½" high, black. Iron _____ | 16.00 |
| Cat. 9½" high, fluffy gray tiger. Iron _____ | 20.00 |
| Cat. Painted black, green eyes. Iron _____ | 17.50 |
| Cottage. Cast iron _____ | 15.00 |
| Court Jester and Dog. 12" _____ | 21.50 |
| Dogs. Large, iron. Pair _____ | 20.00 |
| Dolly Dimple with Doll. Iron _____ | 16.00 |
| Fiddler tuning his violin. Cast iron _____ | 17.50 |
| Flower in Basket. 8" high. Iron____ | 16.00 |
| Flowers in Basket. Brass _____ | 22.50 |
| Fox, Sleeping. Brass _____ | 25.00 |
| Frog. 4", bronze _____ | 18.75 |
| Frog. Iron _____ | 13.50 |
| German Shepherd Dog. Cast iron. Marked Davison Co. 14" long, 13" high _____ | 21.00 |
| Lamb. Cast iron, painted black __ | 21.00 |
| Lighthouse of Gloucester, Mass. Dated 1920. 11½" high _____ | 10.00 |
| Lion. Large. Iron _____ | 21.75 |
| Little Red Riding Hood and Wolf. Iron. Pair _____ | 18.50 |
| Parrot. Iron _____ | 17.00 |
| Pointer Dog. 9". Iron _____ | 16.50 |
| Scottie Dog. Iron _____ | 16.00 |
| Ship. Mayflower _____ | 10.00 |
| Terrier. Iron _____ | 18.00 |
| The Snooper. 13½" high. Iron ____ | 18.50 |
| Wagon, Conestoga. 7" high, iron__ | 20.00 |
| Wolf. With chain leash. Iron _____ | 18.00 |

Meissen Box. 5½ x 3½ x 3½". Painted
floral decor _____ $250.00

Basket. Handled, round, lat-
ticed. Painted robin in
center, raised flowers, painted
sprigs _____ $120.00
Bed. 6" long, 3" high. Colored
flowers and leaves in sprays,
highlighted with gold _____ 275.00
Bowl. Solid bottom, open "spa-
ghetti" sides, colorful roses.
Marked "Germany." Late _____ 48.50
Candelabras. 2-branch, boy and
girl on each base, applied flowers. Pair _____ 750.00
Chocolate Pot. 10½" high. Schuman
mark. Multi-colored ground.
Floral decor _____ 48.50
Compotes:
9" diam., 4½" high, with 6
matching plates. Red and gold

223

decor with green leaves. Marked
Dresden, impressed F & M _____ 95.00
14'' top diam., 17'' high. Sword
marks on bottom. Finest quality_ 475.00

**Cups and Saucers:**
Demitasse. Fluted, colored flowers, gold trim _____ 48.50
Handleless. German. Circa 1820.
2 dark red roses. Paper thin
porcelain. Fine ''X'' mark in blue
underglaze _____ 50.00
Green dragon _____ 45.00
From chocolate set. Flower band
and scattered flowers _____ 42.50

Plates, Dessert. 6'' diam., hand painted figures, filigree edge, gold.
Each _____ $25.00

Dish. Boat shaped. 14½'' long,
9½'' wide, 2½'' high. Irregular
edge with lavender trim. Blue
orchid and white flowers in center. 4 pierced openings each end 46.00
**Figurine.** Frog musicians. Blue
crossed swords _____ 260.00

**Frames:**
Beveled mirror, Cupids on top
holding flower wreath. Marked__ 195.00
3½x5'', double portrait frames.
Gold border, surface covered
with small pink roses _____ 65.00
9x6½'' overall, scalloped, floral
decor, gilt scrolls. For photos.
Pair _____ 67.50
Jewel Casket. 3½'' high, green with
white enamel decor. Circa 1870__ 95.00

**Lamps:**
5½'' high, 5'' base diam. Shell-
shaped bowl with raised flowers and cupid at sides _____ 160.00
10'' high, cherub on stem, raised
flowers on base and bowl. Cream,
green and yellow _____ 200.00
Mirror. 12x10''. Oval, cupids and
applied flowers _____ 265.00
Place Cards. 3¾'' high. Full figure.
of girl holding 2-tiered lace skirt.
Marked. Pair _____ 40.00

**Plates:**
11'' diam., landscape center,
gilt scrolls _____ 50.00

Soup _____ 22.50

Plate. 9½'' diam. Portrait of
woman _____ $50.00

Teapot. Relief-molded hot water kettle on stand, with burner. Gold
and white, 17'' high _____ $275.00

Shoe. On chariot, being pulled by
Cupid. 5¼'' high. Garland of
roses, blue shoe. Marked KPM __ 85.00
Teapot. Relief-molded hot water
kettle on stand, with burner.
Gold and white. 17'' high _____ 275.00
Teapot. 5'' high, 8'' long, footed,
floral decor _____ 65.00
Tea Set. Teapot, sugar bowl and
creamer, with floral and gold
decor _____ 175.00
Toast Rack. Divided compartments,
small handles _____ 48.50
Tray. 15'' diam., floral and gold
decor _____ 47.50
Vegetable Dish. 8½'' diam., round,
covered. Roses, forget-me-nots
and butterfly decor, knob on
lid _____ 40.00

## DURAND ART GLASS

Victor Durand, reputed to be a de-
scendant of the French family which made
Baccarat Glass, started a factory in
Vineland, New Jersey, in 1924 or 1925, and
sold the product under the name of "Dur-
and Art Glass."

The glass resembled Tiffany in some
respects, especially as to the golden sheen
of some of the designs. Many of the pieces
were made in red and sapphire blue, and
occasionally stars were cut into the pattern.
A Cameo-type of glass was also produced.
The glass was labeled with a sticker "Dur-
and Art Glass" while some items were marked with the letter "V" in the pontil. The
factory closed in 1931, due to the accidental
death of Durand.

Vase. 7'' high. Bulbous, gold with
green leaves _____$210.00

Bowl, Flower. Deep blue with usual
decor, vaseline colored foot.
11'' diam., 2'' deep _____ 270.00
Candlestick. 10'', silvery-blue.
Signed _____ 185.00
Comport. 5¾'' high. Cranberry
feather pattern. Baluster stem___ 275.00
Goblet. Red, with gold iridescent loopings _____ 235.00
Jack-in-Pulpit Vase. 8½'', gold
iridescent _____ 375.00
Lamp Shade. Bell shape. 10'' tall,
2'' opening, 2'' flaring to 9½''
at bottom. Deep green with
outer layer of heavy crackle
over gold lining _____ 275.00
Plate. Medium size. Feathery pattern with 4 stars placed to
form square outside the central
design _____ 220.00
Rose Bowl. Blue color _____ 265.00
Tazza. Gold color _____ 325.00
Vases:
5'' high. Gold iridescent _____ 260.00
7'' high. Bulbous, gold with
green leaves _____ 210.00
7'' high. Gold iridescent _____ 200.00
12'' high. Blue, leaves and
trailing vines of ochre and
green, blue ground. Signed ____ 265.00
13'' high. Deep cranberry with
milk white Nailsea-type loopings at base. Signed V. Durand__ 300.00

## END-OF-DAY GLASS

A multicolored or spotted glass, sometimes called "spatter glass," which was
made from about 1885 to 1905. The name
"End-of-Day" is derived from the custom
of glassblowers using the remains of the
day's glass from their various pots (usually
of a variety of colors) and blowing or
molding objects of their own fancy. Some
of the glass was made commercially but
was never very popular as it was considered cheap by persons of distinction.

Barber Bottle. Amber and white __ 49.50
Basket. Yellow, pink and white,
white lining, thorn handle _____ 60.00
Boot. 3¾'' high. Multicolored,
applied clear glass decor _____ 65.00
Candlesticks. Pair _____ 60.00
Carafe with Tumbler. Pink _____ 50.00
Cracker Jar. 9'' high, cased in
white, yellow, red and green
colors, thorny handle _____ 75.00
Lamp, Hand. Pink with clear ap-
plied handle _____ 62.50
Mug. 3¾'' high _____ 24.50
Mug. 4⅛'' high, in red, yellow,
green and blue. Clear glass
handle _____ 45.00
Perfume Bottle. Brass top with
jewel, finger chain and ring ____ 35.00

tables which often consist of receptacles or dishes, usually of elaborate design, with several tiers for holding fruit and sweetmeats, or with vases or receptacles for holding flowers.

Vase. 7½'' high. Yellow, red, pink and black _____ $35.00

Pitcher. 9½'' high. Spattered with blue, red and white. Acid finish__ 98.50
Rose Bowl. Green _____ 30.00
Sugar Shaker. Pink _____ 27.50
Syrup Jug. Pink _____ 57.50
Tumbler. Pink, yellow, blue and deep red _____ 25.00
Vases:
5¼'' high, ruffled top _____ 35.00
7½'' high, clear glass splashed with blue, red, rose, green, yellow and white. Ruffled top, 3 feet. Pair _____ 72.50
8'' high,. mottled brown, red, green, yellow, blue and pink, on pink ground. Fine quality ____ 65.00
8½'' high. Orange, blue and green colors. Late. Pair _____ 16.00

## EPERGNES

Epergnes are ornamental centerpieces for

Cranberry. Milk white bowl with cranberry edge, clear rosettes wound around holders. Venetian glass _____ $180.00

Blue. Crimped top and bowl, with trimming _____ $145.00
Blue. Satin glass, 1 lily _____ 85.00

Clear to opalescent. Rubina Verde.
  2-piece, 12'' high _____  125.00
Cranberry to white. 15'' high _____ 175.00
Cranberry. 3 arms in round metal
  base with mirror. 16¾'' high ____  180.00

English ruby glass. 21½'' high _____ $85.00

Cranberry. Light lower bowl with
  darker pleated top and hobnails
  around darker pleated ends. One
  tube, scattered white flowers___  185.00
Cranberry. Crimped top and lower
  bowl. 3 lilies _____  165.00
Pink. 10¾'' ruffled bowl, 11''
  ruffled lily, silver frame _____  130.00
Rose and pink. 16'' high, upper
  ruffled edge 5'' diam., lower
  edge 9'' diam. _____  175.00
White Milk Glass. Green to white
  opalescent. 19'' high, tall lily
  baskets with two hanging baskets and two stationary baskets  165.00
White Satin Glass. 12½'' high, in
  silver-plated standard. 3 arms
  support ruffled bowls, with
  enamel flowers and leaves _____  325.00

### FAIENCE

The ware is red in color and has a tin
• glaze. Delft and Majolica are made by
the same process of tin glazing.

Hen with chick on back and under
  wings. French. Dark orange with
  black and yellow decor _____ $165.00

Bird in cage. Gilded gold wire,
  white body with flower and leaf
  decoration. Museum quality ____  360.00
Compote. 10'' high. Signed Rouen__   85.00

Plate. 16½'' diam. Rooster decor in
  yellow and dark red. Early type __ $65.00

Plates. 7½'', dull blue ground with
  raised fruit in center. Set of 6__   75.00
Platter. 14½x19½''. Delft-type blue
  decoration  _____   92.50

227

## FAIRY LAMPS

These are small glass candle-burning night lamps, usually consisting of two parts—a base and a shade. They were first made in England by the Samuel Clarke Co., in 1857. A variety was manufactured until 1910, when electricity made the flame lamps obsolete, except in country areas.

The Phoenix Glass Co., Pittsburgh, Pa., was granted the exclusive right to manufacture the lamps in the United States. A wide variety was produced—from cheap colored glass to expensive Art Glass such as Burmese, Nailsea, Satin, Amberina, Peachblow, etc.

**Nailsea-type** Glass. Cranberry loopings, clear Clarke base _____ . $185.00

Amethyst. 2¾" high, 2¼" diam. Resembles Fine Cut, on tall clear Cane standard. 11¼" overall height _____ 85.00
Amethyst. Diamond Point shade. Clear base. Sulphide profiles of Napoleon and Josephine _____ 115.00
Blue. Overshot with silver, swirl ribbed, pyramid shape _____ 50.00
Blue. (Royal). Overlay with faceted panels. Ormolu frame _____ 160.00
Blue. Bristol glass, swirled, enameled flowers _____ 110.00

Brass. With blue and amber glass windows. 8½" high _____ 95.00
Bull Dog Face. Bisque. 4½" high __ 50.00
Burmese shades on "Clarke" candle holder _____ 275.00
Burmese glass shade with enamel flowers and leaves. Royal Doulton base (also holds flowers) decorated with flowers and coin gold __ 425.00
Camphor Glass shade, pattern molded to resemble pine cone. Plain camphor glass base. Aquamarine ___ 150.00
Clarke. Clear glass base with 5½" frosted amber glass top _____ 75.00
Clark's Cricklite. Peacock blue shade, clear base _____ 60.00
Cut Velvet. Rose color with herringbone design, white lining, clear "Clarke" holder _____ 110.00
Diamond Point (amber) Top, clear base, 4" high _____ 40.00
Diamond Point (blue) Top, clear base, 4" high _____ 44.00
End-of-Day. Cased in white. Soft colors of pink, rose, beige and green _____ 110.00
Lithophane. 7¼" high. Ormolu holder with blue enamel saucer- _____ 225.00
Millefiori Shade. Glass base, 4" high _____ 75.00
Monk's Head. Semi-opaque glass__ 135.00
Nailsea. Rose with small matching crimped edge base _____ 185.00
Pyramid. Amber shade with swirled diamond point _____ 35.00
Ribbon Stripe. 4¾" high, yellow and opaque white, matching base. Signed "Clarke" _____ 148.50
Royal Doulton. Ceramic and enameled base, decorated satin shade ____ 275.00
Ruby Red Glass Top. White milk glass base _____ 48.50
Satin Glass. Apricot shading to Peachblow _____ 195.00
Satin Glass. Deep yellow, rib mold. Standard, shade and shade holder are separate _____ 165.00
Satin Glass. Mother-of-Pearl, diamond quilted, ruffled shade and base _____ 235.00
Yellow. Shape of acorn _____ 67.50

## FANS

In the days before electricity, the hand fan was the air conditioner of the period. Various styles and types were available, depending on the owner's economic standing in the community. Some were hand-painted silk set with jewels and others were made of cheap printed "fan-paper."

Advertisement. Cardboard _____ 2.75
Chiffon. Black lace. Shows embossing of Geraldine Farrar _____ 15.00

Red silk with hand painted decor of small blue flowers and green leaves.
13" _____ $28.50

French. Hand painted on heavy
paper. Ivory sticks, fine coloring. 10¼" long, 19½" open _____ 75.00
Ivory. Carved fan with painted silk
insert. Ordinary type _____ 20.00
Ivory. Carved fan with rose satin
center _____ 20.00
Louis XVI. 19" across, 10 high,
carved ivory center _____ 95.00
Ostrich Feather. Black _____ 9.50
Wedding Fan. Carved and pierced
ivory sticks. 10½" long. Hand
painted pink flowers and forget-
me-nots on silk _____ 32.00

Carved ivory sticks with painted
feathers _____ $25.00

Wood sticks with ordinary fan
paper _____ 6.00·
8" high, 16" across. Pastoral scene
with man and woman. Marked R.
N. 1198. 18 fretted metal sticks
with gold finish _____ 75.00

### FINDLAY GLASS, See ONYX GLASS

### FINGER BOWLS

Small bowls made of glass or metal for
the purpose of cleansing fingers at the end
of a meal. The practice of using finger
bowls has fallen into disuse in most homes
and restaurants but a revival of this custom
would add to the charm of gracious living.

Emerald green. Light band through
center. 5½" diam. _____ $25.00

Apple green. Old, blown _____ $20.00
Blue, cobalt _____ 12.75
Blue, light. Old, blown _____ 21.00
Bohemian Glass. Enamel floral
decor _____ 24.00
Brass. Chinese _____ 8.75
Canary yellow. Old, blown _____ 18.00
Cranberry. English, blown _____ 24.75
Cut Glass. With matching plate.
Diamond and Fan pattern _____ 29.50
Green. Old, blown _____ 21.00
Pink (Maiden Blush) _____ 11.00
Silver plated _____ 9.00
Vaseline. Old, blown _____ 21.50

### FIRE EQUIPMENT

In the days before mechanized fire equipment, firefighters utilized manpower for the
job of extinguishing fires. Most of the fire
companies were of the volunteer nature.
Each member owned his own leather bucket
and helmet.
Property owners who carried insurance
displayed a firemark made of iron or brass.
In the last few years reproduction fire-
marks, cast of aluminum, have been placed
on the market.

Bell. Brass. Operated by hand crank.
Made by "New Departure Bell
Co." Polished _____ 75.00
Bucket. Early, leather, owner's name
and date 1807_____ 75.00
Fire Marks:
Hydrant, F. A. 1817_____ 48.50
Tree, 1784, iron_____ 50.00
United Fireman's Ins. Co. Iron 37.50.

Fire Horn with braided tassels ____ $150.00

Helmets:
  Faint painted date "1878." Eagle
  finial _____ 30.00
  Embossed black leather, colored
  insignia. Brass eagle head on
  front _____ 25.00
  Fireman with trumpet finial ____ 40.00
Sheet Music. "The Midnight Fire
  Alarm." Colored litho front cover
  showing engines puled by horses
  racing to fire_____ 4.00

## FIREPLACE EQUIPMENT

Until a half century ago the fireplace
was the main source of heat for each
room in a home. Various types of equipment have been salvaged and offered for
sale by antique dealers.

Trammel Iron. 24½" long _____ $75.00

Andirons:
  Iron, ball on top_____ 26.50

Solid brass, 23½" high_____ 100.00
Bellows:
  Leather, 15" long, flower panel
  on sides_____ 30.00
  Leather in good condition. Small 23.50
Coal Box. Brass. English_____ 110.00

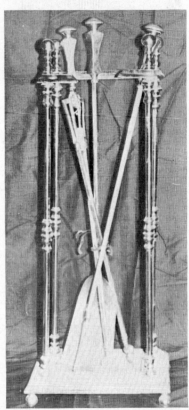

28" high. English. Brass set _____ $80.00

Fenders:
  31" long. Iron base with screen,
  brass top and finials _____ 75.00
  48" long. Brass, 3 claw feet_____ 55.00
Grate. Iron, on legs. 9x17½" _____ 25.00
Lighter, Cape Cod. Brass_____ 18.00

Coal Hod. Helmet-type with scoop. Brass, burnished and lacquered__ $89.50

Screen. Hinged, 3-part. Roman Arch in center of middle section_____ 80.00
Spider. Early _____ 55.00
Stand. 42" high, with shovel, poker and tongs _____ 87.50
Tools, Holder, shovel, poker and tongs. Brass_____ 85.00
Trammel Hook. 39" long, hand-forged iron, extends to 59" for holding cooking pots over fire-place _____ 75.00

## FISH SETS

Fish sets were popular in the 1885 to 1905 period. The plates and platters, usually decorated with fish, were used when fish was served. Many of the sets now in existence are of Limoges or Austrian china.

14-piece "Elite" Limoges Chinaware. Seaweed in dark green, fish in natural colors, edges of burnished gold. In leatherette, satin-lined case _____ $95.00

14-piece "Perle" set. 12 plates, platter and sauce tureen. Limoges china _____ 85.00
7-piece set. "Sie Beck." 6 plates and platter _____ 60.00
7-piece set. Limoges, seashells and fish. 8¼" plates, 9½x16" platter__ 67.50

## FLASKS

Whiskey. Pint. Sterling base cover about ⅓ way, leather above. Sterling top _____ $22.75

Basket of Flowers. Reverse, cornu-copia of fruit. Rare emerald green color, pint, from western New York _____ 85.00
Bust of General Washington. Aqua, pint _____ 85.00
Cornucopia-Urn. Pint, dark olive green _____ 40.00
Eagle, American. Pint. Eagle with ribbon in beak, 5 bars. Reverse floral medallion and oval with 5-pointed star. Light blue_____ 210.00

Eagle-Anchor. New London Glass
Works. ½ pint aqua_____ 40.00
Eagle. Concentric Ring, pint. Yel-
lowish green _____ 400.00
Eagle-Liberty. Willington Glass Co.
½ pint, red amber _____ 36.50
Eagle. Louisville, pint. Obverse,
eagle below 14 stars, and 8-point-
ed star near base. Reverse, same.
Amber _____ 80.00
Eagle. Lyre, pint. 14 stars over lyre
on obverse. Reverse, Louisville
eagle holding ribbon inscribed
"Union." Aquamarine _____ 150.00
Eagle-Masonic Arch. ½ pint, olive
green _____ 42.50
Eagle-Masonic Arch. Pint, olive
amber _____ 37.50
Eagle-13 Stars. U. S. Flag, "For Our
Country." Pint _____ 37.50
Eagle. Willington Glass Co. Pint,
olive green _____ 32.50
Hunter and fisherman. Green glass 55.00
Jenny Lind. Fisherville Glass Works.
Quart, aqua_____ 35.00
Jenny Lind. Calabash, deep emerald 70.00
Lafayette-Eagle. Quart, aqua _____ 75.00
Masonic Arch and Masonic Symbols.
Heavy, grass green, pint_____ 95.00
Perry, Justus. Masonic pint flask.
Deep sapphire blue. Rare ____ 475.00
Pitkin-Swirl Pattern. Pint, green____ 40.00
Pittsburgh area glass factory pink
flask. Eagle with shield and arrow,
ribbon with "Liberty." Light corn-
flower blue. Generally found in
aqua _____ 85.00
Sailing Sloops and 8-pointed star.
½ pint, sapphire blue_____ 180.00
Schoolcraft, Henry. Masonic pint
flask. Initials "H.S." in beaded
oval beneath eagle on reverse.
Scarce _____ 150.00
Sheaf of wheat and star. Green
glass _____ 48.50
Sheaf of wheat. "Traveler's Com-
panion." Quart, amber_____ 40.00
Sheaf of Wheat. Westford Glass Co.
½ pint, amber_____ 36.50
Sunburst Eliptical. ¾ pint. Pale aqua 75.00
Violin. Ring neck, brilliant im-
pression, honey amber, pint_____ 95.00
Violin. Scrolls, dark red amber,
pint _____ 96.50
Washington-Jackson. Pint, olive
green _____ 60.00
Washington-Jackson. ½ pint, olive
green _____ 60.00
Washington-Taylor. Pint, aqua green 65.00
Willow Tree. Reverse, "Good Game"
(Deer). Aqua, pint _____ 65.00

## FLOW BLUE

This term is used to denote Staffordshire
and other china on which the color "ran"
during the "firing" process and, upon being taken from the kiln, had a smudged
blue appearance. Some of the better known
patterns include "Manilla," "Fairy Villas,"
"Scinde" and "Khyber."

Plate. 9". "Kybar" pattern _____ $11.50

Bowls:
13½" diam. "Scinde" pattern___ 70.00
8" diam. "Ayr" pattern _____ 16.00
Butter Dishes:
Covered. "Fairy Villas" _____ 35.00
Covered. "Labelle" _____ 39.50
Butter Pat. Round _____ 2.50
Creamer. "Fairy Villas"_____ 29.50
Cups and Saucers:
"Lorne." Demitasse_____ 10.75
"Manilla" _____ 21.50
"Stanley." Johnson Bros._____ 12.00
."Waldorf" _____ 15.00
Dinner Set. 87-piece. "Louvre" pat-
tern by Meakin. Set_____ 300.00
Dishes:
"Fairy Villas." Deep, small, for
cereal _____ 12.00
"Fairy Villas." Vegetable, covered 48.50
"Kesnick." Oval_____ 12.50
"Scinde." 8½x6¾". Open _____ 30.00
Gravy Boat. With trap_____ 39.50
Pitchers:
Small _____ 30.00
Water _____ 60.00

**Plates:**

"Amoy" pattern:

| | |
|---|---|
| 10" diam. | 12.00 |
| 9" diam. | 10.50 |
| 8" diam. | 9.75 |
| "Chusan." $8\frac{3}{4}$" | 8.50 |
| "Coburg." 9" | 10.00 |

"Fairy Villas" pattern:

| | |
|---|---|
| $10\frac{1}{2}$" | 12.75 |
| 9" | 11.50 |
| "Formosa." $9\frac{1}{2}$" | 8.00 |
| "Hong Kong." $9\frac{1}{2}$" | 10.50 |
| "Indian Jar." $9\frac{1}{2}$" | 10.50 |
| "Jeddo." $10\frac{1}{2}$" | 11.50 |
| "Khyber." $8\frac{1}{2}$" | 11.00 |

"Manilla" pattern:

| | |
|---|---|
| 8" | 12.00 |
| $7\frac{3}{4}$" | 11.00 |
| 7" | 10.50 |
| "Nankin." 7" | 8.75 |
| "Oregon." $10\frac{1}{2}$" | 11.00 |
| "Oriental." 8" | 10.50 |
| "Scinde." 7" | 12.75 |
| "Shanghai." 8" | 8.00 |
| "Shell." $7\frac{1}{2}$" | 8.00 |
| "Sobraon." 7" | 8.00 |

"Temple" pattern:

| | |
|---|---|
| $9\frac{1}{2}$" | 11.00 |
| $8\frac{1}{2}$" | 12.00 |
| 7" | 10.50 |
| "Tonquin." 9" | 10.75 |
| "Waldorf." $9\frac{1}{2}$" | 12.00 |
| "Watteau" | 10.50 |

**Platters:**

| | |
|---|---|
| "Blantyre." By Alcock | 22.50 |
| "Chusan". Clemson. 14x18" | 50.00 |
| "Khyber." 10" | 20.00 |
| "Lucerne." Light blue | 30.00 |
| "Manilla." By Podmore, Walker & Co. 12x15$\frac{1}{2}$" | 42.50 |
| "Scinde." Large | 42.50 |

"Sobraon" pattern:

| | |
|---|---|
| 10x14" | 32.00 |
| 13" | 27.50 |
| "Tonquin." 10x14" | 38.50 |
| "Waldorf." 9x11" | 32.00 |

**Sauce Dishes:**

| | |
|---|---|
| "Fairy Villas" | 6.00 |
| "Scinde" | 8.00 |
| Saucer. "Manilla" | 6.00 |

**Soup Dishes:**

| | |
|---|---|
| "Amoy." 11" diam. Davenport | 16.00 |
| "Nonpariel." Burgess & Leigh | 10.00 |
| "Scinde." $10\frac{1}{2}$" | 12.75 |

**Sugar Bowls:**

| | |
|---|---|
| "Arabesque" | 37.50 |
| "Hong Kong." No lid | 21.50 |
| "Manilla" | 42.50 |

**Tureens:**

| | |
|---|---|
| "Melbourne." Small, with tray and ladle | 60.00 |
| "Scinde." Large size with platter | |

and rose knob _____ **280.00**

## FRAMES, See FURNITURE

## FRY GLASS

The H. C. Fry Glass Company began operations in 1900, at Rochester, Pa. The main product for the first 15 years or more was fine cut glass. As the demand waned, other types were produced.

A fine type of colored glass known as "Foval" is of interest to collectors now even though production did not begin until after 1925.

The glass is best described as being in pastel shades of smoky-blues, pinks, greens and creams. Usually a combination of two colors was used together. For example, a compote bowl would be pink and the standard blue; whereas, another would have a blue bowl, a knobbed stem of clear glass and a blue base.

A worker in the factory reported that not all pieces were stamped with the name "Fry," as just an occasional piece bore the mark. It was further reported that gold was used in the batches of glass in making "Foval" items.

The glass was expensive when retailed in its period and collectors are beginning to recognize its beauty and quality. The concern went bankrupt in 1929.

| | |
|---|---|
| Sugar Bowl and Creamer. Each $3\frac{1}{4}$" high. Deep blue handles, blue base on creamer. Set | **$165.00** |
| Candlesticks. Pair | 250.00 |
| Celery. Cream top, green base. $6\frac{1}{2}$" high | 95.00 |
| Cologne Bottle with Stopper. No trim, 6" tall | 55.00 |
| Compotes: 10" high. Pink bowl, blue foot | 120.00 |

12" high. Blue bowl and base,
clear ball connector _____ 100.00
14" high. Blue flared dome
base under Foval bowl _____ 135.00
Creamer _____ 115.00
Cup and Saucer _____ 65.00
Custard Cup. Dated 1919 _____ 6.00
Ewer. Foval. Bluish-opalescent in
classic urn shape, applied
orchid handles. 8x7¼" at top ____ 120.00
Pitcher _____ 165.00
Plate. 9½" diam. Blue trim on
rim _____ 37.50
Sherbet. Stemmed and plate. Pink
shaded color _____ 75.00
Sugar Bowl. Covered _____ 120.00
Teapot. On 8-footed hotplate.
Smoky opalescent body, green
handle and spout. Marked "Fry."
Heat resisting glass _____ 115.00

Vase. 7" high. Clear crackle glass
with applied blue glass leaves __ $60.00

Vases:
Green base, cream body with
blue band around top edge. 7½"
high, 7" across top _____ 85.00
Pink, with green base. 12"
high _____ 90.00
8" high. Cream body with flared
top, green band around top.
Green base _____ 125.00

## FURNITURE

Prices vary considerably on furniture.
The quality of workmanship, kind of wood,
the maker's name, if known, style and condition are determining factors in influencing
the price.

An attempt has been made to arrive
at an average price on each item listed.
It is hoped that this list will serve as a
guide. However, the above enumerated
factors must be taken into consideration
in arriving at a representative price.

### —FURNITURE STYLES—
### —APPROXIMATE DATES—

William and Mary _____ 1688-1710
Queen Anne _____ 1710-1750
Chippendale _____ 1754-1780
Hepplewhite _____ 1786-1800
Sheraton _____ 1790-1810
Empire _____ 1810-1830
Duncan Phyfe _____ 1800-1840
Early Victorian _____ 1830-1868
Late Victorian _____ 1870-1900

### BEDS

Bed Steps. Sheraton. Three steps,
original carpet inlay, lift-top lids,
bed chamber under lower step __ 225.00
Brass. Circa 1890 _____ 175.00
Brass and Iron. Full size. Lacey
ornamentation _____ 50.00
Cannon Ball Rope. Soft wood. Refinished _____ 125.00
Jenny Lind-type Beds:
Half size. Soft wood _____ 100.00
¾ size. Walnut _____ 125.00
Full size, spindle foot, solid
headboard. Original finish in
rough condition _____ 175.00
Day Bed. Opens into double bed,
with pad and pillows _____ 115.00
Maple. Full size. Pineapple-
carved posts. 4' high _____ 100.00
Maple. Full size. Turned posts.
40" high _____ 87.50
Maple Canopy. Turned posts. 6'
high. Refinished _____ 750.00
Sheraton Canopy. Maple. Twin size,
flame finial. Posts 74" high.
Circa 1810 _____ 900.00
Sheraton Canopy. Pine headboard,
square headposts. Fully reeded
with turned footposts _____ 500.00

### BENCHES

Cobbler's Benches:
Leather Seat. Nail drawer _____ 160.00
Restored and refinished _____ 175.00
Pine. 44" long, 17" wide, 2"
solid plank _____ 170.00
Mammy Bench. Made in western
Pennsylvania. Original green
paint. 6' long _____ 415.00

Church Bench. 36'' high, 48'' long.
Pine _____ **$50.00**

Cobbler's Bench. Complete with
nail drawer and leather seat.
Good condition _____ **$160.00**

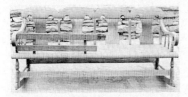

Mammy Bench. 6' long. Made in
western Pennsylvania. Original
green paint. Good condition __ **$415.00**

Water Bench. Pine trough lined
with zinc. 35'' high _____ **65.00**

High Chair. Bent wood _____ **$45.00**

Arm Chair _____ 29.50
Child's High Chair _____ 45.00
Cradle. Scarce _____ 150.00

## BOOK CASES

Oak. 5 slats, 6 shelves on a large
round pedastel base that re-
volves. $17\frac{1}{2}$'' square, $42\frac{1}{2}$'' high__ 95.00

## BOXES

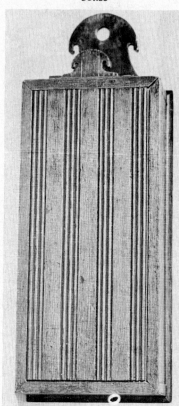

Candle Box. English, oak. Circa 1850. 7 x 4 x 18'' ............ $37.50

## CABINETS

Curio. Rosewood. Red lacquer, lined with tea paper. 45'' high, 24'' wide, 13'' deep ............ 175.00

## CANDLE STANDS

Candle Stand. Windsor, turned, dish tray. Early 18th Century. All original ............ $975.00

## CHAIRS AND ROCKERS

Chairs:
Adam Style. 32'' high, cane seat, original black and gold decor... 210.00
Arrowback. Plank seat. Set of six ............ 525.00
Arm Chair. Maple. Cane seat and rounded back ............ 29.50
Bamboo. Maple. Rush seats. Painted light tan with black in joints. Set of twelve ............ 3000.00
Belter Carved Rosewood. Upholstered in blue velour. One arm chair, 4 side chairs. Set ...... 2000.00

Chippendale Country Chair. Slat back, 18th century. Split rush seat _____ 220.00
Chippendale. Mahogany frame, rush seat _____ 320.00
Curly Maple. Refinished. Set of 8 _____ 500.00
Empire. Mahogany, carved. Set of 4 _____ 200.00
Empire Side Chair. Mahogany __ 67.50
Empire Side Chair. Walnut _____ 50.00
Empire. Mahogany. Fiddle back, slip seat. Original condition ___ 48.50

Windsor Chair. Brace-back, 9 spindles _____$275.00

Hitchcock-type. Fancy turnings, rush seat. Refinished _____ 100.00
Hitchcock _____ 89.50
Hitchcock. Stenciled. Circa 1812. Set of 6 _____ 525.00
Hitchcock. Baltimore. Set of 6__ 450.00
Ladder-back. Splint seat. Original _____ 21.50
Ladder-back. Splint seat. Refinished _____ 36.50
Louis XV. Beechwood. Occasional Armchair. Serpentine frame, covered with textured gold fabric _____ 500.00
Maple. Plank seat, spindle back. Set of 6 _____ 100.00

Chair. Early Windsor. Yew wood. Early 19th Century _____ $295.00

Belter Side Chair. Rosewood. Back scrolls, bunches of grapes and roses. Original _____ 275.00
Bent Half-Arrow. Original stencil decor _____ 95.00
Bentwood Arm Chair. Austrian. J&J Kohn burled inside cane seat rim. Sweeping curves _____ 75.00
Captain's. Pine. Unfinished ____ 60.00
Captain's. Roll-back type. Refinished _____ 125.00
Captain's Highchair. Foot rest. 28'' high. Original red paint ___ 55.00
Child's Arrowback. Plank seat __ 75.00
Child's Captain's Chair. Hickory plank seat. Original condition _____ 55.00
Child's. Tiger Maple. Shaped slat back. Rush seat. 17½'' high__ 175.00
Child's Highchair. Windsor-type arms _____ 67.50
Chippendale. Corner Marquetry__ 225.00

leaf carved, 4-spindle back. Set
of 4 _____ 300.00

Windsor Arm Chair. Maple legs,
hickory bent-back. Made by
Joseph Henzey, Phila. _____ $600.00

Morris. Oak. Ball and claw feet,
finials on brass rod. Back adjustment _____ 27.50
Morris. Walnut. Carved lion's
paw foot and arms, with ram's
horn and acanthus leaf. Back
adjustment _____ 37.50
New England Pillow-back Side
Chair. Eagle on splat. Original
stencil. Rush seat _____ 125.00
Queen Anne (Scotland). Mahog-
any. Fan decoration, slip seat __ 375.00
Queen Anne. Maple. Booted foot,
scalloped apron. Circa 1770 ___ 850.00
Queen Anne. Circa 1730. Rough__ 300.00
Queen Anne. Country style. Spanish feet _____ 295.00
Queen Anne Pilgrim Armchair.
Bulbous turnings, Spanish feet __ 850.00
Queen Anne. Rhode Island country
style, duck feet _____ 500.00
Regency Side Chair. Carved and
painted, lyre back, upholstered
seat _____ 275.00
Rose-carved. Mahogany. Three-
spindle back, refinished _____ 95.00
Sheraton Windsor. Step down, 7
spindles _____ 145.00
Slip Seat. Mahogany. Rose and

Windsor Side Chair. Made by
Joseph Henzey, Phila. _____ $325.00

Victorian Gentleman's Chair.
Grape and nut carvings, shield
back. Refinished _____ 295.00
Victorian Lady's Chair. Walnut.
Finger carved, oval back _____ 235.00
Victorian Side Chair. Walnut
frame. Needlepoint seat covering 95.00
Victorian Side Chair. Walnut
frame. Refinished _____ 80.00
Victorian Side Chair. Walnut.
Rose back, needlepoint seat ____ 60.00
Victorian Sleepy Hollow Chair.
Curved, serpentine front. Cabriole
legs _____ 300.00
Wm. Penn Style Dining Chairs.
Circa 1790, horsehair seats. Set
of 6 _____ 950.00
Windsor:
Arm. Bow back _____ 185.00
Arm. Maple legs, hickory bent-
back. Made by Joseph Henzey,
Phila. _____ 600.00
Bow Back, 7 spindles, black ____ 45.00
Bow Back. Early. Refinished ____ 75.00
Brace Back. 9 spindles _____ 275.00
Butterfly. Bamboo turnings. Origi-
nal condition _____ 90.00
Child's Bow Back. Shaped arms,
original black paint. Circa 1740__ 300.00

Captain's Chair. Pine. Refinished.. $90.00

Chair. Step-down Sheraton (Windsor). 7 spindles _____ $145.00

Rocker. Arrow-back, with writing arm. Western Pennsylvania origin. Signed S. C. TEBNER. Circa 1825. Original black paint with red and yellow decor. Scarce ____ $600.00

New England Pillow-back Side Chair. Eagle on splat, original stencil, rush seat _____ $125.00

Boston. Painted black _____ 95.00
Boston. Refinished _____ 100.00
Boston. Roll back _____ 100.00
Child's Victorian Rocker. Ring
turnings, knobs on top and arms.
Diagonal slat in back covered
with corduroy. Cane seat _____ 30.00
Comb Back. Painted _____ 120.00
Curved back, rolled seat. Refin-
ished _____ 100.00
Empire. Mahogany _____ 95.00
Ladder-back. Double bearing
arms, 4 slats, finial at top of
posts. Original splint seat, paint-
ed black _____ 70.00
Ladder-back. Splint seat _____ 30.00
Lincoln. Life-size grape carving__ 75.00
Mahogany. Swan head arms, origi-
nal _____ 95.00
Mammy Rocker. Maple and
pine _____ 100.00
Platform. Carpet upholstery ____ 75.00
Victorian. Sleep Hollow type.
Upholstered _____ 125.00
Windsor Arm Rocker. Bird cage.
Refinished _____ 150.00
Windsor. Bamboo turned, 7 spin-
dles. Shaped saddle seat. Rough
condition _____ 100.00

## CHESTS

Chest, Miniature. 13¾" high, 13"
wide. Walnut, ceramic drawer
pulls. 4 drawers _____ $75.00

Apothecary Chest. Pine. 15 drawers, 57" long, 16" deep, 43¼"
high. Strip paneled ends _____ 475.00
Blanket Chests:
Pennsylvania Dutch. 2 drawers.
Chippendale brasses and feet,
stippled light green with dull
red trim _____ 900.00

Hepplewhite Side Chair. Carved,
mahogany. Square stepped back,
fluted urn-shaped splat carved
with drapery swags and crested
with 3 feathers, enclosed by an
arch with fan lunettes and slender
colonnettes, on square tapering
legs ending in square feet. Old
gold striped satin on serpentine-
fronted seat _____ $500.00

Low Back Chairs. 9 spindles. One
armchair and 6 straight chairs.
Set _____ 800.00
Rabbit Ears. Set of 4 _____ 350.00
Seven spindles. Refinished _____ 90.00
Side Chair. Made by Joseph
Henzey, Phila. _____ 325.00
Side Chair. Refinished _____ 150.00
Side Chair. Step-down type ____ 50.00
Stick Back. 8 spindles, bamboo
turnings, saddle seat. Dark finish 75.00
Rockers:
Arrow-back Writing Arm. Wes-
tern Pennsylvania origin. Signed
S. C. Tebner. Circa 1825. Origi-
nal black paint with red and yel-
low decor. Scarce _____ 600.00

Highboy. Queen Anne. Massachusetts origin. Circa 1730. 62" high, 36" wide. Walnut, with herringbone inlay. Original condition __$7500.00

Bride's Chest. Pine. Montgomery County, Pa. Name "Johan Adam Scohr 1784" on front. Original __ $400.00

Pine:
Miniature. Bracket-foot,
19x10x11" high. Original _____ 50.00
One long drawer _____ 200.00
30" high, 40" wide _____ 110.00

Two drawers .Refinished _____ 200.00
Walnut. Somerset County, Pa. Lift top, 3 drawers, $51\frac{1}{4}$" long, 22" wide, $27\frac{1}{2}$" high. Original "Dutch" decoration under paint.
Rough condition _____ 250.00

Chippendale. Walnut. American, 18th century. $63\frac{1}{2}$" high, 41" long _____$1250.00

Bow-front. Mahogany. Late 19th century. $36\frac{1}{4}$" high and $39\frac{1}{4}$" wide   475.00
Camphor Wood. Deep carving on front, sides and ends _____   175.00
Cherry. Refinished _____   300.00
Cherry. Unfinished _____   200.00
Chippendale Bow-front. Cherry, $41\frac{1}{2}$" long, $23\frac{3}{4}$" across top, $34\frac{1}{2}$" high. Refinished _____   975.00
Chippendale. Curly maple. Six drawers with original brasses. New England, circa 1800. 40" wide, 56" high, 19" deep _____ 2000.00
Chippendale. Three drawers, inset quarter columns, molded top. Original brasses. Top $21x34\frac{1}{2}$", $35\frac{1}{4}$" high. Rare _____ 6000.00
Chippendale (Scotland). Original brasses. Mahogany. 37" long, $35\frac{1}{2}$" high _____   800.00
Chippendale. Walnut. Four drawers, inset columns, 3'5" high. Refinished _____ 1650.00

Chest, Bow-front. Mahogany. Late
19th century. 36½'' high, 39½''
wide _____ $475.00

Chippendale Low Chest. Walnut,
4-drawer, plain front. Circa
1780 _____ 1200.00
Chippendale Highboy. 6'3'' high,
3'6'' long. Walnut. Broken arch
top. Refinished _____ 2000.00
Chippendale Highboy. Mahogany.
New England ,circa 1770-80, all
original _____ 2400.00
Commode. Lift top. Original _____ 65.00
Commode. Pine. Small size, lift
top. Off-center drawer. Refinished _____ 125.00

High Chest. Walnut. 6'6'' high, 22''
wide. 9 drawers with brass pulls.
Lancaster County, Pa., origin __$1,800.00

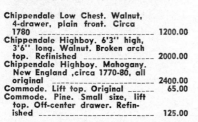

Chest. Hepplewhite. Bow-front. Mahogany inlaid. New England, late
18th century _____$600.00

Lowboy. New England. Walnut, 31''
high, 36'' wide _____ $4,800.00

Curly "tiger-stripe" Maple. Chippendale style. 4 full and 2 half drawers. 45" high, 38" wide, 18" deep _____ 800.00

Hepplewhite. Mahogany inlay. Bowfront. New England. Late 18th century _____ 600.00

Highboy. Cherry. New England origin. 9 drawers with brass pulls, 6' high _____ 2650.00

High Chest. Walnut. Lancaster County, Pa. origin 6'6" high, 22" wide, 9 drawers with brass pulls_ 1800.00

Louis XV. Bombe Chest, inlaid, 2 drawers, 46x20x35½" high ____ 1500.00

Lowboy. New England. Walnut, 31" high, 36" wide _____ 4800.00

Lowboy. Mahogany. Rough _____ 1000.00

Mahogany and Maple. Reeded posts _____ 300.00

Mahogany Chest and Cabinet. Painted panels. 7'10" high, 49" wide. Chippendale style. Circa 1795, English origin _____ 1500.00

Maple. Tiger stripe. Refinished __ 500.00

Maple. 4 drawers, 40" wide, 36" high. Turned legs _____ 200.00

Maple. Turnip feet, 40" high. Circa 1720. Original _____ 750.00

Miniature Chests:
Country-style, pine, paneled end, original _____ 80.00

Sheraton-style. Cherry, 14½x20x9" deep. Refinished _____ 195.00

Sheraton-style. Tiger maple. Paneled end, turned cherry feet. Refinished _____ 250.00

Pine Chests:
Cottage type _____ 85.00

3 long drawers, 34" wide, 29" high, cut-out base. Refinished___ 98.50

4 long drawers, solid ends, cut-out base, 40" wide, 42" high___ 210.00

4 long drawers, paneled ends. Cut-out base _____ 35.00

4 long drawers, 38" wide, solid ends _____ 185.00

4 long drawers, mirror on top __ 125.00

4 drawers, solid ends, 46" high, 42½" long. Original curly maple knobs, turned feet _____ 215.00

Queen Anne. Walnut. Chest on frame. Cabriole legs, drape feet, scalloped skirt, 58½"high, top 22½" x 40" _____ 3500.00

Queen Anne. Birch. 6 drawers on frame. Circa 1750. Original ____ 2500.00

Queen Anne Highboy. Cherry. Two parts, cabriole legs, pad feet, 5'7" high, 40" wide _____ 3000.00

Queen Anne Highboy. Early American. Circa 1790. Rough condition _____ 3250.00

Sea Captain's Map Chest. Refinished _____ 100.00

Sea Chest. Pine. Dovetailed construction, medium size _____ 65.00

Highboy. New England origin. Cherry. 9 drawers with brass pulls, 6' high _____$2,650.00

Sheraton. Walnut. Country type, split top drawers, turned legs. Refinished _____ 400.00

Walnut. Chippendale period. O G bracket feet. Original except for brasses. Refinished _____ 1000.00

Walnut. Victorian. 4 drawers, fruit-carved handles. Refinished _____ 175.00

Walnut. Victorian dresser. Carved pulls, marble insert on top. Swinging mirror. Original _____ 160.00

### COBBLER'S BENCHES, See BENCHES

### CORNER CUPBOARDS

Cherry. One drawer, 2 glass doors at top, 2 solid drawers below. 42" wide, 6'10" high. Original condition _____ $325.00

**Corner Cupboard. Walnut.** Panelled glass door at top, solid door below. 7'4" high. Original "H" hinges, 3 shelves. Good original condition _____$875.00

**Cherry.** Chippendale influence, bow-front, all original _____ 1650.00

**Corner Cupboards:**
**Cherry.** Queen Anne period. Two-piece, 7'8" high. Arched doors with glass panels, butterfly shelves. Original brass "H" hinges on doors _____ 2450.00

**Chippendale. Mahogany.** Philadelphia. 7½' high. Ball and claw feet, gadroon molding. Broken arch top with frame finials _____ 2000.00

**Chippendale Style. Walnut.** Pennsylvania. Scrolled broken-arch top, 3 brass finials and scrolled bracket feet. Solid doors. Refinished _____ 1750.00

**Corner Cupboard.** 2-piece. 7' 10" high. Pine. Bow-front doors with glass panes. Dental molding, solid doors below _____$1,000.00

**Dutch.** Pennsylvania. Pine and maple. Flat-back type, carved pillars. Refinished _____ 600.00

**Pine Corner Cupboards:**
Bow-front doors, with glass panes. 2-piece, 7'10" high. Dental molding, solid doors below _____$1000.00

Butterfly shelves, 6' high. Raised panel door, "H" hinges. Refinished _____ 450.00

Corner Cupboard. Philadelphia Chippendale. Mahogany. 7½' high. Ball and claw feet, gadroon molding. Broken arch top with flame finials _____$2,000.00

Flat-back, double glass doors, 6'10" high, 4' wide. Refinished _____ 375.00
Shell carved. Early New England, 7'3" high, 4" across. Rare ____ 6000.00

Corner Cupboard. 2-piece, 7' 8" high. Cherry. Queen Anne period. Arched doors with glass panels, butterfly shelves. Original brass "H" hinges on doors _____$2,450.00

Single glass panel door. Refinished _____ 350.00
Two paneled doors, center drawer, rough condition _____ 1250.00
Walnut Corner Cupboards:
Chippendale. American. Narrow, circa 1790-1800 _____ 900.00
Solid doors. 6½' high, good rough condition _____ 135.00
Two paneled doors, 82x40". Refinished _____ 300.00
Two glass doors. Refinished ____ 350.00
Jelly Cupboard. Pennsylavnia Dutch. Rough condition _____ 95.00
Wall Cupboard. Pine. 36" wide with cut-out shelves _____ 160.00

## CRADLES

Early Primitive Cradle. 4 turned posts, solid headboard with roll top. Solid splayed sides, solid footboard, rockers.

| | |
|---|---|
| Original red paint _____ | 50.00 |
| Pine. 13x34'' open sides. Original__ | 48.50 |
| Pine. Hooded, dovetailed, 14x37''. Refinished _____ | 85.00 |
| Pine. 43'' rockers. Refinished ____ | 65.00 |
| Walnut. Hooded _____ | 100.00 |
| Walnut. Open-spindle type construction. Arms extend from high back _____ | 110.00 |
| Walnut. 45''. Original condition __ | 50.00 |

## DESKS

Slant-front Desk. 44'' high, 24½'' deep. Walnut, 4 drawers, brass pulls. Original good condition _____$750.00

| | |
|---|---|
| Chippendale Style. Cherry. Slant-front. 3'6'' high, 32'' wide at feet _____ | 1400.00 |
| Chippendale. Cherry. Slant-front. Refinished _____ | 1275.00 |
| Chippendale. Maple. Slant-front. Late 18th century. 40½'' high, 45'' wide. Scrolled bracket feet__ | 1000.00 |
| Curly Maple. New England. Chippendale. Slant-front, Writing height 31¼'', 43½'' to top, 35¾'' wide. Refinished _____ | 1250.00 |
| Hepplewhite. Early Pennsylvania. Eagle inlay, feet missing. Original condition _____ | 3500.00 |
| Hepplewhite. Inlaid. 6 drawers, 6 cubbies. Original hardware __ | 500.00 |

Slant-front Desk (Scotland). Mahogany. 36'' long, 40'' high ___ $700.00

Desk. Chippendale, slant-front. Maple. Late 18th century. 40½'' high, 45'' wide. Scrolled bracket feet _$1,000.00

| | |
|---|---|
| Hepplewhite Slant-top. Solid mahogany case. Pine-veneered drawer fronts with original brass bail pulls. Inlaid interior around drawer edges. Circa 1790-1800 | 400.00 |
| Lady's Desk. Victorian, walnut with 4 drawers below writing lid. 28'' wide _____ | 120.00 |
| Lady's Slant-top Desk. Maple. 36'' wide. Good writing interior ____ | 750.00 |
| Lap Desk. Mother-of-pearl inlay decor. 16'' long, 9¼'' wide _____ | 45.00 |
| Mahogany. Block front, small. Rough condition _____ | 800.00 |

Desk. Early Pennsylvania Hepplewhite. Eagle inlay, feet missing.
Original condition _____ $3,500.00

Slant-front Desk (Scotland). Mahogany. 36'' long, 40'' high _____   700.00
Traveling Lap Desk. Rosewood. 10x
7¼x3¾'' thick. Small brass inlaid
qlaque on lid. Interior compartments with two-part writing surface. Lock and key. Original
finish _____     30.00

## DOUGH TROUGHS

Chestnut. With lid, 4 slender pine
legs. 18x28x28'' high. Refinished__ $125.00
Old American. 41x15x5½'' _____   115.00
Pine. Medium size. Rough condition.    80.00
Pine. Pennsylvania Shaker-type.
30¾'' high, 32'' long, with lid.
Splayed legs with stretchers.
Rare _____   195.00
Pine. Square, tapered legs _____    85.00
Poplar. With cover _____    60.00
Tulip Wood (Poplar). With cover,
turned legs, dovetailed, 21x36'',
28'' high. Pine colored finish ___   100.00
Walnut. Splayed legs, dovetailed
corners, 20x39x27'' high.
Refinished _____   160.00

## DRY SINKS

Dry Sink. Copper liner, soft wood.
4'1'' wide, 42'' high.
Redecorated _____ $ 195.00

Pine. Well top, one door at base.
30x16½x32'' high. Original condition _____ $120.00
Pine. Well top. One drawer, two
doors. Refinished _____   225.00
Pine. One drawer, two doors. Refinished deep well _____   220.00
Poplar. Splash board, no drawers,
49x19½''x33'' high. Refinished____   175.00
Poplar and Pine. High back, 4'2''
high. Two drawers with 2 doors

Lap Desk. Mother-of-pearl inlay
decor. 16'' long, 9¼'' wide _____$45.00

Pine. Slant front. Sheraton legs.
One deep drawer, well for chair.
32'' wide, gallery at back. Refinished _____   500.00
Pine. One drawer. Rough _____    75.00
Plantation Desk, Pine. Rough _____   100.00
Schoolmaster's Desk. Walnut. Rough    87.50
Schoolmaster's Desk. Kneehole type.
4 drawers on each side, compartments on top. Mahogany veneer
drawer fronts. Top is 59x25'' ___   150.00

below. Refinished _____ 260.00
Poplar. High back with two drawers
  above. 46" high, 21" wide, 44"
  long. Refinished _____ 280.00
Poplar. Low back, 2 doors below__ 85.00
Walnut. One drawer, 2 doors below. 44" long, 33" high. Unfinished _____ 115.00

## FLAX WHEELS

Flax Wheel. 54" high, $16\frac{1}{2}$" wide,
  $11\frac{1}{2}$" deep _____ $60.00
Flax Wheel. Small American. Complete with distaff _____ 85.00

## FOOT STOOLS

Mahogany. England. Fluted leg, slip
  seat, 17" high, 16" wide _____ $150.00
Mahogany Veneer. Beading around
  edge, slender Cabriole legs,
  $14x10\frac{1}{2}x10$" high _____ 60.00
Mahogany Veneer. Empire style.
  Short round legs. 12x8x8" high__ ~48.50

## FRAMES

Picture Frame. Pine, stripped to
  natural wood. 14 x 16" _____$18.50

Curly Maple. $17x15x1\frac{1}{2}$" wide ____ $42.50
Gold Leaf Frames:
  $7\frac{1}{2}x20\frac{1}{2}$" opening _____ 22.50
  8x21" opening, for motto _____ 21.50
  $12\frac{3}{4}x10\frac{1}{2}$". Raised berries and
  leaves on top, bottom and sides_ 20.00
Pine. Stripped to natural wood.
  14x16" _____ 18.50
Walnut Frames:
  (Measurements given are for size
  of opening)
  $8\frac{1}{4}x8\frac{1}{2}$". Pair _____ 35.00
  $8\frac{3}{4}x11$" _____ 20.00

$11x15\frac{1}{2}$". Carved, with criss-
  cross corners _____ 18.50
12x8". Cross-bar corners _____ 14.50
$13\frac{1}{4}x9\frac{1}{2}$" _____ 24.00
$16\frac{3}{4}x21$". Deep _____ 25.00
$17\frac{3}{4}x22$". Gold liner _____ 28.00
$18\frac{1}{4}x27\frac{1}{2}$". Deep, leaf carving
  around edge, gold liner. Pair __ 45.00
$20\frac{1}{2}x8$". Pair _____ 35.00
Shadow Box. 28x32". Double liner
  of gold and ebony, 7" deep __ 47.50
Oval:
14x12" _____ 28.50
14x12". Refinished _____ 32.50
14x12". Gold liner _____ 20.00
$15\frac{1}{2}x13\frac{1}{4}$". Gold liner. Pair ____ 48.50
18x11". Brass liner. Pair _____ 60.00
19x16" _____ 75.00

## HAT RACKS

Hat Rack. Expands to 18". Wood,
  12 pegs _____$22.00

Walnut. Accordion type. Porcelain
  tips on pegs. Refinished _____ 18.75
Walnut. Accordion style. 7 porcelain tips _____ 18.50
Walnut. Accordion. Star shape, 12
  pegs with porcelain tips. All
  original _____ 22.50
Wood. Expands to 18". 12 pegs __ 22.00

## ICE CREAM PARLOR FURNITURE

Chairs:
  With arms _____ $65.00
  Straight, heart-back _____ 48.00
  Straight, loop-back _____ 45.00
Stool. High _____ 39.50
Table. 27" square, oak top _____ 85.00

Ice Cream Parlor Chairs. 14" diameter wooden seats replaced. Set of 4 matching chairs _____ $75.00

## LOVE SEATS

Hepplewhite. Walnut. Spade feet, bellflower inlay. Refinished and re-upholstered _____ $ 600.00
Victorian. Late. Walnut _____ 120.00
Victorian. Walnut. Large size _____ 200.00
Victorian. Walnut. Large size, rose carving on 3 crests. Refinished and recovered _____ 495.00
Victorian. Walnut. Mirror-back. Original condition _____ 200.00
Walnut. Finger carved. Refinished__ 275.00

## MAGAZINE RACKS

Oak. 13½x18". Turned spindles, pressed carving, brass studs _____ $16.00
Wall Rack. Victorian. Walnut. 13½x26". Eastlake style. Carved turned posts each side, scrolled and cut-out design. Original ___ 48.50

## MANTELS

Adam-style. Carrara marble. Shelf, 70" long, 42x51". Eagle, acorn and wheat motif _____ $600.00
Pine. Circa 1810-1820. 52½" high, 68" wide. Curved top section__ 110.00
Pine. Victorian. Painted white _____ 75.00

Convex Regency Wall Mirror. Carved and gilded eagle. 34' high, 27" wide _____ $650.00

Bird's Eye Maple Dressing Mirror. One drawer with glass _____ $160.00
Brass Standing Mirror. Oval for dressing table. Cupids and floral decorations. 15" high, 16" wide _____ 55.00
Chippendale. Brass eagle finial, 27½x14", old glass, with 10x17" liner _____ 225.00
Chippendale. Inlaid mahogany, gilt and banding. 21x40" _____ 300.00
Convex Regency Wall Mirror. Carved and gilded eagle. 34" high, 27" wide _____ 650.00
Courting Mirror. 12x16½". Circa 1780 _____ 435.00
Dresser Mirror. English. Oval. Applewood. 26" high _____ 85.00
George I Style. 80x34", carved wood with antique gilt _____ 695.00
Mahogany. Two-section mirror. Original glass, painting in top. 18½x34" _____ 95.00
O. G. Mirror. 28x42" _____ 65.00
O. G. Mirror. Pine. 22½x32½". Thin old glass. Refinished _____ 80.00
Picture Top. Gold leaf. Medium __ 55.00

Dresser Mirror. English. Apple wood. Oval, 26'' high _____ $85.00

Queen Anne. 18th century, 62'' long, walnut frame with gilt ____ 600.00
Sheraton. Carved maple frame, 21x29'', reeded pilaster, cornice. Unfinished _____ 100.00
Victorian. Oval, gold leaf, 42x38'' Ornate _____ 375.00
Walnut. Circa 1870. Reverse painting on glass above. Old glass. 12x19'' _____ 60.00

## SECRETARIES

Empire. Veneer. 6' high, 15'' desk when open. Low bookcase, 3' high. Refinished _____ $375.00
Empire. Mahogany veneer. Scroll front, bookcase top, 39½'' wide, 67'' high _____ 200.00
Hepplewhite. Cherry. Broken pediment top, French bracket feet. 7'8'' high _____ 1650.00
Hepplewhite. Mahogany. Tambour type, sliding doors _____ 800.00
Regency. Mahogany _____ 675.00
Sheraton. Mahogany. Four drawers, arched door panels. Circa 1815.__ 700.00
Sheraton. Mahogany. Inlaid,

small reeded legs, 40'' wide, 54'' high. Original _____ 715.00

Hepplewhite Secretary. Cherry. Broken pediment top, French bracket feet. 7'8'' high _____ $1,650.00

## SETTLES

Arrowback _____ $260.00
Mammy Bench. 54'' long. Original__ 300.00
Pennsylvania Dutch. Hitchcock-type. 6'4'', 17'' high, 20'' deep. Hitchcock turnings, half spindles,

deeply curved arms. Original
paint _____ 450.00
Windsor-type. Bamboo-style turnings, 6'7'' long, 37½'' overall
height. Refinished _____ 675.00
Windsor-type. ''Duck Bill'' arms.
8 legs, 6½' lonf, 36½'' high,
seat 17'' wide. Circa 1815.
Original decoration _____ 660.00
Windsor-type. ''Duck Bill'' top.
47'' long, 37'' high. Hickory and
pine. Small size. Refinished ____ 525.00

## SEWING STANDS

Tiered Sewing Table (England). Mahogany. 22'' wide, 26'' high ____$175.00

Mahogany. Two drawers, turned
legs _____ 135.00
Oriental Sewing Stand. Dragonhead
feet. Bone and ivory fittings.
Top 26x19'', 29½'' high. Black
finish with gold decor _____ 185.00
Victorian. Walnut. 30½'' high _____ 90.00
Victorian. Walnut, 17½'' top diam.
28'' high, 3 legs _____ 120.00

## SIDEBOARDS

Sideboard. Hepplewhite, inlaid mahogany, serpentine sideboard.
Late 18th century. 52'' high,
6'6'' long _____ $2,000.00

Chippendale. Walnut. Cabriole legs,
hand-carved trimmings. 38'' high,
81'' long, 23'' wide. Original

Sewing Stand. Victorian, walnut.
17½'' top diam., 28'' high. On
3 feet _____ $120.00

Drop Leaf. Cherry and walnut. Two
drawers _____ $150.00
Empire Drop Leaf. One drawer __ 160.00
Mahogany. Tiered. (England). 22''
wide, 26'' high _____ 175.00

brass pulls. Made by Virginia craftsmen _____ $4,800.00

Empire. Mahogany, with cherry top and ends. 45'' long, 21'' wide, 48'' high. Large drawer at bottom, pie crust molding trim. Refinished _____ 495.00

Georgian. Circa 1715. 78x26x38'' high. Original finish _____ 1600.00

Sideboard. Hepplewhite, mahogany. American, late 18th century. 41'' high, 6' 1'' long _____:$1,800.00

Hepplewhite. Inlaid _____ 1400.00

Hepplewhite. Mahogany. American, late 18th century. 41'' high, 6'1'' long _____ 1800.00

Regency Style. 5'6'' long, 37'' high. Tapered legs, acorn toes. _ 575.00

Sheraton. Mahogany, 6 legs _____ 1250.00

## SOFAS

Belter Carved Rosewood. Circa 1845. Back enclosed by scrolls and crested with busts of famous persons, including Geo. Washington. Casters. 6'2'' long _____ $650.00

Victorian. Walnut. Miniature. Re-upholstered in avacado velvet.

68'' long, 32'' high. Two matching side chairs. 3 pieces _____ $585.00

Victorian. Walnut. Nut carving, 39'' high, 6' long. Re-upholstered in ivory brocade _____ $385.00

## SPICE BOXES

Spice Box. Wood, porcelain knobs. 8-drawer. 17'' high, 5'' wide __ $75.00

Oak. 8 drawers _____ $45.00

Walnut. 6 drawers _____ 47.50

| | |
|---|---|
| Walnut. 8 drawers. Refinished ____ | 65.00 |
| Walnut. 8 small drawers, 1 large drawer, 19½'' long, 10¼'' wide___ | 67.50 |
| Wood. 8 drawers, porcelain knobs. 17'' high, 5'' deep _____ | 75.00 |
| Wood. Round. 7 individual containers _____ | 18.00 |

### SPINNING WHEELS

Spinning Wheel. Continental-type. Complete _____ **$87.50**

| | |
|---|---|
| Continental-type. Complete _____ | $87.50 |
| Standard-type. Complete and refinished _____ | 80.00 |
| Standard-type. Small. Complete, original _____ | 65.00 |

### SPOOL CABINETS

Spool Cabinet. Corticelli. 15'' high, 21'' wide. Oak, 5 drawers, plate glass display fronts _____ **$45.00**

| | |
|---|---|
| Maple. 15x21x9'' high. Two drawers | $30.00 |
| Oak. 22x30x15'' high. Lift top, 4 drawers _____ | 40.00 |
| Walnut. 17½x17½x11½'' high. "Goffs Best Braid," 3 drawers, 6 original melon-shaped brasses _____ | 32.50 |

### STANDS

Night Stand. Sheraton. Cherry. 2-drawer, 28'' high, top 18 x 22'' $135.00

Candle Stands:
| | |
|---|---|
| Cherry. Spade feet. Small _____$ | 175.00 |
| Curly Maple. Cut-out, tilt top___ | 265.00 |
| Hepplewhite. Pine. 16½'' square top, 28¾'' high. Natural finish___ | 32.50 |
| Mahogany. Tilt-top, bird-claw feet _____ | 95.00 |
| Maple _____ | 145.00 |
| Maple. Tripod base _____ | 80.00 |
| Pine. 27'' high, 17'' square top, tapered Hepplewhite legs _____ | 69.50 |

Cherry Stands:
| | |
|---|---|
| Bedside. Small, square tapering legs. One drawer _____ | 75.00 |
| Dropleaf. One drawer. Refinished _____ | 135.00 |
| Dropleaf. Two drawers _____ | 145.00 |
| Dropleaf. Two curly maple drawers _____ | 165.00 |
| Hepplewhite. One drawer. Refinished _____ | 135.00 |
| One drawer. Refinished _____ | 100.00 |
| Two drawers. 29'' high, 21'' square top, turned legs. Refinished _____ | 150.00 |

**Mahogany Stands:**
Dropleaf. Two drawers. Pedestal. 185.00
Duncan Phyfe Card Table. Turned
reeded legs, with stretchers ____ 450.00
**Maple Stands:**
Dropleaf. Two drawers _____ 160.00
One drawer _____ 85.00
**Pine Stands:**
Bedside. One drawer, square
tapered legs _____ 80.00
Corner. American. Two shelves,
one drawer, 36" high _____ 225.00
18x23" top, dovetailed drawer __ 70.00
**Rosewood Stands.** Marble top,
bamboo design, 32" high. Pair __ 300.00
**Sheraton Night Stand.** Cherry. Two
drawers, 28" high, 18x22" top__ 135.00
**Spool Magazine Stand.** 16½" long__ 40.00
**Wash Stands:**
Hepplewhite. English mahogany__ 215.00
Mahogany-veneer Corner Stand.
English, 34" high _____ 200.00
Victorian. Walnut, 31" high,
15½" wide, 28" long. One drawer,
refinished _____ 125.00

## TABLES

Chippendale Card Table. Marlboro-
type. All original _____ $465.00

Queen Anne Dropleaf Table. Maple.
New England origin. Minor restor-
ations on the rounded leaves. Pad
foot, cut-out ends. 48" long, 15"
wide at top, leaves 16" at widest
point _____$1,500.00

Banquet Table. Cherry, dropleaf,
rosewood veneer apron, 42"
wide, 92" long _____$1500.00
Banquet Table. Hepplewhite (England). Mahogany, three sections,
9'4" long, 29" high _____ 1650.00
Birch Dropleaf Table. Two drawers,
veneer fronts. Turned legs, 8½"
leaves, 18" square top, 29½"
high _____ 125.00

Hepplewhite Mahogany Pembroke
Table. Maryland, late 18th century.
28½" high, 40" wide _____ $1450.00

Bird Cage Tilt-top Table. American.
Cherry, 39" diam., 27" high __ 565.00

Sheraton Mahogany and Satinwood Card Table. American, Circa 1800-1810. 30" high, 34" open _____ $1150.00

Bird Cage Tilt-top Tea Table. Mahogany, 28½" high, 32" wide 650.00

Card Tables:

Cherry Inlaid. Fold top, turned legs _____ 300.00

Chippendale. Walnut. Ball and claw feet. 33" wiae, 27½" high__ 625.00

Chippendale. Marlboro-type. All original _____ 465.00

Duncan Phyfe-type. Circa 1870__ 325.00

Queen Anne with Gaming Top. (England). Mahogany. 35½" long, 30" high _____ 800.00

Queen Anne Dropleaf Table. Walnut. Philadelphia origin. 48" long, 17½" across top. Leaves 19" deep. Tri-fid foot, scalloped skirt, cut-out corner _____ $3,000.00

Sheraton. American. Cherry. 29" high, 36" wide _____ 320.00

Sheraton. American. Mahogany and Satinwood. 30" high, 34" open. Circa 1800-1810 _____ 1000.00

Sheraton. Mahogany. Carved pedestal. 31" hiah, 38" wide with leaves open. Circa 1820 _____ 1150.00

Sheraton. Mahogany. 4 reeded legs, ¾ circle cutaway corners, one leg swings out. 30" high, 17½x35½" top closed _____ 300.00

Sheraton. Mahogany. Reeded legs, serpentine front, maple inlay. 30½" high, 36" long, 19" wide__ 295.00

Dropleaf Table. 6-leg. Cherry. Small turned legs. 30" high, 24" leaves. Refinished _____ $300.00

Cherry Dropleaf. Six legs, slender turnings, 45" wide, 60" long. Drawer in end. Refinished _____ 275.00

Cherry Dropleaf. Six turned legs, drawer in either end. 46" long __ 380.00

Cherry Dropleaf. Six legs, 64x46"__ 300.00

Cherry Dropleaf. Rope legs. Seats six. Refinished _____ 395.00

Chippendale. American maple. Swing leg. Center of top is 43x13". Leaves are 15" wide____ 550.00

Chippendale Dropleaf. Mahogany. Ball and claw feet with casters. 42" wide, 30" high _____ 675.00

Curly Birch Dropleaf. Six legs, refinished _____ 320.00

Duncan Phyfe. Mahogany dining room table. Two end drawers, 28½" high, 58" wide with leaves open _____ 395.00

French Marquetry Table. Mahogany 200.00

Harvest. Pine, 5' long. Leaves replaced _____ 190.00

Harvest. Pine, 6' long, 21" wide__ 185.00

Table, Round (Late). Oak. 48"
 diameter _____ $60.00

Harvest. Pine, 7' single board
 top. 21" wide, 9" leaves,
 turned legs. Refinished and restored _____ 450.00
Hutch. Pine, round, 49" diam. ___ 315.00
Hutch. Pine. Round, 39" diam.,
 29" high, maple legs. Refinished _____ 365.00
Hutch. Pine. B/B. top, 34" wide,
 60" long. Maple chair base is
 28½" high _____ 400.00
Lazy Susan. Pine, 57" top, 37"
 susan _____ 375.00
Pembroke Tables:
 Cherry. Original condition ____ 300.00
 Cherry. Hepplewhite legs _____ 315.00
 Mahogany. Hepplewhite. Late
 18th century, 28½" high, 40"
 wide _____ 1450.00

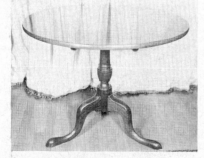

Tilt-top Table. Queen Anne style.
 Slipper foot, 36" diam. Circa
 1770 _____ $475.00

Mahogany (Scotland). Dropleaf.
 37" long, 29" high _____ 300.00
Poker Table. Oak. Round, 36" diam.
 Swivels on round, iron pedestal
 base. Compartment for chips
 underneath _____ 110.00
Queen Anne Breakfast Table. Walnut, circa 1725. Refinished,
 brasses replaced _____ 850.00
Queen Anne Country Style. Walnut, circa 1765. Duck or club
 feet. 29½" high, top 31¼x51½"__ 750.00
Queen Anne Dressing Table (Scotland). Mahogany. 28" high, 30"
 long, original brasses _____ 1500.00
Queen Anne. Maple. New England-
 type. 50" across top, 26½" high,
 46" long, mule or biscuit feet.
 Early _____ 1400.00
Queen Anne. Walnut. Drake feet,
 4'2" long, 28½" high. Early ____ 2250.00

Table. Vetrine, French. 35½" wide,
 gold finish, with beveled plate
 glass _____ $450.00

Serving Table. Walnut. Virginia,
 18th century. 28½" high, 48"
 wide _____ 795.00
Sheraton. Mahogany. Four reeded
 legs, butterfly drop leaves,
 30½" high, 42½" long. Refinished _____ 450.00
Tavern. Pine. Tapered legs, long
 drawer in front. Wide, one-
 board top. Original condition __ 165.00
Tavern. Pine. 20x31x37" high. Refinished _____ 200.00
Tilt-top. Maple, serpentine-edge
 top. 36" square, slipper-foot base 410.00

Tip-top. 17½'' diam. Refinished____ 275.00
Walnut. Dropleaf. Square, tapered
legs. Medium size _____ 80.00

## TABLES — MARBLE TOP

Marble Top Table. Small, oval, walnut base. 29'' high. Marble top is
18'' across and 14'' wide. Refinished _____ $135.00

Large. Fancy carved base with
pedestal _____ $300.00
Medium. Oval, carved base _____ 160.00
Medium. Square _____ 125.00
Small. Walnut base. Oval, 29'' high.
Top is 18'' across and 14'' wide.
Refinished _____ 135.00
Turtle Top. Wa'nut base. 34'' long,
22½'' wide, 30'' high. Refinished__ 165.00
Walnut. Serpentine, stretcher,
carved, curved legs. 26x36'' ____ 200.00

## TEA CADDY

Mahogany. Coffin-shaped. 10x6½x6''
high _____ $65.00

## TEA WAGON

Tea Wagon. Refinished _____$70.00

Tea Wagon. Refinished _____ $70.00
Walnut. Dropleaf. Two large and
two small wheels. Silver drawer
on one end with pull-out ashtray
on other end. Large tray for
top _____ 75.00

## WAGON SEATS

Wagon Seats _____ $90.00

Leather. Upholstered. 37'' wide,
21'' high, low spindle arms with
iron braces _____ 80.00
Wagon Seat _____ 90.00
Wagon Seat. Original scallops, old
paint _____ 50.00
Wagon or Buggy Seat. Windsor-
type. 32 turned spindles, heart
design cut on either side. Refinished _____ 95.00

## WARDROBE

Kas or Shrank. Cherry. Typical
Dutch style. Circa 1720-1730.
41'' wide, 6' high _____ $1,150.00

## WHATNOTS

Corner Whatnot. Soft wood, 5
  shelves _____ $110.00
Walnut Whatnots:
  Corner. Cupboard bottom with
  4 shelves above. 6' high _____ 185.00
  5-shelf. 5' high, 3' wide at
  bottom shelf _____ 195.00
  5 molded-edge, graduated serpentine shelves. Scroll back.
  Original finish _____ 125.00
  Hanging. Leaf carved, 19x13'',
  folding type _____ 32.50

## WICKER ITEMS

Arm Chair. Painted white _____ $35.00
Bassinet. Oval. Painted white.
  38'' long, 22'' wide, 34'' high

with casters. Removable top ____ 40.00
Doll Carriage _____ 35.00
Rocker. Painted white _____ 45.00
Tray. Oval. Butterfly and fern
  under glass. 12'' long, 8'' wide __ 10.00

## YARN HOLDER

Maple. Polished, 6 tree branches.
  Wooden clamps _____ $18.00

## YARN WINDERS

Double-Spool Winder. Scarce ____ $55.00
Walnut. Complete _____ 25.00
Walnut. Refinished. Complete ____ 40.00

## SHERATON FURNITURE

The Golden Age of English Furniture
(1754-1805) came to a close with the designs of Thomas Sheraton. He was the last
of the great designers of the 18th Century. The era began with Chippendale who
was followed by the Adams Brothers and
Hepplewhite.

Sheraton was sometimes referred to as
the "English Louis XVI" for his style was
inspired by the classic fundamentals of outline and ornamentation which were characteristic of the French design. A prominent feature of his work was a delicate
beauty of form along with correct geometrical proportions. At all times his work
showed dignity, fineness of feeling and re-
straint.

His designs, like Hepplewhite's, were
delicate looking yet very strong in struc-
ture. One impressive feature of his furniture was the beauty and purity of perpen-
dicular lines. He never employed short
curves but instead used bent lines which
became a graceful sweep.

A number of other characteristics marked
his style. He employed the oval to a considerable degree. Typical ornamentations
were the lyre, lattice work, urns, the star,
cockle-shell, fan shapes, small disks and
swags. Another feature of his designs was
the free use of reeding and fluting which
was chiefly used on legs of chairs and
tables.

Often, in the past, much of the furniture
of the 1750-1800 period was classified with
the generic title "Chippendale." The designs of Chippendale (published in 1754)
were as unlike Sheraton's style (published
40 years later) as the frills on a modern
dress compared to the restrained drapery
of Greek sculpture.

Chippendale's style is unlike Sheraton's
in design, execution and material. He
worked in mahogany; made use of deep
undercut carving and pierced work and
often overlaid his furniture with distinctive
and bizarre ornament. As a rule, Sheraton
used mahogany, rosewood and satinwood.

## ENGLISH ANTIQUE FURNITURE

English Furniture is a new category which has been added to this edition of "Antiques and Their Current Prices." Your compiler made two trips to England to check the various antique markets and to acquire photographs of examples of furniture now being imported into the United States in large quantities.

Dealers in England have been scouring the countryside for good specimens. The sources are not inexhaustible and dealers have recently stated that antiques in England, especially period furniture, are rather difficult to come by. A market for antique English furniture has developed in this country because examples of American—made period pieces are quite scarce and, for the most part, have already been collected.

The styles and types of furniture in demand and being imported here are Chippendale chests, tables and chairs; Sheraton tables, sideboards, chairs and chests of drawers; as well as tables, nightstands, chairs and chests in the Hepplewhite style. The demand is also good for tall case clocks of any period from Chippendale through the Victorian era.

Within the past year dealers in Belgium, France, and Germany have been competing with American importers in the English market and prices have been increasing. It appears that collectors in other countries have been buying antiques as a hedge against inflation and currency manipulations.

It is likely that within the next two or three years English furniture will be considerably more desirable to American collectors and placed in practically the same category price—wise with early American examples. Really, the only difference in English furniture is that it was produced in another country and was often made of imported woods such as mahogany, rosewood, and occasionally, native oak; whereas the native American woods used were usually walnut, maple, and cherry.

In America, it appears that due to the scarcity of good furniture examples, prices are constantly increasing. Also, as stated in the Introduction, the prices in this book are average retail prices and will vary depending on the section of the country in which they are being sold. In the south and far west, prices are generaly higher because of shipping and added labor costs, whereas in the east and midwest, the average prices are some somewhat lower.

Child's Arm Chair.
Rare. 20 × 28 × 17".
Circa 1847 ........ $430.00

Chippendale Chair.
Leather back, mahogany.
Circa 1760.
Set of six ........ $3,390.00

Edwardian Chair.
Rosewood.
Circa 1910... $40.00

Chippendale Chair.
George II. Mahogany.
Circa 1750.
Pair ........ $850.00

Regency Arm Chair.
Mahogany. Circa 1805-1810.
Set of six ........ $1,850.00

Regency Chair. Mahogany.
Circa 1815.    Pair ..... $430.00

Queen Anne. Cabriole legs.  Walnut.
Well-shaped knee and  pad feet of
golden color.    Pair ..... $1,700.00

Queen Anne Side Chair. Walnut.
Drop-in seat. Tapestry.
Circa 1710        ..... $850.00

Regency. Two single. Two arm.
Set of Four ..... $1,060.00

Regency Arm Chair.
Mahogany.
Circa 1805-1810.
Set of Six ..... $1,850.00

Regency Chairs. Sheraton.
Painted. Beech. Circa 1805.
Pair ........ $850.00

Regency Chair. Mahogany.
Circa 1810. Set of four ........ $530.00

Regency Trafalgar Chair. Mahogany.
Black line. Set of four ........ $680.00

Regency Dining Chair. Reproduction.
Sabre legs. Mahogany. Circa 1810.
Set of four ........ $630.00

Hepplewhite. Arm chairs with satin
wood inlay at backsplat.
Oval patere at cross stretcher.
Mahogany. Circa 1795.
Pair ........ $1,380.00

Queen Anne Corner Chair.
Walnut, drop-in seat ........ $1,600.00

Regency Chair. Mahogany.
Circa 1810 ........ $220.00

Regency Dining Chair. Mahogany.
Circa 1815. Set of four ......$530.00

Tub Wing Chair.
Reproduction ........ $480.00

Wing Chair. Deep buttoned in hide.
Reproduction. Mahogany ........ $630.00

Stool. Sheraton. Late 18th century.
Satinwood. 18½ × 20 × 25" ........ $880.00

Music Stool. Sheraton.
Circa 1810.
Mahogany ........ $380.00

Gout Stool. Late Georgian. Circa 1820.
Mahogany ........ $320.00

Gout Stool. Late Victorian.
19 × 12 × 13" ........ $90.00

Bedside Chest. Mahogany.
Modern ........ $120.00

Commode Chest. Regency.
Mahogany. Circa 1805 ........ $630.00

Chest. Queen Anne. Walnut, original handles.
Circa 1710.   20 × 33 × 32½"  ........ $2,400.00

Double Chest. Late Chippendale.
Dressing slide. Mahogany. Circa 1800 ........ $2,400.00

Low Boy. Pad feet with knees and tresses.
Mahogany, original brasses.
29 × 18½ × 28"  ........ $2,350.00

Low Boy. Original brasses. Mahogany.  George II.
Circa 1740. 30 × 18½ × 27"  ........ $2,300.00

Davenport. Rosewood. Circa 1810.
19 ¾ × 25 × 34 " ........ $590.00

Davenport. Victorian. Walnut.
Circa 1860 ........ $230.00

Cabinet. Miniature. Rosewood.
Early 19th century.
12 × 8½ × 22" ........ $290.00

Tea Poy. Regency.
Mahogany. Circa 1810.
17½ × 12 × 32" ........ $380.00

Canterbury. Original drawers and castors.
Mahogany. 1780-1800.
19½ × 15½ × 25" ........ $580.00

Bedside Table. Mahogany.
Modern copy ........ $105.00

Drum Table. Revolving. Mahogany.
Fine quality ........ $790.00

Card Table. Queen Anne. Walnut
35 ¾ × 17½ × 29" ........ $3,000.00

Sutherland Table. Victorian.
Mahogany ........ $50.00

Card Table. Semi- circular.
Adam. Circa 1770. Satinwood.
36 × 17¼ × 29" ........ $1,600.00

Card Table Regency. Circa 1815.
Satinwood, inlaid rosewood ........ $650.00

Corner Table. George II. Mahogany, very fine, slender pad feet. Circb Circa 1740. 29 × 30 × 28" ........ $1,050.00

Coffee Table. Mahogany, brass bound. Oval. Modern ........ $200.00

Occasional Table. Two top. Sheraton. Mahogany 33½ × 19 × 26½" ........ $1,600.00

Pembroke Table. Mahogany. Circa 1770. 35 × 28" ........ $1,150.00

Tea Table. Georgian. Mahogany. Circa 1780 ........ $150.00

Pembroke Table. George II. Mahogany, oval. 38 × 30 × 27½" ........ $600.00

Coffee Table. Sheraton. Mahogany. Circa 1790. 29½ × 20 × 12 ........ $1,320.00

Marble Top Table Marble Top Table. Regency ........ $720.00

Pembroke Table. Hepplewhite. Mahogany. Circa 1790 ........ $630.00

Kingwood Work Table.
Fine. 19th Century.
20 × 28 × 17" ........ $430.00

Work Box. Regency. Mahogany.
Circa 1815. 32 × 16 × 29" ........ $880.00

Work Table . Rosewood. Victorian ........ $130.00

Work Table. Walnut. Victorian ........ $140.00

1 Bed Steps. Mahogany. Late Georgian
   Circa 1825 ........ $200.00
2 Bedside Commode. Mahogany.
   Chippendale. Circa 1780.
   19 × 30" ........ $240.00
3 Bedside Commode. Mahogany.
   Georgian. Circa 1800 ........ $270.00
4 Bedside Commode. Mahogany.
   Circa 1820 ........ $200.00
5 Bedside Commode. Mahogany.
   Bottom section converted to a
   pull-out drawer. Chippendale.
   19 × 18½ ×30" ........ $430.00
6 Bookshelf, Traveling. Collapsible.
   George II. 28 × 6 × 24" ........ $360.00
7 Bookcase. Mahogany.
   Circa 1815 ........ $400.00
8 Library Steps. Georgian.
   Circa 1890 ........ $120.00

Wash Stand. Mahogany.
Small with lift-up top. Hepplewhite.
13¼ × 14½ × 33" ........ $390.00

Wash Stand, Enclosed. Sheraton.
Circa 1785 ........ $660.00

Wash Stand , Enclosed. Mahogany.
Circa 1810 ........ $530.00

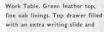

Work Table. Green leather top,
fine oak linings. Top drawer filled
with an extra writing slide and

numerous compartments. Original
covering lids and original
alphabetical lettering .... $2,900.00

Kingwood Work Table. Fine. 19th Century.
31½ × 15¼ × 28½ ........ $1,850.00

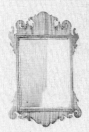

Faded Mirror. Chippendale.
Small, mahogany.
26 × 18" ........ $430.00

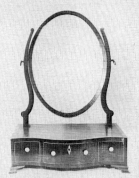

Serpentine Fronted Mirror.
Hepplewhite Mahogany.
Circa 1780-90. 14¼ × 7 × 21" ........ $340.00

Toilet Mirror. Chippendale.
Mahogany. Circa 1765.
19½ × 14" ........ $240.00

Toilet Mirror. Queen Anne.
Walnut, gilt border and old glass.
20 × 13" ........ $570.00

Toilet Mirror. Hepplewhite.
Oval, mahogany. Circa 1785.
19½ × 8¼ × 17½" ........ $240.00

Bowl. Fine dark color. 14½ × 7½ × 10¼ ".
Circa 1790 ........ $850.00

Fruit Bowl. Irish. 12 × 9¾ × 7½".
Circa 1790 ........ $750.00

Fruit Bowl. Irish. Oval. Circa 1790 ........ $675.00

Bowl. Irish. Oval. with turnover edge.
10". Circa 1790 ........ $750.00

Bowl. Green glass, with separate glass stand ........ $250.00
Decanters. Fine quality green glass.
Circa 1830. Pair ........ $195.00

Fruit Bowls. Brilliant diamond and step cutting
and silverplated mounts. 9". Circa 1820.
Pair ........ $975.00

272

Butter Dish. Covered, separate base.
Silver gilt mounted. 9". Circa 1805......$395.00

Decanters. 11". Circa 1805.  Pair .....$250.00

Decanters. English. Various types.
Circa 1820. Each ........ $48.50

Decanters. English. Cut glass.
Circa 1820. Pair ........ $150.00

Decanters. English. 11" high.
Circa 1820. Pair ....... $250.00

Decanters. Late Regency. 12" high.
Circa 1840. Pair ........ $240.00

Ladies' Card Case. 4½ × 3½".
Circa 1850 ........ $25.00

Ladies' Card Case. 4½ × 3½".
Mother of Pearl.
Circa 1850 ........ $25.00

Candy Dish. Victorian, English
Carnival Glass. 8" ........ $40.00

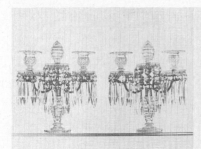

Candelabra. Cut glass with diamond cut pans.
Candle nozzles are cut strawberry diamond.
12 ¼" high, 11 ¼" wide. Circa 1820.
Pair ........ $2,000.00

Candelabra. English. 15" high.
Circa 1790. Pair ........ $4,000.00

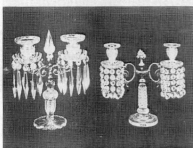

Candelabra. Regency. 12" high.
Circa 1810. Each ........ $300.00

Candlesticks. English. Opaque white glass insets
with base, Ormolu mounts. 9" high.
Circa 1795. Pair ........ $2,250.00

Candlesticks. Regency. 8" high.
Circa 1810. Pair ........ $425.00

Candlesticks. English. 11" high .
Circa 1765. Pair ........ $1,000.00

Candlesticks. English, Cut glass. 9" high.
Circa 1760. Pair ........ $700.00

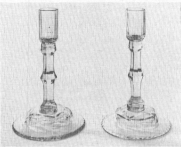

Candlesticks. English. Cut glass. 9¼" high.
Circa 1765. Pair ........ $575.00

Candlesticks. Irish. 11½" high. Circa 1795.
Pair ........ $400.00

Sweetmeat Glasses English. Circa 1730. Each ........ $575.00
Pitcher, Cream. Molded pedestal. 6" high.
Circa 1770 ........ $75.00

Compotes. Irish. Wrist-shaped glass of
unusually large size. 19½" high.
Circa 1790. Pair ........ $1,450.00

Goblets. English. Engraved, with air-twist stems .
11" high. Circa 1745. Pair ........ $1,200.00

### GALLE' GLASS, See CAMEO

### GAMES

Before the advent of automobiles and television a popular evening diversion of the Victorian era was the playing of various types of games.

| | |
|---|---|
| Auto Game. Metal plate shaped like an old touring car. Object is to slide letters around and form word "Automobile." _____ | 8.50 |
| Cribbage Board. Ivory, carved Chinese border _____ | 20.00 |
| Dominoes. Ivory and ebony, in wood box _____ | 12.50 |
| Dr. Busby. Cards, dated 1843 \_\_\_\_ | 8.50 |
| Halma. Dated 1885 _____ | 3.75 |
| Mah Jongg Set. In brass-bound Rosewood box _____ | 27.50 |
| Puzzle Peg. 6½" square. C. 1920. "Lubbers & Bell Mfg. Co." \_\_\_\_ | 3.50 |
| Touring Game. Parker Bros., 1926\_\_ | 7.00 |

### GAUDY DUTCH

Gaudy Dutch is a highly decorated, light-weight, soft-paste china. The ware is unmarked but is reputed to have been made in the Staffordshire section of England around the 1825 period for the Pennsylvania Dutch trade in the Philadelphia, York and Lancaster area. The patterns include Butterfly, Carnation, Dahlia, Double Rose, Dove, Grape, Oyster, Single Rose, Sunflower, Urn (also known as Vase or Flower Pot) and War Bonnet.

Gaudy Dutch should not be confused with Gaudy Ironstone which is a later product, much heavier, usually thicker and generally marked with the maker's name.

Sugar Bowl. Grape pattern _____ $725.00

| | |
|---|---|
| **Butterfly Pattern:** | |
| Bowl. Small _____ | 400.00 |
| Cup and Saucer _____ | 475.00 |
| Plates: | |
| Large _____ | 500.00 |
| 8" diam. _____ | 475.00 |
| **Carnation Pattern:** | |
| Cup _____ | 375.00 |
| Cup and Saucer _____ | 485.00 |
| Plates: | |
| Toddy _____ | 295.00 |
| 8½"diam. _____ | 475.00 |
| 9¾" diam. _____ | 495.00 |
| **Double Rose Pattern:** | |
| Plate. 7½" diam. _____ | 475.00 |
| **Dove Pattern:** | |
| Coffee Pot. 11" _____ | 1800.00 |
| Cup and Saucer _____ | 485.00 |
| Plate. 9¾" diam. _____ | 525.00 |
| Sugar Bowl. Covered _____ | 750.00 |
| **Oyster Pattern:** | |
| Cup and Saucer _____ | 450.00 |
| Plate. 6⅜" diam., sectional border | 475.00 |
| **Single Rose Pattern:** | |
| Cup and Saucer _____ | 465.00 |
| Plate. 8" diam. _____ | 515.00 |

Plate. Urn pattern _____ $485.00

| | |
|---|---|
| **Urn Pattern:** | |
| Plate. 7½" diam. _____ | 540.00 |
| **War Bonnet Pattern:** | |
| Creamer. 4" high _____ | 700.00 |
| Plate. 8¼" diam. _____ | 600.00 |

### GAUDY IRONSTONE

Gaudy Ironstone was introduced in the early 1850's to create more interest in ironstone ware. Staffordshire ware was being issued in various colors and color combinations during this period.

Gaudy Ironstone was decorated in the Imari style and some of the designs have a resemblance to Gaudy Welsh. The ware did not prove to be popular and after a few years of production was discontinued. It is relatively scarce today and commands a good price.

| | |
|---|---|
| Cup and Saucer. Cobalt blue with orange and green flowers _____ | $98.50 |
| Cup and Saucer. Blackberry decor in orange, red and blue _____ | 40.00 |
| Pitcher, with red, blue, green and yellow floral decorations. Dolphin handle. Marked "Mason's" with crown mark _____ | 67.50 |
| Pitcher. 5" high, blue, orange and green _____ | 70.00 |

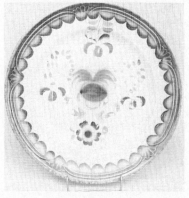

Plate. Seeing Eye or Niagara pattern . ___ ___ ___ ___ ___ ___   $42.50

**Plates:**

| | |
|---|---|
| Dinner. Seeing Eye or Niagara pattern _____ | 42.50 |
| Soup. Grape design in multi-colors _____ | 30.00 |

**Platters:**

| | |
|---|---|
| 20" long. In purple, yellow, orange, black, green and blue | 95.00 |
| 13x18". Marked "Meason." Polychrome colors of pink, orange and green on ivory ground; some leaves in dark blue _____ | 90.00 |

## GAUDY WELSH

A type of chinaware made after 1850. Although the designs are along those of Gaudy Dutch, they are cruder. The body texture and weight also differ from Gaudy Dutch. One of the characteristics of the ware is its bluish-purple coloring. Among the existing patterns are: Flower Basket, Morning Glory, Grape, Oyster, Shanghai, Strawberry, Tulip, Urn and Wagon Wheel.

| | |
|---|---|
| Plate. 5½" diam. Oyster pattern __ | $24.00 |

**Daisy and Chain Pattern:**

| | |
|---|---|
| Creamer _____ | 55.00 |
| Plate _____ | 48.00 |
| Sugar Bowl, Covered _____ | 62.50 |
| Teapot _____ | 85.00 |

**Flower Basket (also known as "Urn" or "Vase" Pattern):**

| | |
|---|---|
| Bowl. 10½" diam. _____ | 98.50 |
| Mug. Handled _____ | 37.50 |
| Plate. 9" diam. _____ | 50.00 |
| Plate. 9½" diam. _____ | 55.00 |

**Grape Pattern:**

| | |
|---|---|
| Cup and Saucer. Handled ____ | 48.75 |

| | |
|---|---|
| Cup and Saucer. Handleless ____ | 54.50 |

**Morning Glory Pattern:**

| | |
|---|---|
| Cup and Saucer _____ | 52.50 |
| Plate. 10'' diam. _____ | 57.50 |

| | |
|---|---|
| Platter. 13½'' ___ ____ ____ ___ | $550.00 |

**Oyster Pattern:**

| | |
|---|---|
| Creamer _____ | 54.50 |
| Cup and Saucer _____ | 45.00 |
| Mug. 3'' high _____ | 30.00 |
| Pitcher. Milk _____ | 75.00 |

**Shanghai Pattern:**

| | |
|---|---|
| Creamer _____ | 55.00 |

**Strawberry Pattern:**

| | |
|---|---|
| Creamer _____ | 57.50 |
| Plate. 8¼'' diam. _____ | 52.50 |
| Teapot _____ | 87.50 |

**Tulip Pattern:**

| | |
|---|---|
| Cup Plate _____ | 12.50 |
| Cup and Saucer _____ | 50.00 |
| Pitcher. Milk _____ | 88.50 |

**Wagon Wheel Pattern:**

| | |
|---|---|
| Plate. 8'' diam. _____ | 48.50 |

### GIBSON GIRL PLATES

Charles Dana Gibson, eminent American artist, produced a series of 24 drawings entitled "The Widow and Her Friends" and the Royal Doulton works at Lambeth, England, reproduced the drawings on plates around the beginning of the present century.


A Message from the Outside World
And Here Winning New Friends
A Quiet Dinner with Dr. Bottles
Failing to Find Rest and Quiet in the Country She Decides to Return Home
Miss Babbles Brings a Copy
Miss Babbles, the Authoress, Calls and Reads Aloud
Mrs. Diggs is Alarmed at Discovering

She Goes to the Fancy Dress Ball as "Juliet"
Prices for the following range from $35.00 to $42.50

### GIRANDOLES

Collectors and dealers generally refer to girandoles as mantel garnitures. A set consists of a centerpiece with a 3-branch candelabra and two side pieces for holding a single candle. The bases are usually made of marble or alabaster and the main body is cast of brass. Long cut prisms hang from the top.

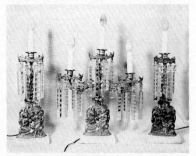

3-piece Set. French, 3-candle centerpiece, single candle side-pieces. 2-piece marble bases. "Paul and Virginia" figures at base. Long prisms _____ $225.00

Bronze figures of Indians. (Scarce-type). 3-candle centerpiece, 18½'' high; 16'' side-pieces. Marble bases. Original finish. 3-piece set **$350.00**

3-piece Set. Two-step marble and brass bases. 20'' centerpiece has 3 figures; 18'' side-pieces have 2 figures. Star-cut prisms. Original finish ----------------------- 195.00

3-piece Set. 3-candle centerpiece, single candle side-pieces. Single marble bases. Scene of bear robbing beehive. 40 colonial prisms suspended from grape-cluster bobeches ----------------------- 200.00

### GLASS DECANTERS
See DECANTERS, GLASS

### GLASS MUGS

Miniature. 2'' high. Clear glass .... **$1.50**

**SMALL, PRESSED GLASS, MOLDED HANDLES:**
**AMBER.** Daisy and Cube -------- 10.00
**BLUE:**
  Basketweave ------------------ 14.50
  Clear glass. McKinley -------- 10.75
  Grape ----------------------- 8.25
  Milk glass. Classic head in medallion ---------------------- 9.75
  Milk glass. Fruit vine --------- 10.00
**CANARY.** Deer and Dog -------- 12.00
**CLEAR:**
  Cats fighting ---------------- 8.50
  Cherries and sweetheart. 3'' -- 12.00
  Geometric design ------------- 6.00
**EMERALD GREEN** Gold decor on base -------------------------- 9.50

**SMALL, BLOWN GLASS, APPLIED HANDLES:**
**BLUE.** Milk glass. White enamel trim -------------------------- 12.50
**WHITE.** Translucent, or "Clams-broth." Plain ------------------ 7.75
**MEDIUM, PRESSED GLASS, MOLDED HANDLES:**
**AMBER:**
  Diamond and Fan -------------- 12.00
  Enamel decor, handled -------- 10.00
  Fine Cut --------------------- 11.50
  Hobnail ---------------------- 12.50
**BLUE:**
  Daisy and Button with "V" ---- 12.75
  Daisy and Cube -------------- 14.00
  Diamond and Fan ------------- 12.00
  Geometric design ------------ 9.00
  Hobnail, cable handle -------- 15.00
  Hobnail, thumbprint handle ---- 15.00
  Sapphire. Classic head in medallion ---------------------- 12.50
**CANARY.** Daisy and Button with "V" ------------------------- 11.50

Clear Glass. Red Riding Hood. 3½'' high -------------------------- **$7.00**

**CLEAR:**
  "By Jingo" ------------------ 9.75
  "God Speed the Plough" ------ 14.00
  Gooseberry pattern ----------- 14.50
  Hobnail, swirl handle --------- 10.50
  Humpty-Dumpty --------------- 9.50
  Lotus pattern. Handled ------ 10.50
  McKinley --------------------- 10.50
  Rabbits near tree and house -- 9.50
  Ribbed, cherries on branch -- 9.75
**LAVENDER.** Swan, bullrushes ---- 12.00
**PURPLE SLAG.** Bird with nest of eggs ------------------------- 36.50

**RUBY. WITH THUMBPRINT BAND.**

| | |
|---|---|
| Sunburst on bottom _____ | 10.50 |
| VASELINE. Diagonal fluting ____ | 10.75 |
| WHITE. Milk glass. Painted flowers | 11.00 |

**MEDIUM, BLOWN GLASS, APPLIED HANDLES:**

| | |
|---|---|
| AMBER. Colored enamel flowers__ | 12.75 |
| AMBERINA. Thumbprint _____ | 75.00 |
| BLUE. Bristol, gold trim. "Remember Me" _____ | 18.00 |
| CLEAR. Enamel Salem witch on broom _____ | 13.50 |

**RED:**

| | |
|---|---|
| Bohemian. Hunter with gun and bird in woods _____ | 24.00 |
| Bohemian. Etched "Remember Me" _____ | 22.00 |

## GOOFUS GLASS

Goofus glass was first made after 1900 and was the original glass given away at carnivals. From about 1910 to 1920 this glass, first known as Mexican, competed with Carnival glass as we know it today, with Carnival Glass winning out in the later years.

The glass had an embossed rose design which was painted in red, pink or purple. Next, bronze or gold metallic paint was applied to stems and leaves, making the pieces very flashy. Over the years the paint has oxidized, making the pieces look dull and drab. The colors, in some cases, can be brought back by gently using silver polish on areas which have not peeled.

Several factories in the Ohio Valley and surrounding area produced the glass. LaBelle Glass Co., Bridgeport, Ohio; Crescent Glass Co., Wellsburg, W. Va.; Imperial Glass Co., Bellaire, Ohio and the Northwood Glass Co. at Indiana, Pa. produced this type product.

| | |
|---|---|
| Bowl _____ | $5.75 |
| Dish, Jelly. On standard _____ | 7.50 |
| Jar, Pickle _____ | 6.00 |
| Lamp Base _____ | 12.00 |
| Plate _____ | 7.00 |
| Vase _____ | 6.50 |

## GRANITEWARE

Graniteware derives its name from iron utensils which were enameled with a speckled glaze resembling granite. For example, blue is mottled blue and white while gray is gray and white mottled.

The ware became popular after 1900 and is now collected for decorative uses.

**Bowls:**

| | |
|---|---|
| Blue. 5½" _____ | 3.75 |
| Gray. 5½" _____ | 3.00 |
| Green. 5½" _____ | 3.50 |

**Coffee Pots:**

| | |
|---|---|
| Blue _____ | 10.00 |
| Gray _____ | 8.00 |
| Green _____ | 9.00 |

**Mugs:**

| | |
|---|---|
| Blue _____ | 2.50 |
| Gray _____ | 2.00 |
| Green _____ | 2.25 |

**Pitchers:**

| | |
|---|---|
| Blue _____ | 10.00 |
| Gray _____ | 8.50 |
| Green _____ | 9.00 |

Plate. 8" diam. Gray _____ $4.50

**Plates, Dinner:**

| | |
|---|---|
| Blue _____ | 3.50 |
| Gray _____ | 3.00 |
| Green _____ | 3.25 |

**Plates, Pie:**

| | |
|---|---|
| Blue _____ | 3.00 |
| Gray _____ | 2.25 |
| Green _____ | 2.75 |

**Teapots:**

| | |
|---|---|
| Blue _____ | 8.75 |
| Gray _____ | 7.00 |
| Green _____ | 8.00 |

## GUNS
### (PISTOLS AND RIFLES)

The invention of the pistol dates back to the early part of the 15th century (Circa 1425) when the Matchlock was devised. The pistol was designed for one-hand use. Most authorities agree that the name "pistol" was derived from the town of Pistola, near Florence, Italy, where many of the arms were first manufactured. Another explanation of the name is from the word "pistallo"—a pommel; a weapon used by mounted troops in the 15th Century.

## CARTRIDGE PISTOLS AND REVOLVERS

Pair of English Pistols. Flintlock-
type. 14" long, brass barrels.
Each ............................ $250.00

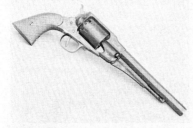

Pistol. Remington. 1858 Model. Octagonal. 8" barrel ............ $350.00

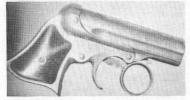

Knuckle Duster Pistol ......... $185.00

Philadelphia Derringer ........ $150.00

ALLEN. Cartridge Derringer. 41
cal. ............................ 100.00
BACON ARMS CO. 32 cal. revolv-
er ............................. 70.00
CHICAGO FIRE ARMS. Palm pistol 160.00
CONNECTICUT ARMS. Hammond
Bull Dog. 44 cal. ............. 110.00
DERRINGER (Philadelphia). 22 cal.
revolver ...................... 125.00
FOREHAND & WADSWORTH. Ar-
my, 44 cal. ................... 150.00
FOREHAND & WADSWORTH. Im-
proved model or 44 cal. Fron-
tier .......................... 375.00
HOPKINS & ALLEN. Army XL-8, 44
cal. .......................... 230.00
IVER JOHNSON. 38 cal., 5 shot .. 50.00
MARLIN. 32 cal. standard re-
volver ........................ 69.50
MERWIN-HULBERT. Model 1876,
Army 44 cal. .................. 200.00
MERWIN & HULBERT. Pocket Army 44
cal. .......................... 155.00
MOORE'S. Revolver, 7 shot, 32 cal.
RF. ........................... 72.50
NATIONAL NO. 1. 41 cal. Der-
ringer ........................ 180.00
NATIONAL NO. 2, 41 cal. Der-
ringer ........................ 175.00
PLANT CUP PRIMER. Army, 42 cal. 150.00
PRESCOTT. Revolver, Iron frame,
Army .......................... 250.00
REID DERRINGER. Knuckle duster,
32 cal. ....................... 185.00
SHARPS. Pepperbox. No. 1, 4 shot,
22 cal. ....................... 125.00
SHARPS & HANKINS. Pepperbox,
32 cal. ....................... 140.00
J. STEVENS. A & J Co. Chicopee
Falls, Mass., U. S. A. 32 cal.
Single shot, wood grips, nickel
plated. Overall length 9" ..... 48.50
STEVENS. Hand target. 8" barrel,
22 cal. ....................... 110.00
WHITNEYVILLE. Armory revolver,
32 cal. ....................... 75.00

## COLT PISTOLS AND REVOLVERS

COLT-PATERSON. 1836 model re-
volver, 9" Hex barrel, marked
"Patent Arms Mfg. Co." ....... 7850.00
COLT. Walker Model 1847 ...... 9250.00
COLT. Dragoon 1st model ...... 3000.00
COLT. Dragoon 2nd model ...... 2650.00
COLT. Dragoon 3rd model ...... 1800.00
COLT. Shoulder. Stock for 3rd
model dragoon ................. 900.00
COLT. 1848 Baby Dragoon ...... 1000.00
COLT. 1849 Pocket, 31 cal. .... 400.00
COLT. 1849 Pocket model with
Thuer conversion .............. 4000.00
COLT. 1851 Navy Model. Ships
engraved on cylinder .......... 525.00

COLT. 1851 Navy, 36 cal. _____ 425.00
COLT. 1851 Navy, 36 cal. Square
 back trigger guard _____ 800.00
COLT. 1851 Navy, 36 cal. Marked
 Colt, London _____ 575.00
COLT. 1851 Navy converted to 38
 cal. _____ 400.00
COLT. 1851 Navy. Thuer conver-
 sion _____ 4000.00
COLT. 1851 Navy, cut for shoulder
 stock _____ 1650.00
COLT BREVETTE. 1851 Navy _____ 1000.00
COLT. Pocket or Navy, cal. often
 called Model 1853 _____ 350.00
COLT. 1860, 44 cal. with fluted
 cylinder _____ 725.00
COLT. 1860. Army, converted to
 44 CF _____ 320.00
COLT. 1860 Army, converted to 44
 CF (Thuer Converson) _____ 3250.00
COLT. 1861 Navy. 36 cal., round
 barrel _____ 500.00
COLT. 1862 Police or Belt Model 300.00
COLT. 1862 converted to 38 CF. 275.00
COLT. New Model Pocket (Roots
 Pat.) 31 cal. _____ 375.00
COLT FRONTIER. 45 cal. Army,
 7½'' barrel _____ 500.00
COLT FRONTIER. High no.'s smoke-
 less powder _____ 425.00
COLT FRONTIER. 45 cal., factory
 C engraving _____ 575.00
COLT FRONTIER. Flat top, cal.,
 32-20 _____ 1000.00
COLT FRONTIER. Flat top, 38 cal.
 Big handle marked 14 Pall Mall,
 London _____ 1500.00
COLT FRONTIER. Storekeeper's
 model without eject _____ 550.00
COLT BISLEY. Flat top, 38 cal.
 special 7½'' barrel _____ 480.00
COLT BISLEY. Cal. 38-40, 5½''
 barrel _____ 275.00
COLT. Double action Frontier or
 Army 45 cal. _____ 345.00
COLT. Old line, 22 cal. Open
 top _____ 135.00
COLT DERRINGER. No. 1, 41 cal. 375.00
COLT DERRINGER. No. 2, 41 cal. 240.00
COLT DERRINGER. No. 3, 41 cal. 225.00
COLT. Army Model. (New York)__ 325.00
COLT. House pistol, 41 cal. Clover-
 leaf _____ 250.00
COLT. House pistol, 41 cal. round
 cylinder _____ 240.00
COLT. Model 1872 type 1860, 44
 cal. _____ 840.00
COLT. New line, 32 cal. _____ 150.00
COLT. New line police. 38 cal.
 Known as police-thug _____ 295.00
COLT. New double action. (Light-
 ning) _____ 115.00
COLT. New service target, 45 cal._ 285.00
COLT. U. S. Marine model 1905,
 38 cal. _____ 230.00
COLT. Officer's model target, 7½''

barrel, 38 cal. _____ 240.00
COLT. P. P. 22 cal. target _____ 230.00
COLT. Automatic 1900 Model, 38
 cal. _____ 265.00
COLT. Automatic 1902 Model, Navy,
 38 cal. _____ 240.00
COLT. Automatic 1903 Model,
 pocket, 38 cal. _____ 225.00
COLT. Automatic 1905 Model, 45
 cal. _____ 200.00
COLT. Automatic 1911-A Model, 45
 cal. com. _____ 195.00
COLT. Automatic, 45 cal. (Na-
 tional Match) _____ 285.00
COLT. Automatic Ace, 22 cal. ____ 275.00
COLT. Army revolver, 1917 Model,
 45 cal. _____ 195.00
COLT. Automatic, 45 cal., govern-
 ment model _____ 155.00
COLT. Automatic, 45 cal., commercial (Pre-War) _____ 175.00

### FLINTLOCK PISTOLS

BELGIUM. Army _____ 135.00
BRITISH. Baldwin _____ 155.00
BRITISH. Pair, British Blunder-
 buss Pistols. Funnel barrels,
 flintlock action, 12'' long.
 Pair _____ 575.00
BRITISH. Double barrel center
 hammer marked D. Egg _____ 150.00
BRITISH. Wheeler, marked London__ 160.00
BRITISH CAVALRY. Marked G. R.
 Tower _____ 165.00
BRITISH NAVY. Marked G. R.
 Tower _____ 145.00
EVANS, O. E. Model 1808 _____ 600.00
EVANS, W. L. Navy, Model 1826__ 525.00
FRENCH. Army Model 1763 _____ 140.00
FRENCH. Army Model 1777 _____ 150.00
FRENCH. Brass trim _____ 130.00
FRENCH. Double barrel _____ 265.00
FRENCH. Side by side double.
 Travelers (silver trim) _____ 215.00
HARPER'S FERRY. Model of 1808 __ 750.00
HENRY, J. Model 1807, marked
 J. Henry, Phila. _____ 650.00
ITALIAN. F/L High Art Silver
 Inlay _____ 150.00
ITALIAN. Miquelet (highly orna-
 mented) _____ 155.00
JOHNSON, R. Model 1836 _____ 180.00
KENTUCKY. With brass ornaments__ 1250.00
MILES. Model 1803 marked Miles
 and C. P. _____ 650.00
NORTH. Model of 1808 _____ 650.00
NORTH. Model of 1810 _____ 725.00
NORTH. Model of 1811 _____ 600.00
NORTH. Model of 1813 _____ 550.00
NORTH. Model of 1813, Navy ____ 500.00
NORTH. Model of 1816 _____ 325.00
NORTH. Model of 1819 _____ 375.00
NORTH. Model of 1836, Navy ____ 550.00
ORIENTAL. Silver trim _____ 185.00
PERKINS. Model 1807 marked I.
 Perkins _____ 700.00

PERSIAN RAT TAIL. All silver
stock _____ 340.00
RICHMOND. Pistol dated 1812____ 1050.00
SPANISH. Miquelet lock _____ 150.00
SPRINGFIELD. 1815 _____ 1650.00
SPRINGFIELD. Model 1818 _____ 1150.00
WATERS, A. H. Model 1836 _____ 275.00

## PERCUSSION PISTOLS AND REVOLVERS

ALLEN & THURBER. 6 shot
Pepperbox _____ 95.00
ALLEN & WHEELLOCK. 31 cal.
5 shot Pepperbox _____ 140.00
ALLEN & WHEELLOCK. 36 cal.
Navy revolver _____ 210.00
ALLEN & WHEELLOCK. 44 cal.
Army revolver _____ 240.00
ALLEN'S PATENT. 31 cal.
Gambler's pistol _____ 80.00
ALSOP. 36 cal. Navy revolver ____ 200.00
AMES. Army, marked U. S. R.,
box lock _____ 215.00
AMES. Navy, marked U. S. N.,
box lock _____ 275.00
ASHTON, H. Pistol _____ 250.00
BACON & CO. 36 cal. under
hammer _____ 140.00
BACON MFG. CO., 31 cal.
revolver _____ 150.00
BUTTERFIELD ARMY REVOLVER.
41 cal. _____ 825.00
COOPER. 36 cal. Navy _____ 150.00
DERRINGER. Pocket Pistol _____ 300.00
DERRINGER. Model 1843, marked
U. S. R. box lock _____ 335.00
DERRINGER. Dated 1847, marked
U. S. N. box lock _____ 335.00
EAGLE ARMS CO., N. Y. 25 cal.,
rim fire. Pat. 1859 _____ 65.00
ELGIN CUTLASS. Pistol _____ 1500.00
FREEMAN'S PATENT. 44 cal. _____ 475.00
JOHNSON, I. N. Model 1842 ____ 245.00
JOSLIN. Revolver _____ 385.00
LE MAT. 9 shot, 85-90% perfect __ 895.00
MANHATTAN. 36 cal. Navy _____ 80.00
MASSACHUSETTS ARMS CO.
31 cal. revolver _____ 275.00
MASSACHUSETTS ARMS CO.
Wesson & Leavitts. Patent. 40 cal. 1000.00
METROPOLITAN ARMS CO. 31 cal.
revolver _____ 285.00
METROPOLITAN ARMS CO. 36 cal.
Navy revolver _____ 265.00
METROPOLITAN ARMS CO. 36 cal.
Pocket Navy revolver _____ 280.00
PALMETTO. Armory Model 1842 __ 320.00
PETTINGILL'S PATENT. 36 cal. Navy 400.00
PETTINGILL'S PATENT. 44 cal. ____ 385.00
ROBBING & LAWRENCE. Pepperbox 240.00
ROGERS & SPENCER. Army.
Revolver _____ 325.00
SAVAGE NORTH. 36 cal. _____ 150.00
SAVAGE NORTH. Navy. Figure
Eight Iron Frame _____ 1500.00
SPRINGFIELD ARMS CO. Warner

Patent. 36 cal. revolver _____ 375.00
STARR. Double action Army _____ 200.00
STARR. Double action 36 cal. Navy 315.00
STARR. Single Action Army _____ 290.00
STEVENS. 32 cal., Lord model.
Silver engraving on barrel,
mother-of-pearl handles. W. F.
Cody (Buffalo Bill) on back of
grip _____ 4500.00
STEVENS, J. 25 cal., single shot.
Pat. 1864 _____ 50.00
TRYON DERRINGER. 41 cal. _____ 225.00
UNION ARMS CO. 31 cal. revolver 115.00
WALCH. 31 cal., 10 shot. Pocket
revolver _____ 350.00
WALCH. 36 cal. Navy _____ 1575.00
WARNER'S PATENT. 31 cal. _____ 215.00
WATERS. F/L pistol converted to
percussion _____ 400.00
WATERS, A. H. Model 1836.
Original _____ 375.00
WHITNEY. 36 cal. Navy _____ 285.00
WHITNEY. First model, 31 cal., two
trigger _____ 260.00

## REMINGTON HAND GUNS

Army. Old model, 44 cal. _____ 300.00
Navy. Old model, 36 cal. _____ 320.00
Army. New model, 44 cal. _____ 270.00
Navy. New model, 36 cal. _____ 320.00
Belt model. 36 cal. _____ 285.00
Police. New model, 36 cal. _____ 245.00
New model police conversion _____ 150.00
New model pocket _____ 300.00
New model pocket conversion ____ 140.00
New model conversion, 44 cal. CF 265.00
Beals Navy, 36 cal. _____ 290.00
Beals Army, 44 cal. _____ 360.00
Beals 1st model _____ 295.00
Beals 2nd model _____ 320.00
Beals 3rd model _____ 370.00
Rider patent, Navy, 36 cal. _____ 350.00
Rider. Pocket, 31 cal. _____ 150.00
1875 model Frontier _____ 400.00
1890 model Frontier _____ 520.00
Navy. 50 cal. 1st model, 1865 ____ 750.00
Navy. 50 cal. 2nd model, 1867 ____ 250.00
Army. 50 cal. 3rd model, 1871 ____ 260.00
Double Derringer. 41 cal. _____ 260.00
Double Derringer. Engraved _____ 300.00
Elliott. Ring trigger. 32 cal. _____ 145.00
New line (smoot). 38 cal. _____ 110.00
Single shot, target, 22 cal. model
1891 _____ 200.00
Elliott Derringer. 41 cal. _____ 250.00
Rider magazine pistol. 32 cal. ____ 265.00
Automatic. 380 ˙al. _____ 140.00

## SEMI-AUTOMATIC HAND GUNS

BELGIUM. High power, cal. 9mm.__ 145.00
BELGIUM BERGMAN. 30 cal. _____ 125.00
BORCHARDT PATENT. Cased set.
Complete _____ 1050.00
CZECHOSLOVAKIA. 25 cal. _____ 60.00

FIALA. Repeating target with set
of 3 barrels _____ 180.00
GERMAN LUGER. 9 mm. _____ 210.00
ITALIAN BERETTA. 380 cal. _____ 75.00
JAPANESE. Nambu _____ 67.50
JAPANESE. Baby Nambu _____ 120.00
LUGER. Carbine _____ 310.00
LUGER. Eagle, 30 cal. _____ 150.00
LUGER. 8'' barrel _____ 140.00
LUGER. Navy, 6'' barrel _____ 165.00
MAUSER. Military, cal. 7.63 _____ 120.00
P 38. German army, cal. 9mm. ____ 85.00
RADOM, F. B. Polish, cal. 9mm. __ 87.50
RUSSIAN TOKAREV. Cal. 7.62 ____ 82.50
SAVAGE. 1907 model, 32 cal. ____ 85.00
SAVAGE. Military, 45 cal. _____ 250.00
SWEDISH LAHTI. Cal. 9mm. _____ 95.00
WALTHER. Model 9, 25 cal. _____ 90.00
WALTHER, P. P. Pre-war, 32 cal. __ 87.50
WALTHER, P. P. 22 cal. _____ 135.00
WALTHER, P. P. K. Pre-war,
32 cal. _____ 87.50

## SHOULDER GUNS

Rifle, Muzzle Loading. Made by
Todd Sherwood, Dodridge County, W. Va. Brass patch-box and
silver ornamentations _____ $450.00

CZECH VZ. 24 cal. 8 mm. _____ 160.00
DOUBLE BARREL SHOTGUN. F/L,
unmarked _____ 185.00
GERMAN K43. Semi-automatic with
scope _____ 285.00
HUNGARIAN. 8 mm. M35 model
98-40 _____ 145.00
ITHACA. 4-E single trap 12 gauge_ 465.00
JAP. Carbine. 7.7 cal. _____ 100.00
JAP. Rifle, 25 cal. _____ 120.00
JAP. Takedown rifle. 6.5 cal. ____ 110.00
JENNINGS. Breech load rifle. 34
cal. Dated 1850 _____ 625.00
JENNINGS. Repeating rifle. 54 cal.
Dated 1852 _____ 1100.00
KENTUCKY. Curly-maple stock, brass
patch-box. 38'' barrel. No mak-

er's name visible _____ 400.00
KENTUCKY. F/L marked Bedford
County _____ 650.00
KENTUCKY. F/L marked W. Barn-
hart, with silver trim _____ 800.00
KENTUCKY. Percussion marked Bed-
ford County _____ 500.00
LEE NAVY. (Straight pull). 6 mm.
model 1895 _____ 255.00
MAUSER. Model 98 cal. 8 mm.
milled guard _____ 215.00
PARKER D.H.E. Grade 12 gauge__ 575.00
SHARPS. 45-70 Old Reliable model,
target sights _____ 200.00
SPRINGFIELD. Model 1863, convert-
ed to 50-70, dated 1870 _____ 110.00
SPRINGFIELD. Model 1863
percussion _____ 175.00
SPRINGFIELD. Model 1873, cal.
45-70 _____ 90.00
SPRINGFIELD. Model 1873, carbine 115.00
SPRINGFIELD. Model 1903. 30 cal.__ 250.00
SPRINGFIELD. Model 1903, Nat.
match type C stock _____ 275.00
U. S. Burnside carbine, 4th model_ 185.00
U. S. Carbine Simeon North model
1833 _____ 260.00
U. S. Eli Whitney Musket model
1798, 69 cal. _____ 295.00
U. S. F/L model 1808, 69 cal. ____ 450.00
U. S. Harpers Ferry. Model 1803__ 485.00
U. S. Joslyn carbine _____ 195.00
U. S. Krag (made at Springfield).
Model 1896 _____ 210.00
U. S. Model 1861-63, made by
Savage R. F. A. Co. _____ 185.00
U. S. Musket model 1795, Charle-
ville pattern _____ 400.00
U. S. Musket model 1809 (contract
arm) _____ 245.00
U. S. Musket 1812, marked B. Evans 310.00
U. S. Musket model 1821 (contract
arm) _____ 155.00
U. S. Musket 1835 (often called
model 1840) _____ 380.00
U. S. Musketoon model 1840,
marked V. P. & U. S. _____ 440.00
U. S. Musket model 1861 _____ 200.00
U. S. Poultney & Trimble carbine__ 210.00
U. S. Rifle. Model 1817, marked
J. D. Johnson _____ 215.00
U. S. Rifle model 1819 (Hall
patent) _____ 345.00
U. S. Rifle model 1842 (percus-
sion), _____ 195.00
U. S. Rifle carbine model 1855.
58 cal., Springfield _____ 210.00
nard, 58 cal. _____ 210.00
U. S. Rifle, model 1863. Remington
Arms Co. _____ 130.00
U. S. Rifle model 1866 (breech
loading) 50 cal. _____ 125.00
U. S. Rifle model 1870, rolling
block, 50 cal. _____ 120.00
U. S. Rifle model 1873, officer's
model, cal. 45-70 _____ 375.00

U. S. Rifle model 1878. Hotchkiss Patent, Navy marks. Manufactured by Winchester _____ 220.00
U. S. Rifle model 1884, with ram-rod bayonet _____ 220.00
U. S. Model 1917. Cal. 30-06, Eddystone _____ 160.00
U. S. Rifle model 1917, made by Remington _____ 150.00
U. S. Rifle model 1922 M-2, 22 cal. _____ 290.00
U. S. Sharps carbine _____ 170.00
U. S. Sharps, 45-70 rifle _____ 210.00
U. S. Spencer. Breech loading repeating carbine _____ 195.00
U. S. Springfield. Model 1812 ____ 210.00
U. S. Star carbine, 50 cal. _____ 245.00
WHEELOCK. Austria. Circa 1550 __ 795.00
WINCHESTER. High side musket, 32-20 cal. _____ 275.00
WINCHESTER. High side s/s Schuetzen, cal. 30-06 _____ 410.00
WINCHESTER. Model 95 marked U. C. Full stock _____ 385.00
WINCHESTER. Model 95 U. S. carbine _____ 375.00
WINCHESTER. Model 1866, 44 cal. _____ 250.0C
WINCHESTER. Model 1866, military musket with bayonet _____ 260.00
WINCHESTER. Model 1873 _____ 190.00
WINCHESTER. Model 1873, full mili-tary stock _____ 515.00
WINCHESTER. 1873, one in 1,000__ 7500.00
WINCHESTER. Model 1876, plain sporting rifle _____ 330.00
WINCHESTER. Model 1886 carbine 50 Express _____ 255.00

## SMITH & WESSON HAND GUNS

American model 1 SA, 44 cal. ____ 285.00
Hand Ejector, 1st model _____ 280.00
Hand Ejector, 32-20 cal. Target __ 200.00
K22 Pre-World War II masterpiece 230.00
Ladysmiths 1st model _____ 415.00
Ladysmiths 2nd model _____ 335.00
Ladysmiths 3rd model _____ 310.00
Ladysmiths 3rd model with 6'' barrel _____ 500.00
Ladysmiths 3rd model with 6'' barrel target sights _____ 795.00
Military and police 4'' barrel. 38 cal. _____ 190.00
Model No. 1, first issue, 22 cal. __ 530.00
Model No. 1, second model _____ 148.50
Model 2, 38 cal. Often called Little Russian _____ 185.00
Model No. 3, American, 44 cal. __ 310.00
Model 3, Russian, cal. 44 _____ 240.00
Model No. 3, Russian markings ___ 310.00
Model 3 SA, Russian target, cal. 38-44 _____ 250.00
Model 320, repeating rifle _____ 425.00
Model 320, repeating rifle with stock _____ 410.00

Model 1917, 45 cal., automatic ____ 175.00
New Century, 44 cal. Triple lock __ 315.00
New Century, target, 44 cal. _____ 400.00
New Century or triple lock. Cal. 455 _____ 200.00
New Departure, 38 cal. 1st model_ 220.00
New Departure, 38 cal. 2nd model_ 120.00
Perfected model, 38 cal. _____ 265.00
Regulation police, 38 cal. _____ 200.00
Safety first Issue, 32 cal. _____ 165.00
Schcfield Patent, 45 cal. _____ 275.00
23-22 target, 22 cal. _____ 220.00
Volcanic arms 41 cal. 8'' barrel __ 435.00
Volcanic marked cast steel, 41 cal. 16.5 barrel _____ 450.00

## HAND PAINTED CHINA

The period, 1890-1915, was when hand painted china became a fad. Women from towns of considerable size would organize clubs to seek instruction from the private teachers available.

The craze could be considered the ''Grand-daddy'' of ''do-it-yourself'' projects. The era passed with the end of World War ·I, but not before millions of pieces were painted. Most of the blanks were imported from France and Germany.

The average price on plates ranges from $12.00 to $20.00, depending on the size, colors and quality of work. Large hanging plaques bring from $25.00 to $45.00, with the same conditions being taken into consideration. See Haviland China section following hardware.

Plate. 8'' diam. Red currants with green and rust colored leaves, gold rim ___ ___ ___ __ __ ___  $16.50

| Jug, Cider. Painted with apples and leaves | 28.50 |
| Pitcher, Wine. 15'' high. Roses on pink to deep rich red ground. Handle gold color | 45.00 |
| Plates: | |
| 11½'' long, 10'' wide. Red and yellow roses with green leaves. Gold decorations around the edge. Hand painted | 24.50 |
| Trinket Box. Pink and yellow roses, gold trim. Small | 12.75 |
| Vase. 11'' high. Rose decorations with gold trim | 32.50 |

## HARDWARE

Most of the hardware made before 1830 was hand wrought. Many of the items are being used in the restoration of old homes.

| Door Knob and Bell. Iron | $15.00 |

| Door Handle. Hand forged, 9'' long. Circa 1820 | 18.50 |
| Door Knobs. Brass. Circa 1815. Pair | 9.00 |
| Door Latch. Butterfly | 22.50 |
| Door Locks: | |
| Early, Pennsylvania. Iron | 25.00 |
| In walnut case | 21.00 |
| Large, one brass knob | 10.00 |
| Hinge-pintles. Pair | 6.00 |
| Hinges, Strap: | |
| 12'', slender, decorative ends. Pair | 9.00 |
| 18'', same | 11.50 |
| 36'', same | 16.75 |
| Hooks, Rafter. Crude | 4.00 |
| Key. Large, brass | 6.75 |
| Lift Latch. Complete, heart or spade | 18.00 |
| Pintle. Rat tail, heart twist | 6.00 |
| Shutter Fasteners. Iron | 3.50 |

## HAVILAND CHINA

The history of Haviland China is complicated and confusing because of the various combinations of partnerships of the Haviland brothers and their sons. .

David Haviland, a New York china importer, established a china factory at Limoges, France, in 1842, under the name of Haviland & Co. The products were sold through the American firm of D. G. & D. Haviland Co., of which David Haviland was a partner.

In 1852 two other brothers were admitted to the firm of D. G. & D. Haviland Co., and the name Haviland Bros. & Co. was established. The firm was discontinued in 1865.

Chronology of the various Haviland firms and partnerships:

1835-36. Edmund and David Haviland, New York china importers.

1837. David Haviland established his own importing business.

1838. David's brother Daniel joined him to establish the American firm of D. G. & D. Haviland.

1842. David Haviland established a factory at Limoges, France, under the name of Haviland & Co. His brother Daniel was a silent partner and continued to manage the New York importing firm.

1852. Daniel and David admitted two brothers, Robert and Richard, to the D. G. & D. Haviland firm. The name was then changed to Haviland Bros. & Co.

1863. David withdrew from Haviland Bros. & Co. to devote full time to the Limoges factory.

1865. Haviland Bros. & Co. suspended business as importers and distributors.

1866. Daniel G. Haviland withdrew as a partner from the French Limoges factory.

1874. David Haviland's sons, Charles Edward Miller and Theodore, entered into partnership with their father as Haviland & Co.

1879. David died and his sons, Charles Edward and Theodore, continued business through 1891.

1892. The brothers, Charles Edward Miller and Theodore, dissolved partnership. Charles continued business under the name of Haviland & Co. while Theodore began operations as LaPorcelaine Theodore Haviland, at Limoges, France, where he acquired a factory. The white ware was marked "Theodore Haviland" in a horseshoe with "France" within, all in green. The decoration marks varied. In 1892 the T. H. monogram with "Limoges France" printed in red, and "Porcelaine Mousseline" above was used. In 1914 the mark was "Theodore Haviland" (in italics) with "Limoges" below and "France" under that. The mark was usually in red with an occasional green coloring. In 1920 the italicizing of the name Theodore was discontinued after his death. The business was then conducted by his son, Wm. David Haviland. 1936. The company decided to make china-ware in America because of tariff regulations and rising costs in France.

1941. The assets of Haviland & Co. were obtained from the French heirs of Charles Edward Miller Haviland by Wm. David Haviland for the Theodore Haviland Co. The mark after 1941 was "Theodore Haviland, New York" in a vignette with "Made in America" below.

Chronology of the Charles Field Haviland firms:

1858. Chas. Field Haviland, a son of David's brother Robert, married the granddaughter of Francois Alluaud, owner of the Alluaud factory.

1859. Chas. Field Haviland established a decorating shop with blanks furnished by the Alluaud works.

1870. Chas. Field Haviland & Co. was formed in New York between Chas. Field Haviland and Oliver A. Gager.

1876. Chas. Field Haviland became manager of Casseaux Pottery Works, successor to the Alluaud Pottery. He used the mark "Ch. Field Haviland."

1881. Chas. Field Haviland retired from manufacturing; sold his interest in Chas. Field Haviland & Co. in New York to Oliver A. Gager who continued in the business until 1889 when he died. The firm name was changed to Haviland & Abbott. It ended operations about the time of World War I.

Creamer and Sugar Bowl. White background. Floral decor. Gold trim.
4½'' high _____ $25.00

| | |
|---|---|
| Bone Dish _____ | 10.00 |
| Bouillon Cup and Saucer. Gold trim _____ | 8.50 |
| Butter Dish. Covered, with insert__ | 29.50 |
| Butter Pat. Princess Feather _____ | 4.00 |
| Candlesticks. 4'' high, gold lustre. Pair _____ | 18.00 |

Cat. 10''. Yellow with white face, black eyes, nose and whiskers   $80.00

| | |
|---|---|
| Chocolate Pot. Blue-green flowers, fern-like leaves, gold trim _____ | 40.00 |
| Chop Plate. 13'' diam., pink rose decor, wide scalloped edge ____ | 29.50 |
| Coffee Set. 3 pieces. 10'' covered coffee pot, 7'' covered sugar bowl and creamer. Allover Morning Glory decor, gold knobs and cross bar _____ | 90.00 |
| Creamer. Marked "C. F. H." Cupids in design, gold handles and gold edge _____ | 20.00 |
| Cups and Saucers: | |
| C. H. Field, Haviland Limoges, G. D. M., decorated with flowers and gold _____ | 16.00 |
| Demitasse. Pink roses in swags, tied with blue bows, gold trim__ | 8.75 |
| Decanter. 9'' with stopper and exquisite flowers. Marked Haviland Limoges _____ | 18.00 |
| Dinner Sets: | |
| Autumn Leaf pattern, service for 8 _____ | 300.00 |
| Marie pattern, service for 12 __ | 360.00 |
| Wedding Ring pattern, service for 12 _____ | 340.00 |
| Wedding Ring pattern, service for 6 _____ | 215.00 |
| Dish, Covered. Haviland & Co., 8'' diam. Silver Wedding pattern | 33.50 |
| Fish Platter. 21¾x8¼''. Scene of trout caught in net, gold corners_____ | 36.50 |

Fish Set. 24" platter, 12 8¾" plates,
hand painted fish in high relief,
gold edges and scrolls _____ 125.00
Game Set. 16½" platter, 6 8¼"
plates, hand painted game.
Signed _____ 89.50
Gravy Boat. Princess pattern, on
standard _____ 20.00
Gravy Boat attached to tray. Blue
forget-me-not decor _____ 22.50
Ice Cream Set. Large oblong platter and 6 plates. Blue and white
with folded corners _____ 57.50
Mayonnaise Bowl, on plate. Trailing Arbutus decoration _____ 22.50
Mayonnaise Set. Gold decor on
white ground. 3-piece set _____ 27.50
Pitcher, Water. 7½" high. Yellow
rose clusters on white background. Scalloped rim, gold
trimmed handle _____ 27.50
Plates:
Bread and butter plate _____ 5.00
Chop. 12½" diam. Pink roses
around edge plus larger ones
forming inner circle _____ 19.75
Oyster plate. Blue cornflowers __ 15.00
6½" diam. Pink rose sprays,
scalloped edge _____ 14.00
8½" diam. Morning Glory decor
Set of 6 _____ 60.00
9½" diam. Princess pattern. Made
by Haviland & Co., Limoges ___ 14.75
Platters:
8x9½" _____ 18.50
10x14½" _____ 21.00
14", French Mignonette _____ 25.00
Powder Box. Marked Haviland.
Hand painted violets. Large
hinged lid, heavy gold trim ____ 35.00
Ramekin, with unattached saucer.
Blue bead festoons, foliage _____ 9.00
Sauce Dish _____ 4.00
Sugar Bowl. Covered _____ 20.00
Sugar Bowl. Covered, cupids in
design, gold handles, gold top
and finial (C. F. H.) _____ 29.50
Sugar Bowl and Creamer. Marked
"Haviland & Co." Set _____ 44.50
Tea Set. Teapot, sugar bowl,
creamer, 4 cups and saucers. Pink
floral decor _____ 75.00
Tea Set. Wedding Ring Pattern,
service for 8. Large teapot, cov-
ered sugar bowl, creamer, open-
handled cake plate, sauce dishes,
cups and saucers _____ 145.00
Teapot. 5" high, cupid design,
gold trim (C.F.H.) _____ 45.00
Tray. 14x20", white with gold border. Signed Theo. Haviland __ 23.50
Tureens:
Miniature, with tray _____ 20.00
Soup. Blue flowers with brown
vine decor, with ladle _____ 50.00
Vegetable, 7½x11". Covered ____ 25.00

## HEISEY GLASS

The A. H. Heisey Co. started operations
in April 1896, at Newark, Ohio. In addition to producing crystal pattern glass,
a wide variety of colored glass, including
milk and custard, was also made. The factory operated for a period of 60 years,
closing in 1957. The trademark is the
letter "H" inside a diamond.

Heisey Glass Advertising Plaque. In
glass with trade mark _____ $10.00

Ash Tray. Heavy, star shaped. 5½"
diam., signed _____ $7.50
Baskets:
Cut and etched florals and
butterflies. 13" to top of handle, 6" opening _____ 38.50
Panelled. Clear, oblong, 8¼x6",
10¾" high. Signed _____ 18.00
Rayed bottom, ribbed with etched
band. 5" deep, 9" to top of
applied handle. Signed _____ 18.00
8 scalloped top panels, each
crosshatched, petaled flowers
and leaves. Octogan-shape base.
15" high. Signed _____ 52.50
Berry Sets:
Six pieces _____ 30.00
Ring Band Custard Glass. Bowl
and six sauces _____ 150.00
Scalloped edge. 8½" bowl and six
sauces _____ 27.50

**Bowls:**
Fruit. Clear, panelled, scalloped
edge. 8'' _____ 8.00
Green footed. Scalloped edge,
11'' diam. _____ 18.00
Orange w/heavy gold rim, black
enamel decor _____ 18.00
Pink, Diamond Quilted. Impressed
star base. 6'' diam., 1$\frac{3}{8}$'' high.
Signed _____ 10.00
Butter Pat. Clear, signed _____ 2.00

Candelabra. 10$\frac{1}{2}$''. Signed. Pair ____$125.00

**Candlesticks:**
Crystal, 8''. Marked _____ 15.00
Peg, with Flower Bowl. Optic bowl
with waved top. 2 pieces _____ 28.50
**Celerys:**
Greek Key. 12'' _____ 15.00
Green. 12''. Rayed type base and
8-sided shape _____ 18.00
**Champagnes:**
Clear. Melody pattern _____ 5.00
Green stems, clear diamond-quil-
ted bowls. Signed _____ 11.50
Coaster. Green, 5$\frac{1}{4}$'' _____ 4.50
**Compotes:**
Candy, covered. Vaseline glass.
Signed _____ 22.50
Clear, diamond-quilted bowl with
green stem and foot. 6$\frac{3}{4}$'' diam.,
4$\frac{1}{4}$'' tall. Signed _____ 15.00
**Cruets:**
Blown with embossed pineapples.
Stopper pineapple shaped.
Signed _____ 18.00
Faceted stopper. Marked _____ 12.50
Kalonyal pattern. Marked and
blown. 8''. Original stopper ____ 27.50
**Dishes:**
BonBon. Pink. 10 swirled panels.
7x5$\frac{1}{2}$''. Signed _____ 9.50
Candy, covered. 8'' pedestaled.
HP and marked _____ 9.00
Candy. Yellow with a frosty
crackle-like finish. 6'' diam., two
handles _____ 12.00
Console. Large Greek Key pat-
tern. Signed _____ 10.00

Covered. 5'' diam., HP, embossed
design border in green, blue and
gold trim. Rayed base with cut
outside panels. Cut knobbed dome 15.00
Relish. Oval, clear. 12'' long,
4'' wide. Ray design in bottom,
panelled sides _____ 6.50
**Sauces:**
Thumbprint and plain panels. 4$\frac{1}{4}$''
diam. _____ 2.50
Octagon shape with open handles
on either side. Green. 4$\frac{1}{4}$'' across
2'' panelled sides, 9$\frac{1}{4}$'' long, 3$\frac{1}{4}$''
wide, 4'' curved ends. Signed __ 18.00
Sundae. Clear, stemmed, 6$\frac{1}{2}$''
tall _____ 3.50
**Goblets:**
Block pattern _____ 9.00
Drape pattern. High stemmed.
Marked _____ 6.50
Hair Receiver. Covered. Star base.
Signed _____ 8.00
Lamp Base. Crystal, 9$\frac{1}{2}$'' tall,
single socket, pull chain.
Marked _____ 22.00
Lemonade Set. Kalonyal pattern
with wide gold trim. Marked.
Pitcher and 5 glasses _____ 55.00
Mustard Pot, Covered. Green with
a swirl pattern. Marked _____ 7.50
**Pitchers:**
Panelled side, 6'' high, 5'' diam.
Dated 4/15/13 _____ 15.00
Water. Diamond-quilted pattern
w/set-in cover. Round pontil and
applied handle. Signed _____ 25.00
**Plates:**
Cup. Clear, signed _____ 2.00
Dessert. Pink, 6'', signed _____ 15.00
Luncheon _____ 2.50
Platter, Bread. Large _____ 15.00
Powder Jar, Covered. Brass lid____ 8.00
Punch Cup. Signed _____ 25.00
Rose Bowl. Quilted design, 7'' tall,
22$\frac{1}{2}$'' diam. Marked _____ 13.50
Salt and Pepper. Etched. Original
stoppers _____ 7.00
Salts. Sawtooth, clear. Serrated
edge. Set of six _____ 15.00
Sherbet. Lariat pattern. Signed __ 3.50
Sugar Bowl. Sterling overlay.
Signed _____ 12.00
Sugar and Creamer, Covered, with
silver filigree in fancy design.
6'' plate with cut-star base.
3 pieces _____ 25.00
Syrup. Etched. Signed _____ 12.00
Tobacco Jar. Dome top, metal in-
sert. Signed _____ 35.00
**Toothpicks:**
Ring Band. Red roses _____ 55.00
Ring Band. Signed Sheboygan __ 40.00
Tumbler. Custard glass. Beaded and
roses _____ 20.00
**Wines:**
Dinner. Park Avenue _____ 6.00
Platinum band. Signed _____ 5.00

## HOLLY AMBER, See COLORED GLASS SECTION

## HORN

Animal horns have been utilized in making various items such as drinking cups, small dishes, powder horns and snuff boxes, by the hornsmiths of past generations.

Snuff Container. In shape of powder
horn. 3" long, screw top _____ $15.00

Bird. Made with several pieces of
horn _____ $12.00
Napkin Ring _____ 2.25
Snuff Box _____ 8.00

Snuff Box. 2¾" long, 1¾" high. Removable lid with small brass ring __$12.50

Spoon. 9¾" long, bowl 3¼" wide___ 8.75
Texas Longhorn Steer Horn. 40"
long with historical engraving
of Washington, Jefferson, Monroe,
General Green, General Gates
and General Schuyler_____ 575.00
Tumblers:
2½" high, inset horn bottom ____ 8.00
4½" high _____ 9.50

## IMARI

An oriental type of gaudy decorated chinaware which was mainly imported into this country from Japan during the period 1875 to 1895. The ware dates back to about 1650 in Japan. Some was brought to Colonial America by Dutch traders. Imitations of this ware were made at Worcester and other potteries in England during the 19th century.

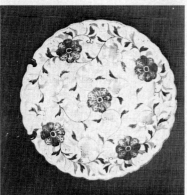

Plate. 16" diam. Orange, cobalt
and gold floral decor. Scalloped
edge _____$110.00
Bowls:
Punch. Large _____ $250.00
8½" diam., footed, 6" high. Decorated inside and out with
rabbits, birds and trees _____ 125.00
10" diam. Typical colors and
decor on teakwood stand _____ 69.50
11" diam., footed. Royal blue,
turquoise, tangerine and gold in
all over enamel decoration ____ 135.00
Brush Pots. Pair _____ 48.50
Chargers:
16" _____ 150.00
18" diam. Peacock center_____ 215.00
Cup and Saucer. Five colors with
blue and rust predominating __ 27.50
Ginger Jar. 8½" high, with cover,
red & black color _____ 85.00
Jardinieres:
7½" high. 7½" diam. _____ 75.00
8" high, 12" diam. In blues,
greens and reds _____ 95.00

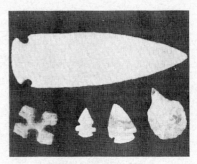

TOP: Spearhead. 5¾'' long. White
flint, from New York State _____ $15.00
LEFT TO RIGHT: Gorget _$20.00. Bird
Point _$1.00. Arrowhead__$1.00.
Drill__$2.50

| | |
|---|---|
| Pipe. Clay _____ | 8.75 |
| Spear-head. Pink flint, 3¼'' ____ | 4.50 |
| Spear-head. Black flint, 3'' _____ | 4.50 |

Charger. 15¾'' diam. Cobalt blue,
orange and gold decor on white
background _____$110.00

Plates:

| | |
|---|---|
| 6 panels, red and blue floral decor, green foliage _____ | 46.50 |
| 10'' diam., alternating floral decorated panels, terra cotta, green and deep blue colors _____ | 55.00 |
| 11½'' diam., dark blue, red basket of flowers in center _____ | 57.50 |
| 12'' diam. _____ | 68.50 |
| 15'' diam., border decorated in floral panels, oriental trees in center _____ | 80.00 |
| Tray. 12'' diam. Scalloped edges | 67.50 |

Vases:

| | |
|---|---|
| 8'', typical colors and design __ | 85.00 |
| 10½'' high, 8'' diam. _____ | 95.00 |

## INDIAN ARTIFACTS

People have long been fascinated by the
arts and crafts of the primitive people who
were here to meet the white man. Columbus and the early explorers called them
Indians because they were under the impression that a new route to India had
been found.

Items vary in age from 200 years to
more than 2000 years. The majority of
relics in which collectors show interest today are made of stone and, for the most
part, are plentiful.

| | |
|---|---|
| Arrow-head. Medium size _____ | .75 |
| Arrow-head. Bird point _____ | .50 |
| Beads, Trade. Green Cantonese. 3-ft. strand _____ | 11.00 |
| Drill. Large stone, 3½'' long ____ | 8.00 |
| Lot: 6 arrow-heads, 2 flint drills, 1 spear and 1 scraper _____ | 12.00 |

## INDIAN TREE PATTERN

The Indian Tree pattern came into popularity during the last half of the 19th century. The name is derived from an oriental
shrub or tree. The ware, with its soft greens,
blues and pinks, is most attractive and is
still collectible in sets.

The pattern was made by numerous English potters. They included: Burgess and
Leigh, Minton, Coalport, Cauldon, Maddox
and others.

Plate. 10'' diam. Johnson Bros. _____$11.00

| | |
|---|---|
| Butter Dish. Covered, "Burgess & Leigh" | $27.50 |
| Cake Plate. Ear-like handles | 22.75 |
| Creamer | 18.50 |
| Cups and Saucers. Fluted-type. Each | 14.00 |
| Demitasse Cup and Saucer. "Maddox" | 9.00 |
| Plates: | |
| 9" diam. Fluted, gilt rim | 11.50 |
| 10" diam. Johnson Bros. | 11.00 |
| 10½" diam. "Cauldon" | 17.50 |
| Platter. 15" long | 35.00 |
| Platter. 15½" diam. Impressed "Burleigh & Leigh" | 36.00 |
| Salt and Pepper Shakers. Shape of beehive. "Coalport." Pair | 21.50 |
| Sauce Dish | 4.50 |
| Sugar Bowl. Covered, "Minton" | 25.00 |
| Teapot. Covered | 45.00 |
| Tureen. Without ladle | 52.50 |
| Waste Bowl. "Spode" | 9.50 |

## INKWELLS

Inkwells have been in use since man first used fluids for writing. Recently, a small village, buried for more than 2000 years, was discovered to have been occupied by a group of holy men known as the "Essenes." The group is believed to be responsible for writing some of the "Dead Sea Scrolls." Upon excavating a building, an inkwell showing evidence of dried ink, was found among the ruins.

Dore' bronze with glass well. 10½" ____ $40.00

| | |
|---|---|
| Bottle. Crystal, 3¾" high. French, gray cover. Homan Mfg. Co. | $12.75 |
| Brass. Crab, 8" wide, 6½" high, hinged cover with glass well, heavy cast brass | 25.00 |
| Brass. Elk head. Clear glass insert | 16.00 |
| Brass. Ornate. English. Circa 1880 | 45.00 |
| Brass. Solid brass stand, 15" long, | |

| | |
|---|---|
| 3¾" wide, with 2 fancy hinged lids at either end, milk glass inserts, 2¼x2¼" | 18.75 |
| Bronze. Mephistopheles. Crouching figure with ears as pen holders. Glass insert for ink. 2⅜x3" | 48.50 |
| Bronze, Vienna. Cat, 6" lifelike pose and coloring | 28.00 |
| China. 4¼" square, 2⅝" well. Pink hand painted roses, green leaves. Domed swirled lid, wide brass connection | 22.50 |
| China. 2" diam., 2½" high. Small melon mold, purple flowers and pink roses on buff background, hinged lid, brass connections | 18.50 |

Sanford's Fountain Pen Filler _____ $9.50

China, German. White 3-step stand, 4¼" long, 4" wide, 2" at top where well rests. Black imp with cap forms lid. Red, blue and yellow decor _____ 15.00
Cloisonne. 6" square. Irregularly shaped tray resting on a stone wall _____ 30.00
Delft. 2¾" square, 3½" high. Crossed mallets and windmill decor, domed lid, wide brass connector 33.50
Glass. Admiral Dewey, clear glass cover _____ 35.00
Glass advertising inkwell. Large round top with legend. "N. Y. Ledger, The Great Home Advertising Medium" _____ 15.00
Glass. 1⅝" square, 2" high, with hinged glass top and brass connector _____ 9.75
Glass. 2" square, 3" high, with a rounded high brass hinged lid. 10.50
Glass. 2¼" square, 2½" high, semipyramid shape with embosed silver lid _____ 11.50
Glass. 2¼" square, 3½" high, early swirled glass with matching lid. Sterling connection _____ 15.00
Glass, Cut. 4" long, 1¾" wide, 1¾" high. Star on bottom, blown well in glass, domed Sterling lid _____ 14.00
Horse's head with horseshoe base and cowboy rider. 4" high. French gold plate _____ 16.75
Iridescent. Green glass, hinged brass mask lid, 3½" high _____ 24.50
Iron. Crab, 5", black enamel ____ 15.00
Iron, Cast. Camel, 9½" long, 6" high _____ 18.75
Jacobus. Eclipse trade mark, green base, clear dome _____ 9.75
Milk Glass. 4" high. Hound dogs made of milk glass. Iron base and stand _____ 60.00
Porcelain. Raised floral and leaf decor. Brass top with 2 large and 3 small wells, 1¼" diam. Small removable glass insert in center well, acorn finial, hinged lid 40.00
Pottery. Frog. Brown color _____ 10.00
Pottery. Lion. Light tan color ____ 22.50
Racing Car. Old style, 2 occupants wearing goggles, 2 wells under hood of car _____ 60.00
Reindeer, with doe and fawn. 3¾x4¾". Glass well _____ 16.50
Rockingham. Sanded surface, bird and snake, eggs in nest, pastel color. Large _____ 65.00
Rookwood. 9x6½". Green birdshaped tray, glass insert, 1921 __ 20.00
Satin Glass. Blue swirl _____ 67.50
Staffordshire. Greyhound _____ 30.00
Staffordshire. 3½" high, square, hinged top, pink and white with

alternating floral stripes _____ 22.50
Tiffany. 3¼" square, 2⅞" high. Iridescent green with filigree trim of roses and leaves in floral effect in silver over copper, hinged lid _____ 85.00

## INSULATORS

The collecting of insulators, which were used on telephone and electric lines, is one of the latest hobbies. In the past year or two, price guides have been published and interest in collecting has increased.

Whitall #9A in clear glass _____ $2.00

Brookfield. 1865 date only _____ $8.00
Brookfield X2. Aqua _____ 2.00
Brookfield. Aqua, no number ____ 1.00
Gayner #48-400. Aqua _____ 6.50
Hemingray #1. High Voltage, triple petticoat, green _____ 10.00
Hemingray #2. Provo _____ 18.00
Hemingray #9. Clear _____ 1.00
Hemingray #9. Purple, May 2, 1893 _____ 10.00
Hemingray #13. Clear _____ 3.50
Hemingray #14. Vaseline _____ 35.00
Hemingray #16. _____ 1.00
Hemingray #19. Coablt blue ____ 25.00
Hemingray #23. Turquoise blue __ 10.00
Hemingray #50. Trans-position ___ 10.00
Hemingray #62. Blue-green _____ 10.00
P. R. R. Signals, green _____ 3.00
Whitall-Tatum #1 _____ 1.25

Hemingray Insulator. #42 in green glass _____ $4.00

## IRON

Kettle. Footed, with bail. Medium__ $10.00

Andirons:
  14'' long, snake feet. Pair ____ $22.50
  14'' long, knob top. Pair _____ 28.75

19'' long, large ball finials, horse-
  shoe feet. Pair _____ 30.00
  30'' long. Pair _____ 32.00
Anvil. Miniature _____ 4.00
Apple Peeler. Made by Reading
  Hardware Co., Reading, Pa. Pat.
  March 5, 1872 _____ 8.00
Belaying Pin. 17'' long _____ 8.50
Boot Jack. Beetle _____ 12.50
Boot Scraper. 6¼'' high, 4'' wide.
  Scroll center and ends _____ 11.50
Bowl. 12½'' diam., 3¼'' deep ____ 12.75
Buggy Steps. Each _____ 5.00
Cake Mold. Shape of lamb _____ 10.75
Cannon, Miniature. Navy model,
  7½'' long, 4 iron wheels _____ 42.50
Ceiling Hook for Lamp _____ 3.00
Cherry Seeder _____ 6.75
Cord Ball Holder _____ 10.50
Cuspidor. Shape and size of stove-
  pipe hat _____ 21.00
Door Stops, see ''Door Stops''
Eagle. Wings out, head down, 31''
  long, 10'' high. Weighs 40
  pounds. _____ 85.00
Elephant Cigarette Dispenser ____ 8.75
Fence. Victorian iron fence, 100 feet
  with gate, 38'' high. Good con-
  dition _____ 245.00
Fence. 150 feet with gate and posts 289.50
Fireplace Items:
  Crane. 38'' arm _____ 67.50
  Kettle. Urn-shaped, spike legs,
    iron lid and bail _____ 15.00
  Milk Warmer. Quart, spike legs,
    long iron handle _____ 12.75
  ''S'' (Pot) Hooks, to use on crane 2.50
  Shovel, tongs and poker in stand.
    Set _____ 21.00
  Swinging Skillet. 13'' diam.,
    short feet _____ 18.75
  Tongs. Plain _____ 8.00
  Tongs and brush. Set _____ 14.50
  Trammel. Hand wrought _____ 65.00
  Trammel. Hook. 24'' long, hand
    forged, eye bolt, hinged hook
    for kettle _____ 12.75
  Waffle Iron. Trumpets and lyre
    design on lid _____ 18.00
Foot scraper. Attached to oval
  fluted pan _____ 11.00
Foot Scraper. Scroll ends _____ 10.00
Girandole. 15'' high. 12 crystal
  prisms on each of 3 branches __ 60.00
Hand Cuffs. Chain joint, screw
  release _____ 20.00
Harpoon, early. 6'3'', cane shaft
  barbed iron head _____ 18.00
Hat, Gentleman's. High, circa
  1880. _____ 20.00
Hat Rack. 6 curved swinging
  arms _____ 9.75
Hitching Post. Horse's head, circa
  1880. _____ 100.00
Hoop. 23½'' diam. Iron holder ____ 20.00

Irons:
Branching iron for tobacco bales
and boxes. 18'' overall length __ 6.50
Charcoal _____ 8.50
Flat. Pair _____ 6.50
Fluting _____ 6.00
Kettles: Footed, with bails —
Small _____ 8.00
Medium _____ 10.00
Large _____ 12.00
Kettle Trivet. 15½'' diam., 13''
high. Hand forged _____ 12.50
Ladles:
Small _____ 6.50
5¼x6'' bowl with pouring lip on
either side. 22'' handle _____ 7.75
Lamp. Bracket. Lacy frame, com-
plete _____ 14.00
Lantern. English bird cage, fros-
ted glass _____ 25.00
Mailbox. Cast iron _____ 8.00
Match Box. Mechanical, eagle picks
up matches _____ 11.00
Match Holders:
Hanging. 5½'' long, hinged cover.
Dated 1863 _____ 8.75
Hangs or stands. Lacy, footed __ 8.75
Hanging moon face _____ 11.50
Mortar and Pestle _____ 11.00
Muffin Mold _____ 6.00
Pans, Muffin. Space for 11 muffins 6.00
Paper Clip. Hound head _____ 30.00
Pea Sheller. Dated 1866 _____ 7.50
Peach Peeler _____ 9.00
Pistol, Toy. Cork shooter. ''J. D.
Frary, Meriden'' _____ 12.50
Plate. 8½'' diam. _____ 8.75
Plaque. 18½'' round. U. S. Grant
bust with date 1822-1885 _____ 60.00
Poker _____ 3.75
Porringer _____ 10.50
Pot. Footed, 9'' top diam., 5''
high. 9'' handle _____ 18.50
Pot. Small, footed, solid handle __ 12.50
Pump. Cast Iron _____ 12.75
Sausage Stuffer. 13'' long. Marked
Brighton No. 2 Works _____ 15.00
Sconces, Wall. 11'' overall height.
Flower shaped cups extend out
14''. Pair _____ 49.50
Shelf Brackets, Lacy type. 9x7''.
Pair _____ 4.50
Shoemaker's Nail Holder _____ 18.00
Skillet. Rattail-type. Wrought iron,
high feet, 9'' diam. _____ 20.00
Soap Dish. Wall type. Lacy design 4.50
Spurs. Civil War. Pair _____ 15.00
Steelyards. 50 lbs. _____ 7.50
Stove. Pot Belly, cast iron, small
size, one lid on top. 31½'' high 59.50
Stove. Wood burning parlor stove.
Dated 1869. Whiteman & Cox,
Phila., Pa. Water urn on top, 12''
diam. at center, 51'' high ____ 90.00
String Holder. See ''String Hold-
ers''

Tea Kettles:
Covered _____ 10.00
8'' high, 8'' diam. Flat cover
dated 1863, recessed base ____ 14.00
Toaster. 11½'' long _____ 22.50
Tobacco Cutters. See ''Tobacco
Cutters''
Traps:
Bear trap. 11¾'' jaws, drag hoks,
chains, etc. _____ 45.00
Beaver. 22½'' double spring ____ 20.00
Fox trap. Early, hand forged __ 16.75
Wolf. 26'' double spring _____ 16.75
Trivet. Early Pennsylvania Dutch,
handled. Hex sign _____ 28.50
Waffle Iron. Round, no design __ 16.50
Washboard _____ 8.75
Weather Vane, See ''Weather
Vanes''

## IRONSTONE

The first china of this type was patented
in 1813, by C. J. Mason, in England. It was
a thin durable type of ware made from
the slag of iron furnaces ground and mixed
with clay. The thick heavy type now commonly referred to as ironstone is, in reality,
granite ware and unlike the original ironstone. This later product was mass-produced
after 1850 and was popular until about the
1880-1890 period when the vogue shifted to
French porcelains, especially Haviland China.

Teapot. 9½'' _____ $29.50

Bone Dish. Wheat pattern _____ $7.50

**Bowls:**

8" square, Meakin, birds and morning glories ............ 10.00
5½" soup. Meakin, birds and morning glories ............ 7.50
With pitcher. Small, Johnson Bros., England ............ 15.00
With pitcher. Large, with large bunches of roses and gold band decoration ............ 40.00

**Butter Dishes:**

Covered, corn pattern ............ 21.50
Covered, footed, handled ...... 24.00
Covered, Meakin, birds and morning glories ............ 20.00
Butter Pat. Meakin, birds and morning glories ............ 2.00
Cake Plate. Square, Meakin, birds and morning glories ......... 15.00
Coffee Pot. Large, tan and blue decoration ............ 36.00
Compote. 10", footed, ribbed ... 32.00
Corn Pudding Mold ............ 12.50
Creamer. Meakin, birds and morning glories ............ 12.75
Cup and Saucer. Meakin, birds and morning glories ............ 14.00
Cup and Saucer. Wedgwood handleless, laurel pattern ...... 15.75
Door Knobs. Pair ............ 6.00
Egg Cup ............ 5.00
Gravy Boat. Meakin, birds and morning glories ............ 10.75
Gravy Boat. Cable pattern ...... 10.00
Jars. 8½" diam., covered, on Teakwood stands. Pair ............ 40.00
Jug. Octagonal, 7" high. Serpent handle, Blue Willow decor .... 48.00

**Ladles:**

Gravy ............ 10.00
Soup ............ 18.50
Pickle Dish. Meakin, birds and morning glories ............ 8.00

**Pitchers:**

5½" high, Meakin ............ 14.00
8" milk. Lily-of-the-Valley.
Burgess, Burslem ............ 20.00
9" high, corn pattern ............ 27.50
9" high, sheaf of wheat ......... 32.00

**Plates:**

6", Meakin, birds and morning glories ............ 11.00
8½", wheat pattern ............ 12.00
9", wheat pattern ............ 13.50
9", Meakin, birds and morning glories ............ 12.50
10½", Mason's. Imari pattern .. 16.75
Wedgwood, marked "Hyacinth" 12.00

**Platters:**

8" long, wheat pattern ......... 15.75
13" long, Meakin, birds and morning glories ............ 20.00
14½" long, Lily-of-the-Valley .. 22.50
15x11½", Meakin ............ 18.50
18¾", wheat pattern, Elsmore & Foster ............ 22.00

"Our Daily Bread," open handles, turned-down sides ............ 16.50
Sauce Dish. Meakin, birds and morning glories ............ 3.50

**Soap Dishes:**

Covered, oval, 6x4¼", gold band decor ............ 6.50
Covered, wheat pattern ........ 8.50

**Sugar Bowls:**

Covered, corn pattern ......... 18.50
Covered, Lily-of-the-Valley, bud finial. "T. Hughes, Burslem" .. 22.50
Covered, pear finial ............ 21.00
Syrup. Pewter lid ............ 20.00

**Teapots:**

Copper lustre decor ............ 45.00
9" Meakin, square ............ 30.00
10" high, leaf pattern ............ 34.50

**Tureens:**

Covered, Lily-of-the-Valley. Small 20.00
Covered, rectangular, Meakin, birds and morning glories ...... 24.50
12", Edwards, nut finial ......... 32.50
14x10", fancy handles and finial, with ladle ............ 65.00
Soup. Large, wheat pattern, pedestal base. With tray and ladle _ 72.00
Vase. 5½", 8-sided, rust red with green and black. Marked Mason's Patent Ironstone ............ 18.00

**Vegetable Dishes:**

7x10", covered, handled. Lily-of-the-Valley. "Anthony Shaw" .. 16.50
9½", open ............ 8.75
Wheat pattern, medium size .. 11.00

## IVORY

Abacus. Carved, 1½x2" ............ 30.00
Banana. Fine detail. 7" long, from elephant ivory ............ 57.50
Bottle, Wine. 1½" high ............ 15.00
Boy. Figurine of small boy with wheelborrow, driving goose. Lattice fence with vines in rear .. 87.50
Button Hook. Ivory handle ...... 3.00
Cane Handle. Dog's head ........ 12.75
Card Case. Carving of stag and foliage. Red silk lining ........ 35.00
Carving of Deer and Fawn. Oval. Victorian frame, gold liner. 3x 2½" ............ 9.75
Chess Set. In red and white. Tallest piece 2¾" high. Complete .... 65.00
Elephant. Standing, one foot raised. Inlaid with stones and pearls. 5" high, 2" wide ............ 50.00

**Figurines:**

Fisherman. One with hand-net, other with handled net and fish. Each ............ 90.00
Man with axe. 5½" high ......... 85.00
Man with oar. 5½" high ...... 87.50
Letter Opener. Elaborate carving .. 9.00
Madonna. 12", German origin .... 40.00
Match Holder. Feet of polished

brass elephant beads, brass rim
and spear at top _____ 32.50

**Napkin Rings:**
Carved scenes in 3 circles. Pair    15.00
Miniature _____   7.00

**Portraits:**
Miniature. 2¾'', hand-painted,
French, round brass easel-rest
frame. Signed ''Cetta'' _____ 95.00
Miniature. In silver frame, unsign-
ed _____ 87.50

**Scrimshaws:**
6¼'' long, carving of 2 Indians
by tree. Walrus tusk _____ 50.00
14'' long, primitive carving on
walrus tusk _____ 55.00
Etched figures of girl, boy and
woman, pair of teeth _____ 60.00
Victorian lady _____ 55.00

Toothbrush. Carved ivory handle__   3.00
Toothpick Holder. Elephant handle   9.75
Tusks. Carved crocodile one side.
Hole in back for hanging.
Pair _____ 42.50

## JACKFIELD POTTERY

Jackfield is a type of pottery made for table use. It has a red body and is sometimes decorated with scrolls and flowers in relief. It is covered with a thick black glaze but differs from Basalt (made by Wedgwood) which is black throughout.

Vase. 4'' high. Design in relief,
beaded top _____ $28.50

Cats. 12½'' high, black with glass
eyes, gold neck ribbon. Pair __ 120.00
Coffee Pot. 9½'' to top of finial __ 60.00
Cow Creamer _____ 48.50
Cup and Saucer _____ 35.00
Dogs. 10'' high. Pair _____ 42.50
Syrup. Pewter top _____ 44.50

Teapot. 4½'' high, all black glaze.
Small size _____ 50.00

## JACK-IN-THE-PULPIT VASES

Near the turn of the present century, vases of various colors of glass, blown in the shape of a ''Jack-in-the-Pulpit'' flower, were in vogue.

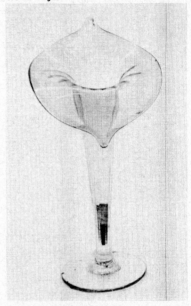

Cranberry Glass. 10'' high _____ $47.50

5''. Pink with frills _____ 25.00
5⅞''. Orange coloring _____ 27.50
6''. Satin glass, blue lining, camphor glass feet _____ 85.00
7''. Clear with green, yellow and
purple _____ 30.00
7''. Millefiori, vari-colored candy
canes _____ 50.00
7''. Ruffled top, clear glass with
shadings of green, purple and
yellow _____ 45.00
7''. Vaseline to opalescent _____ 35.00
7½''. Signed ''Quezal'' _____ 75.00
8''. Pink shading to maroon, white
edge _____ 42.50
9''. Green base blending into
spatter of yellow, gold and pink   44.50

9''. Light green shading to vaseline, clear feet _____ 42.00
10''. Cranberry glass _____ 47.50
12''. Cranberry, ribbed top, scalloped edge, ribbed body with
clear pedestal base, rough pontil _____ 60.00

## JADE

Jade is a semi-precious mineral used
in Burma and China for carving statues,
idols, boxes, incense burners, etc. The
most common color is green. However, it
is found in rare colors of mutton fat,
grey, purple, rose, yellow, black, green
and in mottled colors.

Inkwell. Gray with black top, brass
base _____ $275.00

Box, Round. Covered. $2\frac{1}{4}$'' diam.,
apple green shading to white __ $75.00

Brush Jar. Fei-Ts'ui Period. Round,
carved figures feasting. Greyish-
white jade with blue shading __ 200.00
Figurine. Holding flowers. 8'' high,
on carved teakwood stand ____ 225.00
Frog. 3'' long. Deep green, on
wood stand _____ 50.00
Horse. Being groomed by boy.
Greyish-white jade. $4\frac{1}{2}$'' high __ 195.00
Incense Burner. Carved, mutton fat
jade with Fu-lion masks and lotus
vines. 6'' high _____ 100.00
Inkwell. Gray with black top, brass
base _____ 275.00
Rabbits. Carved, on teakwood
stand. $4\frac{3}{4}$'' long. Ch'ien Lung
Period _____ 225.00
Ring, Thumb. $1\frac{1}{4}$'' diam., greyish-
green _____ 16.50
Snuff Bottle. Shape of pear, on
stand, white jade. Ch'ien Lung
Period _____ 145.00
Tree. Jade in Cloissoine planter.
11'' high, $7\frac{1}{2}$'' wide. Amethyst
turquoise and coral blossoms and
buds, green leaves _____ 150.00
Vase. Carved, mutton fat-type, on
teakwood stand. Lettuce carved
on one side with cricket and
grasshopper. Greenish-white jade.
7'' high, Ch'ien Lung Period ___ 480.00

## JASPERWARE

Josiah Wedgwood described Jasperware
as "a fine Terra Cotta of great beauty and
delicacy proper for cameos." The background of the ware is predominantly blue;
however, green, yellow, red and lavender
shades were also used. The figures are often
done in the Grecian classical tradition
and decorations are usually white.

The product was first made at the Wedgwood Etruria Works in 1775. Probably 90%
of the ware sold in shops today was made
after 1890. Much of it has been brought
into the U. S. within the past 10 years by
importers, and in turn sold by unscrupulous or ignorant dealers as old to new collectors or unsuspecting customers.

Ashtray. German mark. $6x4x\frac{3}{4}$''
high. Indian smoking pipe _____ $20.00
Biscuit Jars:
Covered 5'' high. Blue with
acorn finial and leaf decor on
cover _____ 95.00
5'' high, $4\frac{1}{4}$'' diam. Green, with
silver cover and handle. Im-
pressed "Wedgwood, England" __ 110.00
Bowls:
$5\frac{1}{8}$'' diam., light blue _____ 60.00
7'' diam., light green _____ 72.50
$7\frac{1}{2}$'' diam., $3\frac{3}{4}$'' high, classic figures, 3 white feet _____ 85.00

Creamer. 4''. Blue, classic white figures. Impressed "Wedgwood" ____ $37.50

Cracker Jar. 6½'' high, 5¼'' diam.
Classic white decor on blue. Footed, hinged handle _____ $95.00

Boxes:
  Blue, covered, white chariot in
  relief, scalloped edge. Impressed
  "Wedgwood" _____ 50.00
  Blue, covered, heart-shaped ____ 45.00
  Blue, round, 5'' diam., 2'' deep,
  covered, Classic figures in re-
  lief. England _____ 47.50
  Green, covered, heart-shaped,
  raised bust of man motif _____ 50.00
  White decor. Boys trying to push
  and pull a mule. German origin 37.50
Candlesticks:
  5½'' high, royal blue. Pair ____ 90.00
  7'' high. Dark blue with white
  decor. Marked "Wedgwood".
  Pair _____ 125.00
Cheese Dish. 10'' diam., blue ____ 150.00
Chocolate Pot. Covered _____ 115.00
Cookie Jar. Dark blue, plated silver cover and handle _____ 100.00
Cracker Jars:
  Impressed "Wedgwood." Classic
  scene, figures in white relief on
  blue ground _____ 100.00
  5½x4'', silhouettes of Lafayette,
  Washington and Franklin _____ 195.00
  Impressed "Adams." Deep blue
  with white hunting scene in relief _____ 110.00

Creamers:
  2'' high, 2¾'' diam., blue _____ 42.50
  4'' high, dark blue _____ 52.50
Cup and Saucer. Medium blue,
  classic figures, rope handles,
  early _____ 75.00
Dish. Covered, 10¼'' long. Rabbit
  handle, "game" figures in relief
  around body. Impressed "Wedgwood" _____ 95.00
Jam Jar, with matching plate. Dark
  blue with classic figures _____ 77.50
Jardinieres:
  7¼'' diam., 6¼'' high. Classic
  figures, lion heads and grape
  garlands in relief. Impressed
  "Wedgwood, England" _____ 75.00
  8'' diam., 7'' high, green with
  classic figures _____ 85.00
Jugs:
  5½'' high, blue, Wedgwood, medallions of Washington and Franklin _____ 180.00
  6½'' high, Jasper cover, light
  blue, classic medallions _____ 65.00
  7'' high, blue, hinged pewter lid 75.00
Medallion. Tri-color cameo type,
  2⅛x1¾''. Impressed "Wedgwood" 125.00
Mugs:
  Beer. Dark blue, "Wedgwood,
  England" _____ 78.50
  5½x3½, dark green. "Fill This
  Cup and Drink It Up." Drape
  and floral designs in white relief 72.50

6'' high, blue figures representing seasons _____ 77.50
Mustard Pot with Spoon. Blue with
cameo type cupids. Covered 32.50
Pitchers:
4'' high. Dark blue, classic figures, grape border, twisted handle _____ 40.00
4¼'' high. Dark blue, classic __ 48.00
5¼'' high. Blue, classic _____ 70.00
5¼'' high. Yellow, bulbous _____ 85.00
5½'' high. Green, looped flowers
and figures _____ 70.00
5¼'' high. Dark blue, bulbous __ 69.50
6½'' high. Dark blue, tankard __ 727.00
8'' high. Brown with white classic
figures _____ 48.50
8'' high. Dark blue, tankard ____ 72.50
9'' high. Blue classic figures,
grape border _____ 85.00
Plaques:
4¼'' diam., 3'' high. Green, applied girl's head, not marked __ 32.50
7¼'' high, 5¼'' wide. Shield-
shaped, green. One with girl
playing violin; other with girl
playing bagpipes, vintage border. Pair _____ 60.00
7¾x2½''. Wedgwood. "The Dancing Hour." Circa 1780 _____ 175.00
8''. Head of Goethe. White on
blue _____ 40.00
Ring Tree. 4¼'' diam., 2¾'' high.
Green, "Wedgwood England'' _ 37.50
Salt Shaker. Dark blue, classic
white figures. White Acanthus
leaves and berries around top,
perforated Jasper cover _____ 45.00
Sugar Bowls:
4'', dark blue and white, clas-
sic figures _____ 75.00
Green covered. Wedgwood ____ 65.00
Yellow, covered. Wedgwood.
Rare _____ 160.00
Sugar Shaker. Blue, classic ____ 55.00
Syrup Jug. 7'' high, blue, classic
figures. Wedgwood _____ 72.00
Teapots:
Blue, small, classic figures ____ 50.00
Royal blue, large classic figures,
early _____ 95.00
Dark blue, white classic decor.
Medium size _____ 75.00
Small. 1 cup size, 7'' long. Em-
bossed "Wedgwood'' _____ 48 50
Tea Sets:
Teapot, sugar bowl and creamer.
Dark blue with classic figures. Set 180.00
Teapot, sugar bowl and creamer.
Green with classic figures. Set 195.00
Toothpick Holder. Light blue, with
angel head in blue and green
medallion _____ 25.00
Tray. 10½x7¾''. Dark blue, white
classic figures. Marked "Eng-
land'' _____ 42.50

Tray. 7¾ x 10''. Blue, classic design. Marked "Wedgwood, England'' _____$85.00
Urns:
9¼'' high. Blue, with classic figures, square base. 13'' across
handles _____ 200.00
12'' high. Black with white decor.
Impressed "Wedgwood'' _____ 300.00
Vase. 6½'' high. Green with white
cupids. German origin _____ 32.50

## JEWEL BOXES

Jewel boxes listed in this section are
the so-called Victorian type. The boxes
were common in the 1880-1910 period. For
the most part, they were made of white
metal—similar to the type used by manufacturers for making hollow ware. The
boxes, after being cast, were plated with
either gold or silver. The interior was then
padded lightly with cotton and lined with
satin.

Victorian. Metal, gold plated. Satin
lining _____ $15.00

Kidney-shaped. Pink lining. Gold
color worn _____ 9.00
Large. Footed, lined, ornate design. Gold color _____ 12.50
Medium. Floral design, lined. Gold
color worn _____ 10.50
Small. Lined. Silver color _____ 8.00

## JEWELRY

Jewelry has been used since ancient times
as personal adornment or as symbols of
wealth and status. Primitive people used
bone, iron, wood, seeds, animal teeth,
pebbles and shells for jewelry. Later,
bronze was utilized until gold and silver
were discovered. At a still later date,
precious gems were added to enhance the
appearance and value of an ornament.

In ancient Egypt, jewelry was an important part of the costume of people. Many
items had religious motifs.

In ancient Greece, gold was mainly used
and designs were usually based on animal
and human figures.

In Rome, jewelry was more splendid and
heavier than Greek jewelry. During the
days of the Roman Empire, finger rings
were very popular and people wore them
on every finger and often two rings to a
finger.

In the Renaissance period, design became
more elaborate and jewelry was richly decorated with enamel pearls and gems. In this
period, earrings were considered an important item of a gentleman's costume.
Also, elaborate chains and collars were
worn by the wealthy and the powerful.

In the Victorian period, the common man
was able to buy a variety of items in
jewelry as they became readily available
through manufacturers who issued catalogues to small store owners all over the
country.

Victorian jewelry is popular among collectors today as much of it is still readily
available.

**Bracelets:**
Bangle. Silver, shape of cuff with
repouse buttonholes, buttons and
braid. 1½'' wide _____ $35.00
Diamonds:
Platinum. 5.00 Cts. _____ 1600.00
Platinum. 13.90 Cts. _____ 4800.00
Platinum. 15.00 Cts. _____ 2400.00
**Brooches:**
Classic woman's profile carved in
opal. ½'' size _____ 295.00
Crescent and stars garnets. Large
stones. Gold _____ 90.00
Diamond. 14 K white gold, 1.75
Cts. _____ 700.00
Diamond Platinum. 5.85 Ctc. __ 2500.00
Diamond Platinum. 13.40 Cts. ___ 4900.00

Old Topaz. ¼'' silver mounting,
gold rim. Set with white sapphires
and rose diamonds _____ 195.00
Scotch Agate. Quatrefoil-shaped,
deep red and green, mottling.
Open center banded in engraved
solid silver with 4 silver clovers
at diagonal points. 2'' wide,
1¾'' _____ 30.00
Cameos:
Shell. 1¾'', gold and oval brown
and white. Woman and child.
Early 18th century _____ 75.00
Shell. 1¾'' long, 1½'' wide. Scene
in white on pinkish-tan of young
woman on bench holding swaddled
baby in her arms, large tree,
grasses. Solid gold frame _____ 35.00
Stone. 1½'', gold and oval black-
white-black. Profile of a woman's
head with cluster of grapes in
her hair _____ 175.00
Mother-of-Pearl on dark background. Oval 2x1½'' on 24'' silver
chain. Filigree frame mounting __ 50.00
Three Graces. White on beige
background. Paper thin with figures in high relief, solid gold
mounting. 1¼x1½'' length. Proof__ 50.00
Earrings:
Dangler. 2'' long, filigree tubular with bells on ends _____ 18.50
Drop. 1½'' long, 18K. 3 turquoise
stones and 5 white sapphires,
etruscan work, 2 ribbon-like bands
folded over and joined. New post
backs _____ 110.00
Diamond:
White gold. 1.00 Ct. _____ 330.00
White gold 3.20 Cts. _____ 1050.00
White gold 4.85 Cts. _____ 2000.00
With emeralds. Diamond 3.35 Cts.
emeralds 0.90 Cts. _____ 1800.00
Gold. Small, shaped like cross__ 5.00
Gold. ½'' diam., turquoise center
stone, white sapphires, etruscan
engraving, screwbacks _____ 40.00
Pierced. Siberian Amethyst. Deep
purple stones _____ 275.00
Necklace:
Diamond Platinum. 24.00 Cts. ___ 8200.00
Pendants:
Gold. 2 diamond stones _____ 70.00
Fiery opal surrounded by over-
lapping gold loops to form
circle. ½'' diam., on gold chain__ 25.00
Three Step. Oval designs on
each side. 1½'' diam., on heavy
rope chain _____ 38.50
Opal 1.80 Cts., diamond 0.50
Cts. White gold with chain ____ 380.00
Pins:
Bug. French workmanship. 1½''
long, jade body, gold feelers,
diamond eyes, white gold wings
closely set with diamonds _____ 550.00

Bug. Same as above, except wings are set with sapphires _____ 450.00
Chatelain. Fleur-de-lis. 1'' wide filigree with diamond-shaped center _____ 6.50
Garnet. Flower and crescent design. Deep color, on pinchback mounting _____ 30.00
Miniature. Porcelain, 2½x1¾''. Young girl, long flowing blonde hair, pastel ground, rope mounting _____ 22.50
Scarf or Stick Pin. Gold and porcelain. Two cherubs on black ground _____ 45.00

Rings, Ladies' Diamond:
0.12 Cts., white gold with 10.25 aquamarine _____ 220.00
0.65 Cts. solitaire, white gold oval shape _____ 290.00
0.75 Cts. solitaire, white gold __ 340.00
0.90 Cts., white gold _____ 350.00
0.95 Cts., white gold _____ 380.00
1.00 Cts. solitaire, gold _____ 650.00
1.10 Cts., gold _____ 470.00
1.30 Cts., white gold, emerald cut _____ 650.00
1.40 Cts. white gold, with 2.55 rubies _____ 1000.00
1.45 Cts. solitaire, white gold, pear shape _____ 1400.00
1.55 Cts. white gold _____ 700.00
1.55 Cts., with emeralds, 1.70 Cts. _____ 2200.00
1.75 Cts. white gold, marquise__ 1200.00
2.00 Cts. white gold _____ 1600.00
2.50 Cts. solitaire, white gold, pear shape _____ 2700.00
2.85 Cts. platinum with 3.45 Ct. sapphires _____ 2600.00
3.70 Cts., gold with 2.00 Ct. emeralds _____ 3400.00
3.75 Cts. marquise solitaire, platinum _____ 5500.00
4.00 Cts., gold _____ 4800.00
4.05 Cts., platinum _____ 2100.00
4.15 Cts. solitaire, white gold, pear shape _____ 3700.00
4.40 Cts. platinum _____ 2100.00
5.00 Cts. solitaire, gold _____ 6200.00
5.50 Cts., platinum _____ 3500.00
11.05 Cts., solitaire, gold _____ 11700.00

Rings, Men's Diamond:
0.95 Cts., gold _____ 470.00
1.25 Cts., platinum _____ 625.00
1.55 Cts., gold _____ 800.00
7.00 Cts., white gold, 2.00 star sapphires _____ 340.00

Rings, Diamond Wedding:
1.30 Cts., white gold _____ 550.00
1.50 Cts., white gold _____ 650.00
1.80 Cts., white gold _____ 775.00
2.50 Cts., platinum _____ 850.00

Ring, Opal Cluster. Marquise shape, blue enamel trim. Small diamond in center _____ 125.00

Watches:
Diamond. .50 Cts., white gold __ 290.00
Diamond Bracelet Watch. 2.55 Cts. White gold _____ 1350.00
Hampden. Molly Stark. Gold filled, signed movement _____ 32.00
Illinois. 18S, 14J. Stem wind, lever set in coin silver case ____ 15.00
Ladies:
Longines. 10 size, 14J key wind, In sterling hunting case _____ 15.00
Waltham. 7J. 04 size in solid gold hunting case _____ 30.00
Waltham. Riverside Model 6 in 18K solid gold carved hunting case. Stem wind, lever set _____ 40.00
F. Lagne, Locle Switzerland. 15J size 5, key wind. Lever escape, sterling hunting case _____ 18.00
Men's:
Columbia. 15S, 14J, open face, coin silver case _____ 15.00
Open face, 13 size, 4 jewel thin model. Key wind by B. Hands, Geneva. Sterling silver case, silver vest chain, cylinder escape 15.00
Swiss. 18S, 13J key wind lever escape. Sterling hunting case __ 15.00
Watch Chains, Gold filled:
4 opals, heavy chain _____ 25.00
66'' box type chain link with watch clip. 9K _____ 70.00
Watch Slides, Gold filled:
36'', cameo head _____ 30.00
48'', five pearls and one opal __ 20.00
Plain gold _____ 15.00
With single pearl _____ 18.00

### KATE GREENAWAY

Kate Greenaway, born in 1846, was the daughter of an English artist. In her early 20's she started illustrating Christmas cards. Later, she illustrated books. Her drawings were in vogue in the 1880's and 1890's. Staffordshire and German potteries used her illustrations of children on mugs, tea sets, plates, etc., which are now much desired by collectors.

Plate. 8½'' diameter _____ $26.50

Book of Games. 24 colored illus-
trations _____ 18.50
Book. Mother Goose. Engraved and
printed by Edmund Evans, illus-
trated by Kate Greenaway _____ 25.00
Button. "Ring-A-Rosie" _____ 10.00
Child's Set. Plate, cup, saucer ___ 32.50
Coffee Pot. With figures _____ 60.00
Dinner Service for 6. Child's _____ 120.00
Figurines, Bisque. 5¾" high. Boy
and girl in blue and pink out-
fits _____ 40.00
Hot Plate, Baby's. Made in Ger-
many _____ 35.00
Napkin Ring. Figures of children.
Resilvered _____ 20.00
Pepper Girl, in Basket. 3⅜" _____ 18.75
Plate. Blowing bubbles, skipping
rope, learning to walk, etc. ____ 21.50
Plate. 8½" diam. _____ 22.50
Salt Shaker. Girl in yellow coat __ 20.00
Shakers. Salt and Pepper. Little girl
decor. Pair _____ 40.00
Shams. "Good Night" and "Good
Morning" with 72" matching
spread. Greenaway figures in
squares _____ 42.50
Vase, Bud. Small _____ 18.50

## KEW BLAS GLASS

A type of novelty glass made by the
Union Glass Works, Somerville, Mass., in
the 1890's. It can best be described as
an opal or milk glass, flashed or stained
with color, then coated with a clear glass.
Items are usually marked "Kew Blas" on
the bottom of the base.

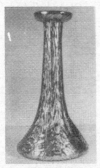

Vase. 11" high. Iridescent deep
blue, silver and gold outer surface, bronze colored lining.
Signed "Kew Blas" on bottom__ $425.00

Candlestick _____ 300.00

Creamer. Green and gold lotus
leaves on creamy pearl background _____ 400.00
Rose Bowl. 5½" diam. Gold festoons
and green Venetian chain on
pearly white ground. Scarce ____ 275.00
Vases:
5" high. Gold iridescent _____ 185.00
7½" high. Creamy pearl with
light green highlights, scalloped
top, gold lining _____ 300.00
11" high. Iridescent deep blue,
silver and gold outer surface,
bronze-colored lining. Signed
"Kew Blas" on bottom _____ 425.00
12" high. Gold iridescent with
brilliant highlights of rose, blue
and green. Signed "Kew Blas" __ 435.00
Wine. Tall, signed _____ 125.00

## KING'S ROSE PATTERN

Soft paste chinaware of the 1820-30 era
produced in the Staffordshire district of
England for the Pennsylvania (Dutch) German trade. The enamel decorations are
usually in soft pinks, dark brick reds, yellows and greens. The colors often flaked-
off with use. Some people refer to the
small rose as "Queen's Rose."

Coffee Biggin. King's Rose. 10½"
high, pine tree border _____ $800.00

Coffee Biggin. 10½" high, pine tree
border _____ 800.00
Cups and Saucers:
Large size _____ 195.00
Regular size _____ 165.00
Plates:
Dinner _____ 200.00
Toddy _____ 120.00

Sugar Bowl and Creamer. Queen's
  Rose. Set _____ $500.00

Sugar Bowl. Queen's Rose _____ 250.00
Teapot. Queen's Rose. 5'' high ___ 300.00

Cup and Saucer. King's Rose. Large_ $195.00

## LALIQUE GLASS

A fine type of late Art Glass first made
by Rene Lalique, a Paris artisan, about
1905. The glass is a combination of press-
ing, blowing, frosting and cutting. The
ware remained in vogue until about 1930.

Annual Plates. See ''COLLECTOR'S
  PLATES.''
Atomizer. 5'' high. ''Made in
  France'' on metal top. 6 nudes in
  sculptured relief on frosty back-
  ground _____ 32.50
Birds. Pair _____ 140.00
Birds. ''The Little Sparrows'' _____ 70.00
Bottles, Perfume:
  Frosted knobs with black enamel
  on points _____ 45.00
  Square-flat shape. Knotted vine

decor. Dome-type stopper. $3\frac{3}{4}$''
  high _____ 35.00
5'' high. ''La Parisien'' on top. 6
  nudes in sculptured relief on
  frosty background. In original
  leather case _____ 65.00

Bowl. $6\frac{3}{4}$'' diam. Fish decoration _ $120.00
Bowls:
  $6\frac{3}{4}$'' diam., green decor on frosty
  opalescent and green leaf body,
  clear casing _____ 110.00
  7'' diam., red, with fish decor.
  Signed, ''R. Lalique'' _____ 120.00
  8'' diam., $3\frac{1}{2}$'' high.
  Opalescent, signed _____ 75.00
Box, Powder. Frosted, green and
  gold trim _____ 24.00
Cherub holding bowl. 4'' high ____ 72.50
Decanters. $14\frac{1}{2}$'' high. Decorated
  with nudes at corner of each side.
  Stoppers are full female figures.
  Pair _____ 300.00
Dish. $8\frac{1}{2}$'' diam., $1\frac{1}{2}$'' high, dragon-
  fly design _____ 48.00
Dragonfly. 8'' long. 8'' wing
  spread. Signed _____ 87.50
Figurine. Nude dancer with arms
  above head, in kneeling position,
  on $2\frac{1}{4}$'' diam. base _____ 95.00
Goblet. Amber, $4\frac{1}{2}$'' high, thin bowl.
  Heavy hollow baluster stem ____ 21.50
Jar, Covered. 6'' diam., clear glass
  with petal formed cover, petal
  edges around base _____ 55.00
Paperweight. Shape of eagle's head.
  4'' high, 5'' wide. Signed _____ 175.00
Rose Bowl. 7'' diam., fantail fish
  decor _____ 75.00

| | |
|---|---|
| Toothpick Holder. Frosted cherubs and grapes. Signed _____ | 18.50 |

Trays:
| | |
|---|---|
| Pin. Approximately 4½" long. Frosted opalescent glass, with nudes in relief _____ | 20.00 |
| Round. 4" diam. Female figure with hair to feet in center holding water lily _____ | 50.00 |
| Tumbler. Frosted, gold band at top _____ | 30.00 |

Vases:
| | |
|---|---|
| 5" high, blue beaded scallops. Signed _____ | 82.50 |
| 6½" high, bulbous, frosted _____ | 95.00 |
| 7" high. 12 birds in high relief in niches. Each surrounded by floral pattern _____ | 145.00 |
| 7½" tapered, frosted. Gazelles and stars in relief _____ | 55.00 |
| Wine. 7½" tall _____ | 18.50 |

## LAMPS
## EARLY LIGHTING DEVICES

The candle was the primary source of light at night until the invention of the fluid lamp. One of the first was the "Betty" lamp—a small device which used lard oil or whale oil. The invention of the Argand lamp by the Swiss scientist of the same name utilized a round wick which produced a draft both inside and outside the burner thus improving the lighting quality of lamps.

Delft base. 19½" to top of painted glass shade _____$165.00

| | |
|---|---|
| Aladdin. French, not electrified ___ | 120.00 |
| Angle, Double. Early, brass. Opalescent shades, brass rope hanging loop. Burnished, lacquered and electrified _____ | 80.00 |

Astral Lamps:
| | |
|---|---|
| 26" high, 9" prism, brass stem, dated 1873. Cut clear and frosted Tulip shade. Electrified _____ | 175.00 |
| All brass, original shades and prisms. Pair _____ | 210.00 |
| Auto, Ford. Kerosene, 9" high, round lenses. Pair _____ | 27.50 |

Banquet Lamp. Red and white stained glass shade _____ $200.00

**Banquet Lamps:**
Britannia metal, brass plated, marble stem _____ 105.00
Brass, painted ball shade. Electrified _____ 98.50
Cherub. Standing, with butterfly in hand. Square base, ornate font, 29½'' high. Burnished and electrified. Large frosted ball shade _____ 115.00
Pink satin glass, brass base, 22'' high, with satin glass and brass connecting large floral embossed pink satin font _____ 125.00
Red and white stained glass shade 200.00

Betty Lamp. Iron _____ $35.00

"Betty" Lamp _____ 25.00
Bicycle Lamp. Oil, "M & W 97" __ 10.00
**Bracket Lamps:**
Iron, lacy frame, mercury glass reflector _____ 20.00
Frame only. Double _____ 11.50
Frame only. Single _____ 9.50
Brass font and base, open shade. Circa 1880 _____ 225.00
**Carriage Lamps:**
20'' Pair _____ 120.00
Brass, beveled lens, red lens in back. Pair _____ 150.00
**Chandeliers.** Lacy iron, clear fonts, bulbous etched chimneys:
4-arm _____ 78.50
3-arm _____ 60.00
2-arm _____ 52.50
**Cosmos Lamps:**
16'' high. Electrified _____ 145.00
Miniature _____ 90.00
Cresolene Lamp. Milk glass chim-

ney _____ 12.00
Cruisie. Early _____ 50.00

Lamp. Brass font and base, open shade. Circa 1880 _____ $225.00

Electrified. With "Pairpoint" stamped on the brass base. Frosted white shade with etched flowers and birds. Red, white and yellow roses around bottom ____ 300.00
Glow Night Light. Small, brass____ 18.50
**Gone with the Wind Lamps:**
29½'' high, with red cosmos flowers and green leaves. Brass base _____ 115.00
Camel scene, burnished. Not Electrified _____ 125.00

**Gone-with-the-Wind-type Lamp.** Electrified. Dark green with Renaissance figures _____ $175.00

Floral decoration, medium size. Electrified _____ 112.50
Electrified. Dark green with Renaissance figures _____ 175.00
Pink background with red rose decor. Electrified _____ 115.00
Red Satin. 26'' high, matching ball shade. Electrified _____ 100.00
Thistle design, all original. Not Electrified _____ 95.00
**Hall Lamps:**
Cranberry, D. Q., burnished __ 80.00
Cranberry, with sharp hobnails 85.00
Cranberry, 12½'' high, 7'' wide, hanging. 4-panelled square sides. Burnished lacy brass frame _____ 90.00
Hanging, with cranberry swirl shade _____ 85.00
Hanging, white milk glass with hand painted floral decor. 8½''

ball shade with burnished brass frame _____ 68.50
**Hand Lamps. Colored:**
Amber, 9'' _____ 35.00
Bull's Eye & Fleur-de-lis, emerald green _____ 38.50
Cranberry. 11½'' high, clear base, striped bowl _____ 59.50
Log Cabin. Amber _____ 72.50
Log Cabin. Clear. Dated Sept. 30, 1868 _____ 52.50
Lemon. 9'' _____ 32.00
Loop. Emerald green, on pedestal 30.00
Milk Glass Hand Lamp. 17'' stem. Floral decoration under glaze __ 45.00
Plume, blue _____ 25.00
Vaseline. 10'' _____ 30.00
**Hanging Lamps:**
14'' China shade, hand painted, 30 prisms. Burnished, electrified 115.00
14'' cranberry Bull's Eye shade, brass font, prisms. Burnished and electrified _____ 280.00
14'' cranberry sharp Hobnail shade, brass font, prisms. Burnished and electrified _____ 325.00
14'' cranberry swirl shade, brass font. Burnished and electrified 195.00
14'' opalescent Hobnail shade, brass font, prisms. Burnished and electrified _____ 190.00
13'' Bristol canopy shade, for kitchen. Up-and down type with iron circle weight. Electrified 65.00
Lard Lamp. Flattened tin, oval font and stem, openwork iron base _____ 25.00
Meissen-type. China with applied flowers and painted decoration. 20½'' high _____ 265.00
Milk Glass. White. Colorful blossoms in relief. Umbrella shade. Electrified _____ 110.00
Miner's Lamp. 4'' high, brass. "Baldwin." Pat'd. 1900-06_____ 30.00
Nutmeg Lamp. Milk glass _____ 30.00
Organ Lamp. Electrified, floral shade. _____ 75.00
Peacock Lamps. 10½'', blue. Pair 115.00
Peg Lamp. Tin, with hook in wooden block _____ 25.00
Pewter. Whale Oil Lamp. Handled, 5'', Morey & Smith _____ 69.50
Piano Lamp. 2 onyx shelves, ornate brass font, turned brass legs, hand painted bail shade. Burnished and electrified _____ 135.00
**Rayo Lamps:**
Brass, burnished, no shade ____ 20.00
Nickel plated _____ 24.00
Painted shade, electrified _____ 48.50
Rochester Lamp. White shade ____ 28.50
Rush Light. Iron, wood base. Early 50.00
Sandwich Glass Parlor Lamp. Ruby cut to crystal font, deep sapphire stem, cut to clear, double mar-

ble base with brass trim. 17''
high. Circa 1860-70 _____ 400.00
Sandwich Glass. Pressed glass font
with shield and scrolls. Opaque
starch blue base. 14'' high ____ 195.00
Sheffield. Early. Pair _____ 225.00
Shoe. Amber, with original chimney _____ 98.50
Store Lamp. Tin shade, brass font,
burnished _____ 75.00

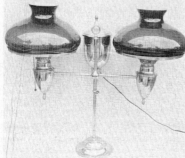

Double Student Lamp. Brass, burnished, electrified _____ $295.00

Student Lamps:
Double. Brass, burnished, electrified _____ 295.00
Double. Buffed, electrified. 8''
shades _____ 275.00
Single shade-type. Glass shade,
brass, electrified _____ 120.00
7'' shades, double _____ 200.00
7'' shades, double. Electrified 245.00
7'' shade, single _____ 125.00
10'' shade. Hanging, double.
Acorn fonts, electrified. Green
shades with white linings. 40''
in length, pulls up or down to
40'', burnished _____ 300.00
Sweetheart Lamp. Green bowl,
white stem _____ 21.00
Table Lamp. 25'' high, Tiffany
Studio. Electrified _____ 100.00
Telephone Lamp. Old desk-type
brass telephone. Electrified ____ 60.00
Tiffany Bronze and Favrille Glass
Lamp. Green opalescent glass
shade. Signed, electrified. 23''
high _____ 520.00
Tin Lamp. Early. 5¼'' high _____ 28.50
Torch Light. Political. Brown sten-
cil design _____ 20.00
Tumbler Lamp. Burns coal oil. Glass
tumbler held by tin contrap-

tion, burner inside tumbler base.
Square wire base _____ 35.00

Lamp. Tin, early. 5¼'' high _____ $28.50

Whale Oil Lamp. Cone-shaped,
with bail _____ 25.00

## LAMPS
### (Illustrated on following page)

1. Clear glass. 9'' _____ 10.00
2. Bowl, opalescent ITP, black
   glass base. 8'' _____ 40.00
3. Bowl, cranberry with ITP in
   opaque white, brass connection to clear base. 9½'' ____ 75.00
4. Bowl, clear bull's eye, brass
   connection to opaque azure
   blue flint glass base. 8½'' __ 55.00
5. Clear, swirled bowl, black
   patterned glass base. 8½'' __ 20.00
6. Clear bowl, brass connection
   to milk glass base. 7¼''. Early 30.00
7. Translucent cobalt blue. 9'' __ 35.00
8. Clear bowl with broad band of
   herringbone pattern. Brass connection to translucent cobalt
   blue base. 9½'' _____ 36.50
9. Fiery opalescent bowl and
   base with brass connection.
   9'' _____ 60.00
10. Flint glass Whale oil lamp,
    with pattern bowl. 8½'' _____ 35.00
11. Clear flint, rough pontil, flange
    footed. 6½'' _____ 27.50
12. Flint glass Whale oil lamp,
    loop pattern, pewter top. 9½'' 50.00
13. Clear pattern glass. 9½'' ____ 11.50

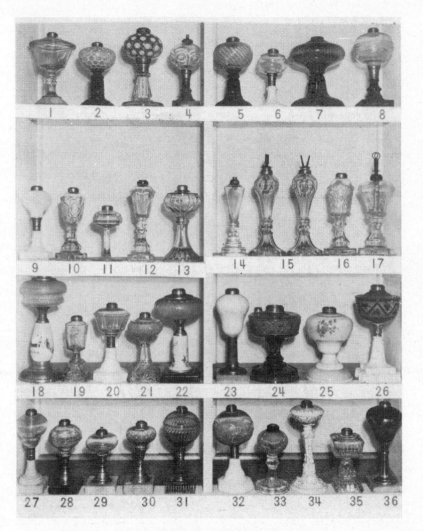

**LAMPS, GLASS**
For descriptions, see pages 308 and 310.

14. Flint glass Whale oil lamp with blown bowl, pewter top. 9'' _____ 45.00
15. Pair of flint glass Whale oil lamps with elongated wheel-cut bowls, pewter tops. 12'' to top of original burners. Pair 165.00
16. Flint glass patterned Whale oil lamp. 10'' _____ 55.00
17. Ring and Cable flint glass Whale oil lamp. 12'' to top of original burner. Rare _____ 77.50
18. Frosted pattern bowl, brass connection to painted winter scene, bulbous stem, brass base. 12½'' _____ 35.00
19. Squatty flint glass Whale oil lamp, Sandwich-type, blown bowl with vintage cutting. 7½'' _____ 37.50
20. Clear panelled bowl, brass connection to milk glass base. 9'' _____ 35.00
21. Clear squatty bowl, medallion pattern. 8'' _____ 11.75
22. Squatty frosted bowl, brass connection to opaque canary stem. Floral decorations on brass connections, painted black square base. 10½'' ____ 30.00
23. Early milk glass, pear-shaped bowl, faded sepia decorations in vintage pattern. Brass stem, marble base. 11'' _____ 48.50
24. Deep amber pattern bowl, patent filler. 9'' _____ 24.50
25. Milk glass, bulbous bowl with floral decorations, with cara-mel bands at top and bottom. 8½'' _____ 29.50
26. Bohemian glass bowl with fros-ted bands, geometrical and vine decoration. Brass connec-tion to milk glass base. 11'' __ 75.00
27. Clear pear-shaped bowl, brass connection to opaque lavender glass base. 9'' _____ 42.50
28. Clear bulbous bowl, brass con-nection to marble base. 8'' __ 23.50
29. Clear bulbous bowl, brass con-nection to marble base. 7'' __ 19.50
30. Clear patterned bowl, brass connection to marble base. 8'' _____ 21.50
31. Clear prism-like pattern glass bowl. Brass connection to brassed stem and base. 9½'' 29.50
32. Clear bulbous pattern glass bowl. Brass connection to milk glass stem and base. 9½'' ___ 32.50
33. Clear Bellflower bowl, scal-loped base, clear stem. 7½'' ___ 48.50
34. Rudolstadt China lamp. Dres-den-ike coloring. 10'' _____ 125.00
35. Square clear pattern bowl, like

Crystal Wedding. 7'' _____ 21.50
36. Bohemian glass pear-shaped bowl, frosted geometrical de-cor. Connected to marble base with brass stem. 10'' _____ 72.50

## LAMPS, MINIATURE

Lamps often referred to in the "old days" as night lamps are now known as miniature lamps. The devices were modeled after the regular lamps of the day but were con-siderably smaller.

(Illustrated on following pages)

Miniature Lamp. Chamber-type. Dated 1873, original chimney ____ $35.00

1. Red satin, footed tulip lamp. 8'' _____ 55.00
2. Green satin glass. 8'' _____ 60.00
3. Embossed milk glass. 8'' ____ 54.50
4. Pink and white swirl overlay. 8'' _____ 75.00
5. Pink melon overlay. 8'' _____ 79.50
6. Cranberry. Mary Gregory. 8'' _____ 110.00
7. White Bristol with blue decor. 8'' _____ 55.00
8. Brass. Aladdin, with yellow overlay shade. 8'' _____ 175.00
9. Dark green, plain. 8'' _____ 49.50
10. Embossed green with gold dec-or. 8'' _____ 57.50
11. Pink Bristol with chimney-type shade _____ 55.00
12. Pink cased embossed glass. 9'' 95.00
13. Pink and white embossed milk glass. 8'' _____ 65.00
14. Red and white End-of-Day glass. 6 applied feet. 8'' ____ 80.00

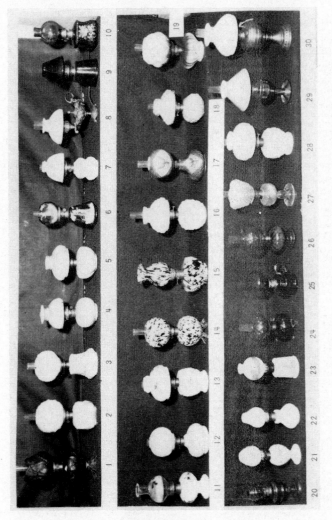

**LAMPS, MINIATURE**
For descriptions, see pages 310 and 313.

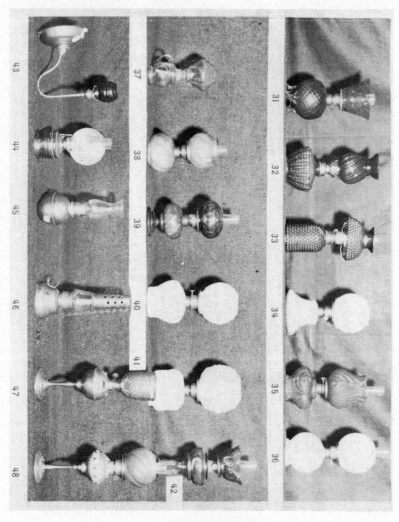

**LAMPS, MINIATURE**
For descriptions, see pages 313 and 314.

15. Blue and white End-of-Day glass. 8'' _____ 77.50
16. Blue diamond quilted. 8'' ____ 79.50
17. Golden eagle with orange colors, yellow and gold. 9'' ____ 55.00
18. Cased glass, yellow basketweave. 7'' _____ 75.00
19. Tulip lamp with orchid and green colors. 9'' _____ 85.00
20. Blue, "Harry's" night lamp. 6'' _____ 57.50
21. Satin glass, white, egg-shaped. 7'' _____ 60.00
22. Milk glass, blue, beaded. 7'' _____ 50.00
23. Milk glass. "Old Dutch Mill." 6'' _____ 49.50
24. Amber, applied feet. 6'' ____ 65.00
25. Blue glass, handled. 6'' _____ 68.50
26. Blue Inverted Thumbprint. 7''__ 75.00
27. Clear glass Hobnail _____ 42.50

28. Cosmos lamp. White milk glass, pink, yellow and blue flowers. 8'' _____ 90.00
29. Brass base with pink overlay shade. 9'' _____ 57.50
30. Junior Aladdin with green ribbed overlay shade. 11'' __ 57.50
31. Cranberry diamond quilted. applied feet. 8'' _____ 85.00
32. Cranberry beaded swirl. 8'' __ 77.50
33. Green Hobnail. 8'' _____ 72.50
34. Blue embossed milk glass. 8''_ 65.00
35. Red satin with tulip shade. 8'' 68.50
36. Bristol with decorations. 10'' to top of chimney _____ 62.50
37. Cranberry. Handled. 6'' _____ 78.50
38. Pink satin swirl with enamel daisy decor. 7'' _____ 89.50
39. Amber Inverted Thumbprint. 7'' _____ 58.50
40. Green milk glass. 8'' _____ 55.00

**LAMPS, MINIATURE**
For descriptions, see page 314.

| | |
|---|---|
| 41. Pink satin glass. 8'' _____ | 85.00 |
| 42. Amber Block and Fan. 8'' ____ | 60.00 |
| 43. Brass wall lamp. "Beauty Night." Burns 40 hours. 6'' __ | 37.50 |
| 44. Brass wall reflector night lamp. 7'' _____ | 47.50 |
| 45. Brass cabin lamp. 7'' _____ | 37.50 |
| 46. Brass skater's lamp with chain. 8'' _____ | 34.50 |
| 47. Miniature brass banquet lamp. Amethyst shade, jeweled base, 10'' _____ | 90.00 |
| 48. Miniature brass banquet lamp. Swirl shade, jeweled base. 10'' | 92.50 |
| 49. Heart pattern clear glass night lamp. 9½'' _____ | 21.50 |
| 50. Reclining elephant milk glass lamp. 9¼'' to top of chimney _ | 100.00 |
| 51. Eagle night lamp. 8'' high, 4'' globe shade _____ | 65.00 |
| 52. Red satin glass. Medallion and plume base, leaf or petal shade _____ | 72.50 |
| 53. Diamond quilted pink satin glass with matching half shade_ | 90.00 |
| 54. Cased glass. Red over milk white with matching half shade _____ | 100.00 |
| 55. Blue hexagon block and star foot. Cathedral stem, plain bowl. Hexagon block and star flare shade. Also found in amber _____ | 67.50 |
| 56. Clear allover spiral pattern, flare or open-top shade. Also found in amber _____ | 31.50 |
| 57. Blue satin glass with matching ball shade, squatty base _____ | 60.00 |
| 58. Same as #57. | |
| 59. Milk Glass with flashed orange color and gold trim _____ | 52.50 |
| 60. Milk Glass with orange decor and daisy spray on base and shade _____ | 49.50 |
| 61. Clear with pressed bar and daisy pattern, matching shade_ | 28.50 |
| 62. Amber with spiral base and stem, matching clear glass shade _____ | 60.00 |
| 63. Milk Glass. Hexagonal, lantern type _____ | 33.50 |
| 64. Milk Glass. "Improved Banner," milk glass chimney ____ | 25.00 |

## LANTERNS

| | |
|---|---|
| Auto. Brass, small _____ | 25.00 |
| Auto Oil Lamp. 14½'' high, brass__ | 55.00 |
| Candle Lanterns: | |
| Copper, pierced. 17½'' high. Rare _____ | 75.00 |
| Tin, folding type _____ | 30.00 |
| Wood, with 4 glass panes, rectangular. Scarce _____ | 65.00 |
| Captain's Ship Lantern. Copper re- | |

| | |
|---|---|
| flector _____ | 72.50 |
| Carriage Lanterns. 15'' high, beveled lenses. Pair _____ | 120.00 |

Skater's Lantern. Brass. Pat. signed "Racke, Sept. 19, 1876 _____ $32.50

| | |
|---|---|
| Dietz Auto Driving Lamp. 10½'' high, 5½'' diam. Red reflector in back. Dated May 10, 1908. Painted black _____ | 50.00 |
| Dietz 1907 Auto Lamp _____ | 30.00 |
| Dietz Carriage Lantern _____ | 20.00 |
| Dietz Farm Lantern. Clear globe __ | 8.75 |
| Dietz Inspector's Hooded Lantern. With bail and handle _____ | 16.75 |
| Hearse Lamps. 31'', silver plated. Pair _____ | 350.00 |
| Iron. Lacy, with 4 glass panes. 12'' high. Circa 1890. Pair _____ | 38.50 |
| Magic Lantern. In box, with slides. Made in Germany _____ | 40.00 |
| Paul Revere. Large, 4 glass panels__ | 45.00 |
| *Pierced Tin _____ | 50.00 |
| Policeman's Hand Lanterns. Pair __ | 18.50 |
| Railroad (B & O). 15'' to top of handle _____ | 15.00 |
| Railroad Lantern. Electrified _____ | 20.00 |
| Railroad Torch. 10'' high. Tole ware _____ | 10.00 |
| Ship's Lanterns. Brass, small size with red and blue lenses. Wired for battery use. Late. Pair _____ | 60.00 |
| Ship's Masthead Lantern. Galvanized iron with old red paint. 12½'' tall. Clear thick beveled cylindrical lense. Kerosene burner | 25.00 |

Railroad Lantern. Made by "Hand-
lan," St. Louis. Alternating red
and green lenses. Kerosene-type __ $48.50

Skaters. Brass, with chain _____ 14.00
Street Post Lanterns. 22" high,
13" canopy. Opalescent globes,
11" high, 8" wide. Matching
pair _____ 135.00
U. S. Ex. Co. Tin with clear globe.
Kerosene, 10½" high _____ 30.00
U. S. Navy. Copper, fitted inside
for candle. 11x8" Circa 1880 __ 35.00

*Reproduced item

## LEEDS WARE

This ware was first made at a factory
established by Charles Green in 1758, in
Leeds, Yorkshire, England. In the 1780's
Queensware was made in competition with
Wedgwood—the quality and style being
as good as the products of the Wedgwood
establishment.

Cream Pitcher. 4¼" high, with yellow blue and green decorations__ 72.50
Cup and Saucer. Handleless, floral
decoration _____ 45.00
Mug. "Watchful Eye, Etc." _____ 50.00
Pepper Pot. Blue feather-stitch
decoration _____ 40.00
Pitcher. 6" high. Colorful flower
decor _____ 110.00

Pitcher. 6" high. Colorful flower
decor _____ $110.00

Plates:
7½", green border, peafowl in
brown and yellow in center ____ 72.50
9", cream with raised flowers __ 29.50
Platters:
Open edge, black transfer center 75.00
13x16¼". Green comb edge _____ 75.00
Teapot. 7½" high, red and green
decoration, shell pattern in body_ 125.00
Tureen. White body with blue comb
decor. 16" long, 25" high _____ 98.50

### LIMOGES CHINA

For information concerning the factories
which produced chinaware at Limoges,
France, see the "Haviland China" section.

Ramekin. Red roses. Marked "C.
Arenfeld" _____ $12.50

Bowl, Punch. Hand painted, decor
of grapes over entire exterior;
interior, roses and green leaves.
Heavy gold trim. With 8 stemmed
cups. Set _____ 225.00
Box, White Heart-shaped. Beaded
design on top _____ 11.00
Candlestick. 8'' high. Blue with
enameled floral decor. Pair ____ 45.00
Chocolate Pot. White, tall, gold
bands _____ 20.00
Chocolate Set. Pot and 6 cups and
saucers. Clover leaf and red
berry decor, gold handles. Set __ 60.00

U. S. Presidential China. U. S.
Grant Dessert Plate (1869-1877).
8¼'' diameter _____ $270.00

Cup and Saucer, Demitasse. Pastel
pink, gold trim _____ 9.50
Cup and Saucer. Green band with
tea rose decor surrounded by
gold bands _____ 15.00
Dinner Set. 80 pieces. A. Lanternier,
decorated with small orchid flowers and leaves _____ 300.00
Dish, Vegetable. 7x9''. Covered,
pink roses and green scroll decor.
Pattern #318 _____ 18.00
Dresser Sets:
3 pieces. Shaped handled tray,
powder bowl and hair receiver.
Embossed with gold, rope trim.
Hand painted violet decor _____ 69.50
5 pieces. Tray, ring tree, 2
round covered boxes, oblong
(7½x2x1½'') covered box. Blue
forget-me-not decor _____ 60.00

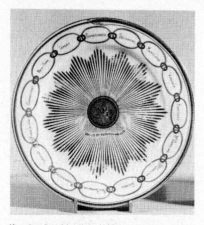

U. S. Presidential China. Benjamin Harrison Dessert Plate (1889-
1893). 8½'' diam. _____ $240.00

Dresser Tray. 12x8'' _____ 18.50
Hat Pin Holder. Blue forget-me-nots
and gold decor. 4'' high _____ 10.00
Patch Box. Hinged, yellow flowers_ 27.50
Perfume Bottle. ''Narbonne,'' green
and gold _____ 11.50
Pitcher, Cider. Red fruit on shaded
green. Dated 1907 by artist ____ 32.00
Pitcher. 7¾'' high. Hand painted
cherry decoration. Marked ''Limoges'' on bottom _____ 40.00
Plaque, Hanging. Arab praying with
2 camels in background. 13x16'',
hand painted. Marked ''J. P.
France'' _____ 45.00
Plates:
Dessert. Cupid center, gold
border. Set of 6 _____ 48.50
9½'' diam., hand painted red and
yellow roses, green and yellow
background. Marked ''LRL'' below
crown, ''Limoges'' in frame _____ 25.00
Oyster. ''France, Depose' Ahren-
feldt Limoges.'' White with pink
and gold edging. With clear
glass sauce dish. Set of 6 _____ 60.00
12'' diam. Hanging-type with
hunting scene painted in bright
colors _____ 40.00
12'' diam., chop. Cream ground,
2'' pink roses outlined in gold.
Green leaves, gold border _____ 35.00
Platter. 16½''. Green and tan border. Gold trim _____ 18.75
Sugar and Creamer. Oval shapes,

pastel ground with small pink
roses on curled gold feet _____ 29.50
Spittoon. Squatty, scalloped rim.
Hand painted floral decor _____ 21.50
Tray. 8x12''. Scalloped gold edges,
cupids in center _____ 54.50

U. S. Presidential China. William
McKinley Dinner Plate (1897-
1901). 8¾'' diam. _____ $160.00

Tureen. 14'' across handles, 8''
wide, 6½'' high, oval. Green band
with tea rose decor surrounded
by gold bands _____ 48.50
Waste Basket. 12½'' high, gold ball
feet, applied gold handles. Wide
gold scroll top, hand painted red
roses. Signed by artist _____ 100.00

## LINENS

Banquet Cloths:
  70x108''. Irish linen, Chrysanthemum pattern _____ 42.50
  70x108''. Linen. Scottish Thistle
  pattern. With dozen 24'' napkins_ 55.00
  73x141''. Irish linen, Rose pattern,
  drawn-work hem _____ 42.50
  Hand crocheted _____ 70.00
Battenburg Lace Handkerchief. 12''
  square _____ 7.50
Battenburg Lace Luncheon Set. 36''
  cloth, 8 napkins, linen centers__ 54.50
Battenburg Lace Scarves:
  17x70'' _____ 9.00
  18x54'' _____ 10.00
Battenburg Lace Table Covers:
  Heavy, round:
  28½'' diam _____ 12.00
  49'' diam. _____ 18.00
  60'' diam. _____ 21.50

Quilt. Red and green design on
white. Fine feather stitching.
Double bed size. Like new _____ $275.00

Bedspreads:
  Brussels net, embroidered, with
  long matching sham _____ 75.00
  Crocheted, new condition _____ 57.50
  72x102''. Handmade, with large
  center medallion of embroidered
  roses, daisies and bowknots,
  Woven border. Pair _____ 85.00
  Large, white, fringed _____ 38.50
  Marseilles, heavy, white, full
  size _____ 42.50
Lace:
  3 yards, 6'' wide. Small scalloped
  edge, fully covered with lus-
  trous darned floral design on
  fine net _____ 18.00
  3 yards, 2½'' wide. Banding with
  scalloped edges on either side __ 9.00
Ladies' Duster. Auto. Fitted princess style, cape collar, 28 pearl
  buttons _____ 16.50
Napkins. Red and white, fringed.
  6 for _____ 17.50
Pillow Shams:
  Embroidered, with ruffled eyelet
  borders. Pair _____ 15.00
  Embroidered red wreath encircling "Sweet Lilies Close Their
  Eyes at Night" and "Open with
  the Morning Light." Each _____ 8.75
  White, with embroidered wreath

and crocheted edge. Each _____ 7.00
Muslin, ruffled edge. Pair \_\_\_\_\_ 8.75
Pillow Slip. 33x17'', cotton, hand-
knitted lace on edge _____ 2.75

Quilts:
Double bed size, red design on
white background, fine stitching.
New condition _____ 75.00
¾ size. Double Irish Chain pat-
tern. Blue calico with white \_\_\_\_ 50.00
60x72''. Wedding Ring pattern.
Flowered percale on white background, scalloped edge, fancy
quilting. Unused _____ 72.50
67x67''. Patchwork squares on
yellow calico background _____ 55.00
77x79''. Appliqued, dated 1858.
4 large eagles and star center,
with small stars. Yellow, light
blue and pink on white _____ 90.00

Samplers:
Made by Jane Thorne. 12 years
of age in 1813. Verse and border. In 14'' square frame _____ 45.00
Made by Eliza Mary Butler, 10
years of age in 1837. In 18½x
13½'' frame _____ 40.00
Sheet, Homespun. 68x90' Fine
condition _____ 18.00
Stockings. Hand knit. Lacy
pattern _____ 4.00

Tablecloths:
52x56''. Dark blue and red with
allover flower and leaf design \_\_ 12.75
56x56''. Red and white, lily
design _____ 14.00
56x64''. Red and white striped
with pansy design _____ 22.50
60x90''. Flower design in red and
natural, fringed _____ 30.00
60x90''. Solid red damask,
fringed _____ 32.50
70x70''. Satin damask, with 12
matching napkins, 26'' square \_\_ 40.00
70x72''. Holly pattern, with 6
matching napkins, handhemmed\_\_ 36.50
72x90''. Cloverleaf center circles
connected with diamond designs.
Lace, not crocheted_____ 42.50
88x90''. Irish linen, damask \_\_\_\_ 28.50

Towels:
25x43''. Plus 4'' knotted fringe.
Wide end border in red and
white with narrow side stripe.
Each _____ 6.00
22x35'' Plus 4'' knotted fringe.
Red and white. Pair _____ 6.50

## LITHOPHANES

Lithophanes are highly translucent porcelains with impressed designs. The picture
is formed by the difference in thickness of
the plaque. Thin parts transmit an abundance of light, while thicker parts represent
shadows. They were first made by the Royal
Berlin Porcelain Works in 1828. Other factories in Germany, France and England later
produced the items. The majority on the
market today was probably made between
1850 and 1900.

Candle Shield. 19½'' high, insert
6 x 7½''. Name ''Petraca'' impressed with K.P.M. 36G _____ **$140.00**

Candle Shields:
5'' high. Flowered and scrolled
pewter holder with candle insert
behind small lithophane _____ 48.50
19½'' high, insert 6x7½''. Name
''Petraca'' impressed with
K.P.M. 36G _____ 140.00
Round, jeweled rims. Pair _____ 65.00
Child on Father's Shoulders. 6¾''
x7¾''. Marked K.P.M. _____ 50.00
Fairy Lamps:
2 scenes of child _____ 95.00

Veilleuse (heating lamp). 3 copper panels, copper and brass mountings _____ 80.00
Girl and Cat. 7¼x9¼ _____ 57.50
Hall Lamp. 7½'' square with cut corners. 4 lithophane panels 6x4'' Brass bound, brass fixture _____ 225.00
Hunter, Young. 4¾x6½'' _____ 32.50
Lamp Shade. Metal frame, 5 panels. Marked _____ 200.00
Picture. 5x6½'', mounted for hanging in colored glass frame _____ 55.00
Plaques. Marked "P. R. Sickle." 5-1/10x4-2/10'':
Cupid and girl fishing (#1849)__ 32.00
Lovers in boat. Approx. 4''x4½''_ 32.00
Monk and girl (#1788) _____ 32.00
Nymph and flowers (#1803) ___ 32.00
Woman gazing at ocean (#894)__ 32.00
Woman in negligee (#1422) ____ 32.00
Woman picking .lowers (#1584)_ 32.00
Plaques. Marked "K. P. M." with torch above (Konigliche Parzellan Manu.aktut, Berlin. Torch mark indicated the item was made after 1882):
Child with glasses, seated at table and reading book. Round, 7'' diam. (#177-Z) _____ 55.00
Couple, Romantic. 5x6½''. Seated in woodland setting with dog. "K. P. M." (#173) _____ 32.50
Dog, flushing bird. Trees and foliage, 3¼x4¾''. (#172-G) _____ 47.50
Girl with rose. 5⅞x7⅜'', K. P. M. (#308G) _____ 58.50
Man and Woman. 4¼x5¾''. Woodland scene _____ 32.00
Mosque-type building, man kneeling in front, 4¾x6½''. (#110-St.) _____ 52.50
Women. 10x11''. One with child on back, two holding rakes, goats in background. Blue glass frame _____ 55.00
Plaques. Unmarked, not as fine grade as K. P. M. listed above:
Madonna and child. 6x7½'' _____ 47.50
Sunset over water, riders and horses on shore. 6½x8⅜'' _____ 42.50
Queen Yasdwiga. 9½x12''. (K.P.M.) 60.00
Stein, Gymnastic _____ 95.00
Stove. Tea or toddy, round brass frame, pewter feet _____ 65.00
Window Panel. 4½x5½'' _____ 20.00
Woman and Child. 4¼x5¼'' Marked "K. P. M. 719'' _____ 35.00
Woman, Reclining. Partly nude. 6x8½'', in lead frame for hanging _____ 46.50

## LIVERPOOL POTTERY

A name applied to wares made at various potteries located in Liverpool, England, from about 1750 to 1840. The leading pottery was that of Sadler and Green which—from about 1790 to 1815—decorated pottery with line drawings by a new process in black on white or cream colored pitchers, mugs, punch bowls, plates, etc. The decorations were often designed for the American trade and consisted of prominent men, eagles, ships and scenes from daily life.

Courtship and Marriage Jug. Trick picture with verses _____ $125.00

Coffee Biggin. Miniature. Transfer in black. 5'' high. Scarce _____ 80.00
Cups and Saucers:
Handled cup. Black transfer ___ 52.50
Transer, pink lustre borders ____ 48.00
Jugs:
4½''. Obverse, bust over cannon, "Decator." Reverse, similar medallion bust of Laurence _____ 135.00
8''. Obverse, medallion bust of Madison surrounded by wreath with names of States. Reverse, frigate with American flag. Eagle under spout _____ 300.00
Marriage Jug. Courtship & Marriage. Trick picture with verse __ 125.00
Masonic. Dated 1817, 11½'' high_ 265.00
9½''. Obverse, medallion bust of Washington, surrounded by wreath with names of States. Reverse, Independence inscription with Eagle and Liberty cap. Eagle under spout _____ 450.00

Plate. 10'' diam. Black transfer of
British frigate. Circa 1785 _____ 57.50
Tea Set. Teapot, sugar bowl and
creamer. Queen Anne shape.
Henna on white _____ 210.00

## LOETZ GLASS

The product was made in Austria just
before the turn of the present century. It
is similar in appearance to Tiffany Glass.
Loetz was a contemporary of Mr. L. C.
Tiffany and worked in the Tiffany factory
before returning to Austria to establish an
operation of his own. The pieces are signed
"Loetz Austria."

Pitcher. 7½'' high. Blue ground with
gold decor. Silver ring with spout
missing _____ $65.00

Bowl. 6½'' high. Ruffled edge, dimpled sides, gold, blue and green
swirled _____ 200.00
Bowl, Rose. Brown iridescent background. Bulbous crimped top
tapering to expanded foot base.
6 peacock feathers over wavy
pattern. Signed _____ 185.00
Pitcher, Water. Green color,
paneled sides, ruffled top,
applied handle _____ 350.00
Vases:
5½'' high. Silvery-green with
bronze green swirls _____ 135.00
6'' high. Blue, deeply dimpled
base, silver-like decor. Signed__ 275.00
7½'' high. Damascene coloring at
base. Signed _____ 350.00
9½'' high. Orange with silvery-
blue tracery design. Signed ____ 400.00
10'' high. Peacock feather design
in shades of blue, gold, bronze,

silver iridescence, silvery-blue
background, signed _____ 475.00

## LOTUS WARE

A type of fine light-weight porcelain
with a warm white color and rich glossy
glaze made by the Knowles, Taylor &
Knowles Pottery Co., in East Liverpool, Ohio,
between 1890 and 1900. It was named
"Lotus Ware" by Mr. Knowles because
it resembled the bloom of the lily. The
first mark was "KTK." This was later
changed to a special mark—the firm name
in a circle enclosing a crescent and star,
a lotus flower above and the name "Lotus
Ware" below. It is now considered scarce
and commands a good price—depending
on the item, its size and elaborateness
of design.

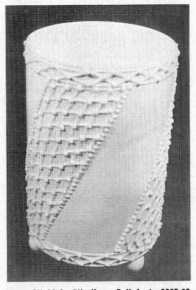

Vase. 8'' high, 5'' diam. Ball feet__$395.00

Bowl. Ruffled edge, ornate handles. 6¾'' high, 4¼'' long _____ 250.00
Bowls, Rose:
Footed. 4'' high. Leaves and
berries in high relief. Leaf
ends form rim _____ 200.00
Large, dated 1895. Raised apple
blossoms in gold along with

small pink and blue flowers _____ 350.00
Creamer _____ 260.00

Vase, Covered. 7¾'' to top of finial. White ground with hand painted violets and green leaves. Hob-
nail-like decoration in gold,
handled _____ $750.00

Dish, Leaf. Small. Turned-in handle _____ 100.00
Jug. 7½'' high. Advertising whiskey 200.00

Tea Service. Sugar bowl, creamer
and teapot _____ $325.00

Pitcher. Flower decoration with
gold. Handle, bamboo design,
with old decor _____ 350.00
Pitcher Vase. Large _____ 300.00
Sugar Bowl. 6'' wide at handles.
4'' high, feather design. Marked
"K.T.K." _____ 300.00

Tea Service. Sugar bowl, creamer
and teapot _____ 325.00
Vase _____ 240.00
Vase. Pitcher type. 7½'' high.
Bulbous, single handle. Colorful
flower decor with gold. Painted
by "J.E.B.", dated 2/92. Marked
K.T.K. _____ 300.00

## LOWESTOFT

The term Lowestoft, when applied to
chinaware, has been called "A Famous
Blunder." It now appears that the name
was derived from the fact that Chinese
porcelain was imported into Lowestoft, England, and decorated there. It was then
exported to other nearby countries and to
the United States. The decorating factory
operated in Lowestoft from 1757 to 1802.
The ware originated from the ports of
Canton, Nanking and other shipping centers
of China, and should be designated as
"Chinese Porcelain."

Teapot. Circa 1760. 6'' high. Blue
and white. Chinese landscape __ $215.00

Bowls:
4½'' diam., blue decor. Circa
1780 _____ 80.00
5½'' diam., 2½'' high. Armorial,
(Export Porcelain). Blue with gold
star decor on top of inside edge 200.00
10'' diam., Pink and yellow
florals in large medalions on front
and back; sepia landscapes on
other 2 small medallions. Surrounded by blue allover decoration, blue border on inside.
Scarce, early _____ 295.00
Deepfor platter. 14½x22''. Coloring in pink and greens. Sepia

border with stripings of gold through the sepia. Arms of the Renny Family. Circa 1775 ____ 600.00

Bowl. 8¾'' diam. Pink decorations on white background _____ $225.00

Cups and Saucers:
Demitasse _____ 50.00
Handleless. Colorful horn-of-plenty decor, wide pink diaper border _____ 58.50

Platter. 12''. Blue decor _____ $95.00

Handleless. Circa 1770, decorated with elk, fighting dogs and rabbit. Iron gray _____ 60.00
Dog. 10'' high. Shown in Lloyd Hyde's Book, Plate 14. Bright terra cotta, green collar with blue charms. Rare _____ 595.00

Bowl, deep for platter. 14½ x 22''. Coloring in pinks and greens. Sepia border with stripings of gold through the sepia. Arms of the Renny Family. Circa 1775 __ $550.00

Hot Water Jug. 5½'' high, covered 125.00
Mug. "Mourning." Diaper design top and bottom. Black and gold side florals _____ 45.00
Pitcher. 4¼'' high. Helmet _____ 95.00
Plates:
Chop. 14½'' diam. Plain _____ 90.00
9'' diam. Armorial, flower border _____ 120.00
Platter. 8½x12'', Circa 1780. Coat-of-Arms, decorated in pink, blues, greens, lavenders and gold 325.00
Tea Caddy. Famille Rose pattern 100.00
Teapots:
Circa 1760. 6'' high. Blue and white. Chinese landscape ____ 215.00
White, small gold decor. Berry finial, entwined strap handle __ 145.00

## LUSTRES (MANTEL)

Lustres are vase-shaped mantle garnitures with glass pendants, or prisms, hanging from the bowls. The glass is of a Bristol-type and is usually colored and decorated with enamel flowers or designs.

Bristol. 8½'' prisms. Top and base 5'' diam. Scarce pastel green color. Pair _____ 225.00

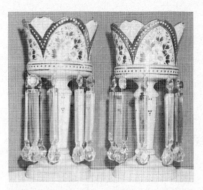

Bristol Glass. Light smoke color, "V" cut top with painted floral decor. Cut prisms. Pair _____ $215.00

Bristol. 11½" high, 6½" across top. Pink, lined with white, 2 rows of cut prisms. Pair _____ 200.00
Bristol. Duck-egg blue, with prisms. Pair _____ 185.00
Bristol. Light smoke color, "V" cut top with painted floral decor. Cut prisms. Pair _____ 215.00
Bristol. Smoke-color. 14¼" high, ten 9¾" cut crystals. Pair ____ 195.00
Ruby-color. 11" high, 1 row of prisms. Each _____ 100.00

## LUTZ GLASS

The name is derived from a type of glass made by Nicholas Lutz, a Frenchman by birth, who came to this country to ply the trade of glass blowing. He was noted for two types—striped, or cane, and threaded glass. He worked at the Boston & Sandwich Glass Co., from about 1870 until it closed in 1888. He then worked for the Mt. Washington Glass Co., and later was employed by the Union Glass Works in Somerville, Mass. This style of glass should be designated as "Lutz Type" for other workmen in the previously mentioned glass houses also made glass of this nature.

Bottles:
  Bellows. 11" long, pink threading, clear rigaree trim _____ 120.00
  Perfume. 3" high, pink thread___ 48.50
  Threaded, rose and white _____ 72.50
Bowls:
  Finger bowl with plate. Gold with

wide green and rose stripes ____ 65.00
Finger bowl with plate. Cranberry with bands of gold thread _____ 63.50
Finger bowl with plate. 6¼" diam. Clear glass with red, white and green stripings _____ 95.00
Small. Clear and white with ruby edge _____ 62.50

Plate. 7" diam. Spiral design in green and white _____ $80.00

Candy Dish. Threaded _____ 58.50
Cologne. Threaded, pink on clear__ 75.00
Creamer. Miniature. Latticino, and blue threads _____ 68.50
Cruet. Heart-shaped mouth, reeded handle, emerald, teal and gold-stone _____ 175.00
Cups and Saucers:
  Clear applied handle, filigree panels of white, blue with gold and white with yellow _____ 67.50
  Miniature. Cup 1¾" high, ruffled edge. Blue, gold and white ____ 72.50
  Rainbow pattern _____ 100.00
Dish. 6½" diam. Gold and white, Latticino design _____ 65.00
Ewers:
  8½" high. Pink ribbon panels laced with goldstone and white filigree. 3-pour lip, handle and base _____ 175.00
  12½" high, 5½" widest diam. Alternating stripes of opaque yellow, opaque white and goldstone on clear crystal background.

Same color combination of canes in hollow reeded handle. Rare __ 375.00

Pitcher, Water. Gold threading, applied rigaree trim _____ 185.00

Plates:
6½'' diam., filigree canes in pink, blue, yellow, green and aventurine (goldstone) _____ 67.50
7'' diam., spiral design in green and white _____ 65.00
7¼'' diam., 1'' deep. Gold swirls in spiral threading _____ 80.00

Slipper. Threaded, pink rigaree on clear. Scarce _____ 95.00

Tumblers:
3¾'' high, 2⅜'' diam., footed Blackberry knobs around lower part, white and gold threading __ 76.50
Blue threading _____ 74.50

Vase, Miniature. 2⅜'' high. Clear with white diagonal threads ____ 72.50

Whiskey. 2⅝'' high. Stripings of pink, white and goldstone _____ 72.50

Wine Glass. Red with gold _____ 65.00

## MAASTRICHT WARE

Maastricht ware was made in Holland from about 1835 to near the end of the 19th century. English workmen and methods were employed. The product found a ready market in the United States and sold in competition with the popular English ware of the period.

Plate. 9''. Early, blue on white ____ $20.00

Bowls:
7¼'' diam., 4¼'' high. Black and tan transfer design on white

ground. Pajong pattern _____ 10.00
7½'' diam., 4¼'' high. Black and tan transfer design on white ground. Pajong pattern _____ 9.75
8½'' diam., 4'' high. Hong pattern _____ 11.50

Cup and Saucer _____ 10.75

Cup and Saucer. Red, blue and green decor on white ground ____ 4.50

Plates:
Red, blue and green decor on white ground _____ 4.75
7¾'' diam. Quilted rims edged with gold; bird and floral centers in deep blue. Set of 6 _____ 30.00
8'' diam., souvenir. Blue and white. Commemorates the Allied Liberation of Holland, 1944. Depicts American soldiers, flags __ 7.50
8¼'' diam. Butterflies in red, green, blue and black decor __ 6.75

Tureen. Large, white, with ladle __ 48.50

**MAGAZINES, See CATALOGUES & MAGAZINES**

## MAGIC LANTERNS

Magic Lanterns were the forerunners of the home movie machines. The period between 1890 and 1910 was the time of their greatest popularity. The earlier ones used kerosene lanterns which were housed inside the machine, hence the name "Magic Lantern." The majority was manufactured in Germany. Colored glass slides were inserted between the lantern and a lens, reproducing pictures on a wall or sheet.

Prices for the machines vary between $30.00 and $45.00, with size and condition being taken into consideration.

## MAJOLICA

The ware is classified as "soft pottery" or "faience." It is covered with a glassy coating which is made opaque by tin oxide.

The name is derived from the Island of Majorca, located between Italy and Spain, where the first history of the ware was recorded in the 12th century. It was later made in Italy, Germany, France and England. Wedgwood & Co., manufactured it in England from the 1850's to about 1900. In the United States the first production was credited to E. & W. Bennett Co., Baltimore, Maryland, in the 1850's. Their ware is marked E. & W. Bennett, Canton Ave., Baltimore, Maryland. After 1856 the initial form was changed to E. B., when William, one of the brothers, retired.

The best known ware in this country was made by Griffen, Smith & Hill Co., at Phoenixville, Pa., and was marked "Etruscan Majolica" or bore the monogram "G.S.H." Beginning in 1880, the product of this plant was used by The Atlantic & Pacific Tea Co., as premiums for baking powder. The factory was destroyed by fire in 1892 and the ware was discontinued.

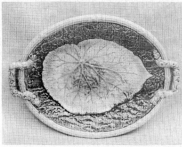

Platter. 12½'' long, oval, 2 handles. Green leaf center surrounded by wide cream band and narrow yellow band on edge, brown handles _____ $32.50

Asparagus Dish and Platter. Top pierced for drain, 4 feet. Asparagus stalks form semi-circular oblong dish in natural colors. Bottom represents fanned-out stalks tied with blue ribbon. 12½'' long, imprinted "V.B.S." _____ 42.50

Asparagus Plate. 16½'' long, in blue, green and white. Unmarked ____ 48.00

Basket. Sanded Majolica. 8½'' long, 5½'' high. Yellow sanded ground with applied gold flowers _____ 40.00

Bottles:
Rabbit. Head is removable as stopper _____ 95.00

Shape of cucumber _____ 17.50
Shape of ear of corn _____ 20.00
Bowl. 9¼'' diam., 5'' high, footed Multicolored daisy decor, pink interior _____ 40.00
Bread Plates:
11'' diam., represents basket with folded white bread cloth with lavender border and fringe, pierced brown handles. Harker imprint _____ 27.50
13'' long. Green ground, white flowers with tinge of pink _____ 28.50
Butter Dish. Raised flower decor with green and yellow predominating _____ 40.00
Butter Pats:
Green, flower center _____ 3.50
Leaf-shaped _____ 5.75
Cake Stand. 5½'' high, 10'' diam. Raised water lilies, green background _____ 36.50
Cheese Dish. 2-piece. 12'' diam. at base. Top is 9½'' high. Brown picket design, red and white flowers, green leaves _____ 62.50
Creamers:
4'' high. Etruscan. Shell and Seaweed pattern _____ 72.00
Small, bulbous, with overall grayish-blue basketweave and brown leaf on either side
Cups and Saucers:
Etruscan. Shell and Seaweed pattern _____ 67.50
Sunflower pattern. Pinks, green and yellows _____ 18.50
Cuspidor. 6¼'' high, raised pink flowers, green leaves, brown stems on yellow stippled background _____ 17.50
Dishes:
9'' long. Deep, leaf-shaped. Brown pierced stem-like handle. Green leaf center shading to blue, lavender, yellow and brown toward edge _____ 22.50
9'' long. Shallow, leaf-shaped with stem-like handle _____ 21.50
9½'' boat-shaped, 6¾'' wide. Light green background, green leaves, small yellow and red pansies ___ 45.00
9½'' long. Shallow _____ 15.00
Egg Server. With hen center _____ 37.50
Flask. Book shape. "Coming Through The Rye'' on back strip, pint size. Cork on top. 4¾''x3½'' ____ 18.50
Fruit Dish. On standard, 9'' diam. Green basketweave designs ____ 30.00
Jardinieres:
Complete with stand. Bowl with 3 dolphins entwined with water lilies. Overall height with stand 35'' _____ 60.00
Plain _____ 22.50
Lamp _____ 50.00

Fish Pitcher. Black body, orange decor at top, green base _____ $30.00

Mugs:
3½'' high, small lavender flowers with yellow centers and green leaf decor on two sides, brown handle _____ 12.00
5'' high. English. Yellow and blue flowers _____ 15.00

Pickle Leaves:
7½'' long, leaf-shaped, without stem. Center, brown shading to blue _____ 12.50
10'' long, overall leaf design of brown and green _____ 15.00
11'' long, plantain leaf shape with pierced brown stem handle. Dark green center shading to light lavender and cream _____ 18.00

Pitchers:
Barrel. Dog head spout, tail handle _____ 32.50
4¼'' high. Blackberry branches and pink blossoms on two sides, cream bark-like background ____ 18.00
4½'' high, Basketweave design on lower part and band, daisies on cream background, butterfly forms spout _____ 20.00
4½'' high. Ear of corn in green and yellow _____ 24.00
5½'' high. Barrel design. 2 metal yellow bands over dark cream staves, raised berry vines and leaves _____ 18.00
6¼'' high. Overall design of light green foliage with 2 brown lilies on either side, pink interior ____ 24.00
6½'' high. Green fish with white belly and brown fins on one side. Reverse shows fish descending. Eel-shaped handle. Dark blue background with narrow yellow band and spout _____ 30.00
7'' high. Stags grazing under overhanging branches of oak leaves and acorns. Brown and green on cream, brown handle, pink interior _____ 27.50
7½'' high. Yellow with green fern decor _____ 24.00
7½'' high. Dark blue with brown rim and handle. Brown butterfly with blue on outspread wings forms spout _____ 27.50
7½'' high. Owl-shaped. Green, brown and white with yellow rim, blue handle, white interior ____ 42.50
8'' high. Basketweave, brown lower part, wide green band of leaves and butterfly, green handle _____ 26.50
8'' high. Square. Brown oak leaves with blue and pink roses on cream background. Basketweave_ 27.50
8¼'' high. Brown basketweave, cream with raised pink floral sprays, green leaves. Top, anchor and chain design on brown band 26.50
9'' high. Ear of corn in green and yellow _____ 30.00
9'' high. Raised flower and leaf decor with green and yellow predominating _____ 32.50
9'' high. Parrot, 5½'' wide with rose lining. Ivory-rose head, gray beak, black claws, brown handle, green and brown bottom 50.00
11'' high. Ear of corn in green and yellow _____ 40.00

Plates:
8'' diam. Clusters of red and white climbing roses on blue background in center with narrow yellow band surrounding the center _____ 17.50
8'' diam. Pink center with yellow cord band, greenish blue to scalloped edge _____ 15.00
8'' diam. Oyster plate, marked Wedgwood _____ 16.50

| | |
|---|---|
| 8'' diam. Shell and Seaweed. Etruscan _____ | 39.50 |
| 9'' diam. Cauliflower. Etruscan__ | 27.50 |
| 9½'' diam. Green leaf in back, asparagus stalks in front _____ | 18.00 |
| 9½'' diam. Footed, green leaf center on white basketweave, yellow edge _____ | 19.50 |
| 9½'' diam. Footed, green leaf center on white basketweave, yellow edge, low pedestal decorated with string of raised green and brown leaves _____ | 27.50 |
| 11'' diam. Center, white dog with brown spots, lying down, with bone on white dish before him. Wide green and brown flower border, with brown scroll handles _____ | 28.50 |
| 11'' diam. Center has seated shaggy dog with doghouse in background. Raised green and brown flower border and brown scroll handles _____ | 30.00 |
| Sardine Dish. 5x6½x2½'' high. Cream basketweave with brown trim, fish for top of lid serves as knob, on pink interior _____ | 37.50 |
| Sauce Dish. 5½'' diam., shallow. Overall leaf design in green on brown _____ | 10.50 |

**Sugar Bowls:**

| | |
|---|---|
| Raised pink and white flowers green leaves on basketweave. Light blue and white bottom ____ | 35.00 |
| Pineapple, covered. Green with pink interior _____ | 40.00 |
| Syrup. 6'' high. Sunflower, conical body, metal top _____ | 37.50 |

**Teapots:**

| | |
|---|---|
| 4½'' high. Design on two sides. Open fan with bluebird on fan, flowers on blue background ____ | 28.50 |
| Etruscan. Bamboo pattern _____ | 49.50 |
| Shell and Seaweed _____ | 98.50 |
| Tea Set. 3 pieces. Etruscan, Shell and Seaweed _____ | 225.00 |
| Umbrella Stand _____ | 32.00 |

**Vases:**

| | |
|---|---|
| 4'' high. Pig-shaped. Blue lining__ | 14.50 |
| 5½'' high. Red colored, sanded __ | 25.00 |
| 6'' high. Raised flowers and leaves _____ | 18.50 |
| 6'' high. Sand finish, applied stem, flowers and leaves in white and gold. Pair _____ | 30.00 |
| 9'' high. Sanded, yellow _____ | 35.00 |

## MARBLES

Large glass marbles were produced by several glass houses in Ohio and Pennsylvania from about 1900 to 1920. Some had animals shaped from sulphide in the center while others were made with colored stripes. Sizes varied from about $1\frac{3}{4}''$ to $2\frac{1}{2}''$.

Smaller ones are common and worth only a fraction of the value of the larger.

| | |
|---|---|
| Marble. 1½'' diam. Clear glass with sulphide figure of bear _____ | $20.00 |
| 1½'' diam. Clear glass with sulphide figure of bear _____ | 20.00 |
| 1½'' diam. Clear glass with sulphide figure of running horse _____ | 21.50 |

| | |
|---|---|
| Marble. 1½'' diam. Clear glass with sulphide figure of running horse__ | $21.50 |
| 1⅞'' diam. Sulphide-type, with lamb inside _____ | 22.50 |

2" diam. Sulphide, with cow inside__ 22.50
2" diam. Sulphide, with dog inside__ 22.50
2" diam. Sulphide, with goat inside 18.00
2" diam. Sulphide, with rooster inside _____ 22.50
2¼" diam. Colored stripes inside__ 18.00
Eagle, with outspread wings _____ 24.50

## MARY GREGORY GLASS

A type of painted or enamel-decor-
ated clear and colored glass depicting
men, women, children, flowers and insects. The name is said to have originated from a spinster, Mary Gregory,
who was one of the decorators in the
Boston & Sandwich Glass Factory about
1886-88. The type and style was originated in Europe about 1880, especially
in Bohemia, Germany, France and England,
and was produced until about 1912.

Vases. 7¼". Emerald green. Satin
Glass with enamel decor. Pair __ $95.00

Ale Glasses:
Cranberry, boy with tinted face__ 45.00
6" high, blue with girl decor ____ 35.00
Atomizers:
Blue with boy decor _____ 37.50
Cranberry _____ 44.50
Barber Bottles:
Amethyst with girl decor _____ 62.50
Blue with girl decor _____ 65.00
Pale olive green. Girl picking
flowers. 7" high _____ 60.00
Basket, Fruit. Amethyst, in silver
frame _____ 88.50

Bottles:
Liqueur. 9" high, green with boy,
girl and trees. Clear handles,
blown stoppers. Pair _____ 115.00
Perfume. Clear with gold hinged
top, chain and ring. Girl decor__ 60.00
Perfume. Green with enameled
boy. Faceted surface _____ 60.00
Bowl. Covered, 8½" high. Cranberry
with young children and flowers.
Applied thorn handles _____ 115.00
Boxes:
4", hinged top, girl and flower
decor _____ 80.00
Jewel. Large, blue with white
decor _____ 115.00
Butter dish. Covered, tinted girl
decor _____ 135.00
Candy Jar. Clear glass. 6" tall,
girl in tree in white enamel ____ 35.00
Cheese Dish. Cosmos trim, large
round plate _____ 125.00
Claret. Blue, figure of boy _____ 34.00
Cracker Jar. Emerald green, white
enameled girl, butterfly and lily-
of-the-valley sprays, gold leaves.
Matching glass cover _____ 70.00
Creamer. Green, boy decor _____ 55.00
Cruets:
Wine. Cranberry _____ 72.50
Wine. Emerald green _____ 65.00
Cup and Saucer. Cranberry _____ 67.50
Decanters:
Emerald green _____ 75.00
Light green. Boy's face on one,
girl's face on other. Bell-shaped,
original stoppers. Pair _____ 105.00
Ewer. Emerald green. Boy in white
enamel on garden seat. Crystal
handles _____ 45.00
Goblet. Cranberry with tinted boy
or girl. Late. Each _____ 47.50
Lamp, Hand. Clear bowl, 8" metal
standard _____ 42.50
Mug. Cranberry with girl decor __ 45.00
Pickle Castors:
12" high, in silver-plated frame,
cranberry with white decor and
gold trim _____ 165.00
Clear with boy decor. Silver-
plated frame, cover and tongs__ 95.00
Double. Opaque, blue, enamel
decor, in silverplated frame ____ 295.00
Pitchers:
7" high. Green with white enamel
decor _____ 85.00
Milk. 6" high, green with enamel
decor _____ 72.50
11½" high. Sapphire blue, white
enamel figure of boy playing ball.
Bulbous _____ 95.00
Tankard-type. Blue with boy decor. 12" high _____ 125.00
Water. Cranberry with girl and
boy _____ 115.00

Water. Clear with 2 girls and
flowers _____ 77.50
Plaque. 10½'', cranberry with girl
and scenery. In brass hanger __ 95.00

Pickle Castor. Double. Opaque blue,
enamel decor. In silver-plated
frame _____ $295.00

Rose Bowls:
Blue _____ 58.50
Cranberry. 3x3¼'', with turned-in
6-crimp rim. Panelled body with
white enameled boy picking
flowers _____ 85.00
Stein. 14¾'' high. Blue with white
enamel girl decor. Pewter top
with thumbrest _____ 135.00
Stein. 5¼'' high. Blue, painted girl__ 65.00
Sugar Shaker. Clear with girl and
butterfly _____ 55.00
Tea Strainer. One-piece cranberry
inset In silver holder. 3 scenes
of children in white enamel. With
original burner, cover and handle 65.00
Trays:
6½''x9''. Amber with 2 girls, one
with a doll _____ 110.00
Pin. Amber with girl decor in
white _____ 35.00
Tumblers:
Clear with boy and girl decor __ 35.00
Cranberry with girl decor _____ 45.00
Green w t boy decor _____ 40.00
Vases:
Small, in plated holder _____ 45.00

Vases. 8½'' high. Cranberry inverted
thumbprint, flared top. Boy and
girl in white. Pair _____ $175.00

5½'', cranberry with girl carrying basket _____ 42.50
7'', blue with girl decor, ruffled
top _____ 45.00
8'', blue with boy on one and
girl on other, gold trim. Pair __ 95.00
8½'' high. Cranberry. Inverted
Thumbprint, flared top. Boy and
girl in white. Pair _____ 175.00
9'', green with girl decor _____ 69.50
9½'', cranberry with man and woman in colonial costumes. Gold
band around base, center and
top rim. Pair _____ 160.00
11'', electric blue with enamel
figures of boy and girl. Regaree
sides. Pair _____ 135.00
12'', Cranberry, tinted features
Boy on one, girl on other. Pair 150.00
12½'' high. Cranberry, girl decor
in white, with gold scarf. Applied
clear glass shell decor on sides.
European origin. Pair _____ 185.00
12½'', green with white decor.
Clear shell decor on sides. European origin _____ 95.00
14'',, electric blue with white
figures of boy and girl flying
kite. Pair _____ 150.00
14'', cranberry with white decor,
tinted faces, ruffled tops. Pair 195.00
Wine Decanter. 7'' high. Blue with
white decor _____ 75.00
Wine Glasses:
Clear with enameled figure ____ 20.00
Cranberry. 2'' high _____ 29.50
Wine Set. Cranberry. 10½'' tray,
decanter and 2 wines _____ 175.00

## MASONIC ITEMS

Collecting Masonic Items is comparatively new when compared with collecting china and glass. The majority of collectible items is of the commemorative or souvenir type— national conventions, etc. Most were made of glass but a few were of pottery and metal.

Goblet. 5⅛" high. Pgh., Pa., May 22, 1900 _____ $25.00

Cane. Ivory handle _____ 15.00
Chalices:
   Glass, gold decor. Dated June 1905, Pgh., Pa. _____ 30.00
   Glass, gold and enamel decor. St. Paul, Minn., 1908 _____ 30.00
Champagne Glass. Dated May 27-29, 1912, New Orleans. Alligator decor on sides _____ 30.00
Cup and Saucer. Pgh., Pa., 1906 Orange color _____ 29.50
Gavel. Wood, hand carved _____ 9.00
Goblets:
   St. Paul, Minn., 1908. Round

base _____ 30.00
   Shrine. Pgh., Pa., 1909, with 2 swords _____ 27.50
Hanging Shelf. Masonic _____ 30.00
Mug. Pgh., 1904, fish handle ____ 19.50
Paperweight. Shape of iron Bible. 4" high. Masonic _____ 21.50
Pitchers:
   5¼" Sunderland lustre, Masonic symbols and seven line verse __ 110.00
   9" high. Early. Color transfer and pink lustre decor. Pilgrim Commander #55, E. Liverpool, Ohio 195.00
   Cream. Small, china. 3¼" high. Cream colored ground with red and cold decor. Pilgrim Commandery #55, E. Liverpool, Ohio 22.50
Plates:
   6" diam. May, 1906, Los Angeles 22.50
   8½" diam. Shrine _____ 22.00
   10" diam. 54th Annual Conclave Grand Commandery, Knights Templar, Harrisburgh, 1909 _____ 39.50
Shaving Mug. With emblem and name _____ 30.00
Slipper, Degree. Blue leather ____ 20.00
Spooner. Shrine _____ 21.50
Sword. Old Colony Commandery 45.00
Tumbler. China. Souvenir of Louisville. Scene of Confederate Monument, City Hall and Masonic Temple _____ 22.50
Wine. Shrine, Pgh., 1901 _____ 25.00

## MATCH HOLDERS

In the days of the so-called "barnburner" matches, match holders were a household necessity. Many styles, types and shapes were made.

Milk Glass. 5" high. Standing type. stippled surface on back for striking _____ $20.00

Brass:
   Beetle, hinged lid _____ 15.00

Devil's Head, grapes and leaves.
Wall safe _____ 17.50
China. Hanging type in shape of
girl's head _____ 12.00
China. Man with cane by old tree
stump which holds matches. 6¼"
high _____ 15.00
Clear Glass:
Charlie Chaplin _____ 30.00
Elephant _____ 9.00

Milk Glass:
Butterfly. White, decorated, wall-
type _____ 15.00
Grape and Leaf _____ 10.00
Indian Head. 5" high, standing-
type. Stippled surface on back
striking _____ 20.00
Jester. Black, 4¼" high. Pat.
date, June 13, '76. Rare _____ 22.50
Little Jack Horner. Wall-type in
form of bellows. 5¼" high _____ 21.50
Uncle Sam Hat with stars _____ 15.00

## MATCH SAFES—POCKET

In the period before safety matches became common, many people carried matches
in safes.

There were two main reasons for their
use. First, the convenience of having
matches in a handy container and second,
as a safety feature. A number of instances
have been recorded about friction matches
becoming accidentally ignited and burning the clothes and sometimes the bodies
of the carriers. Wholesale jewelry catalogues of the 1890's and early 1900's offered these items.

Iron. 7½" long _____ $16.50

Iron:
Bacchus _____ 12.75
Barrel-shaped on board fence. 5"
high, 4" wide _____ 9.50
Bird. Mechanical, 4" _____ 16.50
Double. With lid _____ 15.00
Double With lid, dated 1897 __ 17.50
Grape decoration _____ 10.00
Hunting scene. Deer head, hun-
ters at side, emblem, leaves,
bugle. Two pockets _____ 21.00
Rabbit and duck, child holds
matches. Large _____ 14.50
Remer Bros. Coal and Wood.
Wall-type, open coal scuttle,
5x4" _____ 7.50
Single. Open pocket, lacy back 9.00
Wall Safe. Rectangular, decorated
lift-up cover _____ 8.00
Majolica. Peacock, 6" high _____ 24.00

Sterling. 2¾" high. Scene of running nymphs _____ $8.50

Dragon design. Silver, worn ____ 3.75
Floral design on both sides in relief. French gray finish. Silver plated 4.75
Flower and leaf design. German silver _____ 3.50
Flower and scroll design. Sterling silver _____ 5.75
Flowers, leaves and scroll design. Allover hand wrought openwork design. Sterling silver _____ 8.00
Plain metal with Mother-of-Pearl on sides _____ 4.75
St. Louis World's Fair, 1904. Obverse, Electric City. Reverse, Jefferson and Napoleon. Sterling silver _____ 6.75

## MECHANICAL BANKS - See BANKS

## MEDICAL ITEMS

Old medical instruments and bottles are of interest to a special category of collectors—especially doctors and persons closely associated with the medical profession.

Mechanical surgical scarifier with several knives; for blood letting or lancing. Brass, spring-driven __ $39.50

| | |
|---|---|
| Bleeding Cup. Early blown glass | 6.50 |
| Bleeding Lance. Triggered _____ | 15.00 |
| Breast Pump. Early blown glass __ | 7.50 |
| Dental Cabinet. Old _____ | 30.00 |
| Drill. Treadle driven _____ | 29.50 |

Mechanical surgical scarifier with several knives, for blood letting or lancing. Brass, spring-driven 39.50

Bottle. Glass measure on top. Amber color _____ $25.00

Nursing Bottle. Glass nipple. Early blown glass _____ 15.00

## MEISSEN, See DRESDEN

## MEISSEN, ONION PATTERN

A white ware with cobalt blue decorations whose original designation was "Bulb Pattern." Common usage has determined the name to be "Onion Pattern." It was made in the latter part of the 19th century. The first European china factory at Dresden was started in 1710. The words Dresden and Meissen are often used for the same ware because the factory first operated in Meissen and later moved to Dresden. Recent European reproductions of the various items have flooded the market and caused a considerable break in the price of both the new and old ware.

## "ONION MEISSEN"
### (With Crossed Swords)

Plate. 9½". Lattice rim _____ $32.50

Dish. 10" diam. Villeroy & Boch __ **$27.50**

| | |
|---|---|
| Bottles. Vinegar and oil. Pair ____ | 36.00 |
| Bouillon Cup. Matching saucer __ | 22.50 |
| **Bowls:** | |
| 6" diam. _____ | 21.50 |
| 7" square, pierced edges _____ | 27.50 |
| 8" square, pierced edges _____ | 35.00 |
| 8½" square, handled _____ | 38.50 |
| 9" square _____ | 40.00 |
| 10" diam., round _____ | 29.50 |
| 11" diam _____ | 33.50 |
| Bread Board _____ | 10.75 |
| Butter Dish. Covered _____ | 60.00 |
| Candlesticks. 10½" high, with matching bobeches. Pair _____ | 65.00 |
| Cheese Board. Round, with motto __ | 18.00 |
| Cheese Dish. Covered _____ | 67.50 |
| Chocolate Pot. Rose finial _____ | 55.00 |
| Coffee Pot. 9" high, rose finial | 72.50 |
| **Creamers:** | |
| 3½" high, individual _____ | 18.00 |
| 5½" high, porridge _____ | 21.00 |
| **Cups and Saucers:** | |
| Coffee _____ | 22.75 |
| Demitasse _____ | 16.00 |
| Tea _____ | 20.00 |
| **Dishes:** | |
| 5½" diam., sauce _____ | 10.00 |
| 8", leaf-shaped _____ | 35.00 |
| 8½", leaf-shaped _____ | 65.00 |
| 11", square, covered _____ | 72.00 |
| Egg Cup _____ | 9.50 |
| Fish Mold. 4" long, 12" fish-shaped handled, pierced for hanging _____ | 16.00 |
| Flour Scoop. 9" long, 2" wide. Onion decor on bowl and handle | 15.00 |

| | |
|---|---|
| Grater, Vegetable. 9x5" _____ | 12.50 |
| Gravy Boat. On tray _____ | 45.00 |
| Knife, Dinner. Pistol handle _____ | 9.75 |
| Meal Box, Hanging, covered ____ | 19.05 |
| Meat Drainer _____ | 11.00 |
| Meat Tenderizer. Long wooden handle _____ | 14.00 |
| Melon Mold. Handled _____ | 12.50 |
| Mug, Extract. Finger handles, double, ¼ gill top, ½ gill bottom | 18.00 |
| Mustard. 4¾" high, with ladle ____ | 12.50 |
| Pancake Turner. Long wood handle | 14.50 |
| Pie Crust Crimper. 2" with wooden handle _____ | 12.00 |

Plate, Soup. 9¾" diam. _____ $9.00

**Plates:**

| | |
|---|---|
| 6¼'' diam | 12.50 |
| 8'' diam. | 15.00 |
| 8½'' diam. | 17.50 |
| 9¼'', soup | 10.00 |
| 9⅝'' soup | 12.00 |
| 10'' diam. | 24.00 |
| 12'' sandwich | 27.50 |
| 14'', chop | 55.00 |
| 14'', with hot water jacket | 47.50 |

**Platters:**

| | |
|---|---|
| 13'' long | 35.00 |
| 17'' long | 45.00 |
| Pot de Chambre | 27.50 |
| Potato Masher. Large ball, long wooden handle | 14.50 |
| Ramekin. With handles | 17.50 |
| Rolling Pin | 18.50 |
| Salt Box. With cover | 30.00 |
| Salt, Master. 3¼'' diam., footed | 15.00 |
| Sugar Bowl and Creamer | 67.50 |
| Swizel, or Cream Whip. Fluted bulbous end, long wooden handle | 11.00 |
| Teapot. 5¼'' high, with matching footed tea tile | 70.00 |
| Tea Strainer. Wooden handle | 10.50 |
| Tray. 8¾'' diam. | 18.50 |
| Tureen, Soup. 14x10½'', finial on lid, handles | 125.00 |
| Utensil Rack. Large | 40.00 |

## MERCURY GLASS

A type of thin glass, usually in the form of vases, lined on the interior with a flashing of mercury, which gives the article an allover silver-like appearance.

| | |
|---|---|
| Ball Finial. 5'' | $5.00 |
| Ball. 5½'' diam. | 16.50 |
| Ball Finial. 5'' | 5.00 |
| Bowl. 5'' diam. | 24.50 |
| Candlestick. 13'' high, 5'' base diam. White enamel decor | 30.00 |
| Compote. Gold lined, hand painted white enamel flowers outside. | |
| Ringed pedestal base, 5'' diam. | 32.50 |
| Compote. Large | 50.00 |
| Creamer | 44.50 |
| Door Knobs. Pair | 20.00 |
| Flower Holders. For auto. Pair | 22.50 |
| Goblet | 20.00 |
| Gun. Candy container. Circa 1920 | 10.00 |
| Lamp Reflector | 11.00 |
| Lamps. 10'' high, single marble bases, pewter connections. Vintage design on bowls. Pair | 145.00 |
| Match Holder | 14.00 |
| Pitcher, Milk. Applied handle | 60.00 |
| Rose Bowl. 5'' high | 24.00 |
| Salt. 1¾'', open | 16.50 |
| Spooner | 29.50 |
| Sugar Bowl. Covered | 50.00 |
| Tie Backs. Rose. Pair | 25.00 |
| Toothpick | 15.00 |
| Urn. Pedestal base, 3'' high, gold lining | 40.00 |

| | |
|---|---|
| Vase. 7½'' high. Bird decor | $4.00 |

**Vases:**

| | |
|---|---|
| 9½'' high. Decorated. Pair | 32.50 |
| 10'' high. Bulbous bottom, footed. Painted floral decor | 21.50 |
| 10'' high. Applied floral decor | 20.00 |
| 10'' high. White design, gold lining | 20.00 |
| Wig Stand. 10'' high | 15.00 |

Wine. Etched, stemmed _____ 21.00

### METTLACH, See STEINS, also See VILLEROY & BOCH

### MILK GLASS — NOT ILLUSTRATED

Chick on Sleigh. 5'' high _____ 39.50
Compote. Open. Sawtooth pattern.
  8¼'' diam., 10'' high _____ 80.00
Crab. 7¾'' high, on rectangular base 48.50
Dish. Covered. Boar's Head. Red
  eyes _____ 265.00
Dish, Hand and Dove Cover. 8¾''
  long _____ 85.00
Dish. Square, lacy edge, crimped
  top. (Similar to B-136 or M-73) 60.00
Dog. 5'' high, white, old paint ____ 30.00
Hen. 5¼'' high, on basket base,
  white _____ 27.50
Hen. 7'' high, glass eyes, basket-
  type base, white _____ 35.00
Salt & Pepper Shakers. White milk
  glass with "Columbian Exposition
  1893." Pair _____ 24.00
Santa Claus on Sleigh _____ 50.00

American Hen _____$38.50

### MILK GLASS
(Illustrated on following page)

TOP SHELF:
Toilet Bottle. Satin finish, original
  stopper _____ 22.50
Same. Glazed finish _____ 20.00
Compotes. Matched "C" Scroll.
  Each _____ 62.50
Compote. Early flint _____ 65.00
Bottle. Satin finish, no stopper ____ 12.00
Cosmos Water Pitcher _____ 150.00
Tapered cylindrical water pitcher.
  Behind Cosmos pitcher _____ 20.00
Vases:
  Left. Thin, fiery opal, ruffled
    top. 9½'' high _____ 14.00
  Right. Thin, fiery opal, 11'' ____ 16.00
Blackberry Salts. Each _____ 18.50

SECOND SHELF:
Syrup jug. Patented top_____ 21.50
Jewel Boxes. 2 matched Wavecrest-
  type. Tinted, hinged. Each ____ 85.00
Blackberry Creamer _____ 27.50
Blackberry Spooner _____ 18.00
Blackberry Sugar Bowl _____ 40.00
Compote. Early, high _____ 85.00
Goblets. Cane. Each _____ 35.00
Sugar Bowl. Lacy edge, no lid ____ 22.50
Creamer. Satin glass, small ___ 21.00
Plates:
  7½'', Forget-me-not _____ 14.00
  7¼'', Gothic, white _____ 13.00
  5¼'', Gothic, blue _____ 14.50
  7½'', Wicket, white _____ 14.00
  7½'', Wicket, black _____ 16.50
Vase. 7'', raised roses_____ 18.00
Cake Plate _____ 24.00
Bowl. Shallow, footed, 8'' diam.
  (Resting on the cake plate) ____ 17.50
Bowl. Oblong. 4 feet, 6x8'' ____ 12.75
Mug. Large, footed, molded robins 16.75
Syrup Jug. 8½'', pewter top _____ 21.00
THIRD SHELF:
Mug _____ 10.00
Trays. Blackberry, 9½''. Each ____ 36.00
Compotes. Matched pair, floral de-
  cor inside. Each _____ 82.50
Bowl. Satin finish, gadrooned in-
  terior Front, center, by Challinor
  and Taylor _____ 65.00
Box. Covered _____ 11.50
Compote. Covered, pierced handle.
  Small _____ 55.00
Match Holder. Early flint, hanging 18.50
Plates:
  5½'', Peg Border _____ 11.00
  5½'', Peg border, black _____ 12.75
  8'', Scroll with Eye, green ____ 24.00
Lacy Bowls:
  8½'', Lattice _____ 50.00
  7½'', Scroll with Eye _____ 42.50
  12'', center, rear _____ 52.00
  8'', left of center. Deep_____ 40.00
  9½'', Lattice, flower spray _____ 62.50
Bowls. Footed. Double Feather:
  8'', 28.00; 7'', 21.50; 7½'', 24.00;
  6'', 13.50; 4'', 12.00.
BOTTOM SHELF:
Lacy Bowls:
  Closed lattice, ground base, saw-
    tooth-type bottom _____ 54.00
  Lattice. 8½'', ground base, peb-
    bled bottom _____ 55.00
  Flared lace, 10½'' _____ 60.00
  Shallow, 10'', scalloped, oval __ 39.50
  Basketweave. 10'' long, oblong,
    footed _____ 40.00
  9'' square, footed _____ 48.00
Lacy Plates:
  6'', Peg Border _____ 10.00
  11'', Lattice, flower spray _____ 60.00
  8½'', Wicket _____ 19.50
Kitten Plate _____ 12.50
Plates. 2, Star, 5½''. Each _____ 10.50

**MILK GLASS**
For descriptions, see the preceding and following pages.

| Platter. 13½'', dog swimming to | |
|---|---|
| retrieve bird _____ | 79.50 |
| Blackberry spooner _____ | 18.50 |
| Vase. Flange foot _____ | 10.00 |
| Vase. Small, thin _____ | 8.00 |

## MILLEFIORI GLASS

An ornamental glass consisting of slender canes or rods of colored glass fused together and then cut directly across into small sections and imbedded into the glass. The items most often found in this type of glass are paperweights and small vases.

| Box. Covered, round. 4½ high, usual | |
|---|---|
| colorings _____ | $75.00 |
| | |
| Basket. Small, blues and greens __ | 65.00 |
| Bowl. 3½'' diam., 2'' deep, 2 | |
| handles _____ | 57.50 |
| Boxes: | |
| 3'' high, covered _____ | 85.00 |
| 4'' high, knob on cover _____ | 95.00 |
| Covered, round. 4½'' high, | |
| usual colorings _____ | 75.00 |
| Candy Dish. Applied green handle_ | 62.50 |
| Creamer _____ | 100.00 |
| Cruet. Cut stopper _____ | 180.00 |
| Dish. 3'' diam., ¾'' high, ruffled __ | 60.00 |
| Goblet _____ | 110.00 |
| Jug. 2½'' _____ | 57.50 |
| Lamp Shade. 6'' _____ | 95.00 |
| Lamps: | |
| 15'' high. With shade. Complete_ | 250.00 |
| 18½'' high, electrified. Complete_ | 275.00 |
| Salt. Open _____ | 49.50 |

| Toothpick. 4 pinched sides, yellow | |
|---|---|
| and gold _____ | 55.00 |
| Tumbler. 4'' high _____ | 90.00 |
| Urn Vase. 7½'' high. Colored canes | |
| in red, orange, blue, yellow, | |
| white, green, purple and brown, | |
| 3 applied handles _____ | 150.00 |
| Vases: | |
| 4'' high, scalloped top _____ | 75.00 |
| 3'' high, miniature. Green and | |
| blue with white flowers _____ | 60.00 |

### MINIATURE LAMPS, See LAMPS

### MINIATURE PAINTINGS

| Painting on Ivory. Mother and chil- | |
|---|---|
| dren. 2¼ x 3½'', gold leaf frame __ | $85.00 |
| | |
| Painting on ivory. Portrait of woman | |
| in wide-brimmed hat, pearls. Oval | |
| metal frame. Unsigned. 2½'' high | 35.00 |
| Painting on ivory. 3½'' high. Signed | |
| Davidson. Pair _____ | 120.00 |
| Painting on ivory. Man with long | |
| curly black hair, wearing vest, | |
| coat and bow tie. Mother-of- | |
| Pearl case. From area of Phila- | |
| delphia, Pa. Unsigned _____ | 95.00 |
| Painting on ivory. Napoleon's sister. | |
| 3¼x4'' _____ | 75.00 |
| Painting on ivory. Young Napoleon. | |
| Oval, about 2'' _____ | 35.00 |
| Painting on porcelain. Member of | |
| Prussian Royal Family. 1¾x2'' ___ | 90.00 |

Painting on porcelain. Lady in bonnet. 4x5¼" _____ 72.50
Painting on porcelain. Miniature of Princess Louise. Set on papiermache, in gilt frame _____ 24.00
Painting on porcelain. Oval shape, 1½" high. Portrait of woman in square frame _____ 40.00

## MINIATURES

Collecting miniatures is a popular hobby because the field is broad. Examples are plentiful for miniatures have been made of most items produced for everyday use. Their popularity can be attributed to one of the traits of human nature—love of small things—especially children. This trait extends into other phases of human existence and creates a love or desire to possess models or miniatures of larger things.

| | |
|---|---|
| Frying Pan _____ | $2.00 |
| Dustpan _____ | 1.25 |
| Cuckoo Clock _____ | 2.50 |

| | |
|---|---|
| Baby Buggy. Filigree _____ | 9.50 |
| Bell, School. 1¼" _____ | 5.00 |
| Bird Cage. Pewter, with singing bird. 2¾" _____ | 12.50 |
| Bottle, Wine. 1½" high. Ivory ____ | 7.25 |
| Bowl (Wash) and Pitcher. Dark blue, sponge-spatter type with wide bands of flowers _____ | 35.00 |
| Candlesticks. Brass. Pair _____ | 4.50 |
| Castor Set. 4 bottles, 4½" high __ | 14.00 |
| Cauldron. Iron _____ | 5.00 |
| Chair. 3¼" high, 1½" wide. Walnut, upholstered _____ | 12.00 |
| China Set, Child's. 3 doll face cups and saucers, teapot, sugar and creamer _____ | 15.00 |
| Clock. Grandfather's _____ | 10.00 |
| Desk, Victorian. 2¼x4" _____ | 18.00 |
| Goblet. ⅝" diam. Stemmed. Ivory _ | 9.50 |
| Iron. Swan-type with trivet _____ | 9.50 |
| Jug. 1" high. "How Dry I Am" __ | 3.75 |

| | |
|---|---|
| Bed, Canopy Top. 7" long, 6" wide, 4½" wide. Walnut _____ | 35.00 |
| Kettle. Brass _____ | 15.00 |
| "Little Brown Jug." Bronze colored | 4.25 |
| Lowboy. Queen Anne. Walnut. 4" long, 3" high, 2¼" wide _____ | 40.00 |
| Milk Can _____ | 4.00 |
| Mortar & Pestle. Brass. 1" high __ | 7.50 |
| Napkin Ring. Ivory _____ | 5.00 |
| Pail. Copper, 1½" _____ | 4.50 |
| Plate. ¾" diam. Ivory _____ | 8.50 |
| Playing Cards. With gold edges. 2x2½" in leather case. Old _____ | 3.50 |
| Radiator. Iron _____ | 6.00 |
| Scale. Grocer's. Counter-top type, brass pan, 2x4" _____ | 8.75 |
| Skillet. Iron _____ | 1.75 |
| Stove, Gas. 4½" high, 3¼" wide. Cast iron cutouts and trim _____ | 15.00 |
| Table, Gateleg _____ | 9.50 |
| Tea Kettle. Brass, 1" high _____ | 8.50 |
| Tea Kettle. Iron, ½-cup size, swinging lid _____ | 8.75 |
| Tea Tray. 4" long, oval, with handles. English silver gilt, with green enamel border _____ | 16.50 |

## MOCHA WARE

Mocha is a soft-bodied pottery similar to Leeds ware. It is normally cream colored and decorated with seaweed, earthworms, tree silhouettes or other dippedbrush patterns, applied in various colors on bands of black, blue, green, tan, red or terra cotta.

It was first made in Tunstall, England, by William Adams, from 1787 to 1805, and by his son, William Adams, until 1831. According to Edwin Atlee Barber, it was still being made by the descendants of the family in 1903. It appears that the two William Adamses did not mark their ware.

Mocha was also made at the Cambria Pottery in Swansea, England, between 1831 and 1850, and at South Wales Pottery at Llanelly.

Cup. 4½'' diam. Cat's Eye pattern __ $62.50

Bowl. With matching lid. Earthworm pattern in gray, green, brown and white _____ 200.00

Bowl. 8½'' diam. Earthworm pattern, gray ground with black and white decor _____ 115.00

Chamber Pot. 5½'' high, 9½'' diam. White band with blue decoration on tan ground _____ 60.00

Cup. 4¼'' diam. Cat's Eye pattern 62.50

Jug. 5¾'' high. Blue, black and white mottling on red ground __ $120.00

Jugs:
5¾'' high. Blue, black and white mottling on red ground _____ 120.00

6½'' high. Combination of Earthworm, Cat's Eye and Seaweed patterns in green, blue and brown   130.00

Jug. 6½'' high. Combination of Earthworm, Cat's Eye and Seaweed patterns in green, blue and brown _____ $130.00

Muffineer. 4½'' high, gray with tan band. Seaweed pattern _____ 40.00

Mugs:
3¾'' high. Seaweed pattern in black on brown ground, green bands at top _____ 65.00

6'' high. Earthworm pattern in dark brown and black on light brown ground _____ 72.50

Mug. 6'' high. Twig pattern in black, brown and white on blue ground, black bands _____ $77.50

6'' high. Twig pattern in black, brown and white on blue ground, black bands _____ 77.50
Large. Black Seaweed and green band around center, 4 narrow blue bands above and below center band _____ 65.00
Mustard. ¼ pint, handled. Blue with lustre bands, original ladle ____ 62.50
Pitchers:
6'' high. White with blue center band, leaf decorations _____ 80.00
6¼'' high. Earthworm pattern ____ 77.50
6½'' high. Seaweed pattern, brown, blue and white decorations 90.00
7¼'' high. Wide brown band, narrow blue bands and white decor. White spout and handle _____ 90.00
7½'' high. Earthworm pattern in tan, gray and black on white background _____ 90.00
Salt. Open _____ 40.00
Salt Shaker. Earthworm pattern ____ 40.00
Sugar Bowl. Covered, 5'' high, tree pattern. Tan background, black trees, green band. Rare__ 385.00

### MOLDS (FOOD)

Old food molds are used primarily for decorative purposes to create a "homey" atmosphere in the kitchen.

Grape pattern ice cream mold. 5'' long. Pewter _____ $15.00

Basket. 3½'' high, 6'' long _____ 9.50
Billiken _____ 10.75
Cigar. Old, 9 sections _____ 11.50
Ear of Corn. Crockery _____ 11.50
Ear of Corn. 5'' high. Pewter ____ 12.75
Fire Engine. 4½'' long. Pewter ____ 17.50
Fish. 4'' long. Pewter _____ 12.00
Frog. 5'' long. Copper _____ 9.00
Grapes. 5'' high. Pewter _____ 10.00

Heart _____ 10.00
Hen. Small. Pewter _____ 7.25
Lamb. Iron. 14'' long, 9'' high ____ 30.00
Lion. Tin, copper top _____ 12.75
Pineapple. Tin, copper top _____ 13.00
Pomegranate, pears, plums. 8x6x3'' 25.00
Pudding. Copper _____ 21.00
Rabbits:
4½'' high. Copper _____ 9.00
5¾'' high. Tin _____ 9.50
7½'' high. Tin, candy mold ____ 18.50
Rooster. 5½'' high. Tin _____ 7.50
Rose. Tin, copper top _____ 16.75
Santa Claus. Pewter _____ 17.50
Santa Claus. 6¼'' high. Nickel-plated over tin _____ 10.75
Turkey. 3½'' high. 4'' long. Pewter 13.50
Valentine Card. 4x2¾'' _____ 14.00
Witch on Broom. 6'' high, tin __ 8.75
Woodchuck _____ 14.75

### MOORCROFT POTTERY

William Moorcroft established the Moorcroft factory in 1913, in Burslem, England. Practically all items were handcrafted on the potter's wheel and no two pieces were made exactly alike. The founder died in 1945. The business is now operated by his son, Walter.

Vase. 9¼'' high. Cobalt blue with tree decor in light green _____ $27.50

Dish, Nut. 3½'' diam., pedestaled.
  Dark green with dark red flower
  in center _____ 20.00
Lamp. 14'' overall, 6'' wide.
  Scenic trees, reds, yellows on
  olive and deep blue. Original
  finial _____ 200.00
Vases:
  1¾'' high, miniature. Flaring
  sides, 3 tiny handles. Delicate
  blue violets against white.
  Signed W. M. with McIntyre mark
  3½'' high, 2½'' diam. Bulbous ____ 30.00
  shape, cobalt blue background
  with yellow and purple pansies __ 35.00
  5'' high. Ovoid shape, peacock
  feather design. Blue, green,
  yellow. Signed W.M. and marked
  Florian Ware, McIntyre. Circa
  1899 _____ 42.50
  5'' high. 2¼'' diam. Orange,
  purple, and light green flowers on
  cobalt background with light
  green top _____ 45.00
  12'' high, 7½'' diam. at widest
  section. Dark blue with pansy
  decoration _____ 65.00
  12'' high, 6'' diam. at widest
  section. Bulbous base, slendor
  neck. Dark green with large rose
  and blue flowers _____ 65.00

## MOSS ROSE PATTERN CHINA

The Moss Rose was a popular garden
flower in England and potters started
using it to decorate their wares about
1840. The pattern retained its popularity until around 1900.

Teapot. 9'' high _____ $45.00

Coffee Pot. 9'' high. Porcelain,
  E. C. & Co. Gold trim _____ 37.50
Creamer _____ 20.00
Cup and Saucer. Edwards _____ 14.50
Dresser Set. 3 covered boxes,
  pair of candlesticks, tray. Rose
  border _____ 50.00
Pitcher. 7¼'' high, J. M. & Co.
  Ironstone _____ 36.00
Plates:
  Cake. Open handles _____ 15.00
  7½'' diam. Red rim. Ironstone ___ 8.00
  8½'' diam. Knowles, Taylor &
  Knowles (U.S.). Ironstone _____ 10.00
Platter. 12x18'' _____ 18.50
Sauce Dish. Old type _____ 5.00
Shaving Mug _____ 10.00
Sugar Bowl, Covered. Blue edge __ 25.00
Syrup Jug. 8'' high _____ 25.00
Teapot. Tall, bulbous _____ 45.00
Toilet Chamber, Covered. Meakin__ 21.00

## MUFFINEERS

These are containers, usually glass or
silver, used for sifting sugar or a mix-
ture of sugar and cinnamon on muffins.
They are about two to three times larger
than the ordinary salt shaker. They enjoyed
their greatest popularity in England before the turn of the present century.

Sheffield. 7'' high _____ $75.00

China. Cobalt bands, floral decor__ 18.00
China. Stoke-On-Trent, decorated,
  sterling top _____ 18.50

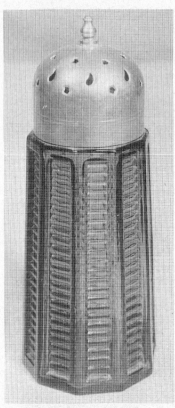

Glass. Green, 5'' high, panelled.
   Sterling top _____ $27.50

Glass. Blue, 5'' high, ribbed sides,
   milk glass criss-cross pattern,
   original metal top _____ 20.00
Glass. Cut. Clear, plated top __ 27.50
Glass. Cranberry, 5'', panelled ___ 35.00
Glass Green, 5'' high, panelled.
   Sterling top _____ 27.50
Silver Plated _____ 17.50
Silver, Sterling _____ 60.00

## MULBERRY CHINA

Butter Dish. Covered. Vincennes
   pattern _____ 32.00

Sauce Dish. 5½'' diam. _____ $6.75

Creamer. Corean pattern _____ 21.00
Cup and Saucer. Handleless. Corean pattern _____ 17.50
Cup and Saucer. Chocolate size.
   Corean pattern _____ 15.00
Dish, Vegetable. Covered. Corean
   pattern _____ 27.50
Gravy Tureen. Covered, with ladle
   and tray. Corean pattern _____ 45.00
Pitcher. Ironstone. Grecian fig-
   ures, large _____ 36.00
Plates:
   7''. Corean pattern _____ 9.50
   8¾''. Ironstone. Corean pat-
   tern _____ 12.00
   10½''. Corean pattern _____ 15.00
   10½'' diam. Unina pattern by
   J. Clementson _____ 15.00
Platter. 10''. Ironstone. Corean
   pattern _____ 24.00
Platter. 11½x15''. Vincennes pattern 32.50
Sauce Dish. 5½'' diam. _____ 6.75
Sauce Dish. Corean pattern _____ 6.75
Sugar Bowl. Covered. Vincennes
   pattern _____ 40.00
Toothbrush Holder. Covered, 8''
   long, 2½'' wide _____ 12.00

## MUSIC BOXES

Swiss Music Box. Cylinder-type,
   with bells, 8 tunes. 9½x15x8''
   high _____ 180.00
GROUP 1. OLD SWISS CYLINDER-
   TYPE. 6 tune, 12½x7x5'', inlaid
   rosewood cover. Clear tone, program attached to cover _____ 160.00

6 tune, "Ideal" rosewood case, 12x28x8½" high _____ 175.00

8 tune, 22x8x6" high. Painted case, light silvered antique finish, plain _____ 180.00

10 tune, 20x9x6" high. Plain light wood, small oval pearl inlay in center of cover _____ 200.00

Nickelodeon. "Regina." Coin operated, 27" discs, circa 1890 ____ $1,000.00

## GROUP 2. SWISS MUSIC BOXES WITH BELLS, DRUMS, ETC.

10 tune, 3 bells, with butterfly strikers. 18x11x8½" high. Mahogany case. Coat-of-Arms of England on lid _____ 215.00

12 tune Swiss Bell and Drum Box, 27x15x13" high. Inlaid rosewood case. 6 chased and tuned bells and drum may be turned on or off at will. Program attached to cover _____ 275.00

6 tune Bell box, 18½x12½x8½" high. Inlaid rosewood case. 6 bells have bee and butterfly strikers__ 225.00

8 tune Drum and Bell Box, 25½x12½x 8½". Inlaid rosewood case, highly polished. 6 bells with tiny hummingbird strikers. Program card missing _____ 310.00

## GROUP 3. SWISS MUSIC BOX WITH INTERCHANGEABLE CYLINDERS.

2 cylinder Swiss box, 51x16x12" high. Matched walnut with lighter woods and ebony borders on 60" matching table. 3-part comb, large double springs. Tune selector, indicator and safety catch. 6 tunes on each cylinder, plays for 1 hour with complete winding 330.00

## GROUP 4. DISC MUSIC BOXES.

15" wide. 19 discs _____ 160.00

Regina. 15" long, 17" wide, 10" high. Mahogany case No. 62,886. 12 discs _____ 250.00

Regina. Coin-operated console, manual selection. Mahogany finish, in operating condition with 12 27" discs _____ 1600.00

Regina. Mahogany case, piano finish, 21x20x12" high. Narrow gold outline stripe, double comb, speed regulator, zither attachment. 25 discs, 15½" diam. _____ 500.00

Reginaphone. Combination music box and phonograph. Piano finish Serpentine case. 20x20x48" high. One of the last products of the old Regina factory. Short bedplate, speed regulator, zither built-in sounding box for phonograph record attachment, detachable record plate. 20 discs, 15½" diam. _____ 500.00

Mira. Plain mahogany case, 26x19x 12" high, single comb mechanism. 18 discs, 15½" diam. _____ 185.00

Olympia. Plain oak case. 21x21x12" high, single comb, speed regulator. 16 discs, 15½" diam. _____ 165.00

"Silvanigia." Mahogany case. 4½" metal discs, spring wind, 7x7x5" high. Scarce _____ 115.00

## GROUP 5. UPRIGHT DISC BOXES AND AUTOMATIC RECORD CHANGERS.

Automatic 20¾" disc. Regina. Mahogany case, piano sounding board back. Plays set of 12 20¾" discs automatically. With set of 12 discs _____ 500.00

Automatic 27½" disc Regina. Mahogany case, piano sounding board back. 12 discs _____ 265.00

Upright Symphonion. Grandfather's clock style. 57" high, 20" wide, 13" deep. Covered with black tooled leather. Operated by lead weights. 16 discs, 13¾" diam. __ 245.00

Polyphone Upright Disc Box. With 2 sets of bells. German, walnut case 65" high. Glass front, originally coin operated. 35 discs, 20" diam. _____ 1000.00

Regina Piano. 9 feet high, 45" wide, 23" deep. Walnut case,

made with piano strings, bells, 2 drums and cymbal. Coin operated, run by large coil spring. 12 discs, 32" diam. _____ 1150.00

Regina. Small mahogany case, 12x9½x7", single comb, 12 discs, 8" diam. _____ 135.00

## GROUP 6. MISCELLANEOUS ITEMS.

Jewelry Box. Swiss, small, 3 tunes __ 60.00

Swiss Chalet Jewel Case. Fine old 2-tune unit. Base, 9½x6x5½" high. Top opens to play and discloses a velvet lined jewel compartment _____ 145.00

Musical Photograph Album. 2-tune, fine tone quality, recovered in maroon velvet _____ 65.00

Singing Bird. In brass cage, base, 6x5x12" high. Tan and brown feathered bird _____ 250.00

Musical Stein. Highly colored tavern scene. 10" high, pewter cover _____ 125.00

Bowl. Oak-leaf shape, bird on one edge, acorns on other. 2 tunes __ 90.00

Music Box. Small, 3x4½x2" high. Papier-Mache case, brass works. Plays 3 tunes _____ 55.00

Music Box. Small, 3½x5x2½", mahogany case, 2 tunes _____ 57.50

## MUSICAL INSTRUMENTS

Accordion. Early, small size, pearl keys, stenciled. Good playing condition _____ 40.00

Accordion. Adolphus Special. 10 ivory keys on right, 4 on left____ 36.00

Banjo. Marked "Vega" and "Vegaphone Professional." Complete with velvet lined case and Tenor Banjo Tuner No. 1742 _____ 115.00

Dulcimer. 15x38". Rosewood _____ 50.00

Glockenspiel. Similar to zylophone. 2 rows of steel bars supported by gut string on brass posts. Also, tubular brass harp on which 14 bars cans be hung and struck while being carried. Produces bell-like sound _____ 45.00

Organ Music Box. In stenciled case, 15x18x12½". 17 rolls. Hand operated. Like new _____ 175.00

Organ, Pump. 32" high, 26" wide. Mason-Hamlin, top closes, working order _____ 115.00

Tuba. Brass, 30", Conn-Helleberg. Rough condition _____ 57.50

Zither. Menzenhauers. Dated 1894__ 30.00

## MUSTACHE CUPS & SAUCERS

Mustache cups were popular in the late Victorian period (1880-1900). The majority was made and decorated by the transfer method in Germany. The rarest items of this group are the "left-handed" cups which were especially made for left-handed men. Prices on these scarce cups range from $250.00 to double the amount quoted. At the present time left-handed shaving mugs are being reproduced so the collector should buy from a reputable dealer with a return guarantee arranged in advance.

Cup and Saucer. Floral decoration, purple leaves, gold beading ____ $21.50

Austrian. Turquoise, gold, pink roses _____ 35.00

Floral decor. Lavender, asters, green rim _____ 19.50

Floral decor. Lavender, mums ____ 21.00

Floral decor. Pink roses, blue forget-me-nots _____ 32.00

Floral decor in pink and lavender__ 21.00

Floral decor. Purple leaves, gold beading _____ 21.50

Floral decor. Red roses, gold trim_ 21.50

John Sumner, 1883, inscribed in white panel. Shocking pink _____ 45.00

"Think of Me." Gold and red ____ 22.50

## NAILSEA GLASS

Glass produced at Nailsea, England, between 1788 and 1883. A characteristic of the glass is the loopings and swirlings of colored glass combined with clear or opal glass. Common color combinations are green and white, and red and white.

Atomizer. 7" high. Clear glass with white loopings _____ 21.50

Bell. English, white to clear loopings _____ 75.00

Bottles:
Cologne. 6½", silver top _____ 85.00
Gemel. 10", clear glass with pink and white loopings _____ 95.00

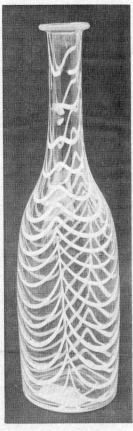

Bottle, 11¾'' high. Clear glass with
white loopings _____ $45.00

Finger Bowl. 5½'', scalloped edge.
Light blue with white loopings __    48.50
Flasks:
Double, 8'' long, blue and white__    89.50
Single, 9'' long, white decor __    49.50
Reclining, white, clear and pink
loopings. Pewter and cork stopper    75.00
Globe. For Gone with the Wind
Lamp. Rose with white loopings__   160.00

Perfume Bottle. 2¼'' high. Metal top.
Green and white stripes _____ $25.00

Lamps:
Fairy. 5½'' high, 8'' diam. Blue,
clear lacy marked holder _____   175.00
Fairy. 5½'' high, 8'' diam. Opaque
white and frosted _____   175.00
Fairy. Pink, double tiered.
Clarke's F. L. base _____   125.00
Fairy. Cranberry with loopings,
clear pressed glass shade holder
and candle cup marked ''Samuel
Clarke, Fairy, Patented'' _____   210.00
Paperweights:
Green with floral spray _____    75.00
Four flowers, 6½'' high. (Berg-
strom #44) _____    85.00
Pipe. 10½'' long, curved stem. Clear
with white loops _____    30.00
Pitcher. 8'' high, blue and white
with clear applied handle _____   150.00
Rolling Pin_____    45.00
Rose Bowl. Green with maroon and
white striping, crimped edge ___    60.00
Tumbler. Green with silver loops__    28.50
Vase. 2½'' high, miniature, blown.
Red on white _____    35.00
Wine Jug. 9'' high, white loopings
on electric blue ground. Crystal
handle and stopper _____    80.00

**Witch Balls:**

| | | |
|---|---|---|
| 3½'', cobalt blue | _____ | 20.00 |
| 4½'', amethyst | _____ | 24.00 |
| 5½'', striped | _____ | 27.50 |
| Large, pink and white | _____ | 55.00 |

## NAPKIN HOLDERS

The period from 1875 to 1915 was one in which the catalogues of jewelers and silver plating companies featured numerous types and styles of napkin holders. Some were plain and inexpensive while others were ornate and rather expensive.

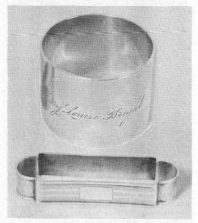

Round. 1¾'' diam., with engraved name. Sterling _____ $10.00
Flat. 2⅝'' long, ½'' wide. Sterling__ $10.00

| | |
|---|---|
| Barrel with grapes on leaf. Resilvered _____ | 18.75 |
| Cart drawn by bullock. Tortoise shell with silver insert _____ | 15.00 |
| Chicken. Resilvered _____ | 17.50 |
| Dog, Scottie. Standing and begging. Floral work on ring, beaded edge. Resilvered _____ | 21.50 |
| Eagle. 4'' high, 4'' wingspread. Resilvered _____ | 24.00 |
| Goat. Meriden Silver Co. _____ | 18.50 |
| Plain. Pierced design, gold liner. Plated. Barbour Silver Co. _____ | 4.50 |
| Plain. With initial ''R''. Needs resilvering _____ | 3.00 |
| Rabbit on side. Ornate design on ring. Pairpont silver plate _____ | 21.50 |

LEFT: Cherub riding dolphin. Resilvered _____ $20.00
RIGHT: Boy holding vase. Resilvered _____ $25.00

Squirrel at side. Fancy design on ring. Needs resilvering _____ 20.00
Woman at each side. Plain ring __ 18.50

## NAZI ITEMS

In recent years a large number of collectors, interested in World War II items, are gathering various items of Hitler's lost cause.

LEFT: Sword. Police-type. Eagle on grip _____ $75.00
RIGHT: Emblem, Swastika. 7¾'' diam. Sewn onto a red banner __ $ 8.50

| | |
|---|---|
| Ammo. Carrier. World War II __ | 7.00 |
| Arm Band. Deutscher Volksstrum Wehrmact with issue stamp ____ | 4.00 |
| Badge. Nazi Crimea. Brass shield with zinc backs, 1941-1942 ____ | 4.00 |
| Banner, Wind. Triangle, 18'' long, 1940. Red with black swastika __ | 5.00 |
| Bayonet. Nazi Police Eagle's head dress, with bone-type grips and police eagle in center. Complete with frogs, etc. _____ | 35.00 |
| Bayonet. Nazi etched blade with black plastic grips _____ | 32.50 |
| Belt Buckle. Army, mixed markers | 4.00 |
| Cross, Mother's. Blue and white enamel with swastika center. Dated Dec. 16, 1938. Original matching blue and white ribbon saying: 'Der Deuchen Mutter.'' Size 1½x1¾'' _____ | 15.00 |
| Daggers: | |
| Navy Officer Dress with etched blade _____ | 54.50 |
| Nazi Youth. World War II _____ | 20.00 |
| SA, with motto blades _____ | 37.50 |
| Eagle, Staff Car. Alloy with fixing bolt _____ | 7.50 |
| Flag. 2x3'. Swastika and German cross _____ | 17.50 |
| Flag, Battle. 2x3'. Kriegsflagger, for Navy motor launch, with halyards and markings _____ | 18.00 |
| Helmet, SS. Large issue-type ____ | 33.00 |
| Knife. Nazi Labour Corps. With motto blade, contractor's name and stag grips _____ | 85.00 |
| Medals: | |
| German Cross. Swastika center, silver plated _____ | 9.75 |
| Serpents death head, swastika _ | 6.50 |
| Plaque, Hitler. 1933 Officer's mess. With famous motto underneath __ | 40.00 |
| Plate, Nazi. With German eagle and swastika emblem. Rosenthal China dated 1941. Carried during Invasion of Russia by Lnt. Bier | 195.00 |
| Transfers: | |
| For Nazi helmets, SS, Army, Luftwaffer, etc. 14 per sheet _____ | 3.00 |
| Massive Luftwaffer staff car eagle with 2 matching smaller types. Set of three _____ | 2.00 |

## NETSUKES

Netsukes are fasteners or buttons for clothing. Carved of Ivory, Jade or other materials, they are a domestic product of past generations in Japan.

| | |
|---|---|
| Boy bending over fishbowl. 1½'' | 35.00 |
| Devil Mask. 1¼''. Wood _____ | 27.50 |
| Double figure. 1¾'' _____ | 40.00 |
| Evil demon. Small _____ | 27.50 |
| Foo Dogs. Entwined. Ivory. 1¾'' __ | 42.00 |
| Frogs, Group. 1¾'' _____ | 32.50 |

| | |
|---|---|
| Ivory. 1⅞'' high. Man with fish ____ | $35.00 |

| | |
|---|---|
| God of Wisdom. Bone _____ | 31.50 |
| Horse. Ebony _____ | 36.00 |
| House Boat. 1½'' high, 2 1/8'' long | 57.50 |
| Man with bag over shoulder. Ivory | 34.50 |
| Man with can and dog. 1¾'' _____ | 32.00 |
| Mask. 1½'' _____ | 31.50 |
| Skull. Ivory. Coiled snake on top. 1¾'' high, 1 3/16'' wide, 1½'' deep. Signed _____ | 33.50 |
| Temple Dog. Ivory _____ | 34.50 |
| Woman. Old. Apple vendor, small | 25.00 |
| Woman playing lute. 1¾'' _____ | 36.50 |
| Worriors (3) with cask. 2'' _____ | 60.00 |

## NEWHALL CHINA

Made at the New Hall Factory, Shelton, Staffordshire, England, it is reputed to be the first true English china. Until 1810 it was hard-paste china with a ''composition'' glaze. The factory later produced bone china. It closed in 1825 and reopened in 1826. In 1842 it moved to Joiner Square under another name.

| | |
|---|---|
| Creamer. Pink lustre decor _____ | 36.50 |
| Cups and Saucers: | |
| Blossom band decoration _____ | 32.00 |
| Family scene in pink, blue, green and brown _____ | 40.00 |
| Flower decor in green, red and yellow _____ | 39.50 |
| Mug. Small. Oriental decor _____ | 25.00 |
| Plate. 7¼'' diam. Rose decor. Early period _____ | 27.50 |
| Platter. 16½x21'' Two scenes: one with sailboat, other with stream and trees _____ | 65.00 |

Cup and Saucer. Blossom band decoration _____ $32.00

Sugar Bowl. Pink lustre decor ____   70.00
Teapots:
  Chinese pattern _____   100.00
  Flower spray _____   85.00
  Pink lustre decor _____   115.00

## NORITAKE CHINA

The ware is of Japanese origin and is considered "late" when compared to most European china. The bulk of the ware was imported some time after 1900.

The best known pattern is "Azalea" and it received wide distribution in the eastern part of the United States when the Larkin Tea & Coffee Company gave it as premiums. Dinner sets of finer china were also made and exported to this country.

Bowls:
  7x3". Nuts in relief _____   15.00
  9½" diam. Azalea _____   12.00
  11" diam. Azalea _____   10.00
Cake Plate. Azalea _____   9.50
Celery. ed ground, blue trim
  with gold _____   6.75
Child's Tea Set. Tinted sunset
  scene, water, bridge, in orchid
  and green with gold trim. 16-piece
  set _____   49.50
Chocolate Pot. 9½" high. White with
  pink blossoms. gold trim _____   21.50
Choco'ate Set. Pot with 6 cups and
  saucers. Pink rose decor with
  blue band. Gold trim _____   34.50
Creamer. Sahara pattern _____   6.25
Cup and Saucer. Azalea _____   8.00
Dinner Set. Hanover pattern. Border design of pink roses, with
  blue and gold. 64-piece set _____   89.50
Pitcher. 6" high. Azalea _____   9.00
Salt and Pepper Shakers. Azalea.
  Pair _____   6.00
Sugar Bowl. Sahara pattern _____   9.00

Chocolate Pot. 9½" high. White with
  pink blossoms, gold trim _____ $21.50

Sugar Bowl and Creamer. Azalea.
  Set _____   11.00
Tea and Toast Set. Azalea. Set
  of 4 _____   21.50

## NUT CRACKERS

Since primitive man first cracked nuts with his teeth or with stones, inventors have been devising ways to make the task simpler and easier. Examples listed below are the fruits of some of their ingenuity.

Dog. Iron, 10½" long, 5½" high.
  Name "Renz" appears on top of
  base _____ $14.50

Alligator. Brass, 7½" long _____   9.00

| | |
|---|---|
| Bear's Head. Wood, 9'' long, 4½'' high | 21.50 |
| Bowl, Turned. 9¾'' diam. Squirrel cracker attached | 15.00 |
| Dog. Iron. 10½'' long, 5½'' high. Name ''Renz'' appears on top of base | 14.50 |
| Parrot. Brass, 2 handles | 9.50 |
| Rooster. Brass, 2 handles | 9.50 |
| Squirrel. Iron | 15.00 |
| Wolf's Head. Iron, ''Pat. June, 1920.'' 4½'' high | 14.50 |

## OLD IVORY CHINA

The china derives its name from the ground color of the ware. The difference in patterns is indicated by a number on the base. It was made in Silesia, Germany, in the latter part of the 1800's. Marked pieces usually bear the Crown Silesia mark.

| | |
|---|---|
| Cup and Saucer. Colorful floral decor. #15 | $19.00 |

| | |
|---|---|
| Berry Set. #7. 9½'' bowl and six saucers | 59.50 |
| **Bowls:** | |
| 9¼'' diam., #200 | 21.50 |
| 9½''. #73 | 24.00 |
| 9½''. #84 | 24.00 |
| 9½''. #28 | 25.00 |
| **Cake Plates:** | |
| #84 | 25.00 |
| #78 | 23.50 |
| #28 | 24.00 |
| #16 | 23.50 |
| #15 | 23.00 |
| #10 | 24.50 |
| **Celery Dishes:** | |
| #84 | 23.00 |
| #16 | 23.50 |
| #10 | 23.50 |
| #7 | 22.50 |

| | |
|---|---|
| Chocolate Pot. Colorful floral decor. #15 | $57.50 |
| Chocolate Set. Large pot and 6 cups and saucers | 92.50 |
| Coffee Pot. #84 | 47.50 |
| Creamer. #15 | 23.75 |
| **Cups and Saucers:** | |
| #15. Colorful floral decor | 19.00 |
| #16 | 18.75 |
| #84. Rose decor | 24.00 |
| #121 | 20.00 |
| #200 | 19.75 |
| Hair Receiver. Thistle pattern, ivory with pink and lavender flowers | 12.50 |
| Pickle Dish. #75. Oval | 12.00 |
| **Plates:** | |
| Cake, individual. #28 | 8.50 |
| 7½''. #16 | 16.50 |
| 12'' diam. Pink roses. #78 | 30.00 |
| Platter. 11½'' long, 8¼'' wide. Painted rose decoration, gold trim. #78 | 25.00 |
| Sauce Dish. #84. 5'' | 8.00 |
| Sugar Bowl. Covered, #84 | 35.00 |
| Sugar Bowl and Creamer. #16. Set | 40.00 |
| Tea Tile. #55, round 6½'' diam. | 22.50 |
| Teapot with 6 cups. #200 | 65.00 |

## OLD PARIS CHINA

A number of French pottery and porcelain factories were situated in Paris during the 18th and 19th centuries. The finer porcelain products bore the generic name of Old Paris. The difference in the ware can be distinguished by the marks appearing under the glaze.

Miniature Tea Service. Teapot, covered sugar bowl, cup and saucer and 2 plates _____ $35.00

Box. 6x5" with matching tray. Handpainted flowers on entire top of lid. Set _____ 48.50
Cake Plate. White with gold trim __ 24.00
Cups and Saucers:
  White with gold trim _____ 16.00
  Maroon and gold border, colorful flowers _____ 20.00
  Tall, decorated with pink rose garlands, green leaves and gold stems. Tall gilt handle and wide gilt border _____ 35.00
Dessert Set. White. 2 cake plates and 8 7" plates _____ 75.00
Figurines. 3½" high. Boy and girl with goats, pastel coloring, oval bases. Pair _____ 120.00
Pitcher, Water. White with gold trim _____ 27.50
Plaque. 12½" diam. Birds on a hut, with foliage, gilt border _____ 75.00
Plates:
  7" diam. Floral decor in center, scalloped border with gilt scrolls. Circa 1820 _____ 20.00
  10" diam. Painted fruit decor in center. Circa 1840 _____ 24.00
Teapot. White with gold trim _____ 25.00
Tea Set. 3-piece. Teapot, covered sugar bowl and creamer. Pink, with blue forget-me-nots and gilt handles. Circa 1840 _____ 115.00
Tureen (No. 128800). Brown decor with water scenes _____ 55.00
Urns. 24" high. Painted flower decor with gold trim. Pair _____ 315.00
Vases:
  12" high. Handled, gold trim. Painted scene on bowls. Pair ___ 395.00
  13" high. Circa 1855. Blue with

rose decor _____ 75.00

Vases. 12" high. Handled, gold trim. Painted colorful scene on bowls. Pair _____ $395.00

24" high. Circa 1840. Hand painted flowers, gold trim. Pair ____ 175.00
24" high. Horses and Italian scenery, gold trim. Circa 1840 Each _____ 135.00

## ΄ONYX GLASS (SILVER INLAY)

Onyx Glass was made in the 1890's by the Findlay Glass Co., Findlay, Ohio. It is a multi-layer of ivory-white color with floral designs covered with real silver which has the appearance of being imbedded in the body of the item. When held to a light, a fiery opalescence appears. The glass was made for only a short time because of the high cost of production and the slack demand.

Bowl _____ 300.00
Butter Dish _____ 245.00
Celery Vase. 6¼" high _____ 225.00
Creamer _____ 195.00
Pitchers:
  Milk _____ 385.00
  Water _____ 575.00
Salt and Pepper Shakers. 3" high. Pair _____ 200.00
Spooner. 4½" high. Fluted rim ____ 175.00
Sugar Bowl. Covered _____ 245.00
Sugar Shaker _____ 190.00
Syrup Jug. Custard colored opaque glass with pattern molded design in relief of flowers and leaves. Raised design in a silvery iridescent color. 7" to top of lid__ 225.00
Toothpick Holder _____ 95.00
Tumbler. Regular _____ 175.00
Tumbler. Barrel shape _____ 230.00

Onyx Glass. Sugar Bowl. Covered__ $245.00

## OPALINE GLASS

This glass derives its name from the Opal—a gem with a milky iridescence. Upon being held to the light it exhibits a play of colors like the Opal. It should not, however, be confused with milk glass.

Basket. Small, with deep blue and
gold trim _____ 72.50
Bottles:
  Perfume. 5'' high. Jade green
  with enamel decor _____ 50.00
  Perfume. 5½'' high. Gold trim
  around neck. Pair _____ 57.50
  Perfume, Green, in stand _____ 49.50
Bowl. 6'' diam., low _____ 52.50
Bowl, Finger. Light blue _____ 32.50
Cheese Dish. White with enamel 120.00
Cup and Saucer. Jade green color 50.00
Hen on Basket. 7''. English _____ 40.00
Lamp. French origin. 12½'' high __ 57.50
Toothpick Holder. Lavender color,
  on small ball feet _____ 35.00
Vases:
  5½'' high. Globular body, slender
  neck, pink with yellow flowers,
  green leaves _____ 35.00

Vase. Regency style. 11½'' high. Circa 1840. Gold decor. Pair _____ $40.00

6'' high. Plain, no decor _____ 60.00
10½'' high. Bud vase. Pink with
  gold enamel decor _____ 67.50
12'' high. Mint green. Pair ____ 115.00
16'' high. Quilted. Blue _____ 75.00

## ORIENTAL ITEMS

The term "Oriental" is applied to articles which originated in or were manufactured in China and/or Japan.

Incense Burner. 9½'' high. On 4 legs, animal decorations. Bronze _____ $85.00

Bowls, Rice. Blue. Each with different designs. Set of six _____ 25.00
Box, Cigarette, with Match Holder. Brass and soapstone _____ 12.50
Box, Cosmetic. Late 18th century. Black and green enamel with dragon on cover. 3'' diam. _____ 48.00
Box. 17x17x8''. Gold lacquered. Chinese scene on lid. Circa 1850 89.50
Burner, Open. 5½'', with soapstone burner _____ 10.00
Candlesticks. Cobra bronze. Pair 35.00
Desk Set. Brass. Hand decorated tray, letter opener, blotter cover, 3½'' wood lined box with hinge __ 20.00
Incense Burners, Bronze:
   4x4'', handled and footed ____ 16.00
   5x5'', with Foo Dog _____ 25.00
   Camel _____ 11.00
   Little Pot _____ 10.00
Figurines:
   Lady. Carved Ivory _____ 29.50
   Lady and Priest. Chalkware. Handpainted costumes, each standing on platform in front of tall, curved bamboo fence. 12½'' high. Pair _____ 50.00
Jars:
   Egg-shaped, covered _____ 29.50
   Ginger, 4½'' high, horses _____ 27.50
   Ginger. 5'' high, white porcelain, handpainted ladies, gentlemen, horse, coolie, 4 Chinese charac-

ters on bottom. No cover _____ 20.00
Jam. Red, gold dancing figures, 2 handles, covered underplate __ 15.00
Lamp, Champleve. Rare _____ 50.00
Plate, Kutani. Allover decor in shades of orange, grey and gold with 2 panels each with a sage, heron and huge carp. 9½'' diam. 22.00
Platter. Chinese Export period. Oval with scalloped rim, blue and white. Deer and pine tree in center. 18th century _____ 90.00
Printing Set. Hand carved Chinese characters. Over 100 pieces ____ 79.50
Rabbit. Bronze, 4¼'' long, signed 45.00
Sword, Samurai. In metal scabbard. Detailed work in copper and brass on Tsuba and other mounts 85.00
Tea Caddy. Chinese porcelain. Pink floral on green. Circa 1830. 8½'' high _____ 38.00
Teapots:
   2¾''. Chinese _____ 32.50
   4''. Chinese _____ 40.00
   8''. Yi-Hsing. Brown unglazed stoneware in form of ''Buddha's-hand citron.'' Circa 1800 _____ 115.00
   Terra Cotta _____ 10.00
Vases:
   6½''. Chinese. Pair _____ 60.00
   4''. Bulbous. Pair _____ 39.50

## ORIENTAL RUGS

The early history of Oriental rugs is obscure for they have only been preserved since the 16th century. The largest number was probably made in Persia (now Iran), while others are attributed to Central Asia, Caucasia and Afghanistan. They became popular in this country during the Victorian era. However, some were in use prior to that time.

The origin of certain rugs can be determined by the style of weave. Some examples are: Bijar, Cabistan, Kazak, Kurd, Mir, Royal Bokhara, etc.

| | | |
|---|---|---|
| 4'x2' | Chinese _____ | 100.00 |
| 4'x2'5'' | Kashan Ivory _____ | 210.00 |
| 4'2''x3' | Yamud Bukara _____ | 160.00 |
| 4'9''x2'5'' | Kashan _____ | 220.00 |
| 4'10''x3'8'' | Meshkin _____ | 140.00 |
| 5'x2'5'' | Kashan Blue _____ | 220.00 |
| 5'x2'6'' | Belouj _____ | 110.00 |
| 5'x2'6'' | Kashan _____ | 220.00 |
| 5'x3' | Chinese _____ | 175.00 |
| 5'x3'2'' | Chinese Ming _____ | 110.00 |
| 5'x3'6'' | Abede _____ | 230.00 |
| 5'x3'6'' | Meshkin _____ | 140.00 |
| 5'x3'7'' | Fine Ispahan _____ | 950.00 |
| 5'x3'7'' | Ispahan Blue _____ | 220.00 |
| 5'1''x3'5'' | Abede _____ | 225.00 |
| 5'2''x3'8'' | Abede _____ | 230.00 |
| 5'3''x2'5'' | Kashan _____ | 220.00 |

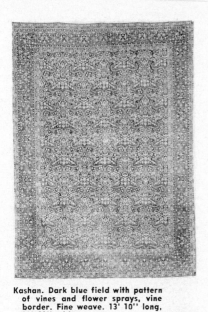

Kashan. Dark blue field with pattern of vines and flower sprays, vine border. Fine weave. 13' 10'' long, 10' 2½'' wide _____ $1,500.00

| Size | Type | Price |
|---|---|---|
| 5'4''x3'8'' | Meshkin | 140.00 |
| 5'4''x3'10'' | Ispahan | 220.00 |
| 5'5''x3'5'' | Meshkin | 140.00 |
| 5'5''x3'9'' | Meshkin | 140.00 |
| 5'6''x3' | Belouj | 130.00 |
| 5'6''x3'6'' | Ardebil | 140.00 |
| 5'6''x3'7'' | Nain | 1000.00 |
| 5'7''x3' | Belouj | 130.00 |
| 5'8''x3'3'' | Meshkin | 140.00 |
| 5'8''x3'7'' | Nain Blue | 1000.00 |
| 5'9''x3'1'' | Belouj | 110.00 |
| 5'9''x3'9'' | Nain Blue | 1000.00 |
| 6'x3' | Chinese | 110.00 |
| 6'x3'2'' | Chinese | 140.00 |
| 6'x3'3'' | Belouj | 140.00 |
| 6'x4' | Keyseri | 275.00 |
| 6'x4'2'' | Aroon | 170.00 |
| 6'2''x3'6'' | Nain Blue | 1000.00 |
| 6'3''x3' | Belouj | 130.00 |
| 6'3''x4'4'' | Aroon | 200.00 |
| 6'3''x5'1'' | Serapi | 260.00 |
| 6'4''x4'4'' | Guohanl | 500.00 |
| 6'6''x3'3'' | Belouj | 130.00 |
| 6'7''x3' | Belouj | 130.00 |
| 6'7''x3'4'' | Belouj | 140.00 |
| 6'7''x4' | Belouj | 170.00 |
| 6'7''x4'5'' | Senna | 600.00 |
| 6'8''x4'6'' | Baktlary | 300.00 |
| 6'8''x4'7'' | Kashan | 180.00 |
| 6'9''x4'4'' | Ardebil | 230.00 |
| 6'9''x4'5'' | Joshigan | 170.00 |
| 6'10''x3'3'' | Belouj | 130.00 |
| 6'10''x4'4'' | Joshigan | 200.00 |
| 6'10''x4'4'' | Kashan Blue | 410.00 |
| 6'10''x4'4'' | Kum | 440.00 |
| 6'10''x4'5'' | Bijar | 600.00 |
| 6'10''x4'6'' | Kum | 500.00 |
| 6'10''x4'9'' | Ardebil | 230.00 |
| 7'x3'4'' | Belouj | 130.00 |
| 7'x3'7'' | Belouj | 150.00 |
| 7'x4' | Chinese | 180.00 |
| 7'x4'5'' | Ardebil | 300.00 |
| 7'x4'5'' | Jozan | 375.00 |
| 7'x4'5'' | Kashan Prayer | 600.00 |
| 7'x4'5'' | Kum Blue | 545.00 |
| 7'x4'6'' | Kashan | 635.00 |
| 7'x4'6'' | Kum | 440.00 |
| 7'x4'7'' | Ardebil | 250.00 |
| 7'x4'7'' | Kashan Hunting | 635.00 |
| 7'x4'7'' | Kum | 440.00 |
| 7'x4'8'' | Ardebil | 300.00 |
| 7'x4'8'' | Kum Mosaic | 515.00 |
| 7'1''x4'5'' | Kum | 435.00 |
| 7'2''x4'4'' | Jozan Ivory | 500.00 |
| 7'2''x4'5'' | Kum | 435.00 |
| 7'2''x4'7'' | Kum | 600.00 |
| 7'2''x4'7'' | Silk Kashan | 1800.00 |
| 7'2''x4'9'' | Kum Mosaic | 515.00 |
| 7'2''x4'9'' | Silk Kashan | 1825.00 |
| 7'3''x4'4'' | Kashan | 600.00 |
| 7'3''x4'4'' | Kum | 435.00 |
| 7'3''x4'6'' | Kashan Ivory | 600.00 |
| 7'4''x4'1'' | Kerman | 500.00 |
| 7'4''x4'5'' | Kum | 435.00 |
| 7'4''x4'6'' | Ardebil | 300.00 |
| 7'4''x4'6'' | Kum | 435.00 |
| 7'4''x4'7'' | Kashan Ivory | 635.00 |
| 7'4''x5' | Anatolian | 550.00 |
| 7'5''x4'5'' | Kashan | 550.00 |
| 7'5''x4'7'' | Ardebil | 215.00 |
| 7'5''x4'6'' | Kashan Ivory | 635.00 |
| 7'6''x4'6'' | Kum | 435.00 |
| 7'8''x5' | Ispahan | 700.00 |
| 8'x5'1'' | Nain | 1700.00 |
| 8'3''x5' | Nain | 1800.00 |
| 9'5''x6' | Fine Tabriz | 1800.00 |
| 10'x4'8'' | Hamadan | 375.00 |
| 11'10''x8'9'' | Silk Kashan | 8000.00 |
| 13'4''x2'8'' | Sarouk | 375.00 |
| 14'6''x3'9'' | Sarouk Ivory | 600.00 |
| 17'x2'10'' | Sarouk | 700.00 |
| 18'10''x3'4'' | Tabriz | 900.00 |

## OWENS POTTERY

The J. B. Owens Pottery Company operated in Zanesville, Ohio from 1885 into 1892. Their products bear the following marks: "OWENS UTOPIAN", "HENRI/DEUX"and "OWENS FEROZA."

Pitcher. Utopian. 6'' bulbous footed body forms handle. High glaze, floral decor _____ $50.00

Pitcher. Utopian. 12'' high gloss, shaded brown and greens. Long side handle, yellow berry decor ... 49.50

Urn. Utopian. 3½'' high, 6'' wide. Mat glaze clover decor. Signed ... 35.00

Vases:

4'' high. Lotus line, green shamrocks on shaded pale green to pink background. High glaze ____ 60.00

5'' high. Deeply swirled bottle shape. Rich browns with pansy decor under glaze _____ 35.00

5½'' high. Signed _____ 39.50

8'' high. Broad shoulder narrows at base. Shades of brown glaze with large orange wild roses and buds on thorny, leafy branches __ 48.00

10'' high. Pansy decor, Matched pair _____ 70.00

11½'' high. Glazed roses decoration _____ 45.00

## PAISLEY SHAWLS

Shawls woven at Paisley, Scotland, in imitation of Kashmir Shawls, during the 1800-1860 era, were often given as gifts but were seldom used. A writer describes them as "a drug on the market in antique circles; in the shops, dust catchers; in the home, moth collectors; their only practical use is for piano covers." Prices of Paisley Shawls range between $45.00 and $70.00, depending on the size and condition.

## PAPERWEIGHTS

The term "Paperweight" in the antiques trade usually refers to a small object of glass used on a desk or table for holding papers in place. Glass paperweights are often highly decorative in that they contain colored flowers, canes, thread twists and/or air bubbles.

Advertising:

National Lead Co. Dutch Boy. Brush in hand, bucket beside him. Weighs nearly 2 pounds_____ 11.00

Prudential Insurance Co. Solid bronze Fiftieth Anniversary, 1875-1925 _____ 12.00

Baccarat:

"Cog" design of wheels in dark blue, rose red, white and green, set on lace background. 3¾'' diam. _____ 900.00

Geometric set-up of delicate jewel-like canes of white, blue, rose, set in wheels _____ 600.00

Multicane or millefleur close-set design. Animal silhouettes in some canes, also date B1848 indicating year of manufacture. Nearly 100 canes form the design. 3½'' _____ 750.00

White flower center. Rare _____ 8500.00

1952 Eisenhower Sulphide ____ 125.00
1958 Virgin of Lourdes Sulphide 125.00

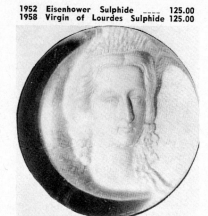

Portrait in high relief of Empress Eugenie. Inscribed "Eugenie Imperatrice de France." 2⅞'' diameter _____ $395.00

Bell. Blue_____ 15.00

Brass. Nude Baby on stomach. 6'' long, 2½'' high. Signed "Fonderia Giorgio," Sommer Napoli_____ 14.50

"Christ in Glory" Emblem, surrounded by laurel wreath and five stars. Red, white and blue scatter field _____ 25.00

Clichy. Canes on lace bed, multicolors of brilliant tints, set on white thread twist bits. 3¼'' diam. _____ 750.00

Clichy. Rare flower on stem over latticino ground. Rose petals, tipped with yellow, green leaves. 3¼'' diam. _____ 1000.00

Clichy. Scattered "fleurettes" or canes of brilliant multicolors, set in crystal clear glass. 3'' diam. __ 600.00

"Don't Forget Your Father." Lincoln photo on pillow background. "Good Luck" with horseshoe center _____ 45.00

d'Albert Weights, Modern:

Columbus. Overlay. Royal Blue___ 175.00

Leonardo da Vinci _____ 75.00

Hemingway _____ 75.00

J. F. Kennedy & Wife _____ 75.00

King of Sweden_____ 65.00

Gen. Douglas MacArthur _____ 75.00

F. D. Roosevelt_____ 75.00

Mark Twain_____ 75.00

Door Stop. 3 tiers of flower sprays. 4'' diam., 4'' high_____ 47.50

Fish Aquarium. Fish among seaweed 16.00

Flower wreath and insignia_____ 72.50

Sandwich Glass. Fruit. Clear cut set with two red pears on green stems. 3 1/16" $385.00

Sandwich Glass. Fruit. Yellow pears surrounded by leaves. Clear glass. 2¼" diam. $550.00

Baccarat. Primrose. 3⅛" diam. Deep pink flower on long green stem surrounded by 5 long green serrated leaves ____$1,100.00

Baccarat. Double Clematis. Weight, 3¼" diam. Dark red flower on green stock with numerous red buds. Clear glass _____$2,350.00

"Friendship" _____ 35.00
Gilliland (Brooklyn, N. Y.), geometric set-up of canes suspended ¼" above latticino background. Soft blues, lavender, yellow and white. Probably made by a worker train-

ed in French glass works who emigrated to the United States____ 500.00
"God Bless Our Home." 3¼" diam. made by Daggenhart at Union Glass Works_____ 49.50
Hand. Camphor glass _____ 24.00

Millville Footed Rose Weight. Clear glass with large flower and three rows of pink petals surrounded by three translucent green leaves. 3½'' diam. _____ $625.00

Kazium Flower. Signed_____ 225.00
Lalique. Carved boar. 3½'' smoky
  gray color_____ 67.50
Lion. Reclining. Frosted. Centennial
  Exposition. Gillinder & Son. 5¾x
  2⅜'' high _____ 48.50
Masonic. ''Grand Master'' inscribed
  inside _____ 25.00
Masonic. Slipper, bronze_____ 9.50
Millefiori-type with multicolored
  canes. Unsigned_____ 225.00
Millville. Mushroom, footed, 4''
  high _____ 250.00
Moses in Bull Rushes. 1876. Frosted,
  oval shape_____ 55.00
Nailsea. Green with silvery white
  petals, long bubbles. 4½'' high__ 75.00
Pairpont. Silver plated. Bee sit-
  ting on top_____ 25.00
Pairpont. Spiral threads, original
  label _____ 57.50
Pear, Iridescent. On black onyx
  base _____ 95.00
Pittsburgh Exposition_____ 25.00
Plymouth Rock, 1876_____ 30.00
Pope John XXIII_____ 135.00
''Remember Father and Mother''__ 39.50
''Remember the Maine''_____ 40.00
St. Louis, ''Crown weight,'' hollow,
  ribbons twist up to central cane
  at top, center. Red, green, edged
  with white, lace background ____ 900.00
St. Louis, dark red 25-petal dahlia-

Yellow Millville Rose weight. Clear glass with large yellow flower. Three rows of cone-shaped petals rurrounded by pointed green leaves. 3¾'' diam. _____ $675.00

like flower, green cane forms
  center, flat. 3½'' diam._____ 650.00
St. Louis Bouquet, 3 flowers and
  green leaves surrounded by alter-
  natings of white and blue canes,
  2½'' diam._____ 600.00
St. Louis. Fruit cluster over latticino basket. Bright yellow, apricot, red cherries, green leaves.
  3½'' diam._____ 700.00
Sand Dunes Motif. 2x3'' _____ 55.00
West Virginia Paperweight_____ 48.00

## PAPIER-MACHE

A literal translation of the French means '' chewed paper.'' Paper is soaked in water and then ground. The resulting mass is molded into forms where they are japanned and dried at a heat of about 300° F. The finished product is tough, durable and capable of withstanding great heat. So-called Chippendale trays, tilt-tops for tables, boxes and Daguerreotype cases were made of this material and decorated.

Box. Oval. 4⅝'' long, 1¼'' high.
  Black and brown with painted
  red and yellow flowers _____ 21.00
Case for Spectacles. Inlaid with
  Mother-of-Pearl _____ 11.50
Dish. 14'' diam., decorated with
  tropical birds and foliage _____ 15.00

popular in the Un_____ _____ about 1860 and continued in public_____ ___il around 1900.

Inkwell. 6 x 8''. Inlaid Mother-of-Pearl decor _____ **$65.00**

Eagle. 11'' high, 15'' wingspread. Scarce _____ 90.00
Figure. Old hag with broom, 7'', head nods _____ 9.00
Funnel. 11'', red color _____ 10.00
Hen on Nest _____ 7.00
Pail, Water. Dated 1883 _____ 15.00
Pitcher. 5½'', red color _____ 16.50
Plaque. Hanging type. 20'' diam. Painting of St. Bernard _____ 18.00
Rabbit. 5'' high, pulling 2-wheeled cart. 12'' long _____ 15.00
Santa Claus. 11¾'' high. Red, gold, black and white colors _____ 11.25
Shelf, Wall. Oriental, gold trim __ 13.50
Snuff Boxes:
  French print _____ 9.75
  Oval, plain case, hinged lid. 2¾'' long, 1¾'' high _____ 10.00
  Round, colored print on lid _____ 9.50
  Silver Inlay _____ 15.00
Spill Holder. Floral and scenic decorations, collared feet _____ 9.50
Tables:
  Tier. 2 round trays, 12'' top, 14'' bottom, 3 bamboo-style legs. Painted black, with chrysanthemum decorations _____ 49.50
  Victorian Tilt-top. 22x26'', 28'' high. Mother-of-Pearl inlay _____ 95.00
Trays:
  8'' diam. Painting of Dog _____ 33.50
  10x17''. Black with floral decor __ 20.00
  25x11''. Black with floral decor __ 25.00

## PARIAN WARE

Parian ware is a true hard-paste, white porcelain known as biscuit-ware, so-called because of the absence of a glaze. The effect is similar to marble which it was intended to simulate. Many of the figurines and groups are of religious or classical subjects. Tea sets, plaques, pitchers, vases and jewelry were made of this ware which originated in England about 1845. It became

Classic Figure. Copeland, 1864. 16'' high _____ **$225.00**

Basket. 5x5''. Cupid sitting at the side, open-top egg, rope of roses entwined around handle _____ 30.00
Bowl. 4½'' diam. ''Pond Lily'' ____ 21.00
Boxes:
  Trinket. Sleeping baby on cover 25.00
  Trinket. Casket-shape, with applied grapes _____ 22.50
Busts:
  Andrew, John A. 13'' high. 9'' wide, pedestal base _____ 55.00
  Apollo. 9½'' high _____ 42.00
  Beethoven. 8'' high _____ 45.00
  Bennington. Marked ''Spring and Autumn.'' 8'' high, pair _____ 48.50
  Cromwell. 8'' high _____ 40.00
  Dante. 5'' high _____ 32.50
  Dickens. 6¼'' high _____ 40.00
  Enid. 11'' high, rampant lion on her vest. Signed Copeland ____ 48.50
  Garfield. 10'' high _____ 50.00
  Garfield. 12½'' high, 8'' wide, pedestal base _____ 55.00
  Goethe. 11½'' high _____ 47.50
  Josephine _____ 45.00
  Napoleon _____ 62.50
  Schiller _____ 47.50
  Scott, Sir Walter. 12'' high ____ 52.50
  Shakespeare. 7½'' high _____ 56.50
  Sumner, Charles. 12½'' high ____ 60.00

Sunflower Maiden. 11'' high ____ 67.50
Venus De Milo. 8'' high, signed __ 46.50
Washington, George. 9'' high __ 68.50
Cornucopia. With 2 dogs _____ 36.50
Creamer. Lily pad pattern _____ 35.00
Cup and Saucer. Lily pad pattern 52.50
Cupid. $9\frac{1}{2}$'' long, holding torch.
  Loop on back for hanging _____ 46.50
Dishes:
  Oval. $10\frac{1}{2}$x8''. Raspberry and
  white _____ 57.50
  Sweetmeat Dish on plate. Cover-
  ered. Lily pad pattern _____ 75.00
  Sweetmeat Dish without plate.
  Covered. Lily pad pattern _____ 52.50
Ewer. Ring handles with small
  masks. Beading and leaves over
  body. $8\frac{1}{2}$'' high _____ 69.50
Figurines:
  $8\frac{1}{4}$''. Ear of corn with 2 girls __ 36.00
  $8\frac{3}{4}$''. Girl kneeling on pillow,
  holding lyre _____ 32.50
  9''. Boy and girl. White. Pair ____ 70.00
  9''. Man and maiden in Colonial
  attire. Pair _____ 85.00
  9''. Girl wearing hat and cape,
  with gun at side, 2 pistols in
  belt. Standing on oval base.
  Pair _____ 49.50
  9''. Girl with long hair, kneeling
  in prayer on pillow with book
  open on knees. Pair _____ 92.00
  10''. Boy eating fruit, short
  jacket and hat, 2 baskets _____ 42.50
  10''. Girl in plumed hat and
  fancy gown. Urn and bird _____ 33.50
  11'' high. Girl with dog _____ 45.00
  13''. "Rock of Ages." 2 girls
  clinging to cross _____ 48.00
  13''. Girls, one holding a sheaf of
  wheat, the other holding a pitcher. Pair _____ 92.50
  19''. Woman, wearing draped
  gown, holding rose garland in one
  hand and a tambourine in the
  other _____ 72.00
  "Red Riding Hood" _____ 37.00
Hands:
  4'' high. Ring holder _____ 40.00
  6'' high. Holding urn _____ 52.50
Hen. 7'' _____ 78.50
Horses. 5'' high, on 6x3'' base.
  Pair _____ 48.00
Jug. $7\frac{1}{2}$'' high. White with classic
  figures _____ 44.00
Lions. Holding front foot on ball.
  Pair _____ 33.50
Match Holder. Life size mouse ____ 22.00
Pitchers:
  4''. Flowers, vines and leaves in
  relief _____ 16.00
  4''. Squirrel _____ 18.75
  $4\frac{1}{2}$''. With birds, berries and leaf
  decor _____ 24.00
  $6\frac{1}{2}$''. Embossed birds _____ 22.75
  $8\frac{1}{2}$''. Lily-of-the-Valley decor ____ 95.00

9''. Daffodil and leaf decor
around body, berries around neck 95.00
$10\frac{1}{2}$''. Wild fowl and game in bold
relief, glazed hound handle ____ 110.00
$11\frac{1}{2}$''. White with American shield
and flag. Geo. Washington in uniform on one side and words
"American Independence" and
"Mother" on other _____ 125.00

Vase. $7\frac{1}{2}$'' high. Grape decoration
with spots of blue _____ $30.00

Plate. 8'' diam. Raised water lilies 25.00
Sugar Bowl. Lily pad pattern ____ 57.50
Tray, Bread. Round 13''. "Get Thy
  Bread with Joy and Thankfulness" 21.50
Vases:
  $6\frac{3}{8}$''. Decor of grape leaves and
  2 bands _____ 42.50

6½". Hand with 2 rings on finger.     35.75
7x4½". Cornucopia. 2 cherubs
standing on pillow base _____     36.50
7½". Grape decoration with spots
of blue _____     30.00

## PEACHBLOW GLASS

A type of Art Glass which derived its
name from the coloring of fine Chinese
porcelain of the same name. It was produced first at Wheeling, W. Va., in 1886.
The New England firms followed with their
ware a year or two later.

There are three existing types of this
glass. Wheeling Peachblow, which is a
red-rose color at the top, shading to a
bright yellow at the bottom. The inside of
the ware is cased or lined with white. Most
of the items have a glossy finish; however,
some were completed with an acid or satin
surface.

New England Peachblow is a red-rose
color at the top, shading to white at the
bottom. The glass is not cased or lined
with white on the interior. The majority of
items has a satin finish.

A third type, Mt. Washington Peachblow,
is a smoky-pink at the top, shading to a
bluish-white at the base.

During the past 10 years reproductions
have come onto the market. These include
goblets (not originally made), rose bowls,
cruets, plates and baskets.

The new items are of the New England
variety but are off-color and can be "spotted" by anyone remotely familiar with the
product.

Baskets:
    Gundersen type _____     395.00
    8½" diam., twisted amber handle,
    gold shading to pink _____    2000.00
Bowls:
    Finger. Ruffled top. 5¼" diam.     295.00
    Sandwich, 4" high, 9" diam.
    Crimped and ruffled 4-scallop
    edge, dull finish _____     500.00
Butter Dish. Wheeling. Glossy
    finish _____     825.00
Celery Vase. Wheeling _____     495.00
Compote. Gundersen type _____     335.00
Creamers:
    Light yellow into dark red.
    Applied amber handle. 4½" high     750.00
    Wheeling. Light yellow into dark
    red. Applied amber handle.
    4¼" high _____     795.00
Cruet. Wheeling. Yellow with
    amber handle and stopper _____     700.00
Cup and Saucer. Gundersen. Deep
    raspberry color, white reeded
    handle _____     235.00
Darner. New England _____     100.00
Decanter. Wheeling _____    1000.00

Basket. 8½" diam. Twisted amber
    handle, gold shading to pink __$2,000.00

Vase. 6½" high. Gold decor _____ $225.00

Finger Bowl. Wheeling _____ 375.00
Goblet. 5¼'' high. Gundersen. Deep
pink bowl with white at bot-
tom, white baluster stem _____ 165.00
Lamp. Hanging. Hall, 15'' high,
9'' diam. Candle-burner. Brass__ 695.00
Lamp Shade. For banquet lamp.
New England type. Ruffled top __ 495.00
Muffineer. Wheeling. 5½'' high,
original metal top. Shades from
deep red into yellow _____ 395.00
Pear. New England. Scarce. Open
end stem. Glossy finish _____ 400.00
Pitchers:
Syrup. Pink shading to white __ 750.00
Water. Wheeling. Deep pink to
yellow. Applied amber handle __ 850.00
Rose Bowl. New England _____ 400.00
Salt. Wheeling. Glossy finish ____ 185.00
Shakers. Pair _____ 375.00
Sugar Bowl. New England. Deep
wild rose color. Applied white
handles _____ 495.00
Toothpick Holder. Wheeling. Glossy
finish _____ 275.00
Tumblers:
New England. Dull finish _____ 375.00
New England. Wild rose decor __ 395.00
New England. Glossy finish, deep
pink to yellow _____ 400.00
Wheeling. Acid. Deep mahogany
to fuschia, into dusky yellow at
halfway mark _____ 375.00
Vases:
4¾'' high. Sandwich. Turned
down top _____ 300.00
7'' high. Gundersen type. Banjo.
Pair _____ 350.00
10'' high. New England. White
shading to deep rose with gold
tracery design on body _____ 675.00
10'' high, 5'' wide. Mt. Washington. Light blue at base shading
to deep rose with shades of lavender. Typical Mt. Washington
style decor of shasta daisies in
raised enamel dots of yellow and
white. Coin gold stems and centers, powder-blue leaves, jade
green dots _____ 1800.00
Wheeling. Done in style of the
Morgan Peachblow vase. Amber-
yellow at base shading to cherry
red at top, chalky-white lining.
Amber glass 4-part mold matching stands:
Glossy finish _____ 850.00
Satin finish _____ 975.00
12½'' Ewer Vase. New England.
Dull finish, applied handle, applied decoration around base of
long narrow neck _____ 875.00
15½'' high, with long neck. Deep
red at top shading to peach at
base. Wheeling _____ 795.00

Vase. 15½'' high, with long neck.
Deep red at top shading to peach
at base. Wheeling _____ $795.00

Water Set. Wheeling. Finest coloring, glossy finish. Bulbous, pitcher
with 6 tumblers _____ 2400.00
Whiskey. New England. Glossy
finish _____ 195.00

## PEWTER

Pewter is an alloy of the metals tin and lead. It was used for tableware and utensils prior to the general use of chinaware. Pewterware made by early American craftsmen is now relatively scarce. According to earlier writers it was melted and used to make bullets during the American Revolutionary War and again in the War of 1812.

Pieces marked "Jas. Dixon & Son, Sheffield" or "Dixon," have the appearance of being pewter but in reality are made of Britannia metal which is known as the hard pewter of the latter part of the 1800's. Although technically there is a difference in the formula of the two, dealers and collectors in America over the years have accepted pieces with the above marks as late pewter.

Candlesticks. With bobeches. 12"
high. Unmarked. Pair _____ $150.00

**Basins:**

| | | |
|---|---|---|
| 6½", unmarked _____ | | 62.50 |
| 8", Austin, R. _____ | | 125.00 |
| 8", Boardman _____ | | 115.00 |
| 8", Danforth, S. _____ | | 120.00 |
| 8", Pierce _____ | | 100.00 |
| 10½", unmarked _____ | | 72.50 |
| 11½", Lovebird _____ | | 98.50 |

**Beakers:**

| | | |
|---|---|---|
| Dixon & Son. Pint _____ | | 45.00 |
| Griswold, A. _____ | | 72.50 |
| Bedpan. Boardman _____ | | 62.50 |

**Bowls:**

| | | |
|---|---|---|
| 8", Boardman, T. _____ | | 125.00 |
| 8", Compton & Leonard _____ | | 57.50 |
| 8", Danforth, S. _____ | | 115.00 |

**Candlesticks:**

| | | |
|---|---|---|
| 6", Dunham _____ | | 65.00 |
| 6", J.B. _____ | | 55.00 |
| 8", saucer-type. Gleason _____ | | 85.00 |
| 9", unmarked. Pair _____ | | 67.50 |
| 10", unmarked. American, baluster turned. Pair _____ | | 72.50 |
| Chalice. Covered. Coat-of-Arms decor. Eagle finial, unmarked ____ | | 80.00 |

Charger. Townsend-Compton _____ $85.00

**Chargers:**

| | | |
|---|---|---|
| 12", unmarked _____ | | 50.00 |
| 13½", rose mark _____ | | 62.50 |
| 17", English mark _____ | | 85.00 |
| 18", English _____ | | 125.00 |
| 20", English _____ | | 132.50 |
| Townsend-Compton _____ | | 85.00 |
| Chocolate Pot. 18th century, Swiss. Black, Engle and Zinn _____ | | 79.50 |

**Coffee Pots:**

| | | |
|---|---|---|
| Boardman _____ | | 120.00 |
| Danforth, Josiah. 11" _____ | | 110.00 |
| Dixon & Son. 10½" high. Wooden handle _____ | | 67.50 |
| Dunham, 12" _____ | | 85.00 |
| Dunham & Sons _____ | | 77.50 |
| Gleason _____ | | 90.00 |
| Leonard, Reed & Barton. 9" __ | | 85.00 |
| Morey & Sons _____ | | 70.00 |
| Porter, F. 11" _____ | | 97.50 |
| Richardson. 11½" _____ | | 93.50 |
| Savage _____ | | 94.00 |
| Sellens & Co., Cincinnati _____ | | 67.50 |
| Smith & Co. 10" _____ | | 72.00 |
| Trask. 9", dome top _____ | | 94.50 |
| Ward & Co. _____ | | 90.00 |
| Whitehouse _____ | | 95.00 |
| Coffee Urn. Reed & Barton. 14" high, footed base _____ | | 97.50 |
| Creamer. H. Yale. Circa 1830. 4"_ | | 65.00 |

Cuspidor. Derby _____ 90.00
Dishes, Deep:
    B. Barns _____ 115.00
    Calder _____ 120.00
    Danforth. 11" _____ 150.00
    G. Richardson _____ 122.50
Flagons:
    Unmarked _____ 97.50
    Calder. 11" _____ 175.00
    Calder. 11", with platter _____ 182.50
    Jas. Dixon & Son, Sheffield.
    $9\frac{3}{4}$" diam. _____ 32.00
    Gleason. 10" _____ 195.00
    Gleason. 10", with platter _____ 210.00
Foot Warmer. Oval _____ 43.50
Funnel. For decanter. Unmarked __ 50.00
Goblet. Late _____ 20.00
Ladles:
    Dated 1792 _____ 67.50
    12", Yates _____ 39.00
    13", wooden handle _____ 37.50
    $14\frac{1}{2}$" _____ 35.00
Lamps:
    Nursing. 2", T.B.M. Co. Pair __ 88.50
    Peg. 7", J. Newells. Pair _____ 115.00
    Ship. Unmarked. Pair _____ 105.00
    Whale Oil:
    Gleason _____ 95.00
    F. Porter _____ 89.50
    Wildes _____ 85.00
Mugs:
    Handled. English. Circa 1825____ 38.00
    Handled. Morey & Smith. 5"
    high _____ 59.50
Mustard Pot. Blue china liner_____ 38.50
Pitchers:
    Gleason. Covered _____ 145.00
    Kayserzinn _____ 75.00
    McQuilkin _____ 130.00
    Porter. F. 6" _____ 120.00
    Unmarked. Covered _____ 95.00
Plates:
    Austin, N. 8" _____ 89.50
    Austin, Richard. 8" _____ 100.00
    Badger, Thomas:
    $7\frac{1}{2}$" _____ 97.50
    $7\frac{7}{8}$" _____ 88.50
    $8\frac{1}{2}$" _____ 100.00
    B. Barns:
    $7\frac{7}{8}$" _____ 95.00
    8" _____ 100.00
    9" _____ 110.00
    Bassett, Fred. 8" _____ 97.50
    Boardman:
    8" _____ 87.50
    12", flat, eagle touchmark ____ 92.50
    Calder, William:
    8" _____ 91.50
    $11\frac{1}{2}$" _____ 105.00
    Danforth, E. 8" _____ 94.00
    Danforth, S. 8" _____ 88.00
    Danforth, Thos. 3rd. 8" _____ 84.50
    Danforth, William:
    $7\frac{3}{4}$" _____ 85.00
    8" _____ 92.50
    Griswold, Ashbel. $7\frac{7}{8}$" _____ 80.00

Kayserzinn. 10" _____ 24.00
Kilbourn, S. 8" _____ 110.00
Pierce, S. 8" _____ 85.00
Smith & Feltman, Albany. 10" __ 77.50
Marked. Maker unknown:
    $7\frac{1}{2}$" _____ 29.50
    8" _____ 32.50
    $9\frac{3}{4}$" _____ 35.00
    12", deep _____ 42.00
Unmarked:
    $8\frac{1}{4}$" _____ 22.00
    $9\frac{1}{2}$". German. Ship design in
    center _____ 54.00
    $13\frac{1}{2}$" _____ 60.00

Inkwell. $4\frac{3}{4}$" diam., $3\frac{1}{4}$" high_____ $55.00

Platters:
    Badger, Thomas. 12" _____ 150.00
    Calder, $11\frac{1}{2}$", deep _____ 170.00
Porringers:
    2-1/16". R. Lee (rare) _____ 175.00
    3", unmarked _____ 57.50
    $3\frac{1}{2}$", heart handle. Lee _____ 78.50
    4-1/8", crown handle _____ 87.50
    $4\frac{1}{4}$", 2 handles. H.K. on handle __ 90.00
    $4\frac{1}{2}$", heart handle. Marked I.C.__ 95.00
    5". Boardman _____ 110.00
    5". crown handle. Marked I.C. __ 85.00
    5", crown handle. Lee _____ 95.00
    $5\frac{1}{4}$", crown handle. Unmarked __ 87.50
    $5\frac{3}{4}$". Hamlin _____ 145.00
Shaving Mug. Richardson _____ 78.00
Snuff Boxes:
    Round, incised lines _____ 27.50
    Shape of 18th century watch ___ 37.50
Spoon Mold _____ 39.50
Spoons:
    Tablespoon. Yates, England ____ 12.00

Teaspoons:
Fiddle-shape _____ 8.50
Holland, crown and rose. Marked
J. M. _____ 15.00
Shell-back. Early. Set of 4 ____ 18.00
Tankard. 14'', unmarked _____ 77.50

Teapot. James Dixon _____ $90.00

Teapots:
Boardman. 8'' _____ 90.00
Boardman and Hart:
7¾'' _____ 110.00
8'' _____ 85.00
Boardman, L. 7½'' _____ 87.50
Dixon, James _____ 90.00
Dunham, R. 7½'' _____ 88.50
Gleason, R. 7'' _____ 92.00
Morey & Ober, Boston _____ 97.50
Porter, F., Westbrook _____ 89.50
Putnam, 8'' _____ 88.50
Richardson, G:
7¾'', G. Richardson, Boston. Rare 160.00
7½'' _____ 110.00
11'' _____ 120.00
Savage. 10'' _____ 75.00
Shaw & Fisher, Suffolk, England.
5¾'' _____ 72.00
Smith & Co. 7½'', wood handle__ 57.50
Unmarked. Early _____ 72.50
Tea Set. Teapot, sugar bowl,
creamer and round tray. Marked
"Genuine." Late _____ 25.00'

## PHONOGRAPHS

This instrument was commonly known as
the "talking-machine" by old-timers. Thomas
A. Edison invented the first successful machine in the 1880's and placed it on the
market. It was manufactured by numerous
firms in later years.

Columbia "Gramaphone." Pat.
1885, 25 cylinders _____ 110.00
Edison Cylinder. With 20 records.
Morning Glory decor on horn __ 95.00
Edison Cylinder-type. Spring-wind,
with horn _____ 115.00

Edison Cylinder-type. Spring-wind,
with horn _____ $115.00

Edison. Disc-type Horn in bottom 90.00
Edison. Record cylinder _____ 1.75
Keeno-Lo-Phone. Circa 1915. Double
doors conceal 2 drawers with
record pockets. Bonnet is ampli-
fier _____ 80.00
O'Neil James Co., Chicago. Miniature, with horn _____ 80.00
Victor. Early, small horn. 6½'' square
cast iron base _____ 95.00

## PICKLE CASTORS

A novelty of the 1880-1900 period which
consisted of a silver plated frame with a
clear or colored glass insert & metal tongs.
The primary use was for decorative or ornamental purposes in a china closet or on
a sideboard.

Amber. Cane Pattern. In holder with
tongs _____ 69.50
Amberina. Inverted Thumbprint.
Spoon holder and tongs _____ 225.00
Amethyst 12''. Enamel decor ____ 65.00
Blue. 12''. Fine Cut _____ 57.50
Blue. Daisy and button in holder,
with fork _____ 48.50
Blue. Inverted Thumbprint. Enamel
flowers _____ 62.50
Castle. Daisy decor at base. 3
parts _____ 30.00
Clear glass. Button pattern. In sil-
ver-plated holder with fork. Small 40.00
Clear. 12'' _____ 25.00
Clear. 12''. Double _____ 45.00
Cranberry. 11''. Enamel decor ____ 75.00
Cranberry. 12''. Plain _____ 87.50
Cranberry. 12''. Enamel decor ____ 100.00
Opalescent base, shading to pink at
top. Heavy printed Hobnail. Sil-

ver-plated holder with lid and
tongs _____ 110.00

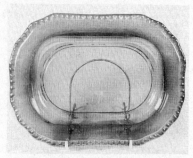

Dish. Deep, 10¼'' long, beading
around edge _____ $25.00

Compotes:
  7½'' high, 9½'' diam. Open scalloped edge _____ 68.50
  16'' high. Cut _____ 90.00
Creamer. 4½'' high. Petal top, clear
  applied handle _____ 40.00
Dish. Large _____ 27.50
Pitcher. 9'' high. Clear applied
  handle. France _____ 95.00
Sugar Shaker. Tin top _____ 30.00
Syrup Jug. Tin top _____ 48.50
Tumbler _____ 18.50
Vases:
  4½'' high. Miniature, 2 clear loop
  handles _____ 24.00
  7¼'' high. Decorated with birds
  and bamboo _____ 48.00
  11¾'' high. Pedestal base, applied
  clear glass scallop on top edge.
  Pair _____ 78.50

### PINK LUSTRE CHINA

Pink Lustre China derives its name from
the pink decoration used on the ware.
The china is normally of the Staffordshire
variety. It is generally believed to have
become popular in the 1840's.

Bowl. Shallow, 7¾x1''. House pat-
  tern _____ 40.00
Creamer. House pattern _____ 45.00
Cup and Saucer. Copper trim ____ 32.50
Cup and Saucer. Schoolhouse pat-
  tern _____ 38.50
Pitchers:
  3½'' high. House pattern _____ 40.00
  6 high. House pattern_____ 75.00
Plates:
  8½'' diam. House pattern _____ 30.00
  Cake _____ 24.50
  Small _____ 20.00
  Soup. 9¼'' diam. _____ 20.00

Pickle Castor. Blue glass insert in
  silver frame _____ $60.00

Red. Satin glass. Silver frame and
  tongs _____ 80.00
Satin Glass. Frosted red with enameled blossom and leaf decor. 11''
  to top of frame _____ 89.50

### PIGEON'S BLOOD GLASS

Pigeon's Blood is a type of red colored glass made around the turn of the
century which derives its name from the
color of a pigeon's blood.

Bottle. 4¼'' to top of stopper ____ 18.00
Bowl. 8'' diam. Beaded top, grilled
  triangular design on sides ____ 40.00
Butter Dish. Covered, 7'' _____ 44.50
Candlestick. 7½'', twisted stem __ 65.00
Castor Set _____ 85.00

Biscuit Barrel. 4½" high. Circa 1860.
With lid and verse _____ $95.00

Mug. 3½" high. Circa 1850 _____ $45.00

Sugar Bowl. House pattern _____  85.00
Teapot. Floral medallion decor. 5½"
high _____  78.00
Teapot. House pattern _____  95.00
Tea Set. Teapot, sugar and cream-
er. House motif _____  135.00

## PINK SLAG

The molded pattern regarded as true
Pink Slag is that of an inverted feather.
Quality pieces shade from pink at the top
to white at the bottom.

This is the most sought after of the slag
wares. The glass is extremely scarce and
commands a good price from advanced
collectors.

Punch Cup _____ $300.00

Bowl, Berry _____  500.00
Butter Dish. Covered _____  675.00
Compote, Jelly _____  500.00
Creamer _____  400.00
Cruet _____  495.00
Lamp Base. Miniature, plain ____  520.00
Lamp. Miniature. In shape of swan.
Rare _____  595.00
Sauce _____  155.00
Sugar _____  400.00
Syrup _____  495.00
Toothpick Holder _____  385.00
Tumblers:
Inverted Thumbprint. 4" high __  295.00
Plain _____  245.00

### PIPES (ILLUSTRATED ON PAGE 366)

1. Meerschaum bowl with carved
   house, fence and men. 5"
   high, 18" overall length. Dated
   1800 _____  35.00
2. Meerschaum bowl with large
   carved dog. 14" long _____  42.00
3. Meerschaum bowl with metal
   cover _____  20.00
4. Meerschaum bowl with wolf.
   20" overall length. Dated
   1841 _____  62.50
5. Indian Head bowl, size of a
   baseball. 17" stem _____  18.50
6. Deer carved all around bowl.
   14" long _____  37.50
7. Horse's Head bowl. Made in
   Italy _____  10.00
8. Face carved all around bowl.
   14" long _____  34.50
9. Meerschaum bowl with large
   dog. 15" long. Dated 1860 __  22.50
10. Devil's Head bowl of porcelain.
    17" stem _____  32.00
11. Plain bowl with metal cover.
    17" wood stem _____  30.00
12. Meerschaum bowl, silver ribs,
    briar bottom. Regimental pipe,
    dated 1862. 12" stem _____  35.00

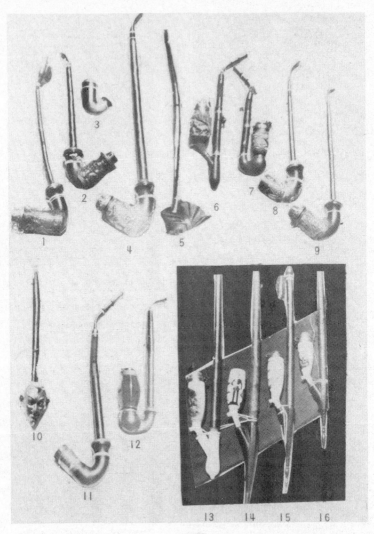

**PIPES**
For descriptions, see the preceding and following pages.

| | | |
|---|---|---|

13. Painted porcelain bowl. 34" stem _____ 26.50
14. Horn bottom. Prussian soldier and girl. Dated 1856, 40" long 30.00
15. Porcelain bowl with gold lettering, black horn bottom. 30" long _____ 24.00
16. Deer painted on bowl, wood stem, horn bottom. 28" long 21.00

## PIPES—NOT ILLUSTRATED

4½". Meerschaum. Fair lady with flowing hair _____ 27.50
5". Meerschaum. Running horse. Amber stem _____ 25.00
5". Meerschaum. Two dogs carved on bowl. Amber stem _____ 24.00
5". Bird devouring bug _____ 30.00
5". Lioness on amber stem____ 28.50
5". Large bowl, tree stump with two wolves _____ 46.50
5". Italian. Steer head with horns _____ 12.00
5½". Bear head carved from walrus tusk. Wood stem __ 15.00
5½". Ivory carved bear head bowl. Wood stem _____ 18.50
5½". Meerschaum. Wolf in relief. Amber stem _____ 29.00
6". Meerschaum. Bowl plain with claw decoration _____ 28.50
7". Meerschaum. Deer pursued by dog _____ 34.50
9". Painted porcelain bowl. Wood stem _____ 18.00
10". Lion and tree stump _____ 48.00
10". Painting of Kaiser Wilhelm 1st. Silver cover _____ 75.00
11". Meerschaum. Fancy carved bowl. Wood base, metal cover _____ 32.00
11". Majolica barrel-shaped bowl with dog at base. Bright colors, wood stem _____ 29.50
12". Meerschaum. Gold cover __ 34.50
12". Regimental pipe. Meerschaum bowl, briar bottom, metal cover, wood stem ___ 39.00
15". Meerschaum bowl. Girl by fence _____ 28.00
15". Meerschaum bowl. Large dog _____ 29.00
15". Porcelain bowl with Meissen mark, cherry wood stem. Green leaf decor on porcelain _____ 27.50
16". Porcelain bowl. Painted decor _____ 19.50
17". Plain bowl, metal cover. Wood stem _____ 30.00
23". Painted porcelain bowl. Wood stem _____ 28.50
28". Painted porcelain bowl. Horn bottom _____ 20.00

32". Painted porcelain bowl. Horn stem _____ 49.50
34". Porcelain bowl. Painted landscape decor _____ 28.50
Opium. Cloissone base. Black background with blue and white water lilies and white crane with blue feathers _____ 48.50

## PITCHERS, GLASS
See Illustration on page 368.

1. Lower part, frosted Hobnail, upper, lemon amber. 7½" ____ 95.00
2. Amethyst. Oaken Bucket. 8" __ 38.50
3. Opaque white with satin finish. Acorns and oak leaves. 7½" __ 62.50
4. Spanish Lace. Light translucent blue, blue handle. 8" _____ 65.00
5. Spirea Band. Amber, 9" ____ 21.50
6. Blue Basketweave. 8" _____ 27.50
7. Opalescent Swirl. Blue, 8" __ 42.50
8. Amethyst, enamel decor. 8½"__ 42.00
9. Clear glass shading to cranberry at top. 9" _____ 75.00
10. Daisy and Fern. Blue, 8½" ____ 55.00
11. Daisy and Fern. Cranberry, clear handle. 8½" _____ 90.00
12. Opalescent Swirl. Blue, 9" ___ 45.00
13. Cranberry with opalescent Daisy and Fern. 8½" _____ 80.00
14. Amberina. Amber handle, 8½"_ 175.00
15. Hobnail. Clear to red, 7½" __ 115.00
16. Amber. 6½" _____ 45.00
17. Amber. Reeded handle. 5" ___ 42.50
18. Hobnail. Clear to red. 7½" __ 85.00
19. End of Day Glass, ITP. Honey amber to opaque white. 8" __ 98.50
20. Clear with opalescent spots and top. 8" _____ 65.00
21. Deep cranberry. 8½" _____ 80.00
22. Clear with opalescent swirl. 8½" _____ 50.00
23. Canary. Heavy raised opalescent swirl, ground pontil. 6½" 60.00
24. Blue. Opalescent spots, ground pontil. 6½" _____ 50.00
25. Clear. Vertical opalescent ribbing. 4½" _____ 30.00
26. Satin Glass. White to deep pink at top, white lining, frosted reeded handle. 8½" _____ 350.00
27. Azure blue over opaque white. Clear handle. 7½" _____ 65.00
28. Cranberry to canary (Rubina Verde). Canary handle. 7½"___ 200.00
29. Cranberry. Clear handle with ground pontil. 7" _____ 75.00
30. End of Day Glass, ITP. Cranberry streaked with opaque white, clear handle. 8½" ____ 98.50
31. Cranberry. 8½" _____ 80.00
32. Light blue. Blue handle, ground pontil. 7" _____ 65.00
33. Light amber. Ground pontil. 7½" _____ 55.00

**PITCHERS, GLASS**
For descriptions, see preceding and following page.

34. Frosted lower part and handle, shading to deep cranberry at top. Raised leaf design. $8\frac{1}{2}$"__ 100.00
35. Light blue. Clear reeded handle. 9" _____ 55.00
36. Milk Glass. Silver and pink decor on lower part, silver and blue on upper. 11" _____ 52.50
37. Amber. Lid, with finial. $11\frac{1}{2}$"_ 65.00
38. Cosmos. Yellow, pink and blue flowers on white. Broad pink banded top. $8\frac{1}{2}$" _____ 150.00
39. Rainbow hues at top, ground pontil. 9" _____ 62.50
40. Two panel. Apple green. $9\frac{1}{2}$"_ 48.50
41. Daisy and Fern. Cranberry, with pink overlay, inside top. Clear handle. $9\frac{1}{2}$" _____ 80.00
42. Milk Glass. Raised net of pink glass threading over entire body. Marked "G.L.F." $9\frac{1}{2}$"__ 48.50

## PITCHERS AND VASES
### (Hand Painted)
### (Illustrated on page 370)

1. Pitcher. Satin finish, floral decor, gold handle. "Pointons, Stoke-on-Trent" _____ 25.00
2. Teplitz Vase. $6\frac{1}{2}$" high, ovoid, satin finish, floral decor on cream background _____ 27.50
3. Slender-neck Vase. $8\frac{1}{2}$", 2 open gold handles, leaf decor flecked with gold _____ 20.00
4. Vase. Bulbous, satin finish, floral spray on cream. "Rudolstadt" _____ 30.00
5. Pitcher. 9", ovoid, slender neck. Flower on high glaze blue background, gold handle, "Pointons, Stoke-on-Trent" ___ 27.00
6. Royal Worcester Pitcher. 5" bulbous, flower sprays _____ 49.50
7. Carlsbad Vase. Bulbous, long slender neck. 2 open dolphin handles. Flower sprays on cream satin background. $8\frac{1}{2}$"_ 27.50
8. Pitcher. Nude female, flowing hair, 9" high. Powder blue background, "Leonard, Vienna" _____ 44.50
9. Vase. Footed, bulbous, gold decor and open gold handles. 8" high. "Burslem, England"_ 33.50
10. Royal Bonn Pitcher. Ovoid, 8" high, flowers and gold ___ 56.50
11. Royal Worcester Pitcher. Powder horn shape, closed spout__ 59.50
12. Carlsbad Pitcher Vase. Gold handle, cream satin background _____ 44.50
13. Pitcher. 8" high, winged dragon handle, cream background _____ 27.50

14. Royal Worcester Pitcher. $6\frac{1}{2}$" high, elephant trunk handle __ 57.00
15. Pitcher. Straight sides, 4-leaf clover shape in cross-section. Blue, pink and lavender flowers on off-white background. Gold handle. $5\frac{1}{4}$" high _____ 19.50
16. Royal Vienna Pitcher. Painting of woman with cupid at fountain. Signed "Loffen." Painting on reverse, cupid and birds in sky. 8" high, gold handle _____ 85.00
17. Carlsbad Vase. Spray of yellow, green, gold and brown flowers. 8" high, ovoid, long neck _____ 30.00
18. Royal Bayreuth Vase. Ovoid, cavalier drinking scene, reverse, wine cellar scene, gold handle. $4\frac{1}{2}$" high _____ 24.50
19. Royal Vienna Vase. $\frac{3}{4}$ length portrait of woman, long hair, flowing robe, in oval medallion, "C" scrolls, Grecian Ruins on blue background. $6\frac{1}{2}$" high __ 72.50
20. Vase. 2 feet, "C" scroll top, pansy decor on white. 7" ___ 18.75
21. Jug. Satin finish, applied floral spray. 4" _____ 16.00
22. Pitcher. Stag-horn shape. Violet decor on white. $5\frac{1}{2}$" _____ 20.00
23. Vase. Flowers on cream shading to pink background. 9"__ 19.50
24. Cream Pitcher. Flowers on cream background. $4\frac{3}{4}$" _____ 21.50
25. Pitcher. Pinched sides, ribbon handle, 2 cupids on white to pink. 3" high _____ 18.75
26. Bud Vase. Firenze ware. Red and yellow roses on cream to green background. $8\frac{1}{2}$" high, signed "D. Pilade" _____ 22.50
27. Royal Bonn Vase. Flowers on cream background, gold handles, $8\frac{1}{2}$" high _____ 24.50
28. Cream Pitcher. Rudolstadt. Scalloped top edged with gold, satin finish, floral spray on cream background. $3\frac{3}{4}$" _____ 18.50

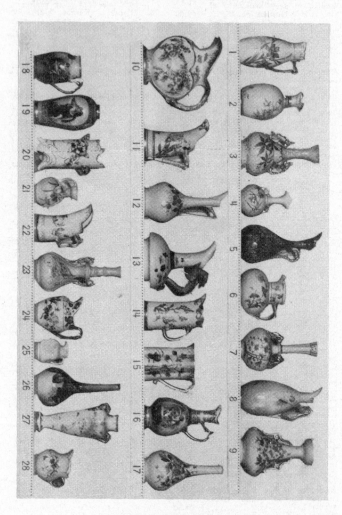

**PITCHERS AND VASES**
For descriptions, see the preceding page.

**PLATES. See PORTRAIT & SOUVENIR PLATES**

## POMONA GLASS

Pomona Glass was invented by Joseph Locke in 1884 and first produced by the New England Glass Co. It has two distinct surfaces. The etched portion has a pebbled surface while the other part is flashed or tinted glass. A pattern is sometimes present but many times the ware is plain.

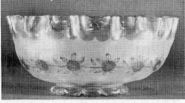

Bowl. 9¾'' diam. New England ____ $275.00

**Bowls:**
| | |
|---|---|
| 4½'' diam. Small. Quilted diamond pattern _____ | 65.00 |
| 8'' diam. New England. Second grind, cornflower and leaf decor, frilled rim _____ | 225.00 |
| Berry. 9½'' diam. _____ | 260.00 |
| Pinch-type. 5'' diam., 3'' high __ | 150.00 |

Celery. No decoration _____ 149.50
Champagne. New England. 3½'' bowl. First grind, not decorated. Deeply etched _____ 120.00

**Creamers:**
| | |
|---|---|
| Cornflower decor, applied feet and handle, crimped top _____ | 160.00 |
| Square mouth, applied handle. 5½'' high _____ | 140.00 |

Dish. Small, with matching plate __ 95.00

**Finger Bowls:**
| | |
|---|---|
| Blue cornflower decor _____ | 110.00 |
| Light amber with frosted base __ | 85.00 |

Jug. 12'' high. Lambrequin. Honey amber rim and handle _____ 180.00
Lamp, Hanging. Strawflower decor on shade. Brass font and frame__ 475.00
Pickle Castor. Silver plated frame, second grind, cornflower decor__ 225.00

**Pitchers:**
| | |
|---|---|
| 5½'' high. Bulbous, cornflowers __ | 315.00 |
| 7''. Amber stained top, blue and amber cornflower design in center _____ | 425.00 |
| 8'' high, 6'' widest diam. 2'' scalloped amber-tint band around collar: band of blue cornflowers at mid-section, undercoated portions are stippled. Applied clear crystal handle _____ | 450.00 |

Water. Thumbprint design _____ 365.00
Plate. 6½'' diam. Straw color, ruffled edge _____ 140.00

**Punch Cups:**
| | |
|---|---|
| New England. Amber, blue cornflowers. First grind _____ | 100.00 |
| New England. Diamond quilted, hand engraved _____ | 85.00 |
| Scroll etching, amber leaf pattern and handle _____ | 75.00 |

Pitcher. 7'' high. Cornflower pattern. First grind _____ $450.00

Ramekin Set. New England. Second grind, undecorated. Diamond quilted, pale amber rim, on plate and dish _____ 90.00
Rose Bowl. 5½'' high, 4¼'' center diam. Straw colored top and base _____ 160.00
Salt Shaker. 4'' high. Second grind, decorated. Pale amber leaves, no color in cornflowers. Original top _____ 100.00
Spoon Holder. 5½'' high. Blue cornflowers, applied amber base _____ 110.00
Sugar Bowl. Midwest, decorated _____ 175.00
Toothpick Holder _____ 145.00
Tray, Ice Cream. 12½x7½''. Cornflower decor in center _____ 110.00

**Tumblers:**
| | |
|---|---|
| Cornflower decor _____ | 89.50 |
| No decor _____ | 70.00 |
| Oak leaf, acorn. Midwest, cranberry stain _____ | 85.00 |

**Vases:**
| | |
|---|---|
| 3'' high. Fan shaped, pinched top, second grind _____ | 89.50 |
| Footed, lily-type, etched _____ | 110.00 |
| 4x7x1¼''. Amber top, inverted thumbprint _____ | 135.00 |

5" high. New England. Footed,
pale blue cornflowers _____ 150.00

## PORTO BELLO WARE

This is an early ware issued by John
& Thomas Astbury about 1739 commemorat-
ing the capture of Porto Bello on the
Isthmus of Panama. It is usually a brown-
ish-red pottery type of product with a
glaze and figures of fortifications, ships
and other scenes. Designs on the first ware
were in white. Its popularity continued
until 1860. Other designs and colors were
applied.

Pitcher. 6½" high. Reddish-brown
with yellow design _____ $85.00

**Bowls:**
4" diam. _____ 55.00
5" diam. _____ 60.00
Jug. J. & T. Astbury, Shelton.
Circa 1760 _____ 65.00
Pitcher. 6½" high. Reddish-brown
ground with design in yellow ___ 85.00

## PORTRAIT PLATES

During the latter part of the Victorian era
it was the fashion of the day to have portrait plates, primarily of female subjects,
hanging in the hall or Sunday parlor. Produced commercially, the subjects were not
of members of the family.

5"___Center of classic figures,
gold borders. Signed
Kaufmann _____ 18.00
7½"__French. Man, woman and
child, garden scene _____ 50.00
8"___Pittsburgh Commandery
Plate. Girl with roses.
Blue border, gold trim _____ 14.00
8¼"__Transfer picture of lady
and cherubs _____ 18.50
9"___Madam LeBrun & Daughter.
Gold border _____ 15.00
9½"__Madonna and Child. Brown
to tan tints _____ 18.00
9½"__Brunette woman. Decorated
in deep rose and gold _____ 24.00
10"_Girl's head in center decoration, gold band surrounds
center. Marked D. & C.
France _____ 29.50

Plate. 9⅞". Portrait of lady on
gray background. Red hair, yellow
ribbon, light pink dress. Red
border with fine gold decor ____ $22.00

10_Queen Louise with scarf ____ 20.00

## POST CARDS
### (BEFORE 1915)

Airplanes. Early _____ 1.00
Angels _____ .10
Autos _____ .45
Boats, Naval _____ .20
Boats, Sailing _____ .25
Bunnies _____ .15
California (before 1900) _____ .35
Capitols (State, U.S.) _____ .12
Chicks _____ .14
Christmas _____ .15
Churches _____ .07
Comics _____ .10
Coney Island, N. Y. _____ .12
Courthouses _____ .08
Crosses _____ .09
Detroit (Maker's name) _____ .24
Disasters (Floods, tornadoes, etc)__ .25
Easter Chicks _____ .15
Easter Crosses _____ .10
Easter (General) _____ .08
Embossed and Airbrush Type _____ .35
Expositions (to 1900) _____ .28
Fairs (before 1900) _____ .24
Florals (mixed flowers, etc.) _____ .14
Florals, Letters _____ .15
Foreign, Colored _____ .07
Gelatin (processed type) _____ .35
Greetings, Birds _____ .10
Greetings, Children _____ .12
Greetings, General type _____ .08
Hall (Mfg.). July 4th., St. Patrick,
etc. _____ .28
Horseshoes _____ .18

"A Stitch in Time Saves Nine"_____ 10¢

Kewpie Christmas Postcards. Each _ 6.00
Leather _____ .45
Massachusetts Views _____ .08
Miscellaneous. Foreign Views _____ .05
Miscellaneous. U.S. Views _____ .07
Newspaper Comics _____ 1.00
New York Views _____ .07
Niagara Falls _____ .08
Ohio _____ .07
Old New England _____ .08
Parades (before 1900) _____ .35
Patriotic _____ .24
Presidents (before 1915) _____ .50
Roses (only) _____ .15
Rotograph Views (colored) _____ .08
Santas _____ .20
St. Patrick _____ .18
Sunbonnet Baby _____ 1.25
Thanksgiving, General _____ .10
Thanksgiving, Turkeys _____ .12
Tinselled _____ .20
Train Wrecks _____ .50
Tucks (Mfg.) Greetings _____ .14
Tucks (Mfg.) Oilettes _____ .25
Utah or Colorado Views _____ .12

U. S. Miscellaneous Views _____ .07
Varnished Surface _____ .25

## POT LIDS

The majority of these lids for containers of hair oil (bear grease), shaving soaps, etc., was made by the Pratt Works at Fenton, Staffordshire, between 1845 and 1880. The various designs were placed under glaze by a multicolor transfer method.

Shakespeare's Home. Stratford-on-Avon. Original lid on original pot $32.50

Fallen Tree. With river in background _____ 28.00
Garibaldi _____ 30.00
Harbor at Hong Kong _____ 32.50
Hide and Seek _____ 27.50
Ning Po River _____ 28.00
Racing Scene at Fair. 4" diam. __ 32.50
Rifle Contest. Wimbledon _____ 32.50
Shakespeare's Home _____ 32.50
The Shrimpers _____ 30.00

## POTTERY

Pottery has been made since ancient times. We are mainly covering items made in the U.S. from about 1800-1900, especially made in New York, New Jersey, Pennsylvania and Virginia.

Pottery with decorations such as swans, ducks, flowers, etc., commands a higher price than pottery with only the manufacturer's name. Eagle decorations bring the highest prices.

Banks, Penny:
Barrel. Gilt hoops _____ 8.00

Cash Register. White with yellow
glaze _____ 9.00
Turnip. Marked "Charity" _____ 10.00

10-gallon Crock. Greensboro, Pa.
Williams & Reppert. Eagle decor $50.00

Bowls:
Milk. Yellow, $9\frac{1}{2}$'' diam. $2\frac{3}{4}$''
deep _____ 15.00
Pennsylvania Redware. $10\frac{1}{4}$'' diam.
Deep red color _____ 50.00
Crocks:
3-gallon. Gray with blue flowers 18.00
3-gallon. 12'' high, blue swan
decor. "Cowden & Wilcox," Har-
risburg, Pa. _____ 28.50
4-gallon, 14'' high. Blue eagle
decor on gray background. By
T. F. Reppert in Greensboro,
Penna. _____ 40.00
4-gallon. 14'' high. Blue floral
decor on gray background. By
Jas. Hamilton & Co., Greensboro,
Penna. _____ 22.50
Lard Crock. By T. F. Reppert,
Greensboro, Penna. _____ 12.50
Foot Warmer. Shape of suitcase.
Marked "Bourne, Denby, Eng-
land." $9\frac{1}{2}$'' long, $4\frac{1}{2}$'' high _____ 21.50

Jug. "Hamilton & Jones." Gray
body with cobalt blue decor ____ $16.50

Jug. 3-gallon, light gray. $15\frac{1}{2}$''
high, bird decor. C. W. Braun,
Buffalo, N. Y. _____ 37.50
Molds:
Fish _____ 10.00
Rabbit _____ 11.00
Turk Head. Pennsylvania Red-
ware _____ 12.00
Wheat _____ 9.50
Pie Plate. 9'' diam. Pennsylvania
Redware _____ 8.75
Pig. Hot water bed warmer _____ 7.50
Pitchers:
New Geneva, Penna. Tan Ware:
$5\frac{1}{2}$'' high _____ 60.00
$6\frac{3}{4}$'' high _____ 65.00
Water, 2-gallon. Made at Greens-
boro, Pa., by James Hamilton,
potter _____ 40.00
Roof Tile. 7'' wide, $14\frac{1}{2}$'' long.
$\frac{3}{4}$'' thick. Early American, red
clay, with rain funnel _____ 10.00
Salt Box. Hanging-type with pine
cover. Blue color with "Salt"
on front _____ 12.50

#### POWDER FLASKS AND HORNS
Containers for gun powder were devis-

ed in a variety of shapes and sizes. The most common types were made of cow and buffalo horns and were sometimes engraved. Patented containers were later produced in brass and pewter.

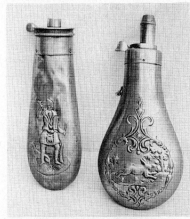

**LEFT:** Hunter and dog. Brass, 7½ high. Patent dispenser _____ **$36.50**
**RIGHT:** Running Rabbit. Brass, 8" high. Patent dispenser _____ **$35.00**

## POWDER FLASKS

| | |
|---|---|
| Civil War. Pistol flask, 4½" long. 2" wide, with eagle holding a pistol and flask in each claw on obverse and reverse _____ | 60.00 |
| Dead Game. 8½" long, brass. James Dixon Co. _____ | 30.00 |
| Eagle, Coat-of-Arms. 5" long, decorated on front and back. Copper with brass top _____ | 35.00 |
| Flower with vines. 7½" high. Patent dispenser. Copper _____ | 30.00 |
| Hunter and Dog. 7½" high. Patent dispenser. Brass _____ | 35.00 |
| Man and Dog. 6¼" long. Copper with brass top _____ | 32.00 |
| Petal Design. 5" long. Brass _____ | 28.50 |
| Petal Design. 7" long. Pewter with brass dispenser _____ | 18.00 |
| Rabbit. Brass, 8" high. Patent dispenser _____ | 33.50 |
| Ribbed. Brass, 7½" high. Patent dispenser _____ | 32.50 |
| Ribbed center. Patent dispenser. Copper _____ | 35.00 |
| Stag and dogs. 8" high. Patent dispenser. Copper _____ | 33.50 |

## POWDER HORNS

| | |
|---|---|
| Brass. European, engraved, 9" high _____ | 35.00 |
| Brass. European, engraved, round, 7½" high _____ | 42.00 |
| **Buffalo Horns:** | |
| 6" long, black, with strap or sling _____ | 18.00 |
| 8" leather. Embossed design of dog and tree _____ | 22.50 |
| Horn. Brass dispenser top, 9" high | 28.50 |
| Ivory. Engraved. 8" high _____ | 48.00 |
| **Plain:** | |
| 8" horn _____ | 14.50 |
| 9½" horn. With plug and measure | 13.50 |
| 13" horn _____ | 17.50 |
| 13" horn. Pewter spout _____ | 28.50 |
| 16" horn _____ | 27.50 |
| **Scrimshaw Scenes:** | |
| Alamo under attack by Mexicans, flag of Texas, dated March 6, 1836 _____ | 175.00 |
| Carved decor of a knight and lion. European origin. Dated 1600 _____ | 180.00 |
| War of 1812. American ship attacking British at Delaware Bay, June 12, 1813 _____ | 185.00 |

## PRATT WARE

Pratt ware was made at the Fenton factory in the Staffordshire district of England, Circa 1775-1805. Characteristics of the ware are the raised figures and decorations which are highly colored in green, blue, black, purple and orange. Transfer pictures were also used on dinner services and other items.

**Compote.** Late, after 1840, with transfer scene in black in center of bowl _____ **$85.00**

Box. Small, "Battle of the Nile"
cover _____ 30.00
Compotes:
9¼" diam., 5" high. English
castle scene _____ 75.00
Colorful transfer picture in
center _____ 75.00
Jug. Tavern scene, with raised
figures, colors of olive-green,
yellow, blue and brown. Circa
1830-1840 _____ 110.00
Pipe. 9¾" long. 4 human masks
in relief on bowl. Mottled black
dog's head stem with blue and
ochre glazes. 18th century _____ 92.50

Pitcher. 4¾" high. Dove of Peace
design in Pink Lustre. Early ____ $175.00

Pitchers:
5½" high, 7" across. Black with
white classic figures _____ 85.00
11" high. Pewter cover, beige
background, colorful seashells.
Circa 1800 _____ 80.00
Plates:
7" diam. Center transfer of man
reading newspaper, "The Times" 30.00
9½" diam. Scene, two boys peep-
ing through doorway into school-
room. Acorn and leaf border __ 40.00
Pomade Jar _____ 18.50
Satyr Mask Drinking Vessels:
4¼" high. Multicolored. Circa
1790 _____ 90.00
5" high. Frog inside, bright
glazes with brown and yellow
predominating. Circa 1790 _____ 95.00
Sugar Bowl, Covered. Black body
with white classical figures ____ 68.50
Teapot. Large _____ 145.00

## PRIMITIVE PAINTINGS

The term is used in the United States
to denote folk art — amateur art, beginning art or untrained art.

The majority was done in the 1800-1900
period. Folk art from the 1825-1850 era
is considered best as itinerant artists
taught the subject and it was "fashionable"
to have painting as a hobby.

Portrait of Girl 10½ x 14½". Signed
Wm. M. Pryor _____ $750.00

Boy and Dog. Boy standing, with
hand on dog's head. In gold leaf
frame. 4½ feet high, 3½ feet
wide _____ 800.00
Farm Scene. Farm house with children on porch, barn, cattle and
buggy. Medium size _____ 210.00
Farm Scene. House, barn, horses
in field, cat on porch, rider
approaching on horseback.
Approximately 30x20", in walnut
frame _____ 195.00
Girl. In blue dress, red background, brown hair and eyes,
with brown dog _____ 1400.00
Girl. Pouring tea. 26x30" gold
leaf frame _____ 825.00
Girl. Small, in red dress, brown
eyes, black shoes _____ 700.00
Man. Seining for fish. Bridge nearby. Trees and mountains in background. 38½x30½" _____ 150.00

**PURPLE SLAG, See COLORED GLASS SECTION**

## QUEZAL GLASS

A fine type of Art Glass produced at Maspeth, L. I., New York, from 1901 to 1920 by Martin Bach, Sr., a former Tiffany Glass Company employee. The glass was of the Tiffany type but generally improved in design. It is an overlay glass with a colored or opaque white over a pure transparent color. The outer layer of glass was drawn into various designs or shapes, often having a drape with a peacock eye at the end of the feather.

The glass was named for the Central American Quezal bird. All pieces are reported to have been signed with the word "Quezal."

After the death of Mr. Bach in 1920 his son-in-law, Conrad Vahlsing, opened a small shop near Elmhurst, L. I., New York, where he produced the same types of ware until 1929 when the glass lost its popularity. In later years Vahlsing marked his glass "Lustre Art Glass."

| | |
|---|---|
| BonBon Dish. Small, shallow. Gold, amethyst, scalloped top. Signed | 48.50 |
| Bowl. 10" diam., 3½" high. Blue, with matching 11" plate, purple and green iridescent | 210.00 |
| Compote. 6" diam., 8" high. Golden iridescence. Signed | 195.00 |
| Dish, Nut. 4" diam. | 55.00 |
| Gas Light Shade. 5¼" high, long lily leaves on opaque green, opaque yellow lining. Signed | 32.50 |
| Gas Light Shades. Bell-shaped, ribbed. Pair | 65.00 |
| Jar (or Vase). 8½" high, bulbous. Mottled green and orange with iridescent satin lining | 90.00 |
| Lamp, Hanging. Bysantine motif in white with feathers | 300.00 |
| Plate. 11¼" diam. Iridescent with rainbow rim | 125.00 |
| Rose Bowl. Footed, 4¼" wide. Deep gold with purple and red iridescence | 150.00 |
| Shade, Lamp. 6½" diam., 4½" neck. Mushroom-shaped. Signed | 65.00 |
| Shade, Lamp. 23" diam., 11¼" high. Vine and leaf decor, with milk maid and bucket | 90.00 |

Vases:

| | |
|---|---|
| 4" high. Iridescent blue, gold and green with red stripes | 180.00 |
| 5" high, 5" wide. Melon-shaped and colored in deep grass-green with lighter green stripes. Iridescent flowers and tendrils with highlights of gold, blue, green and rose. Opalescent pearl colored lining Signed | 195.00 |

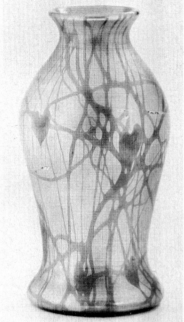

Vase. 8¼" high. Gold iridescent with pale green lines and leaves__ **$220.00**

| | |
|---|---|
| 6½" high. Signed | 210.00 |
| 9" high. Iridescent gold, green, blue, purple and bronze in feather design on emerald background | 225.00 |
| 9½" high. Gold color. Signed | 235.00 |
| 12" high. Green and white, bold stripes outside, gold iridescence inside. Signed | 365.00 |

### QUILTS, See LINENS

### QUIMPER

A type of pottery produced by Henry Quimper of Finistere, France, after 1900. It is usually decorated in bright colors with provincial scenes of the country. It was imported into the United States as a Gift Shop item until the beginning of World War II.

The marks "Henriot Quimper, France" or "Quimper" appear on most articles. It is decorative, fairly plentiful, but not yet particularly valuable.

Plate. 10" diam. Man with staff. White with green, yellow, blue __ **$15.00**

Bagpipe, Hanging _____ 15.00
Bell. 3". Yellow ground with blue
  florals _____ 12.00
Bowls:
  10½" diam., pink and blue _____ 16.50
  12" diam., holes for hanging ___ 21.00
Butter Dish. Covered, marked "Henriot Quimper, France" _____ 17.50
Butter Tub. Covered, 4½" diam.,
  2½" high _____ 14.50
Candleholder. Chamber-type, 5¼"
  high, handled _____ 16.50
Candlestick. Boy with jar on head.
  Marked _____ 12.00
Creamer _____ 10.00
Cup and Saucer. Square _____ 11.50
Inkwells:
  8" long, 4½" wide, pen tray and
  round covered well. Marked ____ 14.00
  12" long, double, decorated ___ 28.50
  14" long, 7" high. Portrait of
  girl in costume _____ 27.50
Knife Rest. Peasant scene _____ 7.50
Nappie. 5¾" diam. _____ 7.00
Pitchers:
  3½" high _____ 9.00
  Water _____ 28.50
Plates:
  5" diam. Signed. Pair _____ 17.50
  6½" diam. Decorated in yellow,
  blue, green, orange _____ 8.50
  7" diam. Portrait center _____ 7.75
  8" diam. Hexagonal. With portrait of girl with rope in center,

floral border _____ 13.50
  9¾", floral center, peasant type
  decor. Border _____ 9.00
Platter. 12" dragonfly center ____ 20.00
Porringer. Double, signed _____ 9.50
Salt. Oval _____ 3.50
Saucer _____ 3.50
Sugar Bowl. Yellow background,
  man and flowers _____ 25.00
Sugar Bowl and Creamer. Marked__ 22.50
Teapot. Small, red and white with
  yellow bands _____ 32.50
Tea Tile. On 4 feet, peasant decor 10.00
Tray. 15x8½", open handles, boy
  and girl center. Marked _____ 24.00
Tumbler. 4½" high. Marked _____ 8.75
Tureen. 14x9". Large, covered ____ 40.00

### RAILROAD ITEMS (PAPER)

Items in this category pertain to paper items such as bonds, passes, tickets and timetables.

SUNBURY & ERIE RAILROAD.
ONE SEAT,
UNION MILLS TO ERIE.
CONDUCTOR WILL TAKE UP THIS TICKET.

Ticket. Sunbury & Erie Railroad.
  Dated Mar. 9, 1861. Scarce _____ **$8.00**

Bonds:
  $1,000 Alabama & Chattanooga
  R.R. Co., 8% Second Mortgage
  Sinking Fund _____ 7.00
  $1,000 The Detroit & Lima Northern Railway Co. First Mortgage
  Gold Bond _____ 7.00
  $1,000 The Utah and Pleasant Valley Railway Co., First Mortgage
  5% Gold Bond _____ 7.00
  7% Gold Loan _____ 5.50
  $1,000 The Washington & Western
  R.R. Co., First Mortgage Gold
  Bond _____ 7.00
  $500.00 Charleston & Savannah
  R.R., Mortgage Loan _____ 5.75
Passes:
  Burlington R.R., 1898 _____ 7.50
  Civil War Soldiers _____ 8.75
  Grand Trunk, 1892 _____ 7.50
  Long Island R.R. Co., 1893 _____ 5.50
  Miss., Kansas and Topeka, 1897__ 7.50
  Missouri Pacific Railway Co.,
  1892 _____ 5.50
  Southern Pacific, 1898 _____ 7.50
  St. Louis, South-west, 1897 _____ 8.75
  Texas Pacific R.R., 1896 _____ 5.75

| | |
|---|---|
| Rules for Ticket Agents and Conductors of NL, NH & Hart. R.R., 1905 _____ | 9.75 |
| Tickets: | |
| B&O., 1876 _____ | 8.00 |
| Grand Trunk, 1888 _____ | 7.50 |
| Texas Pacific, 1896 _____ | 7.50 |
| Union Pacific, 1898 _____ | 7.50 |
| Timetable. Pennsylvania R.R., 1899 _____ | 7.00 |

## REVERSE PAINTINGS ON GLASS

The work was done in a manner to be observed through a pane of glass—the painting being executed on the back. This type of art was in demand in the 1820-1850 period. The popular subjects were men of national prominence, ladies of fashion and children.

| | |
|---|---|
| $5\frac{3}{4}$ x $6\frac{1}{2}$". Building in color. Gold frame _____ | $60.00 |
| Country Scenery. 21x25" _____ | 60.00 |
| Fire Screen. Tole frame with reverse painting on glass of bird and flowers. 23x23". English ____ | 110.00 |
| LaFayette. $12\frac{1}{2}$x$15\frac{1}{2}$" frame _____ | 150.00 |
| "Sweet Little Dear." $6\frac{3}{4}$x10", full length portrait of girl _____ | 100.00 |
| "The Jersey Beauty." Primitive-type, bust of girl. $10\frac{1}{2}$x$11\frac{3}{4}$" ____ | 85.00 |
| "The Young Cavalier." 8x10", framed _____ | 90.00 |
| Washington. 7x10" portrait _____ | 160.00 |
| Washington. $9\frac{3}{4}$x12". Standing at table with scroll in hand, eagle decoration in background _____ | 175.00 |
| Washington. 17x$18\frac{1}{2}$" _____ | 250.00 |

| | |
|---|---|
| Woman in blue gown. $7\frac{1}{2}$x10" ____ | 85.00 |

## REVOLVERS, See GUNS

## RIFLES, See GUNS

## RING TREES

Small tree-like objects of glass, metal or china, with branches for hanging or storing finger rings, are known as "ring trees."

| | |
|---|---|
| Cobalt glass with gold decor of leaves and flowers _____ | $22.50 |
| Bavarian China. Gold trim, floral decor _____ | 14.50 |
| China: | |
| $2\frac{1}{4}$" high. In shape of hand. Painted flowers on base _____ | 11.50 |
| 3" high. Pink floral decor on base _____ | 11.00 |
| $3\frac{3}{8}$" high. Green decor _____ | 12.00 |
| Copeland China. Morning glory and bee decor _____ | 15.00 |
| Cut Glass. In rich blue _____ | 40.00 |
| Metal. Marble base and 6" porcelain figure of man. Ornate _____ | 45.00 |
| Parian. Hand _____ | 19.50 |
| Shape of Hand. Mounted on heart-shaped gold plated metal tray __ | 18.75 |
| Tiffany Silver. $3\frac{1}{2}$" diam. Post $2\frac{1}{2}$" high _____ | 18.50 |

## ROCKINGHAM WARE

The original Rockingham Pottery was situated in the Staffordshire district of England and began operations before 1800. It is heavy and has a brown or chocolate colored glaze. The English type of table service is in white with or without decoration and gold trim. The product was made at many potteries in the United States—including the Ohio River establishments and Bennington, Vermont.

| | |
|---|---|
| Bird Whistle. 3'' long _____ | $27.50 |
| | |
| Bank. Turtle _____ | 29.50 |
| Bird Whistle. 3'' long _____ | 27.50 |
| **Bottles:** | |
|   Shape of potato _____ | 32.50 |
|   4x4''. Pair _____ | 60.00 |
| Bowl. 10½'' diam., mottled brown__ | 45.00 |
| Cat. 5½'' high. Early _____ | 37.50 |
| Coffee Pot. Dome top, acorn | |
|   finial. Scarce _____ | 110.00 |
| Compote. Low, turquoise flower | |
|   border _____ | 31.50 |
| Creamer. Cow _____ | 42.50 |
| Creamer. Squat, silver lustre with | |
|   fluted fan decor _____ | 32.50 |
| **Cups and Saucers:** | |
|   Plain white with rose and gold | |
|   decor _____ | 37.50 |
|   Tea. Green and gold with flower | |
|   sprays _____ | 38.00 |
|   Toy. Rose decor _____ | 15.00 |
| Lions. Pair _____ | 125.00 |
| Pitcher. 9'' high. Hound handle __ | 100.00 |
| Plate. Pie. Brown, 11'' diam. _____ | 26.50 |
| Poodles. 2 dogs at foot of tree | |
|   on each base. Pair _____ | 98.50 |
| Spill Holder. Bird medallion _____ | 22.50 |
| **Teapots:** | |
|   8-cup size. White and gold _____ | 30.00 |
|   ''Rebecca at Well'' _____ | 38.50 |
|   7¾'' high. 10½'' from handle | |
|   to end of spout _____ | 40.00 |
| Tea Set. Teapot, sugar bowl, | |
|   creamer, 6 cups and saucers __ | 280.00 |
| Tureen. 6'' high, 6½'' diam., | |
|   covered. Flowers and panels of | |
|   gilt and buff, scroll feet and | |
|   handles. Circa 1825 _____ | 77.50 |
| Vase, Wall. 8½'' long, 3'' top ____ | 18.50 |

| | |
|---|---|
| Window Stops. Lion head, high | |
| glaze. 5x4½x4'' _____ | 49.50 |

## ROGERS' STATUARY

John Rogers, who was born in America in 1829, studied sculpturing in Europe and produced his first Plaster-of-Paris statue ''The Checker Players'' in 1859, followed by ''The Slave Auction'' in 1860.

His works were popular parlor pieces of the Victorian era. He ''published'' at least 80 different subjects and the total number of groups produced from the originals is estimated to be over 100,000.

One of his best and largest pieces is ''The Council of War'' which shows President Abraham Lincoln, Gen. U. S. Grant and Edwin M. Stanton. Rogers' groups are not classified as works of art but are fine genre' items showing the life and times of the people of the Victorian period.

| | |
|---|---|
| ''Checkers up at the farm'' _____ | $70.00 |
| | |
| A Matter of Opinion _____ | 69.50 |
| A Frolic at the Old Homestead __ | 69.50 |
| Castles in the Air _____ | 68.50 |
| Checker Players. 1860 _____ | 75.00 |
| Checkers up at the Farm _____ | 70.00 |
| Coming to the Parson _____ | 72.50 |
| Con and Tatters _____ | 72.50 |
| Fairy Whispers. 1860 _____ | 69.50 |
| Fetching the Doctor _____ | 75.00 |
| Fighting Bob _____ | 80.00 |
| First Love _____ | 62.50 |

| | |
|---|---|
| Football | 92.50 |
| Going for the Cows | 62.50 |
| Ha, I Like That Not | 68.50 |
| Hide and Seek. 1875. With companion piece, boy or girl. Pair | 74.50 |
| "Is That You, Tommy?" Says granny, feeling goat's head. 11" high | 65.00 |
| It is So Nominated in the Bond | 70.00 |
| John Alden and Priscilla | 76.50 |
| King Lear and Cordelia | 67.50 |
| Legend of Sleepy Hollow. 3 subjects | 90.00 |
| Miles Standish | 69.50 |
| Neighboring Pews | 62.50 |
| One More Shot | 87.50 |
| Othello (Group scene) | 62.50 |
| Private Theatricals | 72.00 |
| Rip Van Winkle at Home | 89.50 |
| Romeo and Juliet | 69.50 |
| School Days. 1877 | 75.00 |
| Taking the Oath and Drawing Rations | 89.50 |
| The Bath. 1892 | 75.00 |
| The Charity Patient | 62.50 |
| The Council of War. Lincoln, Grant and Stanton | 175.00 |
| The Country Post Office | 89.50 |
| The Favorite Scholars | 82.50 |
| The Fugitive Story | 69.50 |
| The Photographer. With Companion piece. Pair | 90.00 |
| The Picket Guard | 70.00 |
| The Returned Volunteer | 80.00 |
| The Slave Auction | 70.00 |
| The Slave Mart | 72.50 |
| The Slave's Story | 75.00 |
| The Tap on the Window | 70.00 |
| The Town Pump | 82.50 |
| The Watch on the Santa Maria | 62.50 |
| The Wounded Scout | 74.50 |
| Union Refugees | 72.50 |
| We Boys. 1872 | 80.00 |
| Weighing the Baby | 77.50 |

## ROOKWOOD POTTERY

Rookwood is art pottery and was first made in 1880 by Mrs. Maria Longworth Storer, daughter of a wealthy family from Cincinnati, Ohio. The name was derived from the family estate "Rookwood" which was so named because of "rooks" or "crows" which inhabited the wooded grounds.

The underglaze background colors are usually in soft tints of brown and yellow. The decorations are also underglaze. In the period 1880-1882, the name "Rookwood" and the year of manufacture were incised or painted on the base. Between 1882 and 1886, the firm name, address and date appeared in the oval frame. The date was changed each year.

A reversed "R" and the letter "P" standing together were first used in 1886. In 1887, the same mark was utilized with the addition of one flame. In 1888, two flames appeared around the mark, and so on, until 1900, when 14 flames were present around the mark. Then in 1901, the Roman numeral I was added; in 1902, the numeral II was employed; and so on, to the mark with 14 flames.

The pottery was still in existence in 1952, but is now reported to be out of business. Items most desired by collectors are from the .1880-1900 period.

| | |
|---|---|
| Pitcher. 10" high. Green color, 1903 mark | $75.00 |

| | |
|---|---|
| Ash Tray. Green Alligator shape. Dated 1922 | 32.50 |
| Ash Tray. 1958. Large gray rook with extended wings — on side. 8" long, 4½" high | 30.00 |
| Bowl. Small, green to rose | 27.50 |
| Candle Holder. Chamber-type, 7" square, handled. Floral spray and leaf decor | 49.50 |
| Candlesticks. 3½", seahorse design. Pair | 40.00 |
| Chalice. 3-handled | 65.00 |

Chocolate Pot. 9'' high. Floral
decor. Circa 1890 _____ 72.00
Creamer. Small, signed. 1890 ____ 65.00
Creamer and Sugar Bowl. (1901).
With sprigs of cherries and
berries _____ 110.00
Cruet. Blue top, brown body.
Butterflies and grass decor.
(1884) _____ 70.00
Cup and Saucer. Demitasse size.
Sailing vessel in light blue on
white ground. 1896 mark _____ 32.50
Ewer. $4\frac{1}{4}$x$4\frac{1}{2}$''. 1901. Signed Howard
Altman. Yellow, orange and green
gooseberries on brown ground __ 115.00
Flower Bowl. Small, yellow _____ 32.50
Flower Holder. 4'' diam., medium
blue color _____ 8.50
Fount. Wall type. Figure of St.
Francis. 9'' high, light tan color.
1947 _____ 25.00
Frog. Flower holder, green gloss,
open mouth _____ 30.00
Jardiniere. 8'' diam., gold with
chrysanthemum sprays. Signed
''LTF'' _____ 57.50
Jug. Brown. Dated 1884 _____ 59.50
Lamp. 22'' high, electrified, brass
fittings _____ 110.00
Mask Container. (1930) _____ 27.50
Mug. Beer. $7\frac{1}{2}$ high, shaped like
barrel, banner over group of
drinking dwarfs inscribed ''Cincinnati Cooperage Co.'' Circa
1885 _____ 48.00
Mug. $4\frac{1}{2}$'', left-handed type _____ 42.00
Paperweights:
Elephant glossy, sea green
color. $4\frac{1}{2}$'' base _____ 55.00
$4\frac{1}{2}$x$4\frac{1}{2}$''. Ivory glazed nude girl,
seated. Signed Louise Abel 1928 48.50
Pitchers:
$6\frac{3}{4}$'' high. Tan and brown _____ 69.50
8'' high. Brown to tan, white
rose sprays, twisted twig handle
(1887) _____ 75.00
$8\frac{1}{2}$'' high. (1902). Pansy decor __ 80.00
10'' high. Brown with yellow to
brown floral decor _____ 89.50
Pitcher Vases:
Miniature. Olive green, brown
to orange, 1900. Signed ''LIL''.__ 50.00
Small. Dated 1901. Signed _____ 60.00
$9\frac{1}{2}$'' high, with pinched sides __ 75.00
10'' high. Circa 1891 _____ 80.00
Plaque. 9x12''. ''The Frozen Mirror'' _____ 65.00
Plate. $8\frac{1}{2}$'' diam., pastel floral
design, 4 flames, signed H.E.W.__ 65.00
Punch Bowl. Flame mark _____ 180.00
Rabbit, Standing. $3\frac{1}{4}$'' high, $3\frac{1}{2}$''
long. White mat glaze, 1910 ___ 37.50
Teapot. 7'' high. Dark mat-green
color, handle over top _____ 39.50
Tea Set. Teapot, sugar bowl and

creamer _____ 160.00
Tobacco Humidor. $6\frac{1}{2}$'' high. Yel-
lowish-green ground with black
and orange decor, 6-flame mark__ 70.00
Vases:
$4\frac{3}{4}$'' high. Running deer in green.
Dated 1932 _____ 25.00
$5\frac{1}{4}$'' high. Brown glaze with orange
and yellow blossoms. Signed
Clara C. Lindeman _____ 100.00
$6\frac{1}{4}$'' high. Light brown, 16 flames 50.00
8'' high. Brown with hand painted
flowers. Signed, 1892 _____ 80.00
$8\frac{1}{2}$'' high. Parchment or vellum
finish. Blue, gray and light
pink. Oriental style decoration.
Flame mark _____ 70.00
$9\frac{1}{2}$'' high. Yellow and black
background with clover leaves
and blossoms _____ 80.00
10'' high. Pear-shaped, green and
gold glaze. Floral decor in gold.
Marked, 4 flames (1890) _____ 90.00
$10\frac{1}{2}$'' high. Brown with yellow
to brown autumn leaves. 1898 and
Rookwood mark. Signed _____ 87.50
$12\frac{1}{2}$'' high. Madonna _____ 98.50

### ROSALINE GLASS

Rosaline is a form of rose-colored Jade
glass (colored alabaster glass). However,
due to its popularity, it has been separated into a color group. It was a product
of the Steuben factory.

Compote. Small. Steuben, Brass
base. $2\frac{3}{4}$'' high, $4\frac{1}{4}$'' wide _____ $190.00

Basket. 9'' long, 8'' high. Clouded
clambroth with heavy Rosaline
handle _____ 95.00
Bowl. 3'' high, $4\frac{3}{4}$'' diam. Signed
''Carder'' _____ 125.00
Cologne. $7\frac{3}{4}$''. Slender-type alabaster stopper and base _____ 200.00

**Compotes:**
12", alabaster foot _____ 215.00
Small. Steuben. Brass base. 2¾"
high, 4½" wide _____ 190.00
Cordial. 3½" high. Conical Rosaline
cup supported by slender alabas-
ter stem, round base. Signed
"Carder" _____ 150.00
Goblet, Water _____ 65.00
Sherbet. Alabaster stem and under-
plate _____ 175.00
Tazza. 8" diam., baluster stem ___ 295.00

## ROSE BOWLS

The term "rose bowl" is a general one
which covers a variety of crimped and
pinched-edge bowls. Their primary use
was for decoration. However, in season
rose petals were placed in them and the
pleasing aroma permeated the air. Most
of them are of the Art Glass-type which
were first made about 1880.

Rose Bowl. Yellow satin glass. 5½"
high. Floral decor _____ **$75.00**

Amberina type. Uncased. Honeycomb pattern. 6" _____ 135.00
Amethyst Glass. 8½" high, edged
in gold with enameled flowers __ 65.00
Blue Opalescent Spanish Lace.
4½" high, crimped rim _____ 40.00
Carnival Glass type. 5" _____ 45.00
Cranberry:
3¼" Crimped top, white enamel
decor _____ 40.00
4" _____ 52.50
Peachblow. New England, acid
finish. 4½" _____ 400.00
Satin Glass:
Blue. Herringbone. 4" high _____ 80.00
Light green with purple flowers
and gold decor _____ 55.00

Mother-of-Pearl. Salmon colored,
herringbone. 5" _____ 98.50
Pink to rose. Orange enameled
shell pattern. 3½" _____ 60.00
Yellow. Crimped top. 4" _____ 57.50
Yellow top, fading to white. 4½"_ 67.50
Vasa Murrhina _____ 57.50
Vaseline. Spanish Lace design,
crimped top. 4" _____ 37.50

## ROSE MEDALLION CHINA

Rose Medallion was produced in China.
It was decorated in Canton and exported
from there. The name generally applies to
pieces of glazed china or pottery having
medallions with figures of people, alternating with panels of pink flowers showing
birds and butterflies. The ware is called
"Rose Canton" if all the panels are filled
with flowers. The smaller pieces usually
have four panels; however, large platters
often contain six.

Candle Holders. 8" high. Pair __ **$145.00**

Basket. 6x9x5¼" high. Oval, with
teapot and 2 handleless cups in-
side. Handles, hinges and latch
in perfect condition _____ 90.00
Bottle. 16" high. Butterfly, with
stopper _____ 89.50
Bouillon Cup and Saucer. Covered 21.50
Bowls:
Oval, 10¾" across _____ 115.00
Fruit, with tray. 9½x10¾", open-
work sides, flared rim _____ 95.00
Rice. 4¾" diam., 2½ high _____ 24.50
Round. 9" diam. Common type __ 48.50
Box. 3½x7½", covered _____ 39.50
Creamers:
Helmet-type _____ 49.50
Squatty, bulbous _____ 40.00

## Cups and Saucers:

| | |
|---|---|
| Demitasse | 15.00 |
| Handleless | 22.50 |
| Heavy with thorn handle | 35.00 |
| Cuspidor. Scarce | 100.00 |
| Dish. $7\frac{1}{4}$", leaf-shaped | 24.00 |
| Dish, Vegetable. $9\frac{1}{2}$x11" | 60.00 |
| Ginger Jar. $3\frac{1}{2}$" high, covered | 48.50 |
| Jug. 5" high. Circa 1820 | 75.00 |
| Mug. $4\frac{1}{4}$" high | 25.00 |

Pitchers:

| | |
|---|---|
| Water. $6\frac{1}{2}$" high. Octagonal | 65.00 |
| $8\frac{1}{2}$" | 80.00 |

Plates:

| | |
|---|---|
| 6" diam., scalloped edge | 15.00 |
| $6\frac{3}{4}$" | 18.50 |
| 7" | 20.00 |
| $9\frac{1}{2}$" | 22.75 |
| 12" | 25.00 |

Platter. 11" long _____ **$45.00**

Platters:

| | |
|---|---|
| $7\frac{1}{2}$x$10\frac{1}{2}$" | 35.00 |
| $8\frac{1}{2}$x11" | 39.50 |
| $9\frac{1}{2}$x12" | 42.50 |
| 11" long | 45.00 |
| $12\frac{1}{2}$x$17\frac{1}{2}$" | 49.50 |
| $14\frac{1}{2}$x$17\frac{1}{2}$", oval | 72.50 |
| $16\frac{1}{2}$" long | 75.00 |
| Powder Jar | 18.50 |

Punch Bowls:

| | |
|---|---|
| $11\frac{3}{4}$" diam. | 100.00 |
| $14\frac{1}{2}$" diam., deep 4" rim | 120.00 |
| 16" diam. | 140.00 |
| Rice Spoons | 7.50 |
| Soap Dish. With drain tray | 65.00 |
| Sugar Bowl. Covered, $5\frac{1}{2}$", berry finial, 2 handles | 49.50 |

Teapots:

| | |
|---|---|
| 7" high, china handle. Finest type | 95.00 |
| $6\frac{1}{4}$" high, china handle, gold nut finial | 60.00 |
| In wicker basket, carrier with brass lock | 57.50 |
| Teapot and Cup. In original | |

| | |
|---|---|
| wicker basket | 75.00 |
| Tea Set. 3 pieces. $7\frac{1}{4}$" teapot, $4\frac{1}{2}$" creamer, 5" covered sugar bowl | 115.00 |
| Urn. 16" high, $9\frac{1}{2}$" diam. | 145.00 |

Vase. 12" high. Early type with Oriental decor _____ **$95.00**

Vases:

| | |
|---|---|
| $9\frac{1}{4}$" high | 75.00 |
| $13\frac{1}{2}$" high, $8\frac{1}{2}$" diam. | 98.50 |
| 36" high. Temple vase | 365.00 |
| Vegetable Dish. Covered, oval, gold finial | 79.50 |

## ROSE O'NEILL WARE

Rose O'Neill was a decorator who used Kewpie Dolls as illustrations. China bearing her name was made in Germany about 1900.

Cup and Saucer. Green and orange, impressed fern design with kewpie decoration _____ $25.00

Hair Receiver. Kewpies and flowers all over item. Has 2 handles ___ 33.50
Ice Cream Tray _____ 32.50
Kewpie with large umbrella _____ 35.00
Kewpie. 6¼", action type, "The Thinker." Original sticker with name "O'Neill" _____ 42.50
Mug. Kewpie _____ 24.50
Plate. 7½" diam. Green and orange. Impressed fern design, kewpie decoration _____ 29.50
Sugar Bowl. Covered _____ 37.50
Tea Set. Teapot, sugar bowl and creamer, 6 cups and saucers, blue coloring, decorated with kewpies. Signed _____ 115.00
Vase. 6½". Blue and white Jasper-ware with four kewpies _____ 35.00

## ROSEVILLE POTTERY

Roseville Pottery was made in Zanesville, Ohio, after 1900. Much of it bears the mark "Rozanne."

Baskets:
10" high. Green with rust colored flowers _____ 18.00
10" to top of handle. Soft blue, gray colors with white roses ____ 15.00
Hanging. Suspended on 3 chains, raised flower design _____ 11.00
Bowls:
8" diam. 2 handles. Fuchsia flowers on blue ground _____ 12.75
11" diam. With matching candle-

sticks. Handled. Blue with cream colored lilies _____ 18.00
Candle Holder. Short, blue. Pair__ 8.50
Console Set. 10" footed bowl and pair of candlesticks _____ 21.75

Basket. 10" high. Green with rust colored flowers _____ $18.00

Cookie Jar. Two-handled. Dark green ground with white magnolias. 10½" high, 9" diam. ___ 19.50
Ferner. 8", green poinsettia decor_ 12.75
Frog. Handled. For flowers _____ 6.00
Jug. Handled. 7" high, 4½" diam. Hand painted grapes and blossoms. Signed _____ 29.50
Rose Bowl. 2 handles. 4½" high ___ 5.75
Sugar and Creamer. Blue with whitish-yellow flowers _____ 12.75
Teapot. Blue with white berries and leaves _____ 10.75
Vases:
5" high, 21" diam. Pink floral decor. Handled _____ 10.00
7½" high. Bud. Light green shading to dark green at base. Pair 13.50
8½" high. Blue with white flowers. Handled _____ 15.00
9" high. Wide-type. Blue with pine cone design, twig handles. Impressed "Roseville 1148" ____ 15.75
15½" high. Brown to amber with yellow lilies, green branches beside them. Two handles, flared collar _____ 25.00
Cornucopia-type. High gloss ____ 14.50
Wall Pocket. "R.V." mark _____ 6.50

## ROYAL BAYREUTH

A late type of novelty porcelain made in Germany. The tapestry type, which has the appearance of woven tapestry, is considered the most desirable. The creamers and other objects were made in a variety of designs. The following list is representative of the ware.

Bowl, Vegetable. Tomatoes on pastel
    green. 9½'' diam. _____ $25.00

Apple. Red and yellow, with green
    leaves _____ 20.00
Ash Trays:
    Devil. Arms extend over top, legs
    around base. Small curled tail __ 24.50
    Moose head, antlers form edges_ 18.00
Basket. Rose tapestry, ruffled edge_ 65.00
Bell. Painting of children at play __ 35.00
Bowls:
    Berry. Large, grape design, irreg-
    ular border _____ 60.00
    Salad. Tomato _____ 20.00
    9½'' diam., 2½'' deep. Dutch girl
    and house scene, blue sky, white
    clouds _____ 32.50
Boxes:
    5x4'', covered, black and tan
    with pink roses _____ 18.00
    Spade-shaped with peasant and
    turkey decor _____ 22.50
    Large, covered. Rose tapestry
    with portrait _____ 55.00
Bread and Milk Set. Nursery decor 30.00
Candle Holders:
    Cape Cod scene with Sunbonnet
    babies fishing _____ 38.50
    Chamber-type. Pink roses on
    blue ground _____ 20.00
    Clown holding hat _____ 28.50
    Santa Claus. Saucer-type with
    ring holder _____ 75.00
    5½'' high, handled. Hand painted
    violets with gold trim _____ 31.50
Celery Vase _____ 28.50
Chocolate Pot. Rose tapestry.

8½'' high _____ 165.00
Compote. Small, 2½x4'', pastoral
    scene _____ 24.00
Creamers:
    Alligator _____ 24.50
    Apple _____ 24.50
    Bear _____ 23.50
    "Black Eagle" _____ 24.00
    Cards. 3½'' high. Red devil handle 40.00
    Cat. Black, 5'' high, red glaze
    interior _____ 24.00
    Children running _____ 27.00
    Children sliding down hill _____ 29.50
    Clown. 4½'' high, red body, white
    head spout _____ 24.00
    Coal Hod. 3½'' high. Rose tapes-
    try _____ 36.00
    Conch Shell _____ 20.00
    Corn _____ 23.50
    Cow decoration _____ 21.00
    Dog's head _____ 24.00
    Ducks on green background ____ 17.50
    Eagle, gray _____ 20.00
    Geranium _____ 24.00
    Goats, Mountain. Scenic _____ 17.50
    Goose Girl. Rose tapestry.
    Medium _____ 55.00
    Horses in pasture _____ 20.00
    Lemon _____ 24.00
    Little Boy Blue decor _____ 22.00
    Lobsters:
    3½'' _____ 30.00
    4½'' _____ 35.00
    Oak Leaf _____ 25.00
    Orange. 4¼'' high. Red _____ 21.50
    Pansy _____ 21.50
    Pig _____ 21.50
    Poppy. 4¼'' high. Red _____ 35.00
    Ram's Head _____ 28.50
    Rose Tapestry. 3½'' high. Scenic 65.00
    Shell, Conch. Mother-of-Pearl type
    glaze _____ 28.50
    Strawberry _____ 26.00
    Tomato _____ 24.00
Cups and Saucers:
    Chocolate size. Rose tapestry __ 48.00
    Demitasse. Tomato-shaped, leaf
    saucer _____ 21.00
Dishes:
    Dachshund. 5'' long _____ 30.00
    Lobster. Covered _____ 23.50
    Tomato. Covered _____ 22.50
    Tomato. Covered, with tray ____ 24.00
    Vegetable _____ 27.50
Dresser Set. 3 pieces. Rose tapes-
    try _____ 175.00
Hair Receivers:
    Barnyard Scene. Blue mark ____ 20.00
    Rose tapestry. 3 gold feet _____ 30.00
    Rose tapestry. Turkey decor ____ 45.00
    Sunbonnet Babies _____ 23.50
Hatpin Holders:
    4¼'' high. Red poppy _____ 18.00
    Rose tapestry, with portrait ____ 60.00
Humidor. 7'' high, covered, barrel
    shape _____ 57.50

Inkwell. 4'' diam., covered. Girl
holding dog on leash _____ 28.00
Match Box. Playing card top. Red
devil's head handle _____ 35.00
Match Holder. Devil and cards.
Blue Mark _____ 24.00
Mayonnaise Set. Poppy _____ 24.00
Mug. ''Ye Old Belle'' scene. Cava-
liers drinkng. Green ground ____ 25.75

Mustard Pot. Tomato shape, red
with green decor _____ $14.00

Mustard Jars:
Lobster, covered, with original
leaf spoon _____ 24.50
Tomato, covered _____ 26.50
Pitchers:
Alligator _____ 30.00
Cat handle, black body _____ 32.50
Conch Shell. 3½'' high. ''Atlantic
City,'' marked _____ 21.50
Clown. In bright red. Spout
forms face. Large size _____ 60.00
Corinthian. Large, with portrait 49.50
Cow. Black _____ 36.50
Crow. Black _____ 38.50
Hunting scene. 7½'' high _____ 26.50
Lobster. Large, with bowl.
(Cracker Set) _____ 59.50
Moose. Milk size _____ 30.00
Polar Bear _____ 32.00
Poodle. Gray _____ 32.50
Poppy. 6½'' high. Satinized stem
type handle, pastel yellow and
green _____ 62.50
Robin. Milk pitcher _____ 39.50
Seal. Gray _____ 36.50
Shell, Conch. Mother-of-Pearl type
glaze _____ 40.00
Sunbonnet Babies. ''Mending'' __ 48.00
Plates:
5½''. Leaf, with handles _____ 24.00
7''. Leaf, with handles _____ 29.00

7½'', Pastoral scene, raised shell
border _____ 35.00
7½''. Rose tapestry. Gold decor on
edge _____ 75.00
9''. Black Corinthian _____ 39.50
9¾''. Rose tapestry. Gold decor
on edge _____ 85.00
10''. Rose tapestry. Hanging-type,
deep, with scalloped border, gold
trim _____ 87.50
Powder Jars:
Covered _____ 24.50
Rose tapestry, covered, 3 gold
feet _____ 65.00
Salt. Open, lobster claw _____ 7.00
Salt and Pepper Shakers:
Lobster _____ 23.50
Rose tapestry _____ 60.00
Tomatoes on green leaf _____ 21.50
Sauce Dish. Rose tapestry _____ 25.00
Shoe. Man's brown oxford, laces __ 48.00
String Holder. Hanging. Rooster __ 30.00
Sugar Bowls:
Apple, covered _____ 37.50
Red devil handle. Open _____ 22.50
Sugar Bowls and Creamers:
Footed. 5'' high. Lime green body
decorated with flowers, finial and
handles with gold trim _____ 24.00
Lobster _____ 50.00
Tomato _____ 40.00
Teapots:
Apple _____ 37.50
Rose tapestry _____ 120.00
Sunbonnet Twins _____ 60.00
Tomato _____ 32.50
Tea Sets:
Apple. Teapot, covered sugar
bowl and creamer _____ 140.00
Tomato. Teapot, covered sugar
bowl and creamer _____ 75.00
Tomatoes:
Covered. On ring-handled tray __ 27.50
Covered. On green lettuce plate 23.50
Covered _____ 20.00
Toothpick Holders:
2½'' high. 2 handles, 4 gold feet 16.00
Coal Hod. Rose tapestry _____ 45.00
Trays:
Celery. 12'' long. Conch shell
design, tinted edges _____ 28.50
Dresser. 8x11''. White ground
with pink roses, gold border __ 32.00
Dresser. Rose tapestry _____ 150.00
Tumbler. Mountain scenery _____ 25.00
Turtle. Covered _____ 26.50
Vases:
2½''. ''Little Bo-Peep'' handles 30.00
4¼'' diam., ball-shaped. Deep
blue, with doll seated on log
with frog _____ 42.00
6½'' high. Rose tapestry. Farm boy
and turkeys _____ 95.00
10'' high. ''Don Quixote'' _____ 42.50

## ROYAL BONN

The factory was established in the latter part of the 18th century by Clemers August. The majority of the ware found in antique shops today is from the Victorian period.

Plate. 7¾'' diam. Blue decor _____ **$7.00**

Bowl. 9½'' diam., wild rose and heart decoration _____ 20.00
Celery Tray. Floral decor _____ 15.00
Cheese Dish. Castle mark _____ 35.00
Clock. 15'' high, 12'' base. Blue and gold trimmed rococo case. Pink and red roses. Ansonia works with outside escapement, chime strike. Running order _____ 100.00
Cracker Jar. Daisies and gold decor 37.50
Dishes:
    3-section, handled. 10'' diam., floral and gold decor _____ 36.50
    9x6½''. In claw-foot silver-plated holder _____ 35.00
Ewer. 10½'' high. Delft-type decor 70.00
Plates:
    7¾'' diam. Blue decor _____ 7.00
    9'' diam., hand painted _____ 17.50
    9½'' diam., portrait _____ 21.50
Punch Bowl (or deep Salad Bowl). 10'' diam., 5'' high. Pink with yellow roses inside and out, gold decorated top _____ 85.00
Stein. Large pouring size. Masked spout, blue and white body, raised circle of old men's heads with grape decor. Porcelain __ 195.00
Tray, Dresser. Floral decor _____ 15.00
Vase, Portrait. 15'' high. Leaf stem handles. Bust of girl on shaded

green base, green leaves, pink lilacs _____ 55.00

Pitcher Vase. 7'' high. Cream ground with floral and leaf decor. Gold decorated handle and trim _____ **$35.00**

For ILLUSTRATIONS of Royal Bonn, refer to numbers 10 and 27 under "Pitchers and Vases."

## ROYAL COPENHAGEN

Royal Copenhagen has been produced continuously since the factory was established in 1772. It was under royal management in 1799. Much of the ware was imported into the United States from 1875 to 1900.

BonBon Dish _____ 18.50
Bottle, Wine. 10'' high. Oval picture of Fredercksborg Castle on front, crown on back _____ 32.00
Chocolate Pot. Blue and white with spring-type lid _____ 77.50
Coffee Pot. Underglaze decor in cobalt blue. Gold edge and handles traced in gold _____ 82.50
Compote. Muschel pattern, triangular, early mark _____ 68.50
Cruet. Blue and white, original stopper _____ 59.50
Cup, Saucer and Plate. Blue with white flower decor _____ 29.50
Dish. Oval, blue and white _____ 22.50
Donkey (Collector's Item) _____ 135.00
Plaques:
    5½'' diam. Zodiac signs around angel _____ 45.00

388

5¾'' diam., white marked "B & G" with 5 different subjects including "Night" and "Day." Set of 5 _____ 145.00
13¼'' diam. Mythological figures of winged woman and children with flowers and owl. Pair ____ 250.00
Cherubs making wine. Circa 1815. Pair _____ 80.00

Plate. 8½'' diam., deep. Flower in brown, black and green leaves __ $17.50

Plates:
7½'' diam. Christmas _____ 27.50
9¾'' diam. Blue and white ____ 20.00
Bread and Butter. Blue and white 8.50
Soup. Blue and white _____ 12.00
Soup. 7¾'' diam., open-chain edge, blue decoration, green mark ____ 14.00

Platters:
8x10''. Blue and white _____ 36.00
9x12''. Blue and white _____ 39.50
12x16''. Blue and white _____ 57.50
Stork (Collector's Item) _____ 140.00
Teapot. Blue and white _____ 55.00
Tureen, Vegetable. Covered ____ 70.00
Turtle (Collector's Item) _____ 95.00
Vase. 9½''. Fuchsia flowers and leaves _____ 57.50

### ROYAL CROWN DERBY

The factory now in existence was established in England between 1875 and 1880 and had no connection with an earlier factory which operated around the turn of the 19th century. It is estimated that 99% of the ware found in antique shops today is from the later factory.

Creamer and Sugar Bowl. Miniature. Set _____ 40.00

Urn. Footed, 9¾'' high. Blue color with gold, looped handles _____ $215.00

Cups and Saucers:
Demitasse. Flowered, with blue, gold and green decor _____ 22.50
Pink and blue decor inside and out, deep saucer. Impressed and stamped _____ 29.50
Tea Cup. Blue chinoiserie decor 29.75
Dishes. 10½x7½'', kidney-shaped. Cobalt blue border, rose center, gilt trim. Pair _____ 78.50
Egg Cup. 2'' _____ 14.00
Ginger Jar. 7½'' diam., red mark. Gold and green, red embossed flowers. Signed Tiffany & Co., N. Y. _____ 248.50
Mug, Child's. 2¼'', double gold handles, gold, blue and henna colors _____ 35.00
Pill Box _____ 22.50
Pitchers:
Neptune's Mask. Dolphin tail. Circa 1769 _____ 110.00
Satyr's Mask. Circa 1790 _____ 120.00
White body with blue and gold decor. Pink, purple and white flowers. Circa 1810 _____ 115.00

Salt and Pepper Shakers. In silver-
plated holder _____ 50.00
Teapot _____ 75.00
Tray. 17x13". White body with blue
flowers in swag design. Gold
edge. Handled _____ 85.00
Tureens. 7" long, covered, oval.
Lion's mask, claw feet, handles.
Multicolor painted floral groups.
Pair _____ 230.00
Urn. Footed, 9¾" high. Blue color
with gold, looped handles_____ 215.00
Vase. 10" high, blue and white,
gold trim _____ 85.00

ground with blue and yellow de-
cor. Top 4½x5½" _____ 32.50
Compote _____ 33.50
Creamer. 3½" high. Brown back-
ground with Egyptian figures on
light tan band, Egyptian head
spout _____ 21.00
Cups and Saucers:
Canterbury Pilgrims _____ 16.00
2-handled. Blue, silver trim ____ 12.50
Cuspidor. 9" diameter at bottom,
8" high _____ 18.00
Dinner Set. Service for 12, "Old
Leeds Spray." Octagonal _____ 300.00
Dish, Child's. 8½" diam. "There
Was a Little Man and He Had a
Little Gun" _____ 12.75

## ROYAL DOULTON

A type of decorated hard-porcelain pottery manufactured in England. It is often
decorated with drawings of scenes from
daily life and usually was finished with a
dark brown glaze. The type mainly found in
antique shops today was made after 1890.
Some of this ware is still being manufactured and imported into the United States.

Pitcher. 6¾" high. Black with classic
figures in red robes _____ $49.50

Bowls:
8" diam., 4" deep. Forest scene
with girl walking with basket__ 24.00
Salad. With 12 8½" plates. Pink
and green poppy decor. Set __ 70.00
Cake Stand. 9½" diam., 4¼" high.
Pastel florals on top. Gold scal-
lop edge _____ 45.00
Candle Holder with Portraits ____ 75.00
Cheese Dish. Base 6½x7½". White

Bottle. Zorro. 10½" high _____ $45.00
Figurines:
5½" high. "Tinkle Bell." Girl in

pink costume _____ 36.50
7½" high _____ 30.00
Jardiniere. 8" high, 8" diam.
White with dark blue floral decor _____ 24.75
Mugs:
Name on side _____ 14.00
The Gleaners _____ 15.00
Perfume. Stoneware. 2¾" high.
Hinged top. Sgfritto design. In
blue, brown and white. Silver-
topped cork _____ 42.50
Pitchers:
6". Milk. "Madras" _____ 22.50
6". "Paddy" _____ 25.00
6". "Robin Hood" _____ 27.50
6¾". Black with classic figures in red robes _____ 49.50
7". "He Who Buys Land, Etc."_ 22.75
7½". Colored tavern scene _____ 26.50
8". Morrisian _____ 23.50
9". Hunting scenes _____ 27.50
9½". Tan with leaf and floral
decor in relief _____ 30.00
Shape of blackjack _____ 38.50
6½". Monk's plate. "And He
Peers in the Face of His Lord-
ship's Grace" _____ 16.00
8". Little Bo-Peep nursery rhyme 18.00
8¾". Twelve-sided, parakeets,
flower decor _____ 14.50
8⅞". "Battle of Hastings" _____ 17.00
9". White background with blue
and gold decor _____ 18.50
9". Monk in wine cellar _____ 20.00
9". "Mr. Micawber Delivers Some
Valedictory Remarks." Dickens
character _____ 21.50
10". "Bermuda" coat-of-arms in
center _____ 14.00
10". Pink willow _____ 11.00
10½". Portrait of Shakespeare __ 22.50
10¼". Sailing vessels _____ 20.00
10½". Dickens "Poor Jo" _____ 25.00
10½". Dickens "Old Peggoty" __ 25.00
10½". Dickens "Mr. Squeers."
Signed "Noke" _____ 27.50
10¼". Dickens "Trotty Veck."
Signed "Noke" _____ 27.50
10½". Golfing scene _____ 24.50
10½". Horseless Carriage Series:
"Itch Yer On Guvenor?" _____ 29.50
"Room For One" _____ 29.50
10½". Portrait of Isaac Walton
in center _____ 30.00
10½". "The Gypsies" _____ 22.50
10½". "Solington Tournament,"
dueling knights _____ 20.00
10½". "The Admiral" _____ 21.50
10½". "The Squire." Man in red
coat, yellow vest _____ 23.50
10½". Two men in red coats
drinking _____ 21.50
11". Dickens "Fagin" _____ 27.50
13". White with tall blue flowers _____ 32.00

Platter, Turkey. Painted turkey in
center _____ 65.00
Punch Bowls:
12" diam., 7" high. Gallon capacity. Dark blue and gold decor
on foot. Bowl decorated inside
and outside in lighter shades
of blue and white with gold ____ 92.50
17" diam. Blue background with
hops decor. Grecian Key border
in blue and gold at top and
base _____ 115.00
Set, Child's. 3 pieces. Bowl, plate
and egg cup. "Bunnykins" _____ 18.50
Soap Dish. With drain. Rose and
gold decor _____ 19.50
Teapots:
Stoneware. Brown with tan decor
in relief _____ 42.50
4½" high. Squatty, rose decor __ 40.00
Tobacco Jar. "Dickens ware" ____ 37.50
Toby Jug. Small. Lord Nelson ____ 15.00
Tureens:
12x8", covered, allover hunt
scene _____ 60.00
Soup. With ladle _____ 75.00
Vases:
Small. Iris decor _____ 22.50
8" high. Raised decor in blue
and brown. Signed, dated 1887.
Pair _____ 60.00
10" high. Orange and blue ____ 24.00
12½" high. 2 handles, brown with
monk decor _____ 48.50

### ROYAL DUX

Nude figure in semi-reclining position. 8" long, 6½" high _____ $55.00

Bowls:
5x9½". Applied leaves over body,
with handles. Oval _____ 32.50
6x9½". Green background, rose

391

spray decor, small open-twig
handles _____ 35.00
Box. 5¼x7½". Covered, elephant
finial. Red panels, gold border __ 87.50
Figurines:
  6½" high, 8" long. Nude, in semi-
reclining position _____ 55.00
  7" high. Stalking lioness on oval
base, 13¾x5¼". Pink triangle
mark _____ 150.00
  12" high. Pair _____ 220.00
  14½" high, 12" long. Maiden at
pool. Red triangle mark _____ 95.00
  18" high. Girl with water jug __ 125.00
Planter. 7x11". Woman in Grecian
costume holding vase. Ivory with
gold trim _____ 87.50
Vases:
  9½" hIgh. Horizontal semi-clad
female figures. 19" long at base 97.50
  10" high. Boy spraying flowers
from tank on back. Beige and
brown coloring _____ 57.50
  10" high. Ewer-shaped pitcher
vase. Applied flowers, cherries
and peaches _____ 65.00
  11½" high. Ivory ground painted
with pink flowers and green
leaves. Pair _____ 140.00
  16" high, Lady in carriage coachman at each end. In cobalt, blue,
white and gold _____ 125.00

## ROYAL FLEMISH GLASS

Royal Flemish Glass was made by the Mt.
Washington Glass Works at New Bedford,
Mass., in the late 1880's. This same factory
produced Burmese, Crown Milano and other
Art Glass. The glass is russet-brown with a
satin finish and is decorated with gold.

Vase. 4" high, handled Opaque
enamel decor in russet, tan and
brown with enamel gold decor.
Gold dragon in medallions with
initials "R.F." _____ $875.00

Cookie Jar. Mt. Washington. Gold
coin medallions, silver top and
handles _____ 650.00
Pitcher _____ 900.00

Vase. 14½" high. Chrysanthemum decor on frosted ground. Orange at
neck and base _____ $800.00

Vases:
  4" high, handled. Opaque enamel
decor in russet, tan and brown
with enamel gold decor. Gold
dragon in medallions with initials
"R.F." _____ 875.00
  11" high. Stick type, 7½" high
neck. Bulbous base _____ 895.00
  Bulbous, unsigned. Medallion design with gold dragon _____ 750.00

## ROYAL RUDOLSTADT

The factory was established in 1758 at
Volkstedt and later moved to Rudolstadt in
Schwartzburg. The early mark was the letter "R". Later a mark representing a hay-
fork, part of the arms of Schwartzburg, was
used. Still later, crossed two-pronged hay-
forks were utilized to imitate the Dresden
or Meissen mark.

The majority of the items appearing in
shops today is of the late 19th and early
20th century period.

The late marks show a shield with the
letters "RW", a crown on top, with the
word "Crown" above and the name "Rudolstadt" below the shield. Another mark has
the word "Germany" in place of the word
"Crown" which indicates that ware so
marked was definitely made after 1891.

Plate. Fruit decor _____ **$11.50**

| | |
|---|---:|
| Bowl. 10" berry. Decorated with small pink peonies _____ | 38.50 |
| Cake Set. 7 pieces _____ | 37.50 |
| Celery. Painted violet decoration, gold edge _____ | 12.50 |
| Cheese Dish. Small, slant-top, decorated with roses _____ | 13.75 |
| Compote. Small, covered. Large raised yellow enameled roses, gold trim _____ | 24.50 |
| Cream Pitcher. 3¾" high. Scalloped edge and gold trim at top, satin finish. Floral spray on cream background. (Illustration #28 under "Pitchers and Vases") ____ | 18.50 |
| Cup and Saucer. Newport Belle pattern _____ | 16.50 |
| Dish, Pickle. 8½" long, 4" wide, 1⅛" high. Rose decor, open handles _____ | 9.75 |

Salt and Pepper Shakers. Hand painted floral decor. Pair _____ **$14.50**

| | |
|---|---:|
| Dish, Vegetable. Rose medallions on interior with gold decor, 3 gold ball feet _____ | 19.50 |
| Hair Receiver. 4½" diam., body with off-white decorated with green, orchid and pink flowers _____ | 18.50 |
| Hatpin Holder. Decorated with roses and lavender _____ | 14.00 |
| Lamp. 10" high. Dresden-like coloring in pastel pink, blue and gold. (Illustration #34, under "Lamps, Glass") 6_____ | 125.00 |
| Pitcher. 4½" high. Flower spray medallions with gold decor, serpent handle _____ | 38.50 |
| Plate. Beethoven portrait. Marked__ | 22.50 |
| Plate. 11" diam., rose decor. Marked "Prussia" _____ | 23.50 |
| Platter, Fish. 15", green base color with fish _____ | 32.00 |
| Salt and Pepper Shakers. Hand painted floral decor. Pair _____ | 14.50 |
| Sugar and Creamer. Violet and gold on cream ground. Set _____ | 27.50 |
| Tray, Perfume _____ | 18.75 |

Vase. 8¼" high. Cornucopia with flying dragon. Beige with mocha__ **$65.00**

Vases:
| | |
|---|---:|
| Bulbous, satin finish, floral spray on cream background. (Illustration #4, under "Pitchers and Vases") _____ | 30.00 |
| 9½". Floral decor, gold handles _ | 37.50 |
| 14". Ornate, beige with pastel flowers and gold decor, gold handles _____ | 90.00 |
| 16¼". Grecian motif, light pastel colors _____ | 115.00 |

### ROYAL VIENNA

The factory was founded in 1720 in Vienna, Austria, by a runaway foreman from the Meissen works. In 1744, Empress Maria Theresa brought it under Royal patronage.

The wares were of the Meissen-type and noted for their brilliant colors and technical excellence. The factory closed in 1864.

The so-called "Beehive" mark on the ware was one of its distinguishing features. The majority of the ware on the market today has been produced by other factories who have made modern reproductions. Items made after 1891 have the country of origin (Austria) as well as the "Beehive" mark.

Compote. 8¼" diam., 4½" high. Floral decor in blue and green___ $40.00

Basket. Porcelain, green body and handles, applied red cherries and green leaves _____ 60.00
Bowl, Berry. 9¾" diam. Light pink shading to red, decorated with pink poppies, leaves, bouquet of lilies in center, gold trim on edge 37.50
Cracker Jar. Covered _____ 65.00
Cup and Saucer. Blue. Beehive mark 16.75
Dinner Set. Service for 12. Dark red, gray and gold colors _____ 480.00
Figurines. Porcelain lady dancers. 10" high, 4" bases, colorful costumes. Pair _____ 285.00
Perfume Cruet. Cobalt blue, gold trim, medallion of woman and cupid _____ 48.50
Pitchers:
Satyr's Mask _____ 72.50
10" high. Tankard-type. Beehive mark _____ 65.00
12" high. Red background with gilt sprays. Large picture panel, "Die Hochzeit" (The Wedding), depicting 19 figures, horses and chariot. Signed Huber. Circa 1815, gilt handle _____ 140.00

Dresser Tray. 8¼ x 12". Hand painted violet decor on pale green ground, gold trim _____ $25.00

Plates:
9¼" diam. Portrait of Queen Louise _____ 49.50
9½" diam. Classic figures in center. Red band border with a gold edge _____ 50.00
9¾" diam. Woman with two attendants. Cream and gold, maroon border. Signed Kaufmann 49.50
10" diam. Bathing scene, blue and gold border, maiden, cupid and swan _____ 49.50
15" diam. Hanging-type. Blue border, colorful classic scene, gold scroll decoration on border 115.00
Rose Jar with Lid. Dark red background, gold decor. Portrait of woman, by Wagner, outlined in Jewels _____ 95.00

Fruit Bowl. 9¼" diam. Pierced sides, green and yellow on white ground $15.00

Tea Caddy. 7" high. Red and cream background with gilt sprays. Two large panels of courting lovers. "Amor Und Cephiste" and "Rinaldo Und Almeido." Signed C. Herr. Circa 1820 ____ 115.00

Tea Set. Pot, creamer, sugar bowl, 2 cups and saucers _____ 125.00

Tray, Dresser. 7¼x11". Green with gold. Classic scene. Kaufmann _ 45.00

Urns:
  6" high. Green decor with gold, including handles and knob. Hand-painted panels on sides __ 72.50
  15" high. Covered, flower and figure panels _____ 139.50

Vases.
  8½" high, 9¼" circumference. Scene depicts story of Moses. Mother holding child, children riding lions _____ 150.00
  10" high. Portrait (Klysti). Iridescent blue and gold. Signed Schieslneer _____ 149.75
  19½" high, 9" diam. Ornate ____ 95.00
  Small. Beehive mark _____ 54.50

## ROYAL WORCESTER

The porcelain works was established in 1751 by Dr. John Wall and 14 partners. Dr. Wall died in 1776 and the entire business was sold to Thomas Flight in 1783. Martin Barr was admitted as a partner in 1793 and the firm was known as Flight & Barr. In 1807 the name was changed to Flight, Barr & Barr. It was changed again in 1813 to Barr, Flight & Barr, or "B.F.B." and continued as such until 1840 at which time Chamberlin & Son and Barr, Flight & Barr were consolidated. The works was moved to Dighlis, the home of Chamberlain & Son. The company was sold to Kerr & Binn in 1852 and it is still in existence. Most of the ware encountered in the United States is of the 1870-1900 variety, although an occasional piece of the Dr. Wall or Flight & Barr is found.

Bone Dish. Blue flower decor ____ 9.00
Bowls:
  Medium size. Dr. Wall period __ 100.00
  9" square. 19th century. Butterfly and sprig decorations _____ 67.50
Butter Dish. Dr. Wall period. Circa 1770. Blue and white _____ 125.00
Cache Pot. 2¼" high, 2½" diam. White porcelain with decor of roses, blue bells, berries, dragonfly, etc. Gold trim, on three gold feet _____ 32.50
Camel. Kneeling. 10" long, 7" high (Hadley) _____ 89.50
Candle Holder. Bright gold mouse nibbling on dull gold tallow, sitting on simulated wood platform. Handled. 6" long, 2¾" high __ 100.00
Candle Snuffer. Old gent wearing night cap and bathrobe. Has toothache, 3¼" high _____ 50.00
Chocolate Pot. Cream background 70.00

Vase. 8½" high. Pair _____ $135.00

Cracker Jar. Covered, with matching plate, floral decor _____ 72.50
Creamer. Florals with green decor 45.00
Cups and Saucers:
  Demitasse. Cream ground, rust flowers _____ 18.75
  Demitasse. Cream porcelain. Circa 1885-1900. Multicolored hand decor outlined in gold __ 27.50
  Pink flowers _____ 32.50
Ewer. 8½" high. Old purple mark, cream ground, purple flowers, raised faces and animal heads. Ornate _____ 195.00
Figurine. 10" high. Man and woman, soft tones. Pair _____ 295.00
Flower Holder. Horn-shaped _____ 35.00

**Mugs:**
Child's. 2¼'' high. Shaded flesh color ground with pink and yellow poppy decor _____ 28.50
Chocolate. Enameled peacock, scalloped rim _____ 22.50

**Pitchers:**
5½'' high. Bulbous at base, narrow at neck, green and rust color with cowslips and wild rose decor ___ 55.00
9'' high. Horn-shaped. Cream background _____ 65.00
Large. Portrait spout. Registery #119925 _____ 57.50
10¼'' tankard-type. Floral decor on cream ground with raised design in gold flowers and branches at top. Gold reeded and entwined handle _____ 90.00

Vase. 8'' high. Blue lilies, leaves on white ground, gold trim _____ $20.00

**Plates:**
8''. "Melba." Set of 12 _____ 92.50
8¼''. Floral scene, raised shell edge _____ 29.50
9''. Buckingham pattern. Late __ 15.00
9''. Floral center, leaf border____ 23.50
9½''. Medallion scene, basket-weave border, gold edge _____ 39.50
10¼''. Painted floral decor ____ 28.50
Rose Tree. 7'' high. Circa 1800, in pot decorated with birds, insects and flowers _____ 125.00
Sauce Boat. Dr. Wall period. Circa 1770. Blue and white _____ 100.00
Sugar Shaker. Signed _____ 24.50
Tea Caddy. 5½'' high, marked, gold and blue spatter _____ 57.50

**Teapots:**
Dr. Wall. Circa 1790. Chinese style painted decor. 7¼'' high___ 200.00
Squat. 5-cup size. Satin finish, floral decor _____ 60.00
Tea Set. Teapot, sugar bowl and creamer. Leaf and floral decor, brown twig finials on blue leaf covers _____ 145.00
Tureen. 11½'' high. Blue and gold decor, in oriental style, with platter and ladle _____ 160.00
Urn. 9'' high, floral decor with green lizard forming handles ____ 90.00

**Vases:**
5½'' high. Pitcher. Floral decor 50.00
10½'' high. Circa 1760. Blue and white relief molded, cabbage leaves, leaf band at top. Meissen crossed swords _____ 180.00
11'' high, floral decor and gold. Applied handles _____ 100.00
11½'' high. White with tan, gold acorn design. Pair _____ 225.00
For Illustrations of Royal Worcester, refer to Numbers 6, 11 & 14, under "Pitchers and Vases."

### R. S. PRUSSIA CHINA

A type of china made in the latter part of the 19th century in Prussia, one of the German States. The quality is similar to Haviland and Limoges. The majority of it was factory decorated. However, occasionally a piece turns up bearing the name of a decorator. The ware bears the mark as follows: Letters "R. S." with a green wreath and red star.

Berry Set. Bowl and 6 dishes. Pastel poppies on tinted background, gold scalloped edge. Set _____ 120.00

**Bowls:**
8½'' diam. Green on white ground, gold decor, floral center 60.00
10'' diam. Raised orchid border, rose in center, gold scalloped edge _____ 59.50
11'' diam. Baroque-type, large roses _____ 62.50
12'' diam. Double scallop, gold edge, flowers, pink orchid and white poppies _____ 57.50
Cake Plate. Floral decor, handled 50.00
Celery Holder. Pink roses. Red mark _____ 70.00
Chocolate Set. Pot, 8 cups and saucers. Green on white with gold trim. Set _____ 175.00
Compote. Pedestal type. 7'' high 6½'' diam. Green ground, decorated with shaded roses. Red mark _____ 68.50

Hat Pin Holder. 5'' high _____ $42.50

Cracker Jars:
  Covered. Bulbous. Pink rose decor
  with green wreath and red star
  mark _____ 85.00
  6½'' to top of finial. Green decor
  with gold sprays _____ 75.00
Creamer. Swirled, pearl-lustered
  body with daffodils outlined in
  gold _____ 60.00
Cups and Saucers:
  Demitasse. Green and white floral
  decor _____ 30.00
  Swans and Trees _____ 42.50
  Tea. Flower decor, red star mark 37.50
Hair Receiver. Diamond-shaped __ 30.00
Hatpin Holder. Poppies _____ 27.50
Ice Cream Set. Master bowl and
  6 individual bowls _____ 100.00
Mustard _____ 32.50
Plates:
  6½''. Rose decor. Set of 6 ____ 60.00
  7½'' diam. Rose decor, raised
  border _____ 45.00
  8½''. Pink poppies and white lilies
  of the valley. Irregular edge __ 58.50
  10'' diam. Open handles _____ 52.50
  11'' diam. Swans swimming, gold
  border with blue, yellow and
  green background _____ 60.00
Powder Box. Rose decor _____ 34.50
Relish Dish. Open-handled. 4½x9''.
  Pastel florals and gold _____ 25.00

Ring Tree _____ 30.00
Sauce Dishes:
  Gold scalloped edge, pastel
  poppies on tinted background.
  Set of 6 _____ 60.00
Set. Creamer, sugar and teapot.
  Rose decor _____ 12.00
  All footed, red mark _____ 195.00
Shaving Mug. Pink flowers, gold
  trim, green leaves _____ 85.00
Sugar Bowl. Covered, pink roses
  and green leaves with gold ____ 60.00
Sugar Bowl and Creamer. Footed,
  red rose decor. Set _____ 80.00
Sugar Shaker. Satin finish. Roses
  around base, three handles ____ 25.00
Syrup Pitcher _____ 40.00
Teapot. Footed, red rose and green
  leaf decor with gold trim ____ 80.00
Toothpick Holder. Swirl design __ 20.00
Tray, Dresser. Green, with pink
  roses. 7½x11½'' _____ 80.00
Vases:
  8'' high. Pink and white flowers
  on yellow ground _____ 49.50
  11'' high. Pitcher-type, footed.
  Pink flowers and gold decor __ 62.50

## RUBINA GLASS

    The glass appears to have first been made
by the Geo. A. Duncan & Sons Co., at
Pittsburgh, Pa., in 1885.
    Part of the item was made of ruby glass
which gradually "melted" into a clear body.
Some objects were then frosted which produced a beautiful effect.

Bowl. Small, footed. Red to yellow
  color _____ $110.00

Atomizer Bottle. Swirl design.
Marked "Baccarat" _____ 40.00
**Bowls:**
Finger. Plain _____ 27.50
Hobnail. 5½" high, 5"diam. In
two-handled silvered holder __ 100.00
Rose. 5", ribbed, with green and
gold enamel decor _____ 62.50
Square. Petal edges, sparking
fern pattern in bottom _____ 50.00
Cruet. 7½" high. Hobnail _____ 90.00
Perfume Bottle. 4½" high, 1½"
square. Clear cut stopper ____ 30.00

Pitcher, Water. Hobnail, 7" high,
clear applied handle _____ $125.00

**Pitchers:**
7½" high. Hobnail _____ 135.00
10" high. Inverted Thumbprint
with enameled flowers _____ 140.00
Inverted Thumbprint _____ 130.00
Plain _____ 80.00
Water. Hobnail, 7" high. Clear
applied handle _____ 125.00
Salt and Pepper Shakers. Enamel
floral decor. Pair _____ 69.50
Sugar Shaker. 6" high _____ 32.50
Tumbler _____ 34.50
**Vases:**
8" high _____ 48.50
10", enameled flowers _____ 65.00

### RUBINA VERDE GLASS

A type of colored glass which is now
considered to be in the field of Art Glass.
The first of this ware was made by

Hobbs, Brockunier & Co., Wheeling, W. Va.,
around 1890. The glass shades from yellow-
green to a cranberry color.

Pitcher, Water. Bulbous body. Hobnail. Clear applied handle _____ $195.00

**Bowls:**
Finger. Inverted thumbprint __ 57.50
Fruit. 8" square top, 3½" deep.
Diamond quilted _____ 95.00
Rose. Large _____ 60.00
9" high, 4" deep. Rounded-
down scalloped rim _____ 70.00
9¾x6¾", shallow, crimped top __ 120.00
Butter Dish. Daisy and button pat-
tern, clear base, domed thumb-
print cover _____ 169.50
Candlesticks. Pair _____ 65.00
Creamer. 3¼" high, 2¼" wide at
top _____ 72.50
Cruets. 6½" high. Pale yellow-green
at base shading to cranberry in
the necks. Inverted thumbprint
bodies, applied clear crystal han-
dles, cut crystal stoppers. Pair 190.00
Cup, Punch. Enamel decor _____ 60.00
**Dishes:**
For butter and cheese _____ 148.50
Open, oval, shallow, 5¾x9½" __ 125.00
Epergne. 3 horns with hanging bas-
kets _____ 185.00
Mustard Pot. I.T.P. _____ 48.50
Pickle Castor. Resilvered frame and
lid _____ 130.00
Pitcher, Water. Hobnail, clear ap-
plied handle _____ 195.00
Sauce Dish. 4½" square. Pointed
hobnail, ruffled top _____ 38.50
Shade. Large hall lamp type ____ 135.00
Tumbler _____ 70.00

**Vases:**
  5½" high. Ruffled top, opalescent
  coin spots, clusters of gold and
  pastel flowers _____ 69.50
  7" high. Ribbed green base
  shading to ruffled cranberry top.
  Applied green glass rigaree
  around body _____ 78.50
  8¾" diam. Trumpet-shaped with
  8 scallops at top _____ 80.00
  9½" high. Flared top, 6-pointed
  petals, gold scrolls and flowers 90.00
  12" high. Jack-in-the-Pulpit, with
  applied clear ribbons. Pair __ 100.00

## RUSSIAN ENAMELS

A type of enamel work on metal, especially brass, by Russian craftsmen during the
Czarist period. Each item usually has the
Russian bird or eagle mark. The ware is
not too plentiful and collectors are on the
search for it.

Spoon. Transparent enamel bowl
  with poison container at top ____$175.00

Blotter, Rocker. Knob holder _____ 125.00
Bottle, Scent. Perfume compartment
  at both ends with black enamel
  and silver caps. Opening in
  center _____ 200.00
Bowl. Sloped sides, beaded rim.
  2½" across. Signed _____ 425.00

Brandy Taster. Signed _____ 385.00
Candle Holders:
  7" high. Ornate marble base.
  Pair _____ 325.00
  Spoon-type, with bobeches _____ 250.00
Cup, Borsch. Bird, 3¾" long ____ 265.00
Inkwell and Pen Holder _____ 150.00
Kofsch, 6" long _____ 500.00
Letter Opener. 3" handle on 12"
  wood opener. No. 84 on handle _ 125.00
Match Holder _____ 140.00
Salt Dip. 1⅞" diam., 1" high. Sign-
  ed F. R. 88, silver gilt _____ 225.00
Scoop. 4½" long _____ 295.00
Spoon, Salt. 2⅝" long _____ 85.00
Tie Pin. For bowtie, 2⅛x1", sign-
  ed 84 AA _____ 175.00
Vodka Cup. Signed _____ 425.00

## SABINO GLASS

| | |
|---|---|
| Butterfly _____ | 14.00 |
| Cat _____ | 13.00 |
| Cherub _____ | 12.00 |
| Cluster, 2 birds _____ | 70.00 |
| Cluster, 3 birds _____ | 100.00 |
| Dog, German Shepherd _____ | 13.00 |
| Dragonfly _____ | 45.00 |
| Elephant _____ | 12.00 |
| Feeding Bird _____ | 14.00 |
| Fighting Bird _____ | 14.00 |
| Fish _____ | 13.00 |
| Mini-birds _____ | 9.00 |
| Mocking birds _____ | 34.00 |
| Napkin Ring of birds _____ | 12.00 |
| Pekingese dog _____ | 12.00 |
| Pheasant _____ | 16.00 |
| Pigeon _____ | 12.00 |
| Rabbit _____ | 12.00 |
| Rooster _____ | 16.00 |
| Snail _____ | 15.00 |
| Swan _____ | 12.00 |
| Teasing bird _____ | 32.00 |
| Turkey _____ | 16.00 |
| Turtle _____ | 12.00 |

## SALOPIAN WARE

A type of decorated pottery made at
the Caughley pot-works, Salop, Stroph-
shire, on the Severn River in England. In
1772 Thomas Turner took over the works
and produced fine porcelain.

In 1780 Turner opened his "Salopian"
Warehouse on Portugal St., Lincoln Inn
Fields, London. His mark was "Salopian"
or the letter "S" impressed or painted in
blue underglaze, and occasionally an impressed 8-pointed star. He is noted for the
famous "Willow" pattern which he originated.

Turner retired in 1799 and the works was
sold to John Rose & Co. In 1815 the establishment was moved across the river to
Coalport where the plant is still producing under the name of Coalport.

**Cup and Saucer.** House pattern ___ $135.00

Creamer. House pattern _____ 270.00
Cups and Saucers:
    Deer pattern _____ 125.00
    House pattern _____ 135.00
Plate. 8½'', pastoral scene, yellow
    border _____ 145.00
Saucer. 2 birds and cottage. 4⅞''
    diam. _____ 60.00
Teapot. House pattern _____ 320.00
Tea Set. Blue and white decoration,
    4 handless cups and saucers.
    Covered teapot, covered sugar
    and creamer. Some pieces mark-
    ed ''Caughley''. Set _____ 650.00

## SALT GLAZE

The Staffordshire district of England was considered the center for salt glazed pottery. The ware has a hard glaze which resulted from throwing regular table salt into the hot kiln. The salt vaporized and fixed itself, in fine drops, to the items. It is reported that it is still being produced in England.

Bowl. 8½'' diam., 4'' high, plain__ 27.50
Dish, Olive. 7'' long, 5¾'' wide.
    Late _____ 16.50
Hunt Jug. Blue glaze at top and
    upper part of handle. THOs.
    PEAT ESQ.' 1801 _____ 125.00
Pitchers:
    Basketweave design _____ 55.00
    8'' high. Raised fern and flowers,
    thorn handle. Dated 1835 _____ 60.00
    8½'' high. Stork in lily pads,
    bearded man spout _____ 65.00
    Scene from Tam-O-Shanter. Im-
    pressed Ridway, olive green
    color. 6¾'' high _____ 50.00
Syrup Jugs:
    7¼'' high. Melon-shaped with al-
    ternating blue and white stripes,
    pewter top. Marked ''W.B.
    Flounger, Cobridge'' _____ 55.00

Water Jug. 8½'' high. Circa 1845.
    Cherubs in relief _____ $65.00

9¼'' high. Pewter-type cover,
    Bacchus design in relief _____ 69.50
Figures in high relief. Original
    top _____ 59.50

## SAMPLERS

Examples of samplers date back to the late 1700's. The earliest ones were made in a rectangular shape—being higher than they were wide. Later examples were square. Before the fad died out about 1900 the shape had changed again and they became longer and narrower. A typical sampler was made by embroidering colored thread in a cross-stitch design onto a piece of material. The usual design included flowers, the alphabet, the maker's name and age, and the date.

Genealogical. Listing husband, wife
    and their children as born, with
    dates. 14'' square handspun lin-
    en cloth. Black, green and red
    colors _____ 85.00
Dated 1805. Small, never framed 60.00
Dated 1812. Small, (Name), aged
    12, 1812 _____ 57.50
Dated 1818. 17x20''. Alphabet,
    trees, birds, house, name of mak-
    er ''Elizabeth Voorhees'' _____ 80.00
Dated 1825. Medium, name and
    date. Framed _____ 68.50
Dated 1829. ''Wrought By'' (Name),
    age 11, (Town and State). Wide

embossed border of flowers and
vines. Framed _____ 85.00

Dated April 21, 1836. 13 x 17'',
(Name), Monongalia, Va. _____ **$75.00**

Dated 1831. 8 x 17''. Alphabet and
name of maker "Christina Bau-
man" _____ **$55.00**
Dated 1835. 21'' square. Alphabet,
verse, flowers. Framed _____ 90.00
Dated 1838. Alphabet and embossed
pictures below with flower pots
and trees. (Name), age 11 ____ 82.50
Dated 1848. 12x13'', alphabet and
numbers _____ 68.50
Dated 1848. 23x23'', birds, flowers,
lions, buildings, verse. Framed 85.00

### SANDWICH GLASS

Basket. Overshot, deep cranberry
shading to pink. Twisted thorn
handle _____ 145.00
Bowls:
  5¼x8''. Overshot, reeded feet __ 89.50
  6¼'' diam. Flat, lacy. Tulip and
  acanthus leaf _____ 60.00
  6¼'' diam. Flat, lacy. Princess
  pattern _____ 50.00
  Industry. Lacy, with scalloped
  edge _____ 140.00
Candlesticks:
  Canary yellow, fluted column.
  Pair _____ 125.00
  7'' high. Blown candle cups,
  flaring six-sided stem and heavy

flint glass bases. Clear glass.
  Pair _____ 69.50
Carafe. 9½'' high, 5'' diam. Over-
lay, blue to white to clear. Star
cut stopper. Enamel decor in
panels _____ 130.00
Cheese Dish. Covered _____ 125.00
Creamer. Individual type _____ 27.50
Cup Plate. Opalescent. (Rose-Lee
No. 522) _____ 25.00

Goblet. Star and Punty _____ **$35.00**

Decanter. Blown and engraved.
Applied reeded handle _____ 37.50
Dish. Deep. 10'' diam. Peacock
Feather with Bull's Eye pattern__ 120.00
Ewer. 12½'' high, amber thorn handle, deep pink at top shading
into white at bottom _____ 180.00
Lamps:
  8½'' high. Amethyst _____ 260.00
  11'' high. Canary. Pair _____ 220.00
  Electric blue, 8-panel font _____ 180.00
Paperweight. Scrambled type ____ 72.50
Pitchers:
  Water. Smoky amethyst. High handle with mask at base. Applied
  latticino bands in gold and white
  around base of neck, top and
  spout _____ 120.00
  5½'' high. Milk pitcher, tankard
  shape _____ 27.50
  11½'' high. Overshot white glass
  with bladder for ice. Circa 1865 98.50
  13'' high. Overshot, with bladder,
  naturalistic handle _____ 175.00
Plates:
  7¼'' diam. Roman Rosette _____ 57.50
  9¾'' diam. Beehive pattern _____ 69.50
  Octagonal. Thistle & Starr pat-

tern with scroll and leaf bor-
der _____ 92.50
Salt. Footed, rayed base. 3'' high,
3'' diam. Flint _____ 18.00
Salt, Master. Purple-blue shades.
Crown pattern _____ 139.50
Sauce Dish. 4½''. Lacy, Peacock
Eye Scroll _____ 19.50
Spill Vases. Hairpin loop. Tall,
ribbed stem. Clear flint glass.
Pair _____ 57.50
Sugar Bowl. Covered, acanthus pat-
tern _____ 98.50
Sugar Shaker. Diamond Quilted,
original top _____ 65.00

Pitcher. 10½'' high. Overshot, with
a metal lid _____ $140.00

Tie Backs:
Opalescent, lacy, pewter screws:
3'' diam. _____ 25.00
4½'' diam. _____ 30.00
Toilet Water Bottle. Emerald green,
original stopper _____ 45.00
Tray. 6½x5''. Unidentified pattern __ 40.00
Vases:
5½'' high. Fireglow. Pair _____ 75.00
7½'' high. Amethyst. Pair _____ 195.00
9'' high. Amethyst. Pair _____ 215.00

11¾'' high. Canary. Pair _____ 195.00
15'' high. Mottled red and aventurine, with applied amber rim
and feet _____ 145.00
Whiskey Taster _____ 18.50
Wine. 4'' tall. Ivy pattern _____ 12.50

## SARREGUEMINES CHINA

The factory was established in Germany
in 1770 and operated by Utzchneider & Co.
Later a factory was put into operation at
Degoin, France. They made sets of chinaware, novelties and cameo ware of the
quality of Wedgwood.

Plate. 7¼'' diam., "Songs of Roland" $9.75

Asparagus Set. Celadon green,
embossed asparagus on 12 plates.
Platter with drain. Set _____ 50.00
Dishes:
Covered, 5½'' diam., 4-leaf clover
shape _____ 20.00
Fruit. Blue floral china, in wire
frame _____ 13.75
Pitchers:
Cream. 4¾'' high. Pink interior,
greenish-yellow exterior _____ 13.00
6½'' high. For milk. Originally had
pewter lid. Transfer pictures of
children _____ 18.00
8¼'' high. Pewter top, cherub
decor _____ 26.50
8½'' high. Dark green, picnic
scene in relief _____ 24.50
Man's head _____ 25.00
Plates:
7¼'' diam. "Songs of Roland" __ 9.75
8'' diam. Varicolored flowers __ 10.00
8½'' diam. Napoleonic military

plate with French captions under
picture _____ 14.50
12'' diam. Fruit decor _____ 14.00

## SATIN GLASS

†The glass was brought to perfection in
1886 by Joseph Webb, an Englishman by
birth, who patented the process while working for the Phoenix Glass Co., Beaver,
Penna. ˒

The object was first blown into a mold
with diamond, circular or square shaped
depressions—usually opal or milk glass
was employed. Next, a colored transparent
coating of glass was applied over the core.
The third step in the manufacture was the
application of a colorless transparent covering of glass. The object was then annealed
or tempered by heat. The final step was
to treat the item with hydrofluoric acid
vapor which produced a satin finish to the
surface. It was always acid finished, never
polished or frosted by sandblasting or grind-
ing. The range of colors is broad but pink
and blue are the most prominent.

Compote. 9¼'' diam. Blue, ruffled,
fluted, frosted white edge. Silver
plated base _____ $225.00

Bobeches. Swirled rose pattern with
applied camphor rim. Scalloped,
fluted rim. 5'' diam., pair _____ 40.00
BonBon Dish. 4¼'' high, body 7x6''.
White Mother-of-Pearl, diamond
quilted. Ribbon-crimped rim
folded down on two sides. 4
applied camphor feet, berry pontil _____ 150.00
Bowls:
6'' footed bowl, Mother-of-Pearl
Satin Glass. Deep blue with
applied thorny feet in crystal.

One of the finest examples of
Satin Glass _____ 420.00
Blue. Diamond quilted pattern,
on silverplated stand _____ 195.00
Pink. Berry bowl _____ 100.00
Red. In silver frame _____ 100.00
Boxes:
5¼'' square. Embossed and enameled with pink and blue flower
clusters _____ 95.00
7½'' square. White with pink
lustre scrolls, blue forget-me-
nots, pink lustre scrolled edge __ 125.00

Cracker Jar. Pink glass, shell pattern with enamel decor. Top and
handle resilvered _____ $150.00

Cracker Jars:
Orange shading to yellow with
painted flower decor and silver-
plated lid _____ 100.00
Ribbon pattern in pink. Silver
plated bail and top _____ 250.00
Rose. Diamond quilted Mother-
of-Pearl, with silverplated lid
and bail. Bulbous _____ 125.00
Creamer. Blue Mother-of-Pearl,
scalloped top, threaded handle__ 150.00
Dish. 8½'' diameter, in RARE Rainbow Satin Glass. Delicate shades
of blue, yellow and pink with
fine scroll decor in gold _____ 450.00
Ewer. 7'' high, melon ribbed, deep
rose to pink, herringbone, cam-

phor glass handle and stopper__ 195.00

**Finger Bowls:**
Blue and pink _____ 115.00
With plate. Bowl, 5'' diam., 4¾''
high; plate, 6'' diam. Chartreuse
to cream. Each has folded-down
crimped rim with applied frosted
edging _____ 145.00

**Lamp, Hall.** Blue Mother-of-Pearl,
diamond quilted shade and brass
frame _____ 250.00

**Lamp. Red Satin.** Maple leaf design. GWTW type. Electrified __ 150.00

**Mustard Pot.** 2⅞'' high. White ribbed satin with blue enamel flowers and dots. Resilvered top and
handle _____ 55.00

**Perfume Bottles.** Melon shape, lime
yellow with floral decor. Pair __ 75.00

Vase. Ewer-type. 8½'' high. Shading
from coral at top to pale pink.
Pair _____ $210.00

**Pickle Castors:**
Blue, diamond quilted, in re-
silvered frame _____ 195.00
Mother-of-Pearl, diamond quilted.
Light to deep pink insert, or-
nate holder, re-silvered frame __ 225.00

**Pitchers:**
9'' high. Diamond quilted _____ 300.00
10'' high. Diamond quilted,
with ruffled fluted top _____ 325.00
12¾'' high, 6½'' widest diam.
Rainbow Mother-of-Pearl, applied
camphor glass handle _____ 360.00

**Plate.** 6'' diam. Rainbow Mother-
of-Pearl, ruffled edge _____ 295.00

**Puff Jar.** 5x4'', open, rose decor __ 80.00

**Rose Bowls:**
4'' high. Pink with yellow and
green enamel decor _____ 70.00
4'' high. Pink shading to blue __ 80.00
5½'' high. White Mother-of-Pearl,
egg-shaped. Venetian diamond
pattern, applied camphor thorn
feet, amber stems with canary-
yellow flowers on 3 sides _____ 125.00

**Salt and Pepper Shakers.** Enameled
flower decor. Pair _____ 69.50

**Set.** Creamer, spooner and sugar
bowl. Enameled daisies, silver
lids and top rims _____ 225.00

**Sugar Bowls:**
Ivory shading to rose. Diamond
quilted Mother-of-Pearl _____ 185.00
Pink. Diamond quilted. Covered__ 200.00
Red. With creamer. Silver lid __ 145.00

**Sugar Shakers:**
Blue. Plain _____ 55.00
Melon shape. Cream shading to
blue, floral decor, silver top __ 75.00

**Tumblers:**
Diamond quilted, scarce apricot
color _____ 90.00
Pink, with blue and yellow flow-
ers and brown leaves _____ 80.00
Pink. Diamond quilted _____ 85.00
Yellow swirl _____ 75.00

**Vases:**
5'' high. Green shading to white
with applied white flower with
rose-amber center, amber leaves
and handle _____ 185.00
6'' high. Rose shading to pale
pink with "Hobnail". Mother-of-
Pearl pattern. Rare _____ 200.00
6'' high. Blue, diamond quilted,
ruffled top _____ 200.00
6½'' high. "Jack-in-the-Pulpit."
White body with applied camphor
petal feet. Apple-green lining __ 215.00
8½'' high. Rainbow satin. Decorated with gold enamel. Delicate pastel blue, pink and yellow vertical striplings, sprays of
small leaves, berries and clusters
of blue and red blossoms, light
cream casing _____ 595.00

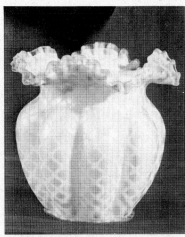

Vase. 7'' high. Ruffled edge, light blue with diamond quilting in white ------------------- **$195.00**

9'' high. Shaded apricot to salmon pink. Mother-of-Pearl with gold and silver decor of birds and flowers. Applied frosted crystal handles ----------------- 400.00

$10\frac{1}{2}$'' high. $5\frac{1}{2}$'' widest diam. Yellow quilted Mother-of-Pearl -- 225.00

$10\frac{1}{2}$'' high. Diamond quilted, white to amber to yellow ------ 200.00

$12\frac{1}{2}$'' high. Bottle shaped, gold leafage, lustreless white satin glass. Mt. Washington --------- 210.00

14'' high. Lavender, red and blue stripes. Bulbous base, slender neck ------------------------- 300.00

## SATSUMA WARE

Named for a Japanese War Lord, Satsuma, who brought skilled ceramic workers to Japan from Korea after a victorious campaign about the year 1600.

Much of the ware on the antique market today was produced by mass production methods during the past 75 years and cannot be compared with the finer handmade items of the previous centuries.

Basket. 9'' long, 6'' wide, 4'' high. Decor of flowers and butterflies in red, blue and black. Gold trim on ivory ground ---------------- 40.00

Bottle, Saki. $6\frac{1}{4}$'' high. 4 panels depicting family life. Rich blue background with gold decor ---- 85.00

Bowl. $6\frac{1}{4}$'' diam. ---------------- 70.00

Box. Covered, $1\frac{3}{4}$'' diam. -------- 48.50

Brush Holder. 5'' high. Decor of colorful flowers and butterflies on cream colored ground ------ 15.00

Plates. $9\frac{3}{4}$'' diam. Each ------------ **$65.00**

Vase. 11'' high --------------------**$125.00**

Buddha. Seated, small ----------- 35.00

Cake Plate. $1\frac{1}{2}$'' flower border. Marked ''B.C.&W.'' ------------ 40.00

Coffee Pot. Peacock among vines and branches with gold scrolls, etc. ------------------------- 65.00

Creamer. $4\frac{3}{4}$'' high. Cream background with red and white flowers, green leaves and gold decor ---------------------------- 58.50

Cups and Saucers:
Demitasse --------------------- 30.00
Gilt faces on men and women. Edges decorated in blue and gold 40.00
Two-handled ------------------ 35.00

Ginger Jar. Covered, square, 6'' high. Figures over body -------- 65.00

Incense Burner. White, known as Awata Satsuma. Circa 1790---- 35.00

Incense Jar ---------------------- 60.00

Inkwell. Butterfly, bird and floral decor. Dimpled hinged top ---- 40.00

Jardinier. 7'' high, resembles 1000 face pattern in blue, green and yellow. Embossed red figures, gold scrolls ------------------ 48.50

Lamp --------------------------- 92.50

Mustard Jar. Covered, gold encrusted design --------------------- 24.00

Pitcher ------------------------- 69.50

Pot-Pourri Jar. $3\frac{3}{4}$'' high -------- 42.50

Rose Jar. 4'', signed ------------- 55.00

Salts. Open. Set of 6 ----------- 44.00

Sugar Bowl, $5\frac{1}{2}$'' high, and Creamer, 4'' high. Set ------------------ 75.00

Teapot. $5\frac{1}{2}$'' high. Cream background with red and white flowers, green leaves and gold decor --------- 67.50

Tea Set. 15 pieces. Teapot, creamer and sugar bowl, 6 cups and saucers. Gold and typical color decorations, crackle, glaze. Signed ------------------------ 165.00

Cup and Saucer. Gilt faces on men and women. Edges decorated in blue and gold ------------------- $40.00

Urn. Large, 3 Fu dogs ----------- 300.00
Vases:
4¼" high. On teakwood stand. "Ladies and the Warrior's" ---- 75.00
6" high, 4" diam., for buds. Decorations on 4 sides depicting groups of figures -------------- 87.50
7½" high. Jeweled. Pair -------- 165.00
12" high, bolted base. Green with red and gold chrysanthemums ----------------------- 110.00
13½" high, warlord on white elephant surrounded by warriors. Much gold -------------------- 125.00

## SCALES

Prior to 1900, the balance scale was commonly used for measuring weight. A variety of styles and types were used by druggists, farmers and storekeepers.

Balance Scales. Iron base, brass trays, 19½" long. Buffed --------- $30.00

Brass:
Arm, 22½" long, "Doyle,

England" --------------------- 87.50
Druggist, enclosed in glass dome. Dozen small weights ----------- 30.00
Wood Base. English. Burnished and lacquered ----------------- 120.00

Balance-type Scale. Circa 1850. Polished ----------------------- $75.00

Iron:
"Eureka". 17¼" high, brass tray, 10¼" diam. Marked John Chatillon & Son, N. Y. Pat. dates 1869 and 1872 ---------------------- 52.50
With two brass pans, 6¼" diam., 1¾" deep ---------------------- 39.50
Jewels Scales. Brass pans, marble-top base, with drawer --------- 40.00

## SCHOENHUT TOYS

Albert Schoenhut came to America from Germany in 1865. In 1872, at Philadelphia, Pa., he established the firm of A. Schoenhut Company, which made standard size and toy pianos.

In 1903 the firm introduced a Humpty Dumpty Circus which was an immediate success. In 1911 the first doll was placed on the market. It had patented steel spring hinges and swivel joints. The wood heads were not hand-carved but were made on a multiple carving machine. Then, in December of 1913 a walking doll was marketed. The manufacture of dolls was abandoned in 1924 due to the importation of cheap German and Japanese dolls.

Albert Schoenhut died in 1912 but the

firm is still being operated by members of the family.

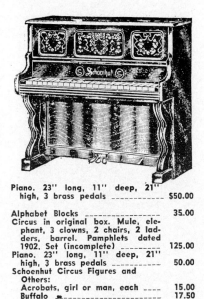

Piano. 23" long, 11" deep, 21" high, 3 brass pedals _____ $50.00

| | |
|---|---|
| Alphabet Blocks _____ | 35.00 |
| Circus in original box. Mule, elephant, 3 clowns, 2 chairs, 2 ladders, barrel. Pamphlets dated 1902. Set (incomplete) _____ | 125.00 |
| Piano. 23" long, 11" deep, 21" high, 3 brass pedals _____ | 50.00 |
| Schoenhut Circus Figures and Others: | |
| Acrobats, girl or man, each ____ | 15.00 |
| Buffalo _____ | 17.50 |
| Clown _____ | 15.00 |
| Elephant _____ | 15.00 |
| Giraffe _____ | 18.00 |
| Hippopotamus _____ | 16.50 |

Schoenhut Mule _____ $12.50

| | |
|---|---|
| Horse _____ | 15.00 |
| Lion _____ | 15.00 |
| Mule _____ | 12.50 |
| Ringmaster _____ | 21.50 |
| Sheep _____ | 14.50 |
| Tiger _____ | 15.00 |
| Zebra _____ | 17.50 |

## SCONCES, WALL

A sconce is a lighting device of the wall bracket type, usually ornamental in design, used for holding candles or lamp fonts.

Brass. 3-arm. French, lacy design.
Pair _____ $85.00

| | |
|---|---|
| Brass: | |
| 2-arm. American. Pair _____ | 45.00 |
| 2-arm. burner. Pair _____ | 45.00 |
| 3-arm. French, lacy design. | |
| Pair _____ | 85.00 |

Brass. 2-arm. American. Pair _____ $45.00

| | |
|---|---|
| Iron. 2-arm, with candle holder. Pair _____ | 32.50 |
| Tole. 14" high, candle type. Early and scarce. Pair _____ | 85.00 |

## SCRIMSHAWS

Items carved of bone or ivory by amateurs, especially sailors, as a pastime. Their period of manufacture falls roughly between 1800 and 1900.

Alamo under attack by the Mexicans, flag of Texas. Dated March 6, 1836. Horn _____ 175.00

Trinket Box. Small, with hinged lid. $32.50

| | |
|---|---|
| Clothes Pin _____ | 10.00 |
| Etched figures of girl, boy and woman. Pair of teeth _____ | 75.00 |
| Hammer. 6½'' long, dolphin head handle _____ | 38.50 |
| Indians (2) by tree. Carved on 6¼'' walrus tusk _____ | 65.00 |
| Lady raising flag over fort. 6½'' walrus tusk _____ | 80.00 |
| Ostrich egg shape with portrait, schooner, compass, etc. _____ | 200.00 |
| Primitive carving on walrus tusk. 14'' long _____ | 45.00 |
| Punch _____ | 8.75 |
| Trinket Box. Small, with hinged lid _____ | 32.50 |
| Victorian Lady _____ | 65.00 |
| War of 1812. American ship attacking British at Delaware Bay, June 12, 1813 _____ | 175.00 |
| Whale's Tooth. ''The Ship Carpenter'' _____ | 100.00 |
| Woman. Holding eagle aloft. Reverse, holds leaves aloft _____ | 85.00 |
| Women. Mounted on lacquered bases. Pair _____ | 95.00 |

### SEWER PIPE FIGURINES

Sewer Pipe figurines were made at various potteries in Ohio and in other states. It is the opinion of some antique dealers that these were not made commercially but were whimseys of some of the workers employed at the potteries. The period of their production is not known exactly but it is believed that most of them were made between 1900 and 1930.

The figurines are light brown and have a high glaze. They are quite heavy despite their rather small size.

| | |
|---|---|
| Bank. Bull dog, 7'' high _____ | 15.00 |
| Chicks. 5'' high. Different poses. Each _____ | 13.50 |
| Duck. 12'' high _____ | 25.00 |

Cat with smug smile. Item has greenish cast. 13½'' high. Approximately 30 years old _____ $48.50

Ducklings. 5'' high. Scarce. Different poses. Each _____ 15.00

Frog. 8'' long _____ $20.00

Frogs:
$5\frac{1}{2}''$ long _____ 11.50
$7\frac{1}{2}''$ long _____ 15.00
8'' long _____ 20.00
Hen. $11\frac{1}{2}''$ high _____ 25.00
Lions:
Reclining. 9'' long _____ 15.00
Standing. 9'' long _____ 15.00
Plaques. 10x5''. Each _____ 11.00
Poodles:
Staffordshire. 5'' high _____ 12.75
Staffordshire. 7'' high _____ 20.00
Puppy. 5'' high. "Nobody Loves
Me'' on base _____ 20.00
Rabbit. 7'' and 8'' high. Each ____ 16.00
Rooster. 14'' high. Scarce _____ 29.50
Shoe, High-Button. 6'' high ____ 11.00
Toad and Log. 7'' long. Scarce __ 16.50

## SEWING ITEMS

A variety of sewing items were found
in practically every home as late as 35
years ago. Sewing and dressmaking were
two of the arts almost every woman
learned.

Among the interesting items used was the
sewing bird. The birds were usually made
of iron or brass with a screw-type fixture
for attaching them to a table or shelf. The
beak or mouth was used to hold cloth
while sewing was accomplished. Later
models had a pin cushion for holding pins
and needles.

Iron. $6\frac{1}{2}''$ high. One cushion _____ $14.50

Clamp with Gage. Ivory _____ 15.00
Sewing Birds:
Brass. One cushion _____ 15.00
Brass Plated. Bird in shape of
dog. Scarce _____ 32.50
Brass. Dated 1853. Double cushion 24.00
Iron. $6\frac{1}{2}''$ high. One cushion ____ 14.50
Iron. $5\frac{1}{4}''$ high. $3\frac{1}{2}''$ bird. 2 pin
cushions. Gold lacquered _____ 16.50
Iron. New red cushion. Fine con-
dition _____ 14.75
Silver. 2 pin cushions _____ 20.00
Wood. No bird, with round mir-
ror, cushion on top _____ 19.75
Shuttle, Sewing. 2 embroidery pun-
ches, crochet hook. All ivory,
set _____ 6.00
Thimbles:
Gold _____ 20.00
Sterling _____ 5.00
Thread, thimble and punch holder.
Ivory _____ 10.00

## SHAVING MUGS
### (Fraternal and Miscellaneous)

A.O.U.W. Colorful _____ $18.00

Anchor and Chain (No name) ____ 22.50
A.O.U.W. Colorful _____ 18.00
B.P.O.E. _____ 20.00
Deer's Head _____ 17.50
Dog _____ 22.50
Eye. Large, 3 links _____ 24.00
Flags, Crossed. United States ____ 28.50
F.O.E. _____ 22.00
Gibson Girls (2) _____ 28.50
Horse's Head. Large gold horse-
shoe _____ 29.00
I.O.O.F. _____ 20.00
K. of C. (Knights of Columbus) __ 21.50
K. of L. (Knights of Labor) _____ 20.00

| | |
|---|---|
| K. of P. (Knights of Pythias) _____ | 22.50 |
| K. T. (Knights Templar) _____ | 24.50 |
| L.O.O.M. _____ | 21.50 |
| Masonic, Square and Compass ____ | 24.50 |
| M.W.A. _____ | 22.50 |
| O.W.M. _____ | 18.50 |
| Rooster _____ | 22.50 |
| Scuttle-type. Soap holder, brush rest, pink poppy decor _____ | 25.00 |
| W.O.W. (With leaf) _____ | 22.50 |

## SHAVING MUGS, OCCUPATIONAL

During the period from 1870 to 1910 shaving mugs of chinaware were manufactured and decorated with the owner's name and occupation. They were usually kept at the owner's favorite barber shop and were for his exclusive use.

| | |
|---|---|
| Tailor, sewing _____ | $65.00 |

| | |
|---|---|
| Accordion _____ | 65.00 |
| Anchor (with name) _____ | 40.00 |
| Anvil and Hammer _____ | 50.00 |
| Anvil, Hammer and Tongs _____ | 55.00 |
| Architect's Emblem _____ | 42.50 |
| Arc Light _____ | 62.50 |
| Athlete. High jump _____ | 75.00 |
| Athlete. Track runner _____ | 82.50 |
| Automoible (early) _____ | 80.00 |
| Baggage Car _____ | 62.50 |
| Baggage Master, Truck and Car __ | 65.00 |
| Baker Working _____ | 65.00 |
| Bakers at Work _____ | 67.50 |
| Bakery Wagon, Horse with Driver__ | 65.00 |
| Bar. Men drinking _____ | 72.50 |
| Barber Shop _____ | 75.00 |
| Bartender _____ | 74.50 |
| Baseball Player _____ | 110.00 |
| Baseball and Bats _____ | 92.50 |
| Beer Barrel, Bottle and Glasses __ | 58.50 |

| | |
|---|---|
| Beer Bottle and Glasses _____ | 52.50 |
| Beer Mug _____ | 55.00 |
| Beer Wagon, Horses with Driver__ | 72.50 |
| Bicycle _____ | 75.00 |
| Bicyclist _____ | 95.00 |
| Billiard Players _____ | 85.00 |
| Bill Poster _____ | 90.00 |
| Blacksmith and Anvil _____ | 70.00 |
| Blacksmith Shoeing Horse _____ | 72.50 |
| Boiler Maker Working _____ | 75.00 |
| Bookbinder Working _____ | 85.00 |
| Bookkeeper _____ | 57.50 |
| Boot and Shoe _____ | 48.50 |
| Brakeman Turning Brake _____ | 68.50 |
| Bricklayer Working _____ | 70.00 |
| Bridge, Steel _____ | 75.00 |
| Buggy, Horse and Driver _____ | 59.50 |
| Butcher's Emblem (Knife, Cleaver, Steel and Saw) _____ | 50.00 |
| Butcher Slaughtering Steer _____ | 65.00 |
| Butcher Store _____ | 65.00 |
| Cabinet Shop. Man sawing _____ | 50.00 |
| Caboose _____ | 67.50 |
| Camera _____ | 100.00 |
| Cannon and Gun Carriage _____ | 87.50 |
| Carpenter at Work _____ | 60.00 |
| Carriage, Horses and Driver _____ | 56.50 |
| Cigar Store _____ | 60.00 |
| Clothing Store _____ | 65.00 |
| Coal Miner at Work _____ | 95.00 |
| Coal Wagon, Horse and Driver __ | 69.50 |
| Cooper Making Barrels _____ | 72.50 |
| Cowboy Lassoing Steer _____ | 80.00 |
| Dentist Pulling Teeth _____ | 120.00 |
| Dentist, with False Teeth _____ | 90.00 |
| Doctor Tending Patient _____ | 175.00 |
| Dray and Driver with Horses _____ | 55.00 |
| Drug Store _____ | 65.00 |
| Druggist Working _____ | 60.00 |
| Drum _____ | 59.00 |
| Dry Goods Store _____ | 63.50 |
| Engine (Stationary) _____ | 57.50 |
| Express Wagon, Horse and Driver__ | 60.00 |
| Farmer Plowing _____ | 52.50 |
| Fire Engine. Motorized _____ | 100.00 |
| Fire Engine (Steam) _____ | 135.00 |
| Fisherman _____ | 55.00 |
| Flour and Feed Store _____ | 69.50 |
| Flute _____ | 45.00 |
| Freight Car _____ | 55.00 |
| Furniture Store _____ | 62.50 |
| Grist Mill Operator _____ | 82.50 |
| Grocery Store and Clerk _____ | 74.50 |
| Grocery Wagon and Horse _____ | 75.00 |
| Guns, Crossed Rifles and Target __ | 72.50 |
| Hardware Store _____ | 80.00 |
| Harness Maker _____ | 82.50 |
| Hatter Working _____ | 68.50 |
| Hod Carrier _____ | 57.50 |
| Hotel Register _____ | 72.50 |
| Ice Wagon, Horse and Driver ____ | 75.00 |
| Jewelry Store _____ | 72.50 |
| Jeweler's Design, Watch Sign ____ | 57.50 |
| Jockey _____ | 78.50 |
| Letter Carrier, Mail Wagon _____ | 80.00 |
| Livery Stable _____ | 90.00 |

## SHAVING MUGS, OCCUPATIONAL

LEFT TO RIGHT. TOP ROW: Engine (Stationary) . . . $57.50; Engine, Traction . . . $80.00; Printing Press . . . $55.00. SECOND ROW: Lathe . . . $65.00; Bartender, men at bar . . . $72.50; Bartender and customer . . . $72.50. THIRD ROW: Baseball Player . . . $110.00; Billiards Players . . . $85.00; Jockey on horse . . . $78.50. FOURTH ROW: Bicycle . . . $95.00; Caboose . . . $67.50; Farmer Ploughing . . . $60.00.

| | |
|---|---|
| Locomotive | 74.50 |
| Locomotive (Wood-burning type) | 77.50 |
| Machinist at Lathe | 65.00 |
| Mail Wagon | 60.00 |
| Marble Cutter at Work | 65.00 |
| Milk Can Maker | 90.00 |
| Milk Wagon, Horse and Driver | 65.00 |
| Miner with Tools | 72.00 |
| Minister in Pulpit | 125.00 |
| Motorman and Conductor | 69.50 |
| Musicians | 57.50 |
| Notary, Hand and Pen | 65.00 |
| Oil Derrick | 70.00 |
| Painter Working | 69.50 |
| Passenger Car (Railroad) | 57.50 |
| Piano Player | 69.50 |
| Plasterer Working | 55.00 |
| Photographer | 90.00 |
| Plumber | 72.50 |
| Policeman | 110.00 |
| Printer Setting Type | 60.00 |
| Printing Press | 55.00 |
| Prizefighter | 240.00 |
| Restaurant and Bar | 65.00 |
| Roller Skater | 50.00 |
| Saloon, Bartender | 72.50 |
| Sawmill | 68.50 |
| Sheep Shearer | 50.00 |
| Shoe | 45.00 |
| Shoe Dealer | 57.50 |
| State Senator | 49.50 |
| Steamship | 66.50 |
| Sulky | 70.00 |
| Surveyor | 75.00 |
| Tailor, Sewing | 65.00 |
| Tailor, With assistants, working | 57.50 |
| Taxi Driver | 79.50 |
| Telegrapher | 58.50 |
| Telegrapher's Key | 50.00 |
| Telephone | 65.00 |
| Tobacco Store | 75.00 |
| Tow Truck and Driver (early) | 82.50 |
| Tug Boat | 125.00 |
| Umbrella | 59.50 |
| Undertaker | 280.00 |
| Watch and Chain | 60.00 |
| Whiskey Wagon | 85.00 |

## SILHOUETTES

Silhouettes are shadow profiles either cut, mechanically drawn or painted.

| | |
|---|---|
| Man. Early, in gold leaf frame. $3\frac{1}{2}$x$3\frac{3}{4}$'' | 57.50 |
| Man. Full length silhouette in original gold leaf frame. 6x9'' | 67.50 |
| Revolutionary General. $3\frac{1}{4}$'' long | 50.00 |
| Taylor, Joseph. Portrait taken in 1819. On black silk background, in oval frame | 65.00 |
| Woman. Circa 1820. In 5'' round frame | 60.00 |

| | |
|---|---|
| Daniel Hayworth. Old Massachusetts man | $25.00 |
| Andrew Jackson. Facsimile signature | $27.50 |
| Woman. Not a silhouette but in pen and ink. Difficult to detect the difference | $10.00 |

Revolutionary General. $3\frac{1}{4}$'' long __ $50.00

## SILK PICTURES, See STEVENGRAPHS

## SILVER

There are variations in the types and composition of silverware.

"Sterling Silver" is a highly refined metal which derived its name from English Coin of the same name.

"Sheffield Silver" is metal annealed to a copper core and shaped into various types of ware. The copper content constitutes the bulk of the weight. Sheffield items were not as expensive as those made of Sterling.

"Plated Silver" production began in the period 1840-1850. By 1855, in the United States, a number of companies were producing the ware in large quantities. The base was usually Britannia metal—10 parts tin and 1 part antimony. After being shaped, articles were plated by an electrolytic method which placed a thin coating of silver over the base metal. Considerably less silver was used when compared with the Sheffield method and consequently the ware was inexpensive enough to find a place in almost every home.

## COIN SILVER

"Coin Silver" was made by melting coins from circulation during the early part of our country, about 1796 to 1850. It appeared that silversmiths were able to obtain this type of silver more readily than sterling. Coin silver consists of approximately 9 parts silver and 1 part copper or other alloy.

Coin Silver Spoons. E. Wheton mark. Set of 12 _____ $100.00

Butter Knives:
Flat, shell design top of handle. By Bailey & Co., Phila. Circa 1848-50 _____ 7.50

Large, grape pattern. By Bacon & Co. Circa 1850 _____ 8.50
Large by Mills, New York, N. Y. Circa 1834-37 _____ 8.00
Fork. Small, grape pattern, 6'' long. By Bacon & Co. Circa 1850 __ 8.00
Sugar Shell. (O. D. Seymour) ____ 10.00
Tablespoons:
Heavy, marked "Pure Coin, Albany." Set of six _____ 55.00
Small. A. Cutler, Boston, Circa 1820-50 _____ 6.75
Small. A. C. Collier. Circa 1820-24 _____ 6.75
Teaspoons:
Jenkins & Clark, Auburn, N. Y. Circa 1820 _____ 6.50
D. Laverack. Circa 1830-40 ____ 6.75
A. Sanborn, Lowell, Mass. Circa 1850. Set of seven _____ 45.00
E. D. Tisdale. Circa 1850. Set of six _____ 35.00
Fiddle-back. Circa 1835. Set of six _____ 40.00
Teapot. Christopher Giffing, New York City silversmith. Circa 1820 825.00

## SHEFFIELD SILVER

Sheffield silver is a plated product made by sandwiching thin sheets of silver over to two sides of a heavy copper sheet. A modern example is our present day coins, other than the cent.

The usual standard was two pounds of silver to eight pounds of copper, however, some unscrupulous silversmiths used as little as six ounces of silver to eight pounds of copper.

The method was in popular use by 1740, however, by 1840, silverplating by the electro-chemical process replaced it.

Sheffield. Wine Cooler. 9½'' high. With crest. Applied silver decor.–$375.00

Candelabra. Three candles. Circa
   1850. Pair _____ 550.00
Candlesticks:
   Fluted, square bases. Circa 1860.
   Pair _____ 225.00
   Georgian design. Circa 1810. Pair  150.00
   Shell-cornered. Circa 1800. Pair  95.00
Candle Snuffer and Tray _____  65.00

Sheffield. Syrup Jug. 2-gill size.
   8½" high _____ $135.00

Coffee Pots:
   Circa 1850 _____  150.00
   10" high, wood handle. Marked
   "Rhodes & Atkins" _____  85.00
Dish, Souffle. Circa 1833 _____  195.00
Epergne. Cut crystal bowls. Circa
   1830 _____  650.00
Syrup Jug. 2-gill size, 8½" high __  135.00

Sheffield. Coffee and Tea Maker.
   21" high. 1785-90 _____ $2,000.00

Tea Service. 4 pieces. Circa 1821  950.00
Tea Urns. Adam design:
   Circa 1760 _____  450.00
   Circa 1780 _____  650.00
   Circa 1800 _____  275.00
   Circa 1820 _____  350.00
Tray. 16x25" _____  175.00
Tureens:
   Adam design. Circa 1790 _____  550.00
   Soup. Baroque design. Circa 1840  1100.00
Wine Coolers:
   Circa 1810. Pair _____  1500.00
   Circa 1816 _____  550.00
   Circa 1830 _____  450.00

### STERLING SILVER

"Sterling Silver" is a highly refined
metal which derived its name from English
Coin of the same name.

Sterling. Bread Tray. 6¼ x 11".
   Marked "Birks" _____ $35.00

Bell. 6", made from marriage cup 150.00
Butter Pick. Marked Sterling and
  Keystone C. W. Embossed scroll
  and floral design _____ 12.50
Cake Server. Marked Gorham with
  an anchor in a shield. Shell de-
  sign, hollow handle _____ 45.00
Candlesticks. 7" high. Pair _____ 200.00
Cheese Server. Not marked. Hollow
  handle, simple design _____ 27.50
Chop Dish. 14½" diam., marked
  "Kirk" _____ 500.00
Cream Jug. 4½" high, marked
  "Kirk" _____ 100.00
Forks:
  Cake Forks. Marked Community
  Plate. Handles taper to dull
  point. Set of 6 _____ 37.50
  Dessert Fork. Marked anchor,
  lion, G. Sterling. Roses and
  beading on handle _____ 18.00
  Dinner Forks. Large, marked
  Weller, ship 90/45. Set of 6____ 75.00
  Sweetmeat Forks. Marked 1889,
  Towle Mfg. Co. Small, 2-tined,
  shell on end of handles. Set of 6 40.00
Grape Shears. Grape design on
  handles _____ 35.00
Hat Pin. Flower top. Sterling_____ 12.00
Knives:
  Butter. Marked E. P. Juichiya &
  Co. Hollow silver handles, bright
  cut. Designs on blade with shell
  pattern on end of handle _____ 22.50
  Fruit knives:
  Marked 1847 Rogers Bros., dot in
  circle. Hollow sterling handles,
  flower festoon on handle. Set of 6 60.00
  Sterling fittings, pearl handles.
  Set of 12 _____ 57.50
  Steak. German steel blades,
  marked J. A. Henckels, Zwilings-
  werk. Twins trademark, plain
  beading on hollow silver handles.
  Set of 6 _____ 75.00
Ladle, Gravy. Marked Sterling,
  eagle within a circle, Griffin.
  Shell design _____ 45.00
Nut Server. Marked Sterling, lion,
  1912, 225/10000. Pierced square
  flat bowl, simple handle _____ 35.00
Spoons:
  Berry. Marked eagle's head,
  hand full of arrows, 3 links and
  Towle Mfg. Co. Large deep bowl 25.00
  Bouillon or Soup. Marked G, lion
  and anchor, Sterling. Chrysanthemums on top, and reverse sides
  of handle and around bowl. Set
  of 6 _____ 95.00
  Demitasse. Marked Sterling.
  Gold plated bowls, embossed on
  both sides of handle with scroll
  work and shell design. Set of 6__ 60.00
  Serving. Marked C. B., lion,

Sterling, anchor. Pierced gold-
washed bowl. Scalloped shell on
front of shell _____ 40.00

Sterling. Gravy Boat. 7¾" long, 2¼"
high, on 3 dolphin-shell feet.
Marked "Birks" _____ $75.00

Sugar Bowl, Covered. By Christo-
pher Giffing, New York City
silversmith. Circa 1820 _____ 895.00
Teapot. 11" high. American made,
Georgian-style _____ 600.00
Tongs, Ice. Marked R & B 647 ____ 25.00
Tray. 11" diam., by "Kirk" _____ 400.00

## VICTORIAN PLATED SILVER

"Plated Silver" production began in the
period 1840-1850. By 1855, in the United
States, a number of companies were producing the ware in large quantities. The
base was usually Britannia metal—10 parts
tin and 1 part antimony. After being
shaped, articles were plated by an electrolytic method which placed a thin coating of silver over the base metal. Considerably less silver was used when compared with the Sheffield method and consequently the ware was inexpensive enough
to find a place in almost every home.

Baskets:
  10" diam., 10" high. Resilvered 35.00
  10¾" diam. Ornate edge and
  etching inside. 4 ornate feet and
  bail. Marked Victor Silver Plate.
  Needs resilvering _____ 24.00
Butter Dishes:
  Ornate, engraved flowers, and
  birds on lid, horse finial, 4 feet.
  Needs resilvering _____ 22.50
  Ornate 4-footed base, handles,
  beaded rim, etchings and finial.
  Needs resilvering _____ 24.00
  Ornate, etched flowers, handles
  and knife rest, cow finial. Needs
  resilvering _____ 18.75

**Silver Plate. Teapot. 14", Reed & Barton. Classic style** _____ **$90.00**

**Goblet.** Ornate, 6½" high, marked "Mfg. and plated by Reed & Barton" _____ 16.00

**Pickle Castors:**
Ornate ribbed base, fan, bail and lid. Sawtooth or zipper-like paneled glass castor. Marked "Triple Plate." Complete with tongs. Needs resilvering _____ 25.00
Vaseline Diamond Point glass castor in square-based circular frame. Ornate base and bail top. Marked "James W. Tufts, Quadruple." Needs resilvering _____ 40.00

**Services:**
5-piece set. Teapot, 8½" coffee pot, sugar bowl, creamer, spooner. "Acme Silver Plate, Quadruple." Needs resilvering _____ 65.00
4-piece set. 6½" teapot, sugar bowl, spooner, creamer. Floral etchings, ornamental spout, finial and handles. "G. Uher Silver Co., Quadruple Plate." Needs resilvering _____ 30.00

**Spoon Holder and Dinner Gong.** 10½" high. Holds 12 spoons. Petaled standard extends from holder. 2 soldiers and 2 dogs stand by handle to guard silver. Marked "Wallingford Triple Plate" _____ 22.50

**Sugar Bowl.** Covered, 7½" high. Ornate handles and finial, 4 feet. Marked "Queen City Silver Co." _____ 20.00

**Silver Plate. Goblet. Meriden Co.** 6¾" high. Resilvered _____ **$18.50**

**Castor Sets:**
4-bottle set. Complete with stoppers and lids. Needs resilvering 37.50
5-bottle set. Etched bottles, ornate handle, complete with lids and stoppers. Needs resilvering__ 39.50
5-bottle set. Unmatched bottles without lids. Needs resilvering__ 22.00

**Champagne Bucket.** 8½" high, 2 handles. "Reed and Barton" ____ 39.00

**Cracker Jar.** Covered, 6" diam., 7½" high. Ornate etching on front, ornate bail and finial. "Crackers" engraved on front. Needs resilvering _____ 20.00

**Cup and Saucer.** Marked "Meridian Quadruple Plate." _____ 20.00

**Dish, Nut.** "Pairpont" silver. 6" long, 3½" high. Deep cranberry glass liner _____ 100.00

Syrup Jug. Ornate handle and lid, ornamental band at bottom and top. Marked "Kan & Co." Needs resilvering _____ 15.00

Teapots:
7½" high, quart capacity. Ribbed bowl rests on base, rose band in relief, ornamental spout and heat-resister handle. Needs resilvering _____ 25.00
14" high. Reed & Barton, classic style _____ 90.00

Vegetable Dish. Covered, 8½" diam. Ornate band around base. Marked "Barbour Bros. Quadruple Plate" _____ 45.00

Water Cooler. "Meridian" plate. Porcelain lined, on holder with two goblets, with tray _____ 85.00

## SILVER

## STERLING FLATWARE

### ALVIN

**Apollo:**

Butter Server _____$ 5.50

**Cellini:**

Butter Serving Knife _____ 6.00
Sugar Spoon _____ 8.50
Tablespoon, 8½" _____ 16.00
Teaspoon _____ 6.00

**Chapel Bell:**

Cream Soup, 6¼" _____ 6.00
Dinner Fork, 8" _____ 8.00
Dinner Knife, 9½" _____ 7.00
Luncheon Knife, 8¾" _____ 7.00
Tablespoon, 8½" _____ 15.00

**Chateau Rose:**

Butter Spreader, F.H. _____ 4.50
Cream Soup, 6¼" _____ 6.00
Dinner Fork, 7⅞" _____ 10.00
Dinner Knife, 9⅝" _____ 8.50
Luncheon Fork, 7¼" _____ 7.50
Luncheon Knife, 8⅞" _____ 6.00
Oyster Fork _____ 5.00
Salad Fork _____ 6.00
Sugar Spoon _____ 8.00
Teaspoon _____ 5.00

**Chippendale** (New):

Butter Spreader, F.H. _____ 5.00

**Chippendale** (Old):

Salad Fork _____ 6.00

**Evangeline** (Inactive):

Luncheon Fork, 6¾" _____ 6.50
Strawberry Fork, 5" _____ 4.50
Teaspoon, 4⅞" _____ 3.00

**Florence Nightingale:**

Butter Serving Knife _____$ 6.50
Luncheon Fork _____ 6.00
Luncheon Knife _____ 5.00
Sauce Ladle _____ 6.50
Serving Fork, 8½" _____ 15.00
Soup, round bowl, 7" _____ 5.00
Sugar Spoon _____ 6.50
Teaspoon _____ 4.50

**Florentine** (Obsolete):

Grapefruit Spoon _____ 6.00
Ladle _____ 8.50
Luncheon Fork, 6½" _____ 10.00
Nut Spoon, pierced bowl _____ 8.50
Pickle Fork _____ 6.00
Teaspoon, 5¾" _____ 5.00

**Francis First:**

Gravy Ladle _____ 12.00
Teaspoon _____ 4.50

**Maryland** (Inactive):

Dinner Knife, 9¾" _____ 5.00
Luncheon Fork, 6½" _____ 4.50
Luncheon Knife _____ 4.00
Tablespoon _____ 16.00
Teaspoon, 5⅝" _____ 5.00

**Morning Glory** (Inactive):

Butter Knife, 7" _____ 8.00
Tablespoon, 8½" _____ 15.00
Teaspoon _____ 6.50
Teaspoon, gold bowl _____ 7.00

**Nuremberg** (Obsolete):

Dinner Knife, 9⅝" _____ 5.00
Fork, 7" _____ 8.00
Teaspoon _____ 6.50

**Raleigh:**

Fork, 7" _____ 7.50

**Romantique:**

Butter Serving Knife, F.H. _____$ 7.50
Butter Spreader, F.H. _____ 4.50
Cocktail Fork _____ 4.50
Cream Soup, 6¼" _____ 4.50
Luncheon Fork _____ 6.50
Luncheon Knife _____ 5.00
Salad Fork _____ 5.00

**Southern Charm:**

| | |
|---|---|
| Butter Spreader, F.H. | 4.50 |
| Cream Soup, 6¼" | 6.00 |
| Ice Teaspoon | 6.50 |
| Luncheon Knife, 8¾" | 7.50 |
| Salad Fork | 6.00 |
| Teaspoon | 5.00 |

**Viking:**

| | |
|---|---|
| Luncheon Fork | 7.50 |
| Salad Fork, 6" | 7.00 |

## DURGIN

**Bead** (Inactive):

| | |
|---|---|
| Fork, 7¼" | $ 8.50 |
| Fruit Spoon, gold bowl | 7.00 |
| Tablespoon, 5½" | 6.00 |
| Teaspoon, 5½" | 6.00 |

**Colfax** (Inactive):

| | |
|---|---|
| Dessert Spoon, 7¼" | 8.50 |
| Fork, 7¼" | 9.00 |

**English Gadroon:**

| | |
|---|---|
| BonBon Server | 7.50 |
| Butter Serving Knife | 9.50 |
| Butter Spreader, F.H. | 5.50 |
| Cream Soup, 6¼" | 7.00 |
| Dinner Fork, 7⅝" | 11.00 |
| Gravy Ladle | 18.00 |
| Lemon Fork | 7.50 |
| Oyster-Cocktail Fork | 6.50 |
| Pickle Fork | 7.50 |
| Salad Fork | 7.50 |

**Essex:**

| | |
|---|---|
| Lemon Fork | 4.50 |
| Sugar Spoon | 6.50 |
| Teaspoon | 5.00 |

**Hampshire:**

| | |
|---|---|
| Dinner Fork, 7⅝" | 9.00 |
| Luncheon Fork, 7" | 8.50 |
| Tablespoon, 8¾" | 18.00 |
| Teaspoon, 5¾" | 6.50 |
| Teaspoon, coffee, 5" | 4.00 |

**Lenox:**

| | |
|---|---|
| Dessert Spoon, 7⅛" | 8.50 |
| Lettuce Fork, 9" | 12.00 |

**Louis XV** (Obsolete):

| | |
|---|---|
| Teaspoon | 6.50 |

**Madame Royale** (Inactive):

| | |
|---|---|
| Dinner Fork, 7½" | $12.00 |
| Luncheon Fork, 7" | 10.00 |
| Teaspoon | 6.50 |

**New Standish** (Inactive):

| | |
|---|---|
| Butter Spreader | 6.00 |
| Dessert Spoon | 8.00 |
| Server, pierced, 9½x2½" | 25.00 |

**Victorian:**

| | |
|---|---|
| Bouillon Spoon, 5½" | 5.00 |
| Cocktail Fork | 4.50 |
| Cold Meat Fork, 8¾" | 16.00 |
| Salad Fork | 5.00 |
| Soup Spoon, 6⅞" | 6.50 |

**Watteau:**

| | |
|---|---|
| Cheese Scoop, gold wash, 8½" | 27.50 |
| Dinner Fork, 7⅝" | 7.50 |
| Sauce Ladle, gold wash | 12.50 |
| Soup Ladle | 40.00 |

## GORHAM

**Albemarle:**

| | |
|---|---|
| Teaspoon | 5.00 |

**Blythe Spirit** (Inactive):

| | |
|---|---|
| Butter Serving Knife, H.H. | 8.50 |
| Butter Spreader, H.H. | 5.00 |
| Cold Meat Fork, 8⅝", 3-tine | 18.00 |
| Sugar Spoon | 8.50 |

**Cambridge** (Inactive):

| | |
|---|---|
| Cheese Scoop | 18.00 |
| Dessert Spoon, 7¼" | 8.00 |
| Dinner Knife | 5.00 |
| Gravy Ladle, 6", gold bowl | 22.00 |
| Luncheon Fork | 8.00 |
| Luncheon Knife | 6.50 |
| Salad Fork, 5⅞" | 8.00 |
| Sauce Ladle, 5", gold bowl | 20.00 |
| Soup Spoon | 6.50 |
| Teaspoon, 5⅜" | 4.50 |

**Camelia** (Active):

| | |
|---|---|
| Butter Spreader, H.H. | 6.00 |
| Demi-Tasse Spoon | 4.00 |
| Luncheon Fork, 7¼" | 9.00 |
| Teaspoon | 6.50 |

**Celeste:**

| | |
|---|---|
| Butter Serving Knife | 8.50 |
| Cocktail Fork | 5.50 |
| Cold Meat Fork, 2-tine | 15.00 |

| | |
|---|---|
| Lemon Fork | 6.50 |
| Sugar Spoon | 7.50 |
| Teaspoon | 6.00 |

**Chelmsford** (Inactive):

| | |
|---|---|
| Teaspoon, $5\frac{3}{8}$'' | 4.50 |

**Cinderella:**

| | |
|---|---|
| Cocktail Fork | 5.00 |

**Clermont:**

| | |
|---|---|
| Cream Soup, $5\frac{3}{8}$'' | 5.00 |

**Cologni:**

| | |
|---|---|
| Cream Soup, $7\frac{1}{2}$'' | 10.00 |

**Esprit:**

| | |
|---|---|
| Butter Spreader, H.H. | 6.00 |
| Dessert Spoon | 8.50 |
| Luncheon Fork | 10.00 |
| Luncheon Knife | 9.00 |
| Salad Fork | 8.50 |
| Teaspoon | 6.50 |

**Etruscan:**

| | |
|---|---|
| Bouillon Spoon, $5\frac{1}{4}$'' | 6.00 |
| Butter Spreader, F.H. | 5.00 |
| Cocktail Fork | 4.50 |
| Cream Soup, $6\frac{1}{4}$'' | 6.00 |
| Dessert Spoon, 7'' | 7.00 |
| Gravy Ladle | 12.50 |
| Luncheon Fork | 8.00 |
| Luncheon Knife | 7.00 |
| Salad Fork | 6.00 |
| Sauce Ladle | 6.50 |
| Tablespoon | 12.00 |
| Teaspoon | 6.00 |

**Fairfax** (Active):

| | |
|---|---|
| Bouillon Spoon, $5\frac{1}{4}$'' | 6.00 |
| Butter Spreader, F.H. | 5.50 |
| Cocktail Fork | 5.00 |
| Dinner Fork, 8'' | 10.00 |
| Luncheon Fork, $7\frac{1}{4}$'' | 9.00 |
| Luncheon Knife, $8\frac{3}{4}$'' | 8.00 |
| Salad Fork, $6\frac{1}{8}$'' | 7.50 |
| Soup Spoon, $7\frac{1}{4}$'' | 8.00 |
| Youth Fork, $6\frac{1}{8}$'' | 5.00 |

**Greenbriar:**

| | |
|---|---|
| Butter Server | 11.00 |
| Cream Soup, $6\frac{1}{4}$'' | 8.00 |
| Dinner Knife, $9\frac{3}{8}$'' | 10.00 |
| Luncheon Fork | 8.00 |
| Luncheon Knife | 7.00 |
| Salad Fork | 7.50 |
| Sugar Tong, $3\frac{7}{8}$'' | 11.00 |
| Teaspoon | 5.00 |

**Hindostance** (Obsolete):

| | |
|---|---|
| Dinner Fork, $7\frac{1}{8}$'' | 5.00 |
| Luncheon Fork, $6\frac{3}{4}$'' | 5.00 |

**Imperial Chrysanthemum** (Inactive):

| | |
|---|---|
| Butter Serving Knife | 10.00 |
| Butter Spreader, F.H., $5\frac{3}{8}$'' | 6.00 |
| Cocktail Fork | 7.50 |
| Demi-Tasse Spoon, gold bowl | 6.00 |
| Dessert Spoon, $7\frac{1}{2}$'' | 12.50 |
| Dinner Fork, 7'' | 7.50 |
| Dinner Fork, $7\frac{1}{2}$' | 12.00 |
| Luncheon Fork | 12.00 |
| Pickle Fork | 7.50 |
| Serving Fork, $8\frac{1}{2}$x2'', gold wash | 35.00 |
| Sugar Spoon | 8.50 |
| Teaspoon | 8.00 |

**King Edward** (Active):

| | |
|---|---|
| Butter Serving Knife | 11.50 |
| Butter Spreader | 5.50 |
| Cheese Server | 9.00 |
| Cocktail Fork | 6.00 |
| Cream Soup, $6\frac{1}{4}$'' | 7.00 |
| Demi-Tasse Spoon | 4.50 |
| Dessert Spoon, $6\frac{3}{4}$'' | 9.00 |
| Luncheon Fork | 9.50 |
| Luncheon Knife | 8.00 |
| Salad Fork | 8.50 |
| Tablespoon, $8\frac{1}{2}$'' | 18.00 |
| Teaspoon | 6.50 |

**King George** (Inactive):

| | |
|---|---|
| Dinner Fork, 8'' | 9.00 |
| Dinner Knife, $9\frac{5}{8}$'' | 7.50 |
| Fruit Spoon | 7.50 |
| Grapefruit Spoon, gold wash | 7.50 |
| Master Salt, gold wash | 6.00 |
| Punch Ladle, 11'' | 95.00 |
| Soup Spoon, $6\frac{3}{4}$'' | 8.00 |
| Sugar Tongs, 5'' | 15.00 |
| Tablespoon, $8\frac{1}{2}$'' | 18.00 |
| Teaspoon | 6.50 |

**Lansdowne:**

| | |
|---|---|
| Salad Fork | 7.00 |
| Teaspoon | 6.00 |

**Lily of the Valley:**

| | |
|---|---|
| Butter Spreader, F.H. | $ 5.00 |
| Cheese Server | 7.50 |
| Luncheon Knife | 6.50 |
| Salad Fork | 7.50 |
| Sugar Spoon | 6.50 |
| Teaspoon | 5.00 |

**Lyric:**

| | |
|---|---|
| Butter Serving Knife | 13.00 |
| Butter Spreader, F.H. | 5.50 |
| Cream Soup | 7.50 |
| Jelly Server | 10.50 |
| Luncheon Fork | 8.00 |
| Olive Spoon | 8.00 |
| Pie Server | 18.00 |
| Salad Fork | 7.00 |
| Sugar Spoon | 7.50 |
| Teaspoon | 6.00 |

**Maryland** (Obsolete):

| | |
|---|---|
| Fork, 7½" | 10.00 |
| Teaspoon, 5" | 6.00 |
| Youth Fork, 6⅓" | 8.00 |

**Newcastle:**

| | |
|---|---|
| Butter Spreader, F.H. | 5.00 |
| Luncheon Fork | 7.00 |
| Teaspoon | 6.00 |

**Old French:**

| | |
|---|---|
| Butter Spreader, F.H., 6¼" | 5.00 |
| Cocktail Fork, 5½" | 5.00 |
| Dessert Spoon, 7⅜" | 7.00 |
| Fork, 7¼" | 7.00 |

**Perspective:**

| | |
|---|---|
| Butter Spreader, H.H. | 8.00 |
| Dessert Spoon, 7" | 10.00 |
| Luncheon Fork, 7⅝" | 12.00 |

**Plymouth:**

| | |
|---|---|
| Butter Spreader, F.H. | $ 5.00 |
| Dessert Spoon, 7⅛" | 6.00 |
| Dinner Fork, 7⅝" | 6.50 |
| Dinner Knife, 9¾" | 6.00 |
| Luncheon Fork, 7" | 7.00 |
| Luncheon Knife, 8½" | 6.25 |
| Salad Fork | 5.00 |
| Tablespoon, 8½" | 12.00 |
| Teaspoon | 4.75 |

**Poppy:**

| | |
|---|---|
| Cocktail Fork, 5⅝" | 7.50 |
| Luncheon Fork, 7" | 12.00 |
| Salad Fork, 5¾" | 7.00 |
| Tablespoon, 8½" | 10.00 |

**Portland:**

| | |
|---|---|
| Luncheon Knife, 8½" | 5.00 |
| Teaspoon | 4.50 |

**Rondo:**

| | |
|---|---|
| Butter Spreader, F.H. | 5.50 |
| Cream Soup, 6½" | 7.50 |
| Luncheon Fork | 9.50 |
| Luncheon Knife | 8.50 |
| Salad Fork | 7.50 |
| Teaspoon | 6.50 |

**Rose Tiara:**

| | |
|---|---|
| Ice Teaspoon | 9.00 |
| Lemon Fork | 8.00 |
| Pickle Fork | 8.00 |
| Tablespoon, pierced, prong on end | 18.00 |

**Royal Oak** (Obsolete):

| | |
|---|---|
| Cream Soup, 6⅝" | 12.00 |
| Luncheon Fork | 12.00 |

**St. Cloud:**

| | |
|---|---|
| Berry Spoon, 9", cut design in bowl, 3x3½" | 35.00 |
| Coffee Spoon, 5½" | 6.50 |
| Demi-Tasse Spoon, gold wash | 6.00 |
| Dessert Spoon, 7" | 12.00 |
| Luncheon Fork, 6¾" | 10.50 |
| Tablespoon, 7⅞" | 15.00 |
| Teaspoon, 6" | 7.50 |

**Sea Rose:**

| | |
|---|---|
| Luncheon Fork | $ 9.50 |
| Luncheon Knife | 8.00 |
| Pie Server | 15.00 |
| Salad Fork | 7.50 |
| Serving Fork, 2-prong | 15.00 |
| Teaspoon | 6.50 |

**Secret Garden** (Active):

| | |
|---|---|
| Cocktail Fork | 6.50 |
| Cold Meat Fork | 18.00 |
| Dessert Spoon | 8.50 |
| Gravy Ladle | 15.00 |
| Ice Teaspoon | 7.50 |
| Luncheon Fork, 7⅜" | 9.50 |
| Nut Server, pierced | 8.00 |
| Pickle Fork | 8.00 |
| Tablespoon | 15.00 |
| Teaspoon | 6.50 |

**Star Dust:**

| | |
|---|---|
| Butter Knife, 6⅞" | 6.00 |
| Luncheon Fork | 8.50 |
| Luncheon Knife | 8.00 |
| Salad Fork | 6.50 |

**Strasbourg:**

| | |
|---|---|
| Butter Spreader | 10.00 |
| Dessert Spoon | 10.00 |
| Dinner Fork | 12.00 |
| Luncheon Fork | 10.00 |

Sugar Spoon `_____` 8.50
Tablespoon `_____` 18.00
Teaspoon `_____` 7.50

## Theme:

Cocktail Fork `_____` 5.00
Dessert Spoon, 7" `_____` 7.00
Lemon Fork, 4" `_____` 6.50
Place Fork `_____` 9.00
Place Knife `_____` 8.00
Salad Fork `_____` 7.50
Teaspoon `_____` 6.50

## Virginiana:

Luncheon Fork `_____` 7.50
Luncheon Knife `_____` 6.50

## HEIRLOOM

### Damask Rose:

Butter Serving Knife `_____`$ 7.50
Butter Spreader, F.H. `_____` 5.50
Cocktail Fork `_____` 6.00
Dessert Spoon, 7" `_____` 7.50
Dinner Fork `_____` 11.00
Dinner Knife `_____` 8.50
Jelly Server `_____` 8.50
Lemon Fork `_____` 6.00
Luncheon Fork `_____` 8.00
Luncheon Knife `_____` 7.50
Pickle Fork `_____` 6.00
Pie Server `_____ _____` 15.00
Salad Fork `_____` 7.50
Sauce Ladle `_____` 8.50
Serving Spoon, 8½" `_____` 15.00
Sugar Spoon `_____` 7.00
Sugar Tong, 3½" `_____` 8.50
Teaspoon `_____` 6.00

### First Frost:

Butter Spreader, F. H. `_____` 4.00
Coffee Spoon `_____` 3.00
Cold Meat Fork `_____` 12.00
Cream Soup `_____` 6.00
Dinner Fork `_____` 7.50
Dinner Knife `_____` 6.50
Gravy Ladle `_____` 11.00
Pastry Server `_____` 11.00
Roast Carving Set `_____` 18.00
Salad Fork `_____` 6.00
Sauce Ladle `_____` 7.00
Serving Spoon, pierced `_____` 15.00
Teaspoon `_____` 4.50

### Heiress:

Butter Spreader, F.H. `_____` 4.00
Cream Soup `_____` 5.00
Ice Teaspoon `_____` 6.00
Luncheon Fork `_____` 8.00

Luncheon Knife `_____` 7.00
Salad Fork `_____` 7.00
Salad Set `_____` 27.50
Teaspoon `_____` 5.50

## Lasting Spring:

Cream Soup, 6½" `_____`$ 5.00
Dinner Knife, 9½" `_____` 6.50
Ice Teaspoon `_____` 6.50
Luncheon Fork, 7¼" `_____` 7.50
Luncheon Knife, 8¾" `_____` 6.50
Tablespoon, 8¼" `_____` 12.00
Teaspoon `_____` 5.00

## Reigning Beauty:

Butter Spreader, H.H. `_____` 6.50
Cocktail Fork `_____` 6.00
Gravy Ladle `_____` 15.00
Luncheon Knife `_____` 9.50
Salad Fork `_____` 6.50
Tablespoon `_____` 15.00
Teaspoon `_____` 6.00

## INTERNATIONAL

### Abbotsford (Obsolete):

Butter Server, 7½" `_____`$ 8.50

### Althea (Obsolete):

Bouillon Spoon, 5⅛"◗ `_____` 5.00

### Angelique:

Butter Spreader, H.H. `_____` 6.00
Luncheon Fork `_____` 8.50
Luncheon Knife `_____` 7.50

### Blossom Time:

Butter Serving Knife `_____` 6.50
Butter Spreader `_____` 4.50
Cocktail Fork `_____` 4.50
Cold Meat Fork `_____` 12.00
Cream Soup Spoon, 6" `_____` 5.00
Dessert Spoon `_____` 5.00
Gravy Ladle `_____` 12.50
Jelly Server `_____` 6.50
Luncheon Fork, 7¼" `_____` 7.00
Luncheon Knife, 9" `_____` 6.00
Nut Server `_____` 6.50
Pie Serving Knife `_____` 12.50
Salad Fork `_____` 6.00
Sauce Ladle `_____` 7.00
Sugar Spoon `_____` 6.50
Tablespoon `_____` 12.00
Teaspoon `_____` 4.50

### Brocade (Inactive):

Butter Serving Knife `_____` 7.50
Cream Soup, 6½" `_____` 7.00

Demi-Tasse Spoon ................ 5.00
Dessert Spoon, $6\frac{3}{4}$'' ................ 7.50
Dinner Fork, $7\frac{3}{4}$'' ................ 11.00
Dinner Knife, $9\frac{5}{8}$'' ................ 9.00
Ice Teaspoon ................ 7.50
Jiffy Server ................ 7.50
Luncheon Fork, $7\frac{1}{4}$'' ................ 9.50
Pickle Fork ................ 6.50
Salad Fork ................ 8.00
Salad Serving Spoon, pierced ................ 15.00
Sugar Spoon ................ 8.50
Teaspoon ................ 6.50
Tomato Server, pierced ................ 22.00

**Continental:**

Cream Soup, $6\frac{1}{8}$'' ................ 6.50
Luncheon Fork ................ 8.00
Salad Fork ................ 7.00
Tablespoon, $8\frac{3}{8}$'' ................ 12.50
Teaspoon ................ 5.50

**Courtship:**

Butter Spreader, F.H. ................ 5.00
Cream Soup, $6\frac{3}{8}$'' ................ 6.50
Luncheon Fork ................ 7.50
Luncheon Knife ................ 6.50
Salad Fork ................ 6.50
Teaspoon ................ 5.00

**Edgewood (Obsolete):**

Butter Serving Knife ................ 8.50
Sugar Spoon ................ 8.00
Tablespoon, $8\frac{1}{8}$'' ................ 15.00
Teaspoon ................ 5.00

**Frontenac (Inactive):**
**Joan of Arc:**

Butter Spreader, F.H. ................ 5.50
Cream Soup, 6'' ................ 9.00
Luncheon Fork, $7\frac{3}{8}$'' ................ 7.00
Luncheon Knife, $9\frac{1}{4}$'' ................ 6.50
Sugar Shell ................ 8.50

**Kenilworth:**

Dessert Spoon, $6\frac{3}{4}$'' ................ 7.50
Teaspoon ................ 5.00

**Lambeth Manor:**

Butter Spreader ................ 5.00
Luncheon Fork, $7\frac{3}{8}$'' ................ 8.00
Luncheon Knife, $9\frac{1}{8}$''. ................ 7.00
Tablespoon ................ 12.00
Teaspoon ................ 5.00

**Moonbeam:**

Butter Spreader, F.H. ................ 5.00
Cream Soup, $6\frac{1}{2}$'' ................ 6.50
Fork, $7\frac{1}{4}$'' ................ 7.00
Salad Fork ................ 6.50
Teaspoon ................ 5.00

**Pine Spray:**

Butter Serving Knife, H.H. ................ 6.50
Butter Spreader, H.H. ................ 4.50
Dessert Spoon, $6\frac{3}{4}$'' ................ 6.50
Luncheon Fork ................ 8.00
Luncheon Knife ................ 7.00
Salad Fork ................ 6.50
Teaspoon ................ 5.00

**Prelude:**

Cheese Knife ................ 7.50
Cocktail Fork ................ 5.00
Cream Soup, $6\frac{1}{2}$'' ................ 7.00
Demi-Tasse Spoon ................ 4.00
Dinner Fork ................ 9.00
Dinner Knife, $9\frac{1}{2}$'' ................ 8.00
Gravy Ladle ................ 18.00
Ice Teaspoon ................ 7.00
Luncheon Knife, 8'' ................ 6.00
Pie Serving Knife ................ 15.00
Salad Fork ................ 7.00
Sauce Ladle, short handle ................ 7.50
Seafood Fork, 3-tine ................ 6.00
Sugar Tong, $4\frac{1}{8}$'' ................ 7.50
Tablespoon, $8\frac{1}{2}$'' ................ 18.00
Teaspoon, 6'' ................ 5.00

**Revere (Obsolete):**

Dinner Fork, $7\frac{3}{8}$'' ................ 7.50
Luncheon Fork, $6\frac{1}{2}$'' ................ 7.50
Soup Spoon, $6\frac{1}{2}$'' ................ 6.50
Tablespoon, $8\frac{1}{2}$'' ................ 10.00

**Richelieu:**

Butter Spreader, F.H. ................ 6.50
Cream Soup, $6\frac{1}{2}$'' ................ 7.50
Fork, $7\frac{1}{8}$'' ................ 8.50
Ice Teaspoon ................ 8.50
Teaspoon ................ 6.50

## LUNT

**American Victorian:**

Bon Bon Spoon ................ $ 7.00
Butter Serving Knife ................ 7.50
Butter Spreader ................ 5.00
Cocktail Fork ................ 5.50
Cream Soup Spoon ................ 7.00
Dessert Spoon ................ 7.50
Dinner Fork, $7\frac{3}{8}$'' ................ 11.00
Dinner Knife, $9\frac{3}{4}$'' ................ 9.00
Ice Teaspoon ................ 7.50
Lemon Fork ................ 6.00
Luncheon Fork, $7\frac{1}{4}$'' ................ 9.00
Luncheon Knife, $8\frac{3}{4}$'' ................ 8.00
Salad Fork ................ 7.50
Sugar Spoon ................ 8.00

Tablespoon, 8½" _____ 15.00
Teaspoon _____ 6.00

## Charles II (Inactive):

Butter Spreader, F.H. _____ 6.50
Cream Soup, 6¾" _____ 8.00
Luncheon Fork, 7¼" _____11.00
Luncheon Knife, 9" _____ 9.50
Salad Fork _____ 8.50
Teaspoon _____ 6.50

## Colonial Manor:

Butter Serving Knife, F.H. _____ 7.50
Butter Spreader, F.H. _____ 5.00
Fork, 7¼" _____ 7.50
Knife, 8⅜" _____ 6.50

## Gadroonette-Manchester:

Cream Soup, 6¼" _____ 6.00
Lemon Fork _____ 5.50
Salad Fork _____ 6.00
Sauce Ladle _____ 6.50
Teaspoon _____ 5.00

## Mt. Vernon (Inactive):

Cream Soup Spoon, 7" _____$ 7.00
Dessert Spoon, 7¼" _____ 8.00
Fruit Spoon _____ 7.00
Luncheon Fork, 7¼" _____ 7.50
Pickle Fork _____ 7.50
Serving Fork, 7" _____ 12.00
Tablespoon, 8½" _____ 12.00
Teaspoon _____ 6.50

## Orleans:

Butter Spreader, F.H. _____ 5.00
Dessert Spoon, 7⅛" _____ 7.00
Dinner Fork _____ 8.50
Luncheon Fork _____ 7.50
Salad Fork _____ 7.00
Sugar Spoon, 6¾" _____ 7.00
Teaspoon _____ 5.00
Teaspoon, Coffee, 5¼" _____ 4.50

## Sweetheart Rose:

Butter Serving Knife _____ 7.50
Butter Spreader, F.H. _____ 5.50
Cream Soup, 6¼" _____ 7.50
Dinner Fork, 7⅞" _____ 10.00
Dinner Knife, 9⅞" _____ 9.00
Luncheon Fork, 7¼" _____ 8.00
Luncheon Knife, 8⅞" _____ 7.50

## Virginia (Obsolete):

Luncheon Fork, 7¼" _____ 7.50
Teaspoon, 5¾" _____ 4.50

## William and Mary:

Butter Serving Knife _____ 8.50
Butter Spreader, F.H. _____ 5.00
Cocktail Fork _____ 6.00
Cold Meat Fork, 7½" _____ 18.00
Cream Soup Spoon, 6½" _____ 6.00
Lemon Fork _____ 6.50
Luncheon Fork, 7⅛" _____ 7.50
Luncheon Knife, 9" _____ 6.75
Nut Server _____ 6.50
Pickle Fork _____ 6.50
Salad Fork _____ 5.00
Sugar Spoon _____ 8.00
Tablespoon, 8⅞" _____ 18.00
Teaspoon _____ 5.50

# MERRIMAC

## Grape (Obsolete):

Butter Knife, 7" _____$ 9.00
Serving Fork, 9", gold tines _____ 28.00
Tomato Server, 6¼" _____ 14.00

# MT. VERNON

## Adolphus (Obsolete):

Butter Spreader, 5¾" _____ 4.50
Sauce Ladle _____ 7.50

## Lexington (Obsolete):

Berry Spoon, 8⅜", gold wash
bowl _____ 12.00

## Sheraton (Obsolete):

Dessert Spoon, 7¼" _____ 12.00
Serving Fork, 9x2", gold tine ____ 28.00

## Princess Elizabeth:

Cream Soup, 6⅛" _____ 6.00
Dinner Fork _____ 9.00
Dinner Knife _____ 8.00
Ice Teaspoon _____ 6.00
Luncheon Fork _____ 7.00
Luncheon Knife _____ 6.00
Salad Fork _____ 6.00
Soup Spoon _____ 6.50
Teaspoon _____ 5.00

## Rosalind (New):

Dinner Fork, 7⅜" _____$ 7.00
Salad Fork _____ 6.00
Teaspoon _____ 5.00

## Rosalind (Old):

Fork, 7" _____ 8.00

**Serenity:**

| | |
|---|---|
| Butter Serving Knife | 7.50 |
| Butter Spreader, F.H. | 5.00 |
| Cream Soup, 6½" | 6.50 |
| Ice Teaspoon | 7.50 |
| Place Knife | 7.00 |
| Teaspoon | 5.00 |

**Silver Melody:**

| | |
|---|---|
| Butter Spreader, F.H. | 5.00 |
| Cream Soup, 6⅝" | 7.50 |
| Dessert Spoon, 6⅝" | 7.50 |
| Ice Teaspoon | 7.50 |
| Place Knife, 9⅛" | 7.50 |
| Teaspoon | 6.00 |

**Silver Rhythm:**

| | |
|---|---|
| Butter Spreader, H. H. | 4.50 |
| Cocktail Fork | 4.50 |
| Dessert Spoon, 6½" | 6.00 |
| Ice Teaspoon | 6.50 |
| Luncheon Fork | 8.00 |
| Luncheon Knife | 6.50 |
| Salad Fork | 6.50 |
| Tablespoon | 15.00 |
| Teaspoon | 5.00 |

**Spring Glory:**

| | |
|---|---|
| Butter Serving Knife | 9.50 |
| Butter Spreader | 6.00 |
| Cheese Server | 8.50 |
| Cocktail Fork | 5.50 |
| Cream Soup, 6½" | 7.50 |
| Dinner Fork, 7¼" | 9.50 |
| Dinner Knife, 9⅜" | 9.00 |
| Luncheon Fork | 9.50 |
| Luncheon Knife | 8.00 |
| Pickle Fork | 7.50 |
| Salad Fork | 7.50 |
| Sugar Spoon | 9.50 |
| Sugar Tong, 4" | 10.00 |
| Tomato Server, 8" | 16.00 |

**Stratford:**

| | |
|---|---|
| Cream Soup, 7" | 8.00 |
| Dessert Spoon, 7" | 8.00 |
| Teaspoon | 6.00 |
| Teaspoon, gold bowl | 7.00 |

**Valencia:**

| | |
|---|---|
| Ice Teaspoon | 9.50 |
| Luncheon Fork, 7½" | 11.00 |
| Luncheon Knife, 9⅛" | 9.50 |
| Nut Spoon | 7.00 |
| Pickle Fork | 7.00 |
| Sugar Spoon | 9.50 |
| Tablespoon | 16.50 |
| Teaspoon | 7.00 |

**Wedgwood (Inactive):**

| | |
|---|---|
| Butter Serving Knife | 10.00 |
| Butter Spreader | 6.50 |
| Cream Soup, 6" | 8.00 |
| Jelly Server | 8.50 |
| Salad Fork | 8.50 |
| Sugar Spoon | 8.50 |
| Tablespoon, 8½" | 15.00 |
| Teaspoon | 6.50 |

**Windemere (Inactive):**

| | |
|---|---|
| Teaspoon | 5.00 |

## STERLING FLATWARE

## REED & BARTON

**Century (Obsolete):**

| | |
|---|---|
| Butter Serving Knife | $ 7.50 |
| Ice Teaspoon | 7.00 |

**Classic Rose:**

| | |
|---|---|
| Butter Spreader | 5.75 |
| Cream Soup Spoon, 6⅝" | 8.00 |
| Dessert Spoon | 8.00 |
| Luncheon Fork | 9.50 |
| Luncheon Knife | 8.00 |
| Salad Fork | 7.50 |
| Sugar Spoon | 8.50 |
| Tablespoon | 16.50 |
| Teaspoon | 6.50 |

**Clovelly:**

| | |
|---|---|
| Bouillon Spoon, 5¼" | 5.00 |
| Butter Spreader | 4.50 |

**Colonial Classic:**

| | |
|---|---|
| Bouillon Spoon, 5½" | 6.50 |
| Butter Spreader, F.H. | 6.00 |
| Cream Soup Spoon, 5⅞" | 7.00 |
| Dessert Spoon, 7⅛" | 7.50 |
| Dinner Fork, 7⅞" | 8.50 |
| Ice Teaspoon | 7.50 |
| Luncheon Fork, 7¼" | 7.50 |
| Soup Spoon, 5⅞" | 7.00 |
| Sugar Spoon, fluted bowl | 8.00 |
| Teaspoon | 6.00 |

**Columbia:**

| | |
|---|---|
| Ice Cream Fork, 5⅛" | 5.00 |
| Teaspoon, 5¾" | 5.00 |

**French Renaissance:**

| | |
|---|---|
| Butter Spreader | 6.00 |
| Cocktail Fork | 6.00 |

Cream Soup, 6'' ------------------- 8.00
Luncheon Knife ------------------- 8.50
Pickle Fork --------------------- 8.00

## Georgian Rose:

Butter Serving Knife ------------- 9.00
ButterSpreader, F.H. ------------- 6.00
Cocktail Fork -------------------- 6.00
Cold Meat Fork, $7\frac{1}{8}$'' ------------ 18.00
Cream Soup, $6\frac{1}{8}$'' --------------- 9.00
Dessert Spoon, $6\frac{3}{4}$'' -------------- 9.00
Dinner Fork, $7\frac{3}{4}$'' ---------------- 11.00
Gravy Ladle --------------------- 18.00
Ice Teaspoon -------------------- 9.00
Lemon Fork ---------------------- 7.00
Luncheon Fork, $7\frac{1}{8}$'' -------------- 10.50
Salad Fork ---------------------- 8.50
Teaspoon ------------------------ 7.00

## Hepplewhite:

Butter Spreader, $5\frac{3}{4}$'' ------------ 4.50
Cocktail Fork -------------------- 4.50
Luncheon Fork, $7\frac{1}{8}$'' -------------- 7.00
Salad Fork ---------------------- 6.00
Sugar Spoon --------------------- 7.00

## Intaglio:

Carving Set, 2-pc. --------------- 40.00
Dessert Spoon, $7\frac{1}{4}$'' -------------- 12.00
Fork, $7\frac{1}{4}$'' --------------------- 12.00
Fork, 8'' ------------------------ 14.00

## The Lark:

Place Fork ---------------------- 8.00
Place Knife --------------------- 7.00
Teaspoon ------------------------ 5.00

## Lexington:

Dessert Spoon, $7\frac{1}{8}$'' -------------- 6.50
Luncheon Fork ------------------- 6.50

## Majestic:

Dessert Spoon, $7\frac{1}{8}$'' -------------- 5.00
Luncheon Fork, $7\frac{1}{4}$'' -------------- 7.50
Tablespoon, $8\frac{1}{4}$'' ------------------ 9.00
Teaspoon ------------------------ 5.00

## Marlborough:

Bon Bon Spoon, shovel type ------ 9.00
Butter Serving Knife ------------- 10.50
Butter Spreader, F.H. ------------ 6.00
Cheese Server ------------------- 9.00
Cocktail Fork -------------------- 7.00
Cream Soup, $5\frac{3}{4}$'' --------------- 9.00
Dessert Spoon, $7\frac{1}{4}$'' -------------- 9.00
Jelly Server -------------------- 10.50
Lemon Fork ---------------------- 7.50
Sugar Spoon --------------------- 9.00

Sugar Tongs, $4\frac{1}{2}$'' ----------------- 11.00
Tablespoon, $8\frac{1}{4}$'' ------------------ 18.00

## Savannah:

Butter Spreader, H.H. ----------- 6.00
Dessert Spoon, $6\frac{3}{4}$'' -------------- 8.50
Gravy Ladle, pourint lip --------- 18.00
Luncheon Fork, $7\frac{3}{8}$'' -------------- 9.50
Luncheon Knife, 9'' -------------- 8.50
Pie Server, serrated edge -------- 10.00
Salad Fork ---------------------- 8.00
Salad Serving Spoon, $9\frac{1}{4}$''
fluted bowl --------------------- 22.00
Teaspoon ------------------------ 6.50

## Silver Wheat:

Butter Spreader, F.H. ------------ 6.00
Dessert Spoon, $6\frac{7}{8}$'' -------------- 9.00
Ice Teaspoon -------------------- 8.50
Jelly Server -------------------- 10.50
Lemon Fork ---------------------- 7.50
Pickle Fork --------------------- 7.50
Sugar Tong, 4'' ----------------- 11.00

## Tapestry:

Place Fork ---------------------- 8.00
Place Knife --------------------- 7.00
Salad Fork ---------------------- 7.00
Teaspoon ------------------------ 6.00

## Tara:

Butter Knife, H.H. -------------- 8.00
Dessert Spoon, 7'' -------------- 7.50

## Trajan:

Butter Server ------------------- 9.50
Coffee Spoon, 5'' --------------- 5.00
Dessert Spoon, $7\frac{3}{8}$'' -------------- 8.50
Dinner Fork --------------------- 10.00
Luncheon Fork, $7\frac{1}{8}$'' -------------- 8.00
Master Salt Spoon---------------- 3.50
Salad Fork ---------------------- 8.00
Sauce Ladle --------------------- 7.50
Sugar Spoon --------------------- 8.50
Tablespoon, $8\frac{3}{8}$'' ------------------ 15.00
Teaspoon, $5\frac{3}{4}$'' ------------------- 6.50

## FRANK SMITH

### Edward VII (Obsolete):

Butter Spreader, F.H. -----------$ 5.00
Cream Soup, 6'' ------------------ 6.00
Salad Fork ---------------------- 6.00

### Golden Age (Obsolete):

Butter Spreader, F.H. ------------ 5.00
Luncheon Fork ------------------- 7.50

Luncheon Knife _____ 6.50
Salad Fork _____ 6.50
Teaspoon _____ 5.00

## Lincoln (Obsolete):

Butter Spreader _____ 6.50
Dessert Spoon, 7¼" _____ 8.00
Gravy Ladle, 7", gold bowl _____ 22.00
Meat Fork, 7½" _____ 16.00
Tablespoon, 8" _____ 16.00

## STIEFF

### Clinton:

Butter Spreader, F.H. _____ 4.00
Cream Soup _____ 5.00
Place Fork _____ 7.00
Place Knife _____ 6.50
Salad Fork _____ 6.50
Tablespoon _____ 10.00
Teaspoon _____ 4.00

### Rose:

Butter Serving Knife _____$ 8.50
Cocktail Fork _____ 5.50
Jelly Server _____ 6.50
Lemon Fork _____ 4.50
Luncheon Fork _____ 7.50
Orange Spoon _____ 6.00
Parfait Spoon _____ 5.00
Pickle Fork _____ 5.00
Pie Server _____ 10.00
Salad Fork _____ 6.50
Seafood Fork _____ 5.50
Soup Spoon, 6⅛" _____ 6.50
Teaspoon _____ 5.50

## TIFFANY

### Wave Edge:

Sauce Ladle, 7½" gold bowl _____ 10.00
Serving Spoon, gold bowl _____ 32.00
Sugar Shell, 7", gold bowl _____ 22.00
Teaspoon _____ 10.00

## TOWLE

### Canterbury:

Dessert Spoon, 7⅛" _____$ 8.00
Luncheon Fork _____ 8.00
Olive Spoon, 8¼" _____ 10.00
Sauce Ladle _____ 9.50
Seafood Fork _____ 5.00
Tablespoon, 8⅛" _____ 10.00
Teaspoon _____ 4.50

### Cascade:

Dinner Fork _____ 5.50
Luncheon Fork _____ 5.00
Salad Fork _____ 4.00

### Contour:

Butter Spreader, H.H. _____ 4.50
Cheese Server _____ 6.50
Lemon Fork _____ 4.50
Luncheon Fork _____ 7.50
Luncheon Knife _____ 7.00
Place Spoon _____ 6.00
Salad Fork _____ 6.00
Sugar Spoon _____ 7.00
Teaspoon _____ 4.50

### Cordova:

Dessert Spoon _____ 8.00
Teaspoon _____ 4.50

### D'Orleans:

Dessert Spoon, 7¼" _____ 8.00
Dinner Fork, 7¾" _____ 9.00
Dinner Knife, 9¼" _____ 7.50
Fish Knife, 8⅞" _____ 7.50
Luncheon Knife, 8⅝" _____ 7.00
Salad Fork _____ 7.50
Soup Spoon, 7¼" _____ 8.00
Tablespoon, 9" _____ 16.00
Teaspoon _____ 6.00
Tongs _____ 12.00

### French Provincial:

Butter Spreader, H.H. _____$ 5.50
Cocktail Fork _____ 6.00
Gravy Ladle ✦_____ 18.00
Jelly Server _____ 8.00
Luncheon Fork, 7⅛" _____ 9.00
Luncheon Knife, 8⅞" _____ 8.50
Pie Server _____ 15.00
Salad Fork _____ 7.50
Tablespoon, 8¼" _____ 15.00
Teaspoon _____ 5.50

### King Richard:

Ice Teaspoon _____ 8.75

### Lady Diana:

Bouillon Spoon, 5" _____ 6.00
Butter Spreader, F.H. _____ 5.00
Demi-Tasse Spoon _____ 4.00
Dessert Spoon _____ 6.50
Dinner Spoon _____ 5.00
Gravy Ladle _____ 10.00
Jelly Server _____ 6.50
Lemon Fork _____ 6.50

Luncheon Fork _____ 6.00
Luncheon Knife_____ 6.00
Pie Server _____ 8.00
Salad Fork _____ 6.00
Sauce Ladle _____ 6.50
Sugar Shell _____ 6.50
Tablespoon, 8½" _____ 10.00
Teaspoon, 5¾" _____ 4.50
Teaspoon, 6" _____ 5.00

## Lady Mary (Inactive):

Bouillon Spoon, 4⅞" _____ 5.00
Cocktail Fork _____ 5.50

## Maderia:

Butter Spreader, F.H. _____ 5.00
Cream Soup Spoon, 6⅜" _____ 7.50
Luncheon Fork, 7½" _____ 9.50
Luncheon Knife, 9" _____ 8.50
Salad Fork _____ 7.50
Teaspoon _____ 6.00

## Mary Chilton (Inactive):

Cocktail Fork, 6" _____$ 6.50
Dessert Fork, 7" _____ 7.50
Ladle, gold bowl _____ 14.00
Lemon Fork 5¼" _____ 6.50
Serving Fork, 7½" _____ 14.00
Sugar Shovel, 6¼" _____ 9.00

## Old Colonial:

Coffee Spoon _____ 7.00
Luncheon Fork _____ 12.00
Luncheon Knife _____ 11.00
Teaspoon _____ 9.50

## Pomona (Obsolete):

Fork, 7" _____ 12.00

## Rambler Rose:

Butter Spreader, F.H. _____ 5.50
Dinner Knife, 9⅝" _____ 10.00
Sugar Spoon _____ 7.50
Teaspoon _____ 5.50

## Royal Windsor:

Butter Spreader, F.H. _____ 5.00
Cream Soup Spoon, 6⅜" _____ 6.50
Dinner Fork, 7⅞" _____ 11.00
Dinner Knife, 9⅝" _____ 10.00
Salad Fork _____ 7.00
Teaspoon _____ 6.00

## Virginia Carvel:

Butter Serving Knife _____ 7.50
Dinner Fork, 7⅞" _____ 7.00
Jelly Server _____ 5.00

Lemon Fork _____ 4.50
Sauce Ladle _____ 6.50
Teaspoon, 5¾" _____ 4.50
Teaspoon, 6" _____ 5.00

# WALLACE

## Carthage:

Butter Server _____$ 7.00
Gravy Ladle _____ 10.00
Place Fork _____ 6.50
Place Spoon _____ 4.00
Sugar Spoon, shovel type _____ 6.00
Tablespoon _____ 10.00

## Dawn Star:

Dessert Spoon, 7¼" _____ 7.00
Gravy Ladle _____ 12.50
Place Fork, 7¼" _____ 8.00
Place Knife, 9¼" _____ 7.50
Salad Fork _____ 6.00
Tablespoon, 8¼" _____ 15.00
Teaspoon _____ 5.00

## Debutante:

Cocktail Fork _____ 6.50

## Eton (Obsolete):

Soup Spoon, 7¼" _____ 12.00

## Irian:

Demi-Tasse Spoon _____ 5.00
Salad Fork _____ 9.00
Teaspoon, coffee _____ 6.50

## King Christian:

Salad Fork _____ 7.00

## Lady Windsor:

Cold Meat Fork _____ 12.50
Dessert Spoon _____ 6.50
Dinner Fork, 7¾" _____ 8.00
Ice Teaspoon _____ 6.50
Jelly Server _____ 6.50
Salad Fork _____ 6.00
Tablespoon _____ 12.00
Teaspoon _____ 5.00
Tomato Server _____ 15.00

## Orchid Elegance:

Luncheon Fork _____ 8.50
Salad Fork _____ 7.50
Teaspoon _____ 6.50

**Princess Mary:**

Salad Fork, 5¾" _____ 6.00

**Rose:**

Ice Cream Spoon _____ 8.50
Teaspoon _____ 6.50

**Silver Swirl:**

Cream Soup, 6" _____ 7.50
Ice Teaspoon _____ 8.00
Lemon Fork _____ 6.50
Pickle Fork _____ 6.50

**Stradivari:**

Butter Spreader, F.H. _____ 5.50
Cocktail Fork _____ 6.50
Cream Soup, 6" _____ 8.00
Luncheon Fork, 7¼" _____ 7.50
Sugar Spoon _____ 8.00

**Waltz of Spring:**

Butter Serving Knife _____ 7.50
Butter Spreader, F.H. _____ 5.50
Cream Soup _____ 6.00
Nut Server, pierced _____ 8.50
Place Knife _____ 7.00
Tablespoon _____ 15.00
Teaspoon _____ 5.00

**Waverly:**

Carving Set, 2-pc. _____ 40.00
Teaspoon _____ 6.50

## WATSON

**John Alden:**

Dinner Fork _____$ 8.00

**King Philip:**

Lettuce Serving Fork _____ 12.00
Serving Fork, 7¼" _____ 10.00

**Lotus (Active):**

Butter Spreader, F. H. _____ 4.50
Cream Soup Spoon, 6⅜" _____ 5.00
Dinner Knife, 9" _____ 6.00
Flat Server _____ 7.00
Jelly Server _____ 5.00
Lemon Fork, 4¾" _____ 4.00
Luncheon Fork, 7¼" _____ 6.00
Salad Fork, 6½" _____ 5.00
Tomato Server, pierced _____ 10.00

## WHITING

**Adams:**

Bouillon Spoon, 5⅛" _____$ 6.50
Butter Serving Knife _____ 7.50
Luncheon Fork _____ 4.50
Luncheon Knife _____ 6.00
Sugar Spoon _____ 6.00
Teaspoon _____ 4.50

**Bead (Obsolete):**

Butter Serving Knife _____ 7.50
Butter Spreader, F. H. _____ 5.00
Luncheon Fork _____ 7.50
Salad Fork _____ 6.50
Teaspoon, 5⅝" _____ 6.00

**Dorothy Vernon:**

Sugar Spoon _____ 8.00
Teaspoon _____ 5.00

**Dresden (Obsolete):**

Berry Spoon, 7¾", gold wash ____ 22.50
Luncheon Fork, 6⅞" _____ 8.50
Soup Spoon, 6¾" _____ 8.50
Teaspoon _____ 5.00
Toddy Ladle, 9½" _____ 22.50

**Duke of York (Inactive):**

Cocktail Fork _____ 7.00

**Egyptian:**

Pastry Fork _____ 5.00
Sugar Spoon _____ 7.00

**Empire:**

Fork, 7" _____ 10.00
Fork, 7½" _____ 12.00
Luncheon Fork, 6⅜" _____ 7.00
Salt Spoon _____ 6.00
Tablespoon, 9" _____ 16.00
Teaspoon, 5⅞" _____ 5.00
Youth Knife/Fork Set _____ 8.50

**George III:**

Dessert Fork, 6½" _____ 8.00
Dessert Spoon, 7" _____ 8.00
Luncheon Fork, 7" _____ 9.00
Teaspoon, 6" _____ 6.50

**Georgian Shell (Active):**

Dessert Spoon, 7½" _____ 9.00
Tablespoon, 9" _____ 16.00

428

## Heraldic (Obsolete):

Demi-Tasse Spoon, 4'' ------------ 5.00
Dessert Spoon, 7⅛'' ------------ 9.00
Dinner Fork, 7½'' ------------ 10.00
Dinner Knife ------------ 7.50
Luncheon Fork, 6⅞''------------ 9.00
Sugar Spoon ------------ 8.50
Tablespoon, 8⅜'' ------------ 18.00
Teaspoon ------------ 7.50

## Imperial Queen:

Butter Spreader, 5⅛'', F.H. ------ 6.00
Cocktail Fork ------------ 7.00
Dessert Spoon, 6⅞'' ------------ 10.00
Dinner Fork, 7½'' ------------ 10.00
Punch Ladle, 12½'' ------------ 65.00
Salt Spoon ------------ 5.50
Soup Ladle, 10¾'' ------------ 60.00
Soup Spoon, 6¾'' ------------ 12.00
Sugar Spoon ------------ 12.50
Tablespoon, 8⅜'' ------------ 15.00
Teaspoon ------------ 7.00

## Ivy:

Luncheon Fork ------------ 8.00
Tablespoon ------------ 12.00

## King Albert (Active):

Butter Knife, 8'' ------------ 8.00
Cheese Scoop, 7½'', gold bowl --- 22.00
Cream Soup, 6⅞'' ------------ 7.00
Dessert Spoon, 7¼'' ------------ 8.00
Gravy Ladle ------------ 18.00
Jelly Server, 7'' gold bowl ------- 9.00
Lemon Fork ------------ 5.00
Luncheon Fork, 7¼'' ------------ 7.50
Luncheon Knife, 8⅝'' ------------ 5.00
Salad Fork ------------ 6.50
Teaspoon ------------ 5.00
Teaspoon, coffee, 5¼'' ------------ 4.50

## King Edward:

Cream Soup ------------ 8.00

## Kings Court:

Butter Serving Knife ------------ 7.50
Cream Soup Spoon, 5⅝'' ---------- 6.50
Gravy Ladle ------------ 10.00
Luncheon Fork, 6¾'' ------------ 7.00
Teaspoon ------------ 5.00

## Madam Jumel:

Butter Spreader ------------ 5.00
Cream Soup, 5⅞'' ------------ 5.00
Salad Fork, 3-tine ------------ 6.50
Salad Fork, 6⅛'' ------------ 5.00
Teaspoon ------------ 4.00
Teaspoon, coffee ------------ 4.00

## Old King (Obsolete):

Dessert Soon, 7⅛'' ------------ 9.00

## Oval Thread:

Butter Knife ------------ 12.00
Fork, 7''------------ 12.00

## Stratford:

Butter Pick ------------ 5.00
Butter Spreader, 5⅞'', F.H. ------ 5.00
Teaspoon ------------ 4.50

## WOODS & HUGHES

## Fiddle Thread:

Fork ------------$14.00
Teaspoon ------------ 7.00

## SILVER DEPOSIT GLASS

Silver Deposit Glass gained popularity around the turn of the present century. As the name indicates, silver was deposited on the glass by using a current of electricity while the glass and a piece of silver were placed in a solution which caused the silver to decompose and pass through the solution to the part of the glass which had previously been outlined into a pattern.

Cologne, 3½'' high ------------ $22.50

BonBon Dish. 8'' diam. _____ 30.00
Bowls:
  Berry. 8'' diam. _____ 40.00
  Fruit. 9'' diam., 2'' high. Flared
  sides _____ 37.50
  Nut. $4\frac{1}{4}$'' diam. _____ 15.00
Box, Puff. $4\frac{1}{4}$'' diam., $2\frac{1}{8}$'' high __ 27.50
Cologne. $3\frac{1}{2}$'' high _____ 22.50
Creamer and Sugar. $2\frac{3}{4}$'' high
  creamer, $2\frac{1}{2}$'' sugar bowl. Set __ 26.50
Cruet. $6\frac{3}{4}$'' high, with fluted steeple
  stopper _____ 25.00
Decanter. $8\frac{1}{2}$'' high _____ 40.00
Marmalade Jar. $4\frac{3}{4}$'' high _____ 32.50
Mustard Pot. $3\frac{3}{4}$'' high _____ 20.00
Perfume Bottle. With stopper, $3\frac{3}{4}$''
  high _____ 16.00
Plate. $6\frac{1}{2}$'' diam. _____ 16.50
Sherbet and Plate Set. 6 sherbet
  cups, $3\frac{1}{2}$'' high and 3'' diam.,
  and 6 plates, $5\frac{1}{4}$'' diam. Set ____ 115.00
Toothpick Holders:
  $1\frac{7}{8}$'' high _____ 8.00
  $2\frac{1}{2}$'' high _____ 10.00
Vases:
  Bud. 6'' high _____ 18.00
  Bud. 8'' high _____ 23.50
  Bulbous bottom, long neck, flared
  top. 8'' high _____ 48.00

### SILVER LUSTRE WARE

The ware was made in large quantities
in the Staffordshire district of England
between 1805 and 1840. After 1840 electro-
plating of metal items brought about a
decline in the demand for metal surfaced
earthenware.

Sugar Bowl. Scroll design on body
and cover _____ $85.00

Candle Holder (Late). Chamber-
type. 6'' diam., embossed scroll

decor at edge. Candle cup is
  gold lustre _____ 25.00
Coffee Pot. $10\frac{1}{2}$'' high _____ 150.00

Footed Teapot. $8\frac{1}{2}$'' to top of lid__ $67.50

Creamers:
  $4\frac{1}{2}$'' to top of handle. Fine ribbed
  design _____ 64.50
  Dolphin handle _____ 70.00
Goblets:
  $3\frac{3}{4}$'' high _____ 60.00
  $4\frac{1}{2}$'' high. Late _____ 36.50
Pitcher. Harlequin, white quilted
  body with silver lustre at top.
  2-quart capacity _____ 150.00
Sugar Bowl with lid. Small open
  handles. Fine ribbed pattern ____ 95.00
Teapots:
  $5\frac{1}{4}$'' high _____ 120.00
  $8\frac{1}{2}$'' high. Footed _____ 140.00
  11'' high. Footed, domed lid ____ 150.00
Toby Jug _____ 135.00

### SILVER RESIST WARE

The ware, first produced about 1805,
is similar to Silver Lustre in respect to
the process of silvering. However, it differs in that a pattern appears on the
surface.

The outline of the pattern was drawn
or stenciled over the body of the item
to be ''silvered.'' A glue or sugar-glycerin
adhesive was brushed over the part which
was not to be lustred. The lustreing solution
was applied and allowed to dry; then the
glue or adhesive was washed off. This glue
or adhesive had caused the drawing or
pattern to ''resist'' the lustreing solution;
and, when fired in a kiln, the lustre-like
glaze covered the entire surface—except
for the pattern.

Cup and Saucer _____ 60.00

Pitcher. 7'' high. Vine and leaf
decor _____ $145.00

Cup and Saucer. Late _____     24.50
Jug. 4¾'' high _____    125.00
Pitchers:
  5¼'' high. Vintage decor _____    100.00
  6¼'' high. Colorful floral medal-
    lion. Flutes and flowering vine
    decor on body _____    120.00
  7'' high. Vine and leaf decor __    145.00

Cup and Saucer. Berry and leaf design _____  $50.00

Teapot. 5½'' high. Vine and flower
decor _____   160.00

## SNUFF BOTTLES

These are small bottles made of porcelain,
glass, or cut from one piece of rock crystal,
agate, coral or jade. They are often intricately engraved on the outer surface and
sometimes decorated with vegetable and
mineral dyes on the interior.

The habit of carrying snuff bottles originated in the Orient during the 18th century
when snuff was introduced as a medical
cure-all. A large number of bottles were exported to Europe from China—especially the
porcelain and glass varieties. In Holland
the bottles were used for unguents or salves.

Painting of woman seated beside a
lake. 2⅛'' high _____   $55.00

Beetlenut. Carved, bird and flower
motif _____    35.00
Chalcidony. Light translucent tan.
On stand _____    95.00
Chinese. 3x2x1½'', with raised por-
celain figures. Signed. Complete     80.00
Chinese. 2½'' high. Amber glass.
Painted Inside with flowers and
birds _____    55.00
Cinnabar. Red with carvings, white
jade top _____   130.00
Cloisonne. Autumn foliage on blue
ground. Cloisonne stopper _____     125.00
Ivory. Man on camel _____     70.00
Ivory. 3'' high. Carved _____     60.00
Jade. 3'' high, carved. Urn-shaped
lion finial _____    95.00
Jade. 3'' high. Muttonfat color __   125.00
Jade. White, 2½x2x1¼'' thick, on
Teakwood stand. Chinese _____     100.00
Oriental character bottles. Carved
ivory, man, 3¼'' high, woman, 3''
high. Each _____    75.00
Peking Cameo. 2½'' high. Red on
translucent white _____    50.00

Porcelain. 3½", white background
with green and orange decor __  55.00
Porcelain. Blue and white, vase-
shaped, on Teakwood stand. With
stopper and dipper _____  48.00
Quartz. 2½" high, on stand _____  58.50

## SOAPSTONE

Soapstone is a mineral called steatite,
commonly known as potstone. Found in
Vermont, Massachusetts and the Delaware
River area, it was extensively used for
table tops, cooking vessels, griddles and
for carvings. Carved figures and vases
marked "China" are often encountered on
the antique market.

Match Holder. With monkey. 4½"
long _____  $15.00

Book Ends. Flower pot and flowers
on each _____  18.50
Chicken. 4" high _____  21.00
Elephant Seated. 5½" high. Dog at
base _____  35.00
Figure of Chinese lady holding
vase. Marked "China" _____  25.00
Figure of Chinese man. 9½" high.
Fine detail. Marked "China" __  22.50
Griddle. Medium size _____  16.00
Match Holder. With monkey. 4½"
long _____  15.00
Monkey. 6" high, with two birds
and small vase _____  25.00
Monkeys (3). 1½" high, 2" long__  10.00
Toothpick Holder with two sections.
Decor of birds and leaves _____  14.00
Vases:
7" high. Intricately carved vines
and leaves _____  27.50
9½" high, carved chrysanthemums
and leaves _____  30.00
Double. 9" high, 5" base width.
Tinted daisies and leaves.
Chinese _____  22.50

## SOUVENIR & COMMEMORATIVE PLATES

The plates referred to in this section had

their beginning at approximately the time of
the Philadelphia Centennial in 1876 and were
still popular at the New York World's Fair
in 1938. They should not be confused with
the earlier Staffordshire historical and pictorial plates which went out of vogue in
the 1850-1860 period.

Plate. 10" diam. Charleston, W. Va.
Staffordshire blue color. Late _  $12.00

Capitol at Washington, D. C. Dark
blue. Marked "R. & M. Co." in
diamond. Staffordshire, England__  12.00
Faneuil Inn. Late Wedgwood, blue  12.00
Indian Hunter Menotomy. Late
Wedgwood, blue _____  12.50
Keokuk, Iowa Plate _____  12.00
Library of Congress. Late Wedg-
wood, blue _____  12.00
Longfellow's home, Portland, Maine.
Wedgwood, deep blue. 9" diam.  12.00
Mt. Vernon. Late Wedgwood, blue  12.00
Niagara Falls. Greenish-brown.
Ridgeway. 9" diam. _____  11.00
"Old Northchurch" Plate. Marked
Wedgwood _____  12.00
Pilgrim Memorial Monument. Late
Wedgwood, blue _____  12.00
Portland, Oregon. Blue and white
Staffordshire plate. 1905 _____  15.00
Portraictuer of Captayne John
Smith, Admiral of New England,
by the Rowland and Marcellus
Co., Staffordshire, England __  11.00
Public Library, Boston. Late Wedg-
wood, blue _____  12.00
The McKinley Home. Late Wedg-
wood blue _____  10.00
"Views of Chicago." Federal Build-
ing in center surrounded by other

well-known structures. 9'' diam. **12.00**
The following late plates, made by shire, England, list at $9.50 each: Atlantic City, Detroit, Independence Hall, New London, Philadelphia City Hall, Plymouth, Richmond.

## SOUVENIR SPOONS, See SPOONS

## SPANISH LACE GLASS

The glass derives its name from the lacy pattern which runs through the glass. The design is found in clear, blue, yellow or cranberry-colored glass.

| | |
|---|---|
| Decanter. Azure blue, 10'' tall, crystal stopper. Blue glass applied handle. Blown _____ | 30.00 |
| Muffineer. Raspberry satin _____ | 49.50 |
| Rose Bowl. Canary _____ | 40.00 |
| Syrup Jug. Blue opalescent Fern pattern. Original top and applied handle _____ | 39.00 |

## SPATTERWARE

The origin and exact period of Spatterware is one of the intriguing mysteries of the antiques world.

· It appears that the majority of the ware, which is a heavy, soft-paste Staffordshire type, has been found among the Pennsylvania (Dutch) Germans. However, some has been found in Ohio, Maryland and New England.

The period of manufacture is believed to have been between 1820 and 1860. A piece impressed ''Adams'' is occasionally found.

The process of spattering was elementary. A fine sponge was dipped into paint and dabbed evenly around the borders and inner surface, or around a previously outlined decoration. After the colors dried a glaze was applied and the item fired in a kiln.

Bowls:
| | |
|---|---|
| 6½'' diam., 3½'' high. Peafowl on front _____ | 100.00 |
| 6½'' diam., rainbow pattern in red and blue _____ | 115.00 |
| Cats. 12½'' high. White ground with purple decor, green eyes. Pair | 150.00 |
| Creamer. 6'' high. Blue with pink flowers _____ | 120.00 |
| Cup Plate. 4'' diam. Blue _____ | 42.50 |

Cups and Saucers:
| | |
|---|---|
| Blue. Fort Pattern _____ | 85.00 |
| Child's. Green, Peafowl _____ | 75.00 |
| Handleless. Blue, Peafowl _____ | 125.00 |
| Light green. Peafowl _____ | 115.00 |

| | |
|---|---|
| Rainbow. Blue and purple _____ | 110.00 |
| Red. Peafowl _____ | 130.00 |

Cats. 12½'' high. White ground with purple decor, green eyes. Pair__ **$150.00**

Pitchers:
| | |
|---|---|
| 7'' high. Red and blue _____ | 165.00 |
| 8'' high. Blue, Peafowl _____ | 185.00 |
| 10'' high. Fort or Castle pattern | 200.00 |

Plates:
| | |
|---|---|
| 8'' diam. Tulip design, blue spatter around edge _____ | 130 00 |
| 8½'' diam. Tulip pattern _____ | 130.00 |
| 8¼'' diam. Rose center, purple border _____ | 115.00 |
| 9'' diam. Peafowl, red _____ | 135.00 |

Plate. 9½'' diam. House pattern. Red house and border, green and black background _____ **$250.00**

9'' diam. Thistle design. Carmine
spatter _____ 130.00
9'' diam. Red and blue _____ 98.50
9'' diam. Soup plate. Red border,
green eagle and shield. Letter
"G" impressed in back _____ 98.50
9'' diam. Red, Peafowl _____ 125.00
9½'' diam. House pattern. Red
house, red border, green and
black background _____ 250.00
9¾'' diam. Thistle or Cock's Comb
pattern. Yellow border, green
leaves and red thistle _____ 130.00

center _____ 155.00
11x14''. Rainbow _____ 125.00
14x17¾''. Blue and red _____ 145.00

Sugar Bowl. Covered. 5½'' high.
Thistle or Cock's Comb design.
Yellow _____ $160.00

Sugar Bowls:
Covered. Blue, Peafowl _____ 150.00
Covered. Blue, Tulip _____ 155.00
Covered. 5½'' high. Thistle or
Cock's Comb pattern _____ 160.00
Yellow spatter. Rose design ____ 165.00

Plate. Peafowl design _____ $125.00

Soup. 10¼'' diam. Rainbow pattern _ $90.00

Soup Plate. 10¼'' diam. Rainbow
pattern _____ 90.00
Platter:
10¼x13½''. Cut corners, purple ___ 120.00
10½x13½''. Cut corners, Peafowl

Teapot. Fort or Castle pattern ____ $215.00

Teapots:
Fort or Castle pattern _____ 215.00
Rainbow _____ 175.00
Thistle pattern. 9'' high _____ 165.00
Tulip design in carmine, blue
spatter ground _____ 200.00
Yellow and red, squat, bulbous
type. Scarce color combination__ 210.00
Wash Set. Bowl, 13½'' diam., pitch-
er, 11½'' high. Rainbow pattern.
Set _____ 240.00

## SPODE CHINA,
### See COPELAND-SPODE CHINA

### SPOONS, SOUVENIR

Souvenir spoons were made especially as mementoes of events, personalities and places. Their period of greatest popularity was between 1880 and 1900.

Spoons of this type are still being produced and feature present day activities. The spoons are finding favor among collectors today. Mr. Albert Stutzenberger, author of "The American Story in Spoons," in a letter to the writer, stated, "They have been the stepchildren of antique dealers too long—but not anymore. They are rapidly being transformed from ugly ducklings into swans, from 'Aschenpudel' into 'Cinderellas' of the antique trade."

Mr. Stutzenberger's book, "The American Story in Spoons," illustrates and discusses old American souvenir spoons and their historical association in individual "spoonographies."

LEFT TO RIGHT: Juarez, Mexico. Sterling __$5.50. Mt. Vernon. Sterling__$6.00. Washington. Sterling__$6.00.

| | |
|---|---:|
| ACTOR'S FUND FAIR. A much sought after spoon. Pictures 5 actresses and 5 actors of the early American theatre | 24.00 |
| AMPERSAND. Fraternal. Sterling __ | 7.50 |
| BERGEN. 1891. Fancy handle, tiny ringlets on hand'e, scene of deer pulling sleigh. fish. Silver plate | 8.75 |
| BUFFALO. 1897. 31st National Encampment. Silver plate | 5.00 |
| BUTTE, MONTANA. Indian face. All copper | 5.00 |
| CADILLAC. Pictures the founder of Detroit who is better known for the auto named after him | 7.50 |
| CHAPLIN, CHAS. Rogers silver plate | 7.50 |
| CHIEF SEATTLE. An Indian orator for whom the City of Seattle, Washington, was named | 7.50 |
| CINCINNATI FOUNTAIN. A heavy spoon of early vintage, with floral design, commemorating a famous Cincinnati landmark | 7.50 |
| COLORADO SPRINGS. "Prospector Panning Gold." Sterling | 8.00 |
| COLUMBIAN EXPOSITION, Chicago, 1893. "Columbus Taking Possession of the New World." Portrait of Columbus on handle | 8.00 |
| COMPLIMENTS OF THE SEASON. Cupid ringing bell, Easter Bunny, Xmas stocking. Sterling | 8.00 |
| DELAWARE WATER GAP, Pa. "The Kittatinny." Sterling | 7.50 |
| DIONNE QUINTS. Silver plate | 5.00 |
| DULUTH, MINNESOTA. Skyline handle. Sterling | 7.50 |
| FORTRESS · MONROE, AT OLD POINT COMFORT. The Moat | 7.50 |
| GRAND RAPIDS, MICHIGAN. Flowered handle. Sterling | 8.00 |
| HOT SPRINGS. An attractive spoon with ornate openwork handle | 8.00 |
| IRISH BRIGADE. Commemorates the courageous action of the Irishborn soldiers from New York City at the battle of Gettysburg. | 8.50 |
| ITHACA, N. Y. Cornell University Library. Sterling | 6.50 |
| KNICKERBOCKER. Personification of the jovial New Yorker | 12.00 |
| LAST SACRIFICE, NIAGARA. Shows Niagara Falls and the Indian Maiden who, according to legend, was sacrificed by her tribe to propitiate the Gods | 7.50 |
| LAW BLDG. Univ. of Mich. Sterling | 7.50 |
| LONGFELLOW. The spoon honored the American poet | 8.00 |
| LOS ANGELES. Sterling, embossed | 7.50 |
| LUTHER, MARTIN. Sterling | 8.00 |
| MACKINAC ISLAND. "Indian Head Landmarks." Sterling | 7.50 |
| MAINE, Feb. 13, 1898. "50,000,000 for Defense." Silver plate | 6.00 |
| MILES STANDISH. "Ruby '91." Sterling | 8.00 |
| MILES STANDISH MONUMENT. Sterling | 8.00 |
| MISSOURI. Enamel State Spoon. Sterling | 8.00 |
| MOLLY PITCHER. An unusual spoon in that it commemorates 2 women of the same name: a heroine of the Revolution and the "last of the witches" (Lynn, Mass.) | 8.50 |

MONTICELLO. Ornate leaf handle. Sterling _____ 7.50

MOUNT WASHINGTON. "Tip-Top House" 1853. Sterling _____ 7.50

NEW HAMPSHIRE. "Fabyan House." Sterling _____ 7.00

NEW ORLEANS. Sterling _____ 8.00

NEW YORK SKYLINE. Shows Statue of Liberty in harbor and skyline of New York City _____.... 8.00

NIAGARA FALLS. Sterling _____ 7.00

OLD POINT COMFORT. "Entrance to Fort Monroe" (military). Sterling _____ 8.50

OSCEOLA. A "soffkee" spoon similar to those used by Seminole Indians in Florida. Bowl pictures their Chief Osceola _____ 10.00

PICKFORD, MARY. Rogers silverplate _____ 7.50

RETURN OF COLUMBUS. A handsome spoon celebrating the discoverer of America. Put out for the Chicago World's Fair in 1893 10.00

ROCKY MOUNT, DENVER. Skyline handle, train going over a trestle (in bowl). Sterling _____ 8.75

ST. PAUL, MINNESOTA. State Capitol Silver plate _____ 6.50

SALEM WITCH. One of the earliest of souvenir spoons, manufactured by Gorham for Daniel Low of Salem _____ 10.00

SALT LAKE, UTAH. Landmarks of the Mormons. Sterling _____ 9.50

SHAKESPEARE. Enameled _____ 8.75

SOUTHERN PINES, N. C. Sterling__ 6.50

STAGE COACH. Shows a coach and horses, fishing rod, rifle and creel _____ 10.00

STATUE OF LIBERTY. Sterling ____ 6.75

STEWART, ANITA. Actress, silver plate _____ 4.50

THOUSAND ISLANDS. "Lachine Rapids." Sterling _____ 6.75

TORONTO, CANADA. Maple leaf handle. Silver plate _____ 5.50

VANCOUVER, CANADA. Enamel coat of arms. Sterling _____ 8.00

VASSAR COLLEGE. Gold bowl, R. L. G. Sterling _____ 7.00

WASHINGTON'S HATCHET. Pictures the hatchet; also on reverse side the cherry tree which Washington is reputed to have chopped down _____ 11.00

WASHINGTON'S TOMB. Shows burial place and home of George Washington at Mount Vernon ___ 8 00

WILLIAMSBURG, VA. Sterling ____ 7.50

WORLD'S COLUMBIAN EXPOSITION. Columbus at top of handle, ship on bowl _____ 7.50

WORLD'S FAIR, CHICAGO, 1892. Sterling _____ 7.00

YALE. Twisted handle, monogram, 1893. Sterling _____ 7.50

YELLOWSTONE ELK AND BEAR. A rare spoon of fine craftsmanship _____ 15.00

YELLOWSTONE PARK. Charging buffalo. Sterling _____ 8.00

YELLOWSTONE PARK. Ornate moose head in high relief. Sterling ____ 8 00

YELLOWSTONE PARK. Old Faithful. Sterling _____ 7.50

YOSEMITE BEAR. The spoon has an unusual rattail handle _____ 9.50

ZODIAC. February. Sterling _____ 10.00

## STAFFORDSHIRE

The Staffordshire District had an abundance of fine clay for pottery making. There were 80 different establishments operating there in 1786; by 1802 the number increased to 149. The district included Burslem, Cobridge, Etruria, Fenton, Foley, Hanley, Lane Delph, Lane End, Longport, Shelton, Stoke and Tunstall. Among the many famous potters located there were Adams, Davenport, Spode, Stevenson, Wedgwood and Wood.

## WILLIAM ADAMS

William Adams of Stoke-upon-Trent produced American views on blue china. Two of his cousins, both of whom were named William Adams, were also potters. One operated at Greengates, Tunstall, and the other at The Brick House Works, Burslem and Cobridge. Neither of the cousins is reported to have made American Historical Views.

Cup and Saucer. Pink, "Columbus." Larsen 351 _____ 45.00

Plates:

6", deep pink. "New York City" _____ 65.00

9" pink, "View Near Conway, N. H." _____ 62.50

10½", black. "Landing of Columbus." Larsen 348 _____ 36.50

10½", soup, pink. "Headwaters of the Juniata" _____ 70.00

Platters:

9⅞", pink. "Schenectady on the Mohawk" _____ 145.00

15", medium black. Columbus and Indian scene. Larsen 356 _____ 100.00

## WILLIAM ADAMS & SON

In 1819 a fourth William Adams, son of William Adams of Stoke, became a partner with his father and was later joined by three brothers to form the firm of William Adams & Sons. In 1829 the father died and William, the eldest of the sons, became manager. The company operated four potteries at Stoke and one at Tunstall. American views were produced at Tunstall in black, light blue, brown, pink and green in the 1830-40 period. William Adams died in 1865 and all operations were moved to Tunstall where the pottery is reportedly still being operated by the Adams family.

Plate. 10¼'' diam. Castle and river
  scene, England. Dark blue _____ $40.00

Creamer, pink. "Palestine" _____ 35.00
Cup and Saucer. "Garden Sports."
  Handleless _____ 32.50
Pitcher. 10'', pink. "Bologna" ____ 65.00
Plates:
  5¾'', pink. "New York, U. S."__ 80.00
  6'', medium blue. "Palestine" __ 21.50
  7¼'', carmine center, green bor-
    der. "Columbus" _____ 29.50
  7½'', deep pink. "Caledonia" ___ 21.50
  7½'', deep pink. "Palestine" ____ 24.00
  8'', rose pink. "Andalusia" ____ 21.50
  8'', black. "Shannondale Springs,
    Va." _____ 48.50
  8'', pink. Same _____ 59.50
  8¼'' soup. "Palestine" _____ 22.50
  8½'', blue and white.
    "Caledonia" _____ 25.00
  8½'', deep purple. "Columbus."
    Camp scene. Larsen 317 _____ 45.00
  8½'', rose pink. "The Sea" _____ 30.00
  9'', dark blue. "Mitchell and
    Freemans China & Glass Ware-
    house" _____ 135.00
  Same. 10¼'', dark blue _____ 145.00

9¼'', pink. "View Near Conway,
  N. H., U. S." _____ 68.50
10½''. Castle and river scene,
  England. Dark blue _____ 40.00
10½'', deep pink. "Caledonia"__ 35.00
10½'', soup, brown. "Headwaters
  of the Juniata" _____ 65.00
10¾'', black. "Catskill Mountain
  House, U. S." _____ 72.50
Platters:
  12½x15½'', black. "Harper's Ferry,
    U. S." _____ 260.00
  16'', pink. Same _____ 270.00
  17'', pink. "Landing of Colum-
    bus" _____ 189.50
Sugar Bowl, brown. "Log Cabin"
  with Harrison medallions on lid__ 50.00
Vegetable Dishes:
  8x10'', pink. "Bologna" _____ 49.50
  9½x13'', black. Open-handled.
    "Lake George, U. S." _____ 110.00

## RALPH & JAMES CLEWS

From sketchy historical accounts that are available it appears that James Clews took over the closed plant of A. Stevenson in 1819, with his brother, Ralph, entering the business a little later. The firm continued until about 1836 when James Clews came to America to enter the pottery business at Troy, Indiana. The venture was a failure because of the lack of skilled workmen and the proper type of clay. He returned to England but did not re-enter the pottery business.

Gravy Boat with Tray. Open-type,
  blue. Landing of Gen. Lafayette
  at Castle Gardens, N. Y. August
  16, 1824 _____ $220.00

Creamers:
  4½''. "Landing of Lafayette" ____ 95.00
  5½'', "Eagle on Urn" _____ 92.50
  Dark blue. "Christmas Eve."
    Wilkie _____ 85.00
Cups and Saucers:
  Dark blue, "Eagle on Urn" ____ 72.50
  Dark blue, "Landing of Lafay-
    ette" _____ 85.00

Dish, Covered. Vegetable, 12½",
dark blue. "The Escape of the
Mouse." Wilkie _____ 175.00
Dish, Vegetable. 11¼x12", dark
blue _____ 69.50
Gravy Boat with Tray. Open-type,
blue. "Landing of Gen. Lafayette
at Castle Gardens, N. Y., Aug.
16, 1824" _____ 220.00
Gravy Tureen with lid and tray.
"Landing of Lafayette" _____ 235.00

Plate. 9" diam. Dark blue,
"States." Building in center with
sheep grazing on lawn _____ $78.50

Plates:
6½", light blue. "Dr. Syntax,
The Garden Trio" _____ 72.50
6½", dark blue. "Dr. Syntax and a
Blue Stocking Beauty" _____ 72.50
6¾", dark blue. "Pittsfield Elm"_ 72.50
7", pink. "Rapids Above Hadley
Falls" _____ 65.00
7¼", dark blue. "Dr. Syntax
Turned Nurse" _____ 72.00
7¾", dark blue. "Landing of
Lafayette" _____ 72.50
8", dark blue. "States." Building
and driveway _____ 82.50
8¾", dark blue. "Christmas Eve."
Wilkie _____ 62.50
8¾", dark blue. "Dr. Snytax
Star Gazing" _____ 62.50
8¼", dark blue. "Dr. Syntax
Returned from His Tour" _____ 68.00
8⅞", dark blue. "Landing of Lafayette" _____ 75.00
9", dark blue. "States." Building

in center, sheep grazing on lawn
in foreground _____ 78.50
9", light blue. "Near Fort Miller,
Hudson River" _____ 67.50
9¾", soup, dark blue. "Dr.
Syntax Mistakes a Gentleman's
House For An Inn" _____ 75.00
10", dark blue. "Dr. Syntax and
the Bees" _____ 77.50
10", dark blue. "Dr. Syntax
Bound to a Tree by Highwaymen" 77.50
10", dark blue. "Landing of Lafayette" _____ 74.50
10", purple and white. "Peace
and Plenty" _____ 82.50
10", blue. Harvard College ____ 87.50
10", soup, dark blue. "Peace and
Plenty" _____ 90.00
10", dark blue. Don Quixote.
"Knighthood Conferred on Don
Quixote." Wilkie _____ 69.50
10⅛", dark blue. "Dr. Syntax
Disputing His Bill with the
Landlady" _____ 85.00
10½", dark blue. "The Valentine."
Wilkie _____ 72.50
10½", purple. "Near Fishkill" __ 55.00
10½", black. "Pittsburgh, Pa."__ 77.50
10½", soup, dark blue. "Winter
View of Pittsfield, Mass." _____ 88.50
10¾", dark blue. "States" _____ 96.50

Platter. 17". Dr. Syntax, "A Noble
Hunting Party." Clews _____ $240.00

**Platters:**

10½x13", dark blue. "Winter View of Pittsfield, Mass." _____ 250.00
11x13", brown. "Hudson, Hudson River" _____ 87.50
11x13¾", black transfer. "Hudson on the Hudson River" _____ 110.00
12½x15½", lavender. "Penitentiary in Allegheny near Pittsburgh" __ 190.00
13x15½", brown. "Newburg, Hudson River" _____ 94.50
14½x19½", blue. "Dr. Syntax Amused with Pat in the Pond" __ 200.00
15", dark blue. "Landing of Lafayette" _____ 285.00
15½", blue. "Dr. Syntax Advertising for a Wife" _____ 200.00
17". Dr. Syntax, "A Noble Hunting Party." Clews _____ 240.00
17", sepia. "Little Falls at Luzerne, N. Y." _____ 110.00
Vegetable Dish. 10", black, rectangular. "New Hudson, Hudson River" _____ 75.00

## J. & J. JACKSON

Job and John Jackson began operations at the Churchyard Works, Burslem, about 1830. The works had formerly been owned by the Wedgwood family. The firm did not produce dark blue china but made black, light blue, pink, brown, green, maroon and purple. In all approximately 40 different American views of Connecticut, Massachusetts, Pennsylvania, New York and Ohio were issued. The firm is believed to have closed about 1844.

Platter. 15½", purple. "Clyde Scenery." (England) _____ $54.50

Basket. 9" long, 3½" high, oval, medium blue, openwork. "Ford Ticonderoga" _____ 100.00
Dish, Sauce. 5", black. "University Hall, Harvard" _____ 48.50

**Plates:**

6", pink. "Girard's Bank, Philadelphia" _____ 64.50
7", black. "At Richmond, Va." _____ 57.50
7", medium blue. Same _____ 62.50
7", brown. Same _____ 65.00
7¾", pink. "Hancock House, Boston" _____ 72.50
7¾", blue. "Race Bridge, Philadelphia" _____ 57.50
8", black and white. "Battery, N. Y." _____ 45.00
8", brown. "Battery & C., N. Y." 59.50
8", pink. Same _____ 57.50
8", purple. Same _____ 66.50
9", purple. "Battle Monument, Philadelphia" _____ 72.50
9", purple. "Shannondale Springs" _____ 74.50
9", blue. "Water Works, Phila." 58.50
9", brown. Same _____ 50.00
9¼", pink. "Race Bridge, Phila." 52.50
10⅜", black. "Hartford, Conn." __ 62.50
10¼", brown. "Boston State House" _____ 65.00
10¼", black. "Hartford, Conn." __ 58.50
10¼", pink. Same _____ 57.50
10¼", brown. "The President's House, Washington" _____ 59.50
10¼", soup, black. "View of Canal, Little Falls, Mohawk River" _____ 66.50
10½", green. "The President's House, Washington" _____ 70 00
10½", medium blue. Same _____ 62.50
**Platters:**
15½", purple. "Clyde Scenery" (England) _____ 54.50
17½", black. "Newburg, New York" _____ 140.00
Tureen, with open handles. 6¼x9", Green, "Lake George" _____ 94.50
Vegetable Dish. 8x9¾", black. "Upper Ferry Bridge" _____ 80.00

## THOS. MAYER

Thos. Mayer operated a pottery at Stoke, Staffordshire, in 1829, where he produced the Coats-of-Arms of the thirteen original States. Teapots and sugar bowls showing Lafayette at the Tomb of Franklin and at the Tomb of Washington were also products of the pottery. In 1829 Thos. and his brothers, John and Joshua, bought the Stubbs works at Burslem where they continued to produce a superior grade of chinaware.

Bowl. 13" diam. "Arms of Maryland." Scalloped and embossed white rim _____ 545.00
Plate. 8¾", dark blue. "Arms of Rhode Island" _____ 225.00
Platter, mulberry, 13x11". Olympic games series, "The Sling." ____ 40.00

Vegetable Dish, dark blue, covered.
"Arms of Virginia" _____ 465.00

## J. & W. RIDGWAY

John and William Ridgway operated a pottery firm from 1814 until 1830 at which time it was dissolved. Previous to this time their father, Job Ridgway, and his brother George, had operated the Bell Bank Works at Hanley since 1792. In 1813 Job built the Cauldon Place Works near Stoke-upon-Trent, with his sons as partners. The firm was run under the name of Ridgway & Sons. After his death in 1814 the brothers operated as J. & W. Ridgway. The establishment was known for its "Beauties of America Series" which included buildings of historic or scenic importance rather than natural views such as Niagara Falls or the Hudson River.

Cup and Saucer. Light blue, Catskill Moss series. Saucer, "Near Troy, N. Y." Outside cup, "Valley of Wyoming, Pa." Inside cup, condensed "Near Troy, N. Y." __ 67.50
Custard Cup. Handled. Dark blue. "Boston State House" _____ 92.50
Gravy Boat, Handled. "Boston State House" _____ 125.00
Plates:
6", light blue. "Valley of the Shenandoah from Jefferson's Rock" _____ 36.50
6⅛", dark blue. "Atheneum, Boston" _____ 74.50
7⅛", dark blue. "Insane Hospital, Boston" _____ 67.50
7¾", rose pink. Log Cabin, "Columbian Star." Harrison souvenir. Larsen 179 _____ 62.50
8", dark blue. "Library, Philadelphia" _____ 68.50
8", light blue. "Washington's Tomb." Catskill Moss _____ 36.50
8¼", dark blue. "Staughton's Church, Philadelphia" _____ 80.00
8½", dark blue, soup. Same ____ 85.00
9", soup, light blue. "Harper's Ferry from the Potomac Side"__ 33.50
9½", light blue. "Meredith, N. H." Catskill Moss _____ 35.00
10", dark blue. "City Hall, N. Y." _____ 72.50
Platters:
10¼", dark blue. "Court House, Boston" _____ 175.00
12½", dark blue. "Hospital, Boston" _____ 165.00
15½x21". dark blue. "Capitol, Washington" with tree and well 280.00
Relish Dish. Leaf-shaped. "Boston State House" _____ 85.00
Sauce Dish. 5", light blue. "The

Narrows, Lake George." Catskill Moss _____ 36.50
Vegetable Dish. 10½", dark blue. "Hospital, Boston" _____ 84.50

## J. & W. RIDGWAY, NARROW LACE BORDER

Cup and Saucer. Light blue. "Crow's Nest from Bull Hill and "Valley of Shenandoah from Jefferson Rock" _____ 48.50
Custard Cup. 2¾", footed, light blue. "Narrows from Staten Island" _____ 46.50
Plate. 8", light blue. "Washington's Tomb." Catskill Moss _____ 27.50
Platters:
9½x11¾", light blue, lattice edge. "Sydney, Sussex College, Cambridge" _____ 49.50
10", light blue. "Peekskill Landing, Hudson River" _____ 62.50
15", black, without border. "View from Fort Putnam" _____ 56.50
Sugar Bowl. Light blue. "Narrows from Staten Island" on cover. "Undercliff near Coolspring" on bowl _____ 62.50
Vegetable Dish. 7¼", light blue, rectangular, cut corners. "President's House, Washington." Catskill Moss ___ _____ 57.50

## JOHN ROGERS & SON

John Rogers and his brother, George, built a pottery near Longport about 1782. George died in 1815. John's son, Spencer, then became a partner in the firm which operated under the name of John Rogers & Son. In 1816 John died but Spencer continued to use the name of John Rogers & Son until he disposed of the business in 1842. The firm produced only four American views of which three were of the Boston State House. The other was the battle between the U.S. Frigate Chesapeake and the British Frigate Shannon. The Shannon was victorious, consequently the subject was not popular in the United States.

Cup and Saucer. Blue. Boston State House _____ 67.50
Plates:
7½", medium dark blue. "Boston State House" _____ 59.50
9¾", soup, medium dark blue. "Boston State House" _____ 65.00
10", medium dark blue. "Shannon." Companion to "Chesapeake and Shannon" platter _____ 148.50
10", soup, dark blue. Frigate "Chesapeake" _____ 82.50
Platters:
13", dark blue. "Boston State

| | |
|---|---|
| House" `_____` | 140.00 |
| 14", dark blue. Same `_____` | 155.00 |
| 18¾", dark blue. Same `_____` | 165.00 |
| 21½", dark blue. "The Chesapeake and Shannon." Well and tree `_____` | 225.00 |
| Teapot. Medium blue. "Boston State House" `_____` | 162.50 |

## RALPH STEVENSON

Ralph Stevenson was operating a pottery at Cobridge, Statfordshire, England, in 1802. It is believed that Williams entered the firm after 1815. The usual mark on the ware was "R.S.W." with an occasional piece being marked "Stevenson" or "R. Stevenson and Williams, Cobridge, Staffordshire." In 1834 the name was changed to "R. Stevenson & Sons." The firm was discontinued in 1840. Most of the views were of the Boston and New York areas.

| | |
|---|---|
| Teapot. State House, Hartford. Dark blue. Scarce `_____` | $500.00 |
| Coffee Pot. 11" high. Black transfer "Vale of Wyoming" (Wilkes-Barre, Pa.) `_____` | 179.50 |
| Jug. 10", dark blue. "Hartford Deaf and Dumb Asylum" and "Alms House, N. Y." `_____` | 195.00 |
| Plates: | |
| 6", dark blue. "Columbia College, New York" `_____` | 140.00 |
| 7", dark blue. "Battery, N. Y."`__` | 130.00 |
| 8½", dark blue. "City Hotels, N. Y." `_____` | 72.50 |
| 10", dark blue. "Capitol, Washington" `_____` | 79.50 |
| 10", dark blue. "Alms House, City of New York." Rare `_____` | 160.00 |
| Platters: | |
| 10½", dark blue. "Brooklyn Ferry," embossed white edge. Rare New York view `_____` | 485.00 |
| 16½", dark blue. "Alms House, Boston" `_____` | 295.00 |
| Teapot, dark blue. State House, Hartford. Scarce `_____` | 500.00 |

| | |
|---|---|
| Tureen. Soup. 15½". "Philadelphia Hospital, Phila., Pa." (R. S. Stevenson) `_____` | 595.00 |

## RALPH STEVENSON & WILLIAMS

| | |
|---|---|
| Plate. 7", dark blue. "Columbia College, N. Y." `_____` | $132.00 |
| Plates: | |
| 7", dark blue. "Columbia College, N. Y." `_____` | 132.00 |
| 7½", dark blue. "Columbia College, N. Y." `_____` | 135.00 |
| 8½", dark blue. "Nahant Hotel near Boston" `_____` | 95.00 |
| 8½", dark blue. "City Hotel, N. Y." `_____` | 89.50 |
| 8¾", dark blue. "Harvard College." Larsen 281 `_____` | 110.00 |
| 9", dark blue. "Hospital, Boston." Vine border `_____` | 89.50 |
| 9½", rose pink. "Erie Canal at Buffalo." Lace border `_____` | 82.00 |
| 10", dark blue. "Capitol, Washington." Vine border `_____` | 84.50 |
| 10", dark blue. "Park Theatre, N. Y." `_____` | 90.00 |
| 10", dark blue. "Water Works, Phila." Acorn and Oak Leaf border `_____` | 125.00 |
| Platter. "Boston State House." Dark blue, about 17". Acorn and Oak Leaf border `_____` | 240.00 |

## JOSEPH STUBBS

In 1790 Stubbs established a pottery works at Burslem, England, which he operated until 1829 when he retired and sold his works to Mayer Bros. It is believed that he produced his views of America about 1825. Many of his scenes were from Boston, New York, New Jersey and Philadelphia. He died in 1836.

| | |
|---|---|
| Creamer. 5½", dark blue. "City Hall, N. Y." `_____` | 95.00 |
| Cup Plate. 3¼", "Woodlands near Phila." `_____` | 65.00 |

Cup and Saucer. Dark blue. Goat
with young kid goat _____ $60.00

Cups and Saucers:
    Dark blue. "City Hall, N. Y." __ 72.00
    Dark blue. Goat with young kid
    goat _____ 60.00
    Rose border. "Boston State
    House" _____ 76.50
Mug. 3½" high, 3½" diam., dark
    blue. "Boston State House" and
    "New York." Rose border _____ 125.00
Pitcher. 4½" high, dark blue.
    "Boston State House" _____ 110.00
Plates:
    6¾", dark blue. "City Hall,
    N. Y." _____ 70.00
    6¾", dark blue. "Woodlands near
    Phila." _____ 55.00
    7", dark blue. "Hoboken in New
    Jersey" _____ 65.00
    8", dark blue. Same _____ 67.50
    8¼", dark blue. "Nahant Hotel,
    near Boston" _____ 60.00
    8¾", dark blue. "Upper Ferry
    Bridge" _____ 60.00
    9¾", dark blue. "Fairmont near
    Phila." _____ 65.00
    10¼", dark blue. Same _____ 70.00
    10¼", dark blue. "Bank of the
    U. S., Phila." _____ 75.00
Platters:
    13½x16½", dark blue. "Mendonhall
    Ferry" _____ 190.00

21", dark blue. "Fairmont near
Phila." _____ 192.50

Pitcher. 4½" high, dark blue. "Boston State House" _____ $110.00

### JOHN TAMS & CO.

John Tams, a potter, operated the Longton Crown Works in Staffordshire, England,
in 1840. During the same year James Tams
from Philadelphia, who was an importer
and relative, sent him an order for campaign plates bearing the portrait of Gen.
Wm. Henry Harrison, Hero of the Thames
River, near Detroit, Michigan, in 1813.

Plate. 7½" diam. Cream background
with blue decor. Made for Harrison's campaign in 1840. Scarce__ $235.00

Bowl. Dark blue, 4x6'' _____ 50.00
Plate. 7½'' diam. Cream background
with blue decor. Made for Harrison's campaign in 1840. Scarce_ 235.00

## S. TAMS & CO.

The firm operated at Longton, England.
The exact date of its beginning is not
known but is believed to be around 1810-
1815. The company produced a number of
American Views including the United States
Hotel, Philadelphia, the Capitol, Harris-
burg, Pa., and the Capitol, Washington,
D. C. About 1830 the firm became ''Tams,
Anderson and Tams.''

Fruit Bowl. 10'' diam., dark blue.
"Capitol, Washington" _____ 180.00
Soup Plate. 10¼'', dark blue.
"United States Hotel, Phila."
Rare _____ 155.00

## ENOCH WOOD & SONS

The pottery was located at Burslem, in
the Staffordshire District of England, and
ran under the name of Enoch Wood & Sons
from 1819 to 1846. Wood began business
in 1783 at Fountain Place, Burslem. His cous-
in, Ralph Wood, was associated with him.
James Caldwell became a partner in 1790
and the firm was then known as Wood &
Caldwell—until Enoch obtained full control
in 1819 and admitted his sons as partners.
He died in 1840 but his sons continued the
business until 1846 under the same name.
The establishment was then sold to the
firm of Pinder, Bourne & Hope. During the
period 1819 to 1840 the pottery produced
more marked American Historical Views
than any other Staffordshire firm.

### ENOCH WOOD & SONS
### REGULAR SHELL BORDER

Plates:
6¼'', dark blue. "Highlands near
Newburg" _____ 87.50
7½'', dark blue. "Erie Canal,
Aqueduct Bridge at Rochester''__ 94.50
7½'', dark blue. "Pass in the
Catskill Mountains" _____ 75.00
7½'', dark blue. "The Capitol,
Washington" _____ 60.00
7½'', dark blue. "View of Trenton
Falls." Mint _____ 67.50
8½'', dark blue. "B. & O. Railroad Incline" _____ 77.50
8¾'', soup, dark blue. "Fall of
Montmorenci, near Quebec" ____ 42.00
9⅛'', dark blue. "Gilpins
Mills on Brandywine Creek" ____ 95.00
9⅛'', dark blue. "Transylvania
University" _____ 92.50

9¼'', dark blue. "B. & O. Railroad Incline _____ 98.50
9¼'', dark blue. "Fall of Montmorenci, near Quebec" _____ 65.00
9¼'', soup, dark blue. "Pine
Orchard House. Catskill Mountains" _____ 63.50
9¾'', dark blue. "Marine
Hospital, Louisville, Ky." _____ 95.00
10'', dark blue. "City of
Albany" _____ 82.50
10'', dark blue. "Marine Hospital, Louisville, Ky." _____ 72.50
10'', soup, dark blue. "City
of Albany" _____ 85.00
10'', dark blue. "Girl Picking
Grapes Behind Arbor" _____ 54.50
10⅛'', dark blue. "Pine
Orchard House, Catskill Mountains" _____ 77.50
10¼'', dark blue. Same _____ 85.00
10¼'', soup, dark blue. "The
B. & O. Railroad." Level view __ 87.50
10¼'', dark blue. "Table Rock
Niagara" _____ 125.00

Platters:
9¼x12'', dark blue. "Military
Academy, West Point" _____ 400.00
12½x16½'', dark blue. "Lake
George" _____ 240.00
15'', dark blue. "Niagara from
the American Side" _____ 265.00
16x20'', dark blue. "Castle
Gardens" and "Battery, N. Y."_ 380.00

### ENOCH WOOD & SONS
### IRREGULAR SHELL BORDER

Platter. 18½'', dark blue, shell border. "Christianburg, Danish Set-
tlement on the Gold Coast of
Africa" _____ $520.00

Plates:
6½'', dark blue. "MacDonough's
Victory" _____ 54.50
7½'', dark blue. "Southampton,
Hampshire" _____ 50.00

7¾", dark blue. "MacDonough's
Victory" _____ 62.50
8½", dark blue. "Chief Justice
Marshall. Troy Line" _____ 76.50
9⅛", dark blue. "MacDonough's
Victory" _____ 72.50
9⅛", dark blue. "Marine Hospital, Louisville" _____ 67.50
9½", dark blue. "The Union
Line" _____ 72.50
9¼", soup, dark blue. Same ____ 67.50
10", dark blue. So-called "Cad-
mus." Ship flying American flag_ 77.50
10", dark blue. "View of Liverpool" _____ 44.50
10¼", dark blue. "MacDonough's
Victory" _____ 79.50

Platters:
8½x11", dark blue. "East Cowes,
Isle of Wight." Sloop with Ameri-
can flag in foreground _____ 136.50
12½x16", dark blue. "Highlands,
Hudson River" _____ 325.00
18½", dark blue, shell border.
"Christianburg, Danish Settle-
ment on the Gold Coast of
Africa" _____ 520.00
Saucer. Dark blue. "MacDonough's
Victory" _____ 28.50
Vegetable Dish. 7½x9¾", dark blue.
"East Cowes, Isle of Wight" __ 85.00

## ENOCH WOOD & SON — VARIED BORDER

Plate. 10½" diam., medium blue.
"Landing of the Pilgrim Fathers
at Plymouth." Circa 1820 _____ $45.00

Bowl, dark blue, 11". "Lafayette
at Franklin's Tomb" _____ 70.00
Cup and Saucer, dark blue, flower
border. "Lafayette at Washington's Tomb" _____ 82.50

Cup and Saucer. Dark blue, flower
border. "Lafayette at Washington's Tomb" _____ $82.50

Plate. 8½", dark blue. "Vesuvius" __ $27.50

Plates:
8½", dark blue. "Vesuvius" ____ 27.50

444

10½'', medium blue. "Landing of
the Pilgrim Fathers at Plymouth."
Circa 1820 _____ 49.50

## UNKNOWN MAKERS

Teapot. Large, light blue. "Capitol
Building at Washington." Maker
unknown _____ $175.00

Cup Plate. River scene. Dark blue
with gold lustre band around
picture. Unknown maker _____ $42.50

Platter. 14½'', blue. Scene of Columbus, Ohio. Unknown maker.
Scarce _____ $615.00

Teapot. 5¾'', dark blue. "Washington at Mt. Vernon." Maker unknown _____ $225.00

## STAFFORDSHIRE FIGURINES

Baden Powell standing in front of
  cannon _____ 30.00
English Queen. Crown and ermine,
  16'' high _____ 39.50
Equestrian figures. Circa 1840.
  Pair _____ 77.50
Farmer and Wife. Jug and wheat.
  13½'' _____ 38.50
Garibaldi. Orange shirt, white
  trousers. 9'' high _____ 50.00
Going to Market—Returning Home.
  Polychrome colors. 8½'' high.
  Pair _____ 67.50
Hunter and Dog. White background.
  Green clothes with brown and
  orange trim _____ 37.50
King John signing the Magna
  Charta _____ 75.00
Milk Maid with Suckling Calf.
  5'' _____ 29.50
Moody. Black and white. 15½'' high 45.00

in blue coat looking at book __ 30.00

Trinket Box. 4'' high. White with gold trim _____ $32.50

Trinket Box. Table and chairs on lid__$35.00

Children (2) and lamb _____ 32.50
Child sitting on couch, pulling on socks _____ 30.00

Young Lady. 13½'' high. Circa 1840.
Pair _____ $100.00

Pastoral Scene. Grazing lambs.
7½'' high _____ 35.00
"Peace on Earth, Good Will Toward Men." 12¾'' high _____ 42.50
Rivals. 3 figures in bower. 15'', colored _____ 37.50
Sankey. Black and white. 15½'' high 40.00
Shakespeare. Standing figure, 18''__ 46.50
"The Huntsman." Orange coat and cap, blue leggings. 15'' high __ 45.00
Wolseley on horse _____ 37.50

## STAFFORDSHIRE ITEMS

Boxes, Trinket:
Angel (winged) and boy dressed

Lamb and baby lamb. White with green, oval, footed. 2x2½x2'' high _____ 30.00
Red Riding Hood and Wolf on cover. 2½'' _____ 30.00
Spaniel reclining on cover _____ 32.50
Wash Stand, Miniature. Cover has bowl, pitcher and mug in front of mirror frame. Footed, gold decor on edges. 1½x1¾x2¼''_ 29.50
Watch and ring on cover _____ 33.50
White with brown and white shell decor. Crossed dolphin tails in back. Green with edge lines in gold. 4⅞'' high _____ 32.50

Candle Holder. Small, leaf shaped 11.00
Dogs:
9½'' high, white, some original gold decor. Pair _____ 60.00
12'' high. White with gold lustre decor. Pair _____ 82.50

Dog. 13'' high. Circa 1850. Pair_____ $150.00

Figurine. 6½'' high. 1850-60. Pair __ $75.00

Hen. 7½'', on base. Typical Staffordshire coloring _____ $95.00

Lions. 13'' long. Green base, orange bodies. Pair _____ $95.00

Dressers:
Anchor and hooks. 2¾'' _____ 32.50
Books and vase. 2'' _____ 35.00
Child, pitcher and cup _____ 38.50
Clock and vase. 2'' _____ 35.00
Goats. Whieldon-type. Early. Pair
Hens:
2½'', miniature _____ 40.00
6½'', brilliant coloring, caramel nest _____ 110.00

7", yellow nest with green
interior ----------------------- 135.00
8", white Staffordshire, brown
nest ----------------------- 72.50
8¾", hen on nest. Light brown
base, black and white hen ----- 100.00

Watch Holder. 9". Indian squaw
with dog. White ground, orange,
blue, green and brown colors __ $35.00

Dog. 8½ high. Circa 1850. Pair ____ $100.00

Swans. For mantel flower arrange-
ments. 1860. 4 x 4". Pair _____ $80.00

Staffordshire Vase. 9" high. Pair __ $150.00

Marriage Bed Series:
  "Last in bed to put out the
  light" _____ 36.50
  "Three O'Clock in the morning"_ 39.50
  "Will we sleep first or now?" __ 42.00
Slippers:
  High-heeled, white with colored
  flowers. Heel rests on 4" pillow 36.50
  5½" long, fluted top. Gold
  sanded rose on front _____ 27.50
Swan. 6" _____ 148.50

## STATUES

Satan. Bronze. 12" high. Ca. 1500_ $245.00

Wild Horses of Mallet. Man in loin
  cloth holding rearing horses.
  French, bronze. Signed _____ 160.00
Woman. 13½" high, semi-nude.
  Ivory head, hands and bust.
  Bronze skirt, washed in gold,
  marble base. Tiara in gold with
  rubies, pearl earrings. Serpent
  arm decoration. French. Signed
  by artist _____ 500.00
Woman. 22" high. Metal. Signed
  Moreau _____ 72.50
Wood Carving. 16" high. Ivory in-
  sets. Italian, 19th century _____ 165.00

## STEINS

Steins are vessels of German origin for
drinking ale and beer which are usually
made of pottery, although some are glass
or various kinds of metal. The surfaces
are usually decorated with a painted picture, a reproduction of a print, or have a
design in relief. The steins generally have
a hinged pewter (or other types such as
porcelain, silver, etc.) top with a thumb-
lift.

## STEINS, METTLACH

Cameo or Wedgwood type. 7" high.
  ½ Litre. Musician, harvester, girl
  with grain, sickle, wine presser,
  dog and hunter. Ceramic mask
  insert in pewter top _____ 165.00
Castle. 8" high. Dark brown ground,
  polychrome figures _____ 140.00
Castle. 8½" high. ½ Litre. Pastel
  red, blue, brown and yellow. Wrr

God pouring bucket of beer on
  befuddled drinker. Marked "V"__  125.00
Castle Mark.  #3024.  13" high.
  Cameo  white  figures  in  relief,
  hinged inlay cover _____  165.00
Drinking Scene. ½ Litre. Pewter top  125.00
Gray  with  blue  decoration.  6¾"
  high. Pewter top _____  110.00
½-L.  #1100  _____   75.00
½-L.  #2086  _____   75.00
½-L.  #1052  _____  135.00
½-L.  #1062  _____  140.00
½-L.  #1258  _____  140.00
½-L.  #1403  _____  225.00

½-L.  #1471  _____  150.00
½-L.  #1649  _____  140.00
½-L.  #1698  _____  125.00
½-L.  #1786  _____  160.00
½-L.  #1900/1178  _____   75.00
½-L.  #1946  _____  190.00
½-L.  #1983  _____  135.00
½-L.  #2002  _____  200.00
½-L.  #2027  _____  175.00
½-L.  #2035  _____  130.00
½-L.  #2044  _____  225.00
½-L.  #2086  _____   80.00
½-L.  #2093  _____  225.00
½-L.  #2140  _____   65.00
½-L.  #2182  _____  110.00
½-L.  #2382  _____  250.00
½-L.  #2632  _____  145.00
½-L.  #2789  _____  110.00
½-L.  #3079  _____  105.00
1-L.  #2131  _____  175.00
3-L.  #2893  _____  160.00
4-L.  #1940  _____  400.00

## STEINS, MISCELLANEOUS

Brown with cameo picture of young
  couple.  Pewter  top  with  eagle
  thumbrest _____   80.00
Monk with stein with word "Mun-
  chen." ½ L. "Gesetzlicht" _____   70.00
Monkey. ½ L. RPM on base _____  105.00
Nun.  ½  L.  Lithophane  scene  of
  woman on bottom. No mark ____   70.00
Romantic scene, colorful. 1 L. Pewter top, unmarked _____   87.50
Shape of tower. 1 L. Gray, with
  pewter  top.  "Gesetzlicht"  on
  bottom _____   95.00
20"  high.  4  Litre.  Lovers  drinking
  a  toast  in  bold  relief  medallion.
  Bright colors _____  150.00
17"  high.  Cream  on  dark  green.
  Hunter  and  old  man  served  by
  maid at table. Pierced vine handle _____   95.00
17"  high.  Serving  stein,  dark  blue
  and  gray.  Bulbous,  high  neck.
  Four  medallions  of  frolicking
  cupids in garlands _____  140.00
11½" high. Sheffield silver.
  Bacchus design _____  325.00
11"  high.  2  green  and  cream  panels,  1  dark  brown  and  green  panel. Lovers, chalet, castle, pierced
  vine handle _____   60.00
10½"  high.  1  Litre.  Blue  and  gray.
  Raised  figure  of  seated  man  being served by maid _____   65.00
10"  high.  ½  Litre.  Firefighting
  scene.  Pewter,  lithophane  scene
  in bottom _____  150.00
10"  high.  Dresden.  White  with
  orange  stripes.  View  of  monument
  in park at Rolandbrunnen. Lithophane scene in bottom _____  135.00

Mettlach  Pitcher  Stein.  #2194.
  Cameo scene, alligator handle __ $225.00

## STEINS, DRINKING

**TOP ROW:** Monkey. $\frac{1}{2}$ L. RPM on base__$105.00. Monk with stein with word "Munchen." $\frac{1}{2}$ L. "Gesetzlicht"__$70.00. Nun $\frac{1}{2}$ L. Lithophane scene of woman on bottom. No mark__$100.00. **CENTER ROW:** $\frac{1}{2}$ L. Brown with cameo picture of young couple. Pewter top with eagle thumbrest__$90.00. Mettlach. #1403. $\frac{1}{2}$ L. Pewter top with porcelain insert__$150.00. Mettlach. $\frac{1}{2}$ L. Drinking scene, pewter top__$140.00. **BOTTOM ROW:** Shape of tower. 1 L. Grey, with pewter top. "Gesetzlicht" on bottom__$110.00. Romantic scene, colorful. $\frac{1}{2}$ L. Pewter top, unmarked__$95.00. Mettlach. $\frac{1}{2}$ L. #1786. Allegorical fire scene, dragon handle__$160.00.

451

Stein. German garden scene. 12''
high. "H. R." mark _____ $125.00

6'' high. Threaded Glass. Rubina
coloring, pewter top with bail
thumbrest, crystal handle _____ 50.00
6'' high. Royal Vienna. Monk scene 450.00

## STEREOSCOPE VIEWERS AND CARDS

The stereoscope came into use in America
about 1850—having been invented in England
a dozen years earlier. The picture is taken
with a dual lens camera and the scene
is reproduced as two pictures. Upon being
seen through a viewer the pictures blend
into one with the scene standing out as it
would if seen by the naked eye.

## CARDS

100 View Sets:
| | |
|---|---|
| Denmark _____ | 9.50 |
| Egypt. With map and book _____ | 10.75 |
| Germany _____ | 9.50 |
| Greece. With map and book ____ | 11.50 |
| Holland _____ | 9.50 |
| Italy. With maps and book _____ | 9.50 |
| Norway. With maps and book __ | 10.75 |
| Panama _____ | 10.75 |
| World War I, 2 boxes of prints. Complete _____ | 24.50 |

Stein. 17'' to top of pewter lid.
Three panels showing frolicking
monks _____ $125.00

9½'' high. 1 Litre. Man with horse,
blowing bugle. Lithophane bottom.
No maker's name _____ 115.00

9½'' high. ½ Litre. Man in foreground, farm and windmill in
back. Bright colors _____ 70.00

9'' high. ½ Litre. Cream with light
brown background. Cavalier,
maid, serpents, C scroll, tracery 60.00

9'' high. ½ Litre. Blue and cream.
Four cavaliers drinking, smoking,
playing mandolin _____ 65.00

8'' high. Owl head cover. Marked
"Hanke, Germany" _____ 72.50

7'' high. Capo-di-Monte _____ 150.00

7'' high. ½ Litre. Dark green ground.
King, Jack and 2 Queens in relief on sides _____ 67.50

6¼'' high. ½ Litre. "V. B. Gwaw-
hutzt"—forerunner of Mettlach.
Gnomes at wine keg _____ 70.00

6½'' high. ½ Litre. Lithophane bot-
tom showing portrait of woman.
German bridge and town scene.
Pewter top. No maker's name __ 110.00

Hand-type viewer, with sliding adjustment _____ 9.50

Double-type. Made of wood. 18''
high, 10'' wide. "Pat. date 1859,
Alex Beckers, N. Y." _____ 89.50

### CARDS-Singles

Prices quoted are for cards in good condition. Folded, mutilated or badly soiled

cards are of little or no value to collectors.

| | | |
|---|---|---|
| Alaska Gold Rush. Each ____ | .75 to | $2.00 |
| American Scenic _____ | .35 to | .45 |
| Anthony. Brady Photographer | | |
| Civil War _____ | 2.50 to | 8.75 |
| Anthony, E. _____ | .75 to | 2.00 |
| Anthony, E. H. & T. _____ | 1.50 to | 4.00 |
| Autos _____ | 1.00 to | 2.75 |
| City Scenes _____ | .25 to | .75 |
| Comics _____ | .25 to | .35 |
| Commercial Advertising Cards | .30 to | .75 |
| Disasters _____ | .60 to | 1.50 |
| Expositions _____ | .35 to | .75 |
| Indians _____ | 1.00 to | 2.00 |
| Lithographed Cards. Some in | | |
| color. Late _____ | .25 to | .30 |
| Panama Canal _____ | .40 to | .75 |
| Presidents _____ | 1.75 to | 3.00 |
| Rogers' Statuary _____ | .65 to | 1.00 |
| Sentimentals _____ | .30 to | .45 |
| Ships _____ | 1.25 to | 2.75 |
| Spanish American War _____ | .30 to | .95 |
| Tissues, American and | | |
| French _____ | 1.00 to | 1.95 |
| Trains _____ | 1.50 to | 3.00 |
| Transportation. Wagons, buggies, etc. _____ | .85 to | 1.25 |
| Western Scenery, etc. _____ | .95 to | 2.00 |
| Whaling _____ | .70 to | 1.25 |
| World War I _____ | .30 to | .65 |

### STERLING, See SILVER

### STEUBEN GLASS

The Steuben Glass Works was started in 1904 by Frederick Carder, a native of England and Thomas G. Hawks at Corning, New York. In 1918, the Corning Glass Company purchased the Steuben Works. Carder remained with the company and designed many of the pieces bearing the Steuben mark.

Bottles:
    15'', fish shape with stoppers.
      Green color. Pair _____ 395.00
    Cologne. 7½'' high. Cerise ruby,
      flame stopper _____ 125.00
Bowls:
    3'' high. Grotesque design.
      Shaded amethyst to crystal _____ 95.00
    7'' high, irregular fluted sides,
      cerise to clear. 12x6'' diam.____ 240.00
    7¼'' high. Large, ivory. 12½x7¼''.
      Base, 3½'' square _____ 375.00
    9½'' diam. Aurene and calcite.
      Gold _____ 200.00
Candlesticks. Blue, signed. Pair __ 160.00
Compotes:
    3½'' high. Rosaline with alabaster
      stem and base. Bowl, 7¾x1½''.
      Round flat base, 3¾'' diam. ____ 195.00
    8''. Jade green base and bowl,
      creamy white stem. Signed_____ 180.00

Candleholders. 12" high. Light green glass. Pair _____ $135.00

Dessert Set. Pink. 8 8½" plates, 1 14" plate. Floral motif on borders. Set _____ 200.00
Flower Pot. 5" high, with matching base. Signed "Steuben Aurene." Set _____ 185.00
Flower Pot. 5¼" high. Jade green with two heavy alabaster threads around top edge. Signed "F. Carder" _____ 250.00
Glass, Iced Tea. 6" high. Amethyst with vertical shadow ribbing ____ 35.00
Goblets.
  7¼" high. Alabaster trumpet bowl and disc foot. Pink and blue Cintra twist stem _____ 150.00
  Red, vintage pattern. Signed ____ 75.00
  Stem. Teardrop _____ 85.00
Mug. 2⅜" high, handled. Clear glass with applied handle. Applied blue-black threading. Signed with fleur-de-lis mark ___ 25.00
Plates:
  8¼" diam. Deep center with swirled rim. Emerald green. Signed with fleur-de-lis _____ 85.00
  8¾" diam. Jade. Signed "Steuben" _____ 70.00
Shade, Gas. Pearl white with green loopings. Signed _____ 50.00
Sherbet. Rosaline _____ 100.00
Vases:
  5½" high. Footed. Clear with cerise ruby threading 1½" high around base of bowl. Concave

sides with 3⅝" top diam. Signed with fleur-de-lis _____ 125.00
7½" high. Ovoid body, short neck, flared rim. Rosaline _____ 275.00
7½" high. Peacock blue, silver sheen, purple tints. 4½" rolled top diam. Spreads to 7" diam., then tapers down for 6" to 3¾" bottom diam. _____ 380.00
8" high. Bud vase. Rosaline, flared tricorne top, short neck, elongated ovoid body overcased with alabaster which forms stem and foot. 2 applied alabaster handles _____ 285.00
8" high. Stick vase. Fully signed _____ 175.00
8" high. Alabaster acid cutback fan vase carved all over with chrysanthemums and leaves. Rim and pedestal carved with leaves 500.00
9½" high. Folded handkerchief. Shaded green crystal. Signed Steuben _____ 185.00
10" high. Ivory. Straight paneled sides. Signed "F. Carder" ____ 300.00
10½" high. Cluthra. Solid yellow-green _____ 575.00
10½" high. Jade, amphora-shaped with 2 applied inverted "w" alabaster handles. Expanded 3¼" base, widest diam. 7", neck 2½" with 4" smooth rim opening. Signed with fleur-de-lis _____ 325.00
12" high. Amethyst, flared top, body and scalloped base joined by clear swirled ball _____ 115.00
14" high. Stick vase. Fully signed _____ 160.00
Wine. Bowl and foot blue. Stem has mica flecks encased _____ 39.50

## STEVENGRAPHS

Stevengraphs are woven silk items with figures in the design. The articles were manufactured by Thomas Stevens, using the Jacquard loom, invented in France by J. M. Jacquard. Thousands of silk pictures were sold at the New York Crystal Palace Exposition, 1853-54 and at the Philadelphia Centennial Exposition in 1876.

Book Marks:
  "Last Rose of Summer" _____ 30.00
  Silk. Stage coaches, framed ____ 50.00
Cannon, Tom. Jockey _____ 70.00
Cody, Wm. F. 5x9½" _____ 75.00
Crystal Palace (Interior) _____ 92.50
Dick Turpin's Last Ride on His Bonnie Black Bess. 2x6" _____ 75.00
Eagle and Shield. 18x20". "E. Pluribus Unum" on ribbon below ____ 75.00
Good Old Days, The _____ 60.00
Landing of Columbus _____ 60.00

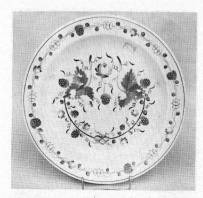

Strawberry China Plate. 10'' diam. $185.00

**Plates:**

| | |
|---|---|
| 8½'' diam. | 165.00 |
| 10'' diam. | 185.00 |
| Sugar Bowl. Covered | 195.00 |

**Teapots:**

| | |
|---|---|
| 5¼'' high, 9½'' long | 200.00 |
| 6'' high, 9½'' long | 225.00 |

### STRING HOLDERS

Grocery and Dry Goods Stores found string holders to be useful items. Usually made of iron there were two common types —the hanging-type and the beehive which was placed on the floor or counter.

George Washington. The Father of Our Country. USA Centennial 1776-1876 _____ $45.00

| | |
|---|---|
| Last Lap (Bicycle Racers) | 65.00 |
| Playing Saint and Angel. 12x10''. Framed | 45.00 |
| Present Time, The | 50.00 |
| Royal Mail Coach | 65.00 |
| Train, Railroad | 57.50 |

### STRAWBERRY CHINA

Strawberry china derives its name from the decoration of the ware. It is an early soft-paste china and a contemporary of Gaudy Dutch and Spatterware. It is scarce and much sought after by collectors.

| | |
|---|---|
| Creamer | 150.00 |
| Cup and Saucer | 140.00 |

Iron. Shape of beehive _____ $15.00

Glass. Beehive, 5'' high _____ 6.75
Iron. Beehive _____ 15.00
Iron. 4½'' high. Hanging-type ____ 12.50
Pottery. 9¾'' high. Cone-shaped,
   glazed interior _____ 9.50

Orange coloring at top shading to
   yellow at bottom _____ 60.00
Scrolled Rib. 4½'' high. Green milk
   glass _____ 22.50
Single Ring. Tin top. Opaque white 11.50

## SUGAR SHAKERS

Sugar shakers, or sifters, as they are
sometimes called, came into general use
in the 1870-80 period. The majority was
made of opaque white glass while some
of a later period was made in colors, such
as cranberry, green and blue.

Milk Glass. 5¼'' high. Painted flowers on body, shell pattern base,
   tin lid _____ $12.75

Acorn. Shape of acorn. Metal top,
   opaque white _____ 20.00
Cranberry. Diamond quilted. Origin-
   al top _____ 49.50
Milk Glass. White. 4½'' high.
   Double tooth band. Tin lid _____ 11.50
Flowered Panels. 4'' high. White
   milk glass _____ 16.50
Satin Glass. Pewter-type top.

## SUNDERLAND LUSTRE

A type of lustre ware with marbled or
spotted decorations which shade from pink
to purple. A solution of gold compound applied over a white body developed many
shades of pink lustreing—from a pale
pink to ruby and purple—the shade being
determined by the metallic film's thickness.
The ware was made by many potters including Wedgwood, Enoch Wood, Bailey &
Batkin, Copeland & Garrett, Adams and
many others.

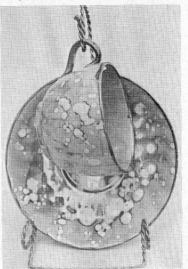

Cup and Saucer. Handled. Allerton
   & Son _____ $40.00

Box. 6x4x2½'', with unattached lid.
   Black transfer of old time English
   people _____ 75.00
Bowls:
   10''. "Sailor's Farewell" and
   "Sailor's Return" verses inside
   and out _____ 150.00
   10'' diam., 4½'' high. View from
   the cast iron bridge _____ 160.00

Cake Plate _____ 75.00
Cups and Saucers:
  "Babes in the Woods" _____ 47.50
  Black and white transfer com-
  memorating death of Princess
  Charlotte _____ 59.50
  Handled. Allerton & Son _____ 40.00
  Mustache. Black transfer of ship
  on front, sailor's poem on back.
  Late _____ 45.00
  Plain _____ 40.00
Goblet. Allover lustre decor _____ 90.00

Jug. $5\frac{1}{2}$" high. Ship with caption.
"Success to the Tars of Old
England" _____$300.00

Jugs (Pitchers):
  5" high. "Home is a name of
  more than, etc." _____ 200.00
  $5\frac{1}{2}$" high. "Sailor's Departure"__ 250.00
  $5\frac{1}{2}$" high. Ship with caption,
  "Success to the Tars of Old England" _____ 300.00
  $6\frac{1}{2}$". Wilkie Comic. Mottling inside and out _____ 260.00
  Pink lustre trim with raised
  figures _____ 150.00
  Quart. Allover lustre decor, 2
  light green hands and three
  verses around bowl _____ 225.00
  Shell. Hunting scene. Medium __ 165.00
Mugs:
  "Faith, Hope" _____ 185.00
  Frog. 5" high, 3" diam. English,
  pink, with mariner's compass and
  figures of John Bull and Britannia

in colors. Large green frog looking up from bottom _____ 125.00
4" high. Verse, "Sailor's Tears"
and ship flying British flag ____ 85.00
$4\frac{1}{2}$" Iron Bridge. With black transfer, ships and peace and plenty
on reverse _____ 89.50
Pepper Shaker _____ 59.50
Pitcher. 6" high. Allover pink lustre. Hunting scene in black,
shell design _____ 100.00
Plaque. 9x8". Angel with horn in
center. "Prepare to Meet Thy
God" in purple border _____ 85.00
Plates:
  7" diam. Pink and floral decor __ 27.50
  8" diam. deep. Lady with harp,
  trees and child _____ 50.00
  9" diam. "Babes in the Woods" 57.50
Platter. $7\frac{1}{2}$x$8\frac{1}{2}$". Picture of Adam
  Clark, Wesleyan minister _____ 115.00
Salt. Round, footed _____ 60.00
Salt Shaker _____ 42.50
Teapots:
  Covered. Large, mottled pink __ 175.00
  Medium, mottled pink _____ 100.00

## TAFFETA GLASS, See CARNIVAL GLASS

### TEA LEAF LUSTRE

A type of gold lustre decoration on late
Ironstone chinaware which is more or less
a form of the oriental tea leaf. It was
known also as "Lustre Band with Sprig."
The ware was an inexpensive type produced
by a number of English and American
potteries.

Gravy Boat. $7\frac{7}{8}$" long. Meakin China _____ $21.50

Bone Dish _____ 7.50
Bowls:
  Covered, vegetable _____ 30.00
  Open, vegetable _____ 10.00
  15" diam. _____ 36.50
Butter Dish. Covered _____ 32.50
Butter Pat _____ 2.75

| | |
|---|---|
| Cake Plate. Meakin _____ | 27.50 |
| Coffee Pot _____ | 37.50 |
| Creamer _____ | 21.50 |
| Cups and Saucers: | |
| Coffee _____ | 15.00 |
| Handleless _____ | 18.00 |
| Tea _____ | 15.00 |
| Demitasse Tea Service. Teapot, sugar bowl, creamer, 4 6'' plates, 4 cups and saucers _____ | 98.50 |
| Gravy Boat _____ | 21.50 |
| Pitchers: | |
| Milk _____ | 22.00 |
| Water _____ | 29.50 |
| Plates: | |
| Cup _____ | 5.00 |
| 8'' diam. _____ | 8.00 |
| 8¾'' diam. _____ | 9.00 |
| 9'' diam. _____ | 9.50 |
| 9'' soup _____ | 7.50 |
| 10'' diam. _____ | 11.00 |
| Platters: | |
| 12'' long _____ | 20.00 |
| 13'' long _____ | 23.50 |
| 14'' long _____ | 25.00 |
| 16'' long _____ | 27.50 |
| 16½'' long _____ | 30.00 |
| Sauce Dish. Meakin, round _____ | 5.75 |
| Shaving Mug. Ribbed, embossed berries on handle _____ | 22.50 |
| Soap Dishes: | |
| Covered _____ | 12.00 |
| Square, covered, handled, with removable insert _____ | 21.50 |
| Sugar Bowl _____ | 28.50 |
| Teapot. Large _____ | 49.50 |
| Tureens: | |
| Gravy. Covered, with tray and ladle _____ | 58.50 |
| Soup. Covered, round, without ladle _____ | 80.00 |
| Vegetable Dish, Covered. 5⅓x9⅓'' __ | 32.50 |
| Wash Bowl and Pitcher. ''Alfred Meakin Royal Ironstone China''__ | 60.00 |

## TEA WAGONS, See FURNITURE

## TELEPHONES

Alexander Graham Bell patented the first telephone in 1876. Since that time a variety of instruments have been designed. One of the most common in the collectors' field is the wooden case wall-type which collectors seek today, mainly for decorative purposes or to create atmosphere.

| | |
|---|---|
| French. Cradle type _____ | 85.00 |
| Wall. Oak case, crank type, with shelf _____ | 65.00 |

## TEPLITZ

A type of late German decorated pottery, usually found in vase form, it was issued in the late Victorian period and was made in quantity for sale to the masses rather than to persons of discriminating taste.

| | |
|---|---|
| Vase. 19½''. Cream ground, red floral arrangement, green leaves, gold trim _____ | $225.00 |

| | |
|---|---|
| Bust of woman. 12'' high. Victorian style _____ | 60.00 |
| Ewer. 7'', oval shaped. Gold handle and trim. Decorated with colorful flowers _____ | 29.50 |
| Figure. ''Tom, Tom, the Piper's Son.'' 5½x8'', 5'' front to back__ | 57.50 |
| Figurines. Boy and girl _____ | 72.50 |
| Vases: | |
| 5¼'' high, ¾ of body in brown, purple at top with woman and cherub, simulated pearls _____ | 22.50 |
| 9'' high, 2 dragon handles _____ | 50.00 |
| 9¾'' high. Flower effect openwork top and handles. Gold decorated base _____ | 30.00 |
| 11'' high. Footed and handled, scalloped openwork top _____ | 50.00 |
| 12¾'' high. Egyptian urn shape. 2 handles _____ | 54.50 |

15'' high. Gold decoration.
Marked "Bohemia" _____  58.50

## TERRA COTTA WARE

This is unglazed red ware which is made of clay. Much of the Terra Cotta ware on the market today is of Oriental origin.

Child's Tea Set. Tray, teapot,
3 cups _____  $16.00

Child's Tea Set. Tray, teapot, 3
cups _____  16.00
Creamer. Royal Terra Cotta Porcelain with colorful Chinese
panels _____  22.50
Cup and Saucer _____  18.50
Plaque. Cupids and dog, hunting__  18.75
Statues. 9½'' high, Chinese subjects, enameled fronts _____  120.00
Teapots:
3⅛''. Tan background with
green and yellow enamel decor.
"Made in China" impressed on
bottom _____  12.00
Individual. Enamel decor.
Oriental _____  7.50
Tobacco Jar. 10'' high. Man in
swallowtail coat, white vest,
skull cap, sideburns _____  48.50

## THREADED GLASS

The glass was originally made in this country at the Sandwich factory. The thread-ing is not impressed but is applied to the outside of the object. The early ex-amples were hand-threaded while later pieces were done by machine.

Basket _____  37.50
Bowl. 5'' high, 3¾'' across.
Applied white feet, rose threaded,
clear trim _____  69.50

Jam Jar. Pink glass. Silver plated
lid and handle _____  $55.00

Finger Bowls:
Blue. 4½'' diam., 2½'' high _____  20.00
Cranberry. Sandwich threaded,
fluted edge, with matching plate  57.50
Rose threaded. Opaque lining, 14
scallops at top _____  48.50
Vaseline _____  18.50
Jug, Wine. Bulbous, clear to amethyst, metal collar, lid and
handle _____  70.00
Lemonade Glass. Sandwich glass,
deep pink threads on crystal
ground. Engraved with pond
flowers and leaves. 5'' high,
applied handle _____  52.50
Pitcher. 11½'' high. Cranberry with
white floral decor. Applied clear
glass handle _____  95.00
Sugar Bowl. Medium blue color __  50.00
Tumbler. Cranberry, Sandwich glass  42.50
Vases. 3'' high. Cranberry with
green shading, bulbous base.
Diamond pattern in threading,
crystal rigaree top. Pair _____  60.00

## TIFFANY GLASS

Louis Comfort Tiffany, the son of a

wealthy New York jeweler, established his own glass house in 1878 to make stained glass for windows.

Around 1890 he began to make vases, lamp shades, tableware etc., in a gold iridescent or lustred glass. Most of the items bore the name "L. C. Tiffany" or the initials "L. C. T." However, in sets, such as goblets, lamp shades, salts or finger bowls, only one item was marked. Some items also carried a number, while others, in addition to name or initials, were inscribed with "Favrille," the French word for color. The ware was discontinued about 1910. Tiffany died in 1933 at the age of 85.

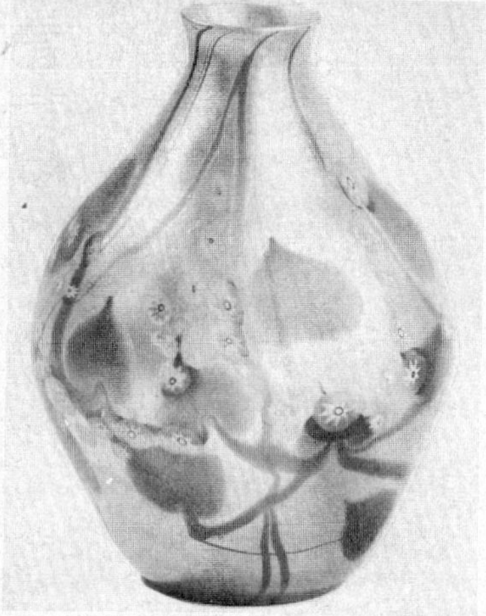

Vase. 8". Gold with green leaves and vines ______ $295.00

Bobeches. Blown, gilt rims. Late. Set of 6 ______ 80.00
BonBon Dish. $5\frac{1}{2}$" diam. Gold ______ 120.00
Bowls:
- $4\frac{3}{4}$" diam. Ruffled top, gold iridescent ______ 140.00
- 6" diam., $2\frac{1}{2}$" high. Gold and blue iridescent. Signed "L.C.T." ______ 150.00
- $7\frac{1}{2}$". Green shading into clear. Opalescent stripings from rim to pontil. Signed ______ 285.00
- $8\frac{1}{4}$" diam. Blue and rose. Signed Favrille #1404 ______ 300.00
- 9" diam. Ribbed, blue, ruffled edge. Signed ______ 345.00
- 12" diam. Etched leaves on bronze base. 5" high. Signed ______ 395.00
- Rose. "Verre Moire" ______ 160.00

Candle Lamps. $9\frac{1}{2}$" high, 5" shade diam. 3 pieces: shade, candle-tube and base. Favrille, gold iridescent. Brass fixtures, push-up type. Signed "L.C.Tiffany." Pair 425.00
Candlesticks:
- $4\frac{1}{2}$" high. Gold and blue. Signed "L.C.T" Pair ______ 195.00
- $7\frac{1}{2}$" high. Signed ______ 125.00
- $7\frac{1}{2}$" high, $3\frac{1}{4}$" top diam., $15\frac{1}{2}$" base circumference. Signed. Pair 250.00
- 10" high. Bluish-gold. Signed ______ 185.00
- $11\frac{1}{2}$" high. Signed ______ 200.00
- $13\frac{1}{2}$" high. Signed ______ 225.00

Centerpiece. With flower holder. 12" diam., 2" deep. 5 green lily pads and vines. Signed ______ 300.00
Champagne. 7", hollow stem. Signed ______ 225.00
Compotes:
- Jelly ______ 175.00
- Small. Signed ______ 200.00
- $11\frac{1}{2}$" high. Gold iridescent. Signed ______ 225.00
- $14\frac{1}{2}$" high, $6\frac{1}{2}$" diam. Feather design. Signed ______ 295.00

Cordial. Gold iridescent. Signed ______ 110.00
Decanters:
- 8" high. Gold iridescent. Signed 250.00
- $10\frac{1}{2}$" high. Original stopper. Signed ______ 400.00

Dish. Square, in 4-legged metal frame ______ 125.00
Finger Bowl and Plate. Gold iridescent, fluted edge. Signed ______ 150.00
Glass, Jui~e. Lily pad decor ______ 160.00
Goblet. Clear, blue and opalescent. Signed ______ 200.00
Inkwell. By Tiffany Studios. Beige mottled panels ______ 50.00
Lamps:
- 3-shower, bronze base. Tiffany Studio. Shades marked "L.C.T." ______ 500.00
- Tulip Table Lamp. 16" diam. Signed ______ 700.00

Nut Set. Bowl, 6 dishes. Signed ______ 225.00
Pen Tray. Zodiac design. Tiffany Studio ______ 40.00
Perfume Bottle. Peacock blue. Original stopper ______ 110.00
Pitcher, Water. Border etched with grapes and leaves. Signed "L.C. Tiffany" and "Favrille" ______ 495.00
Plate. 6" diam. Gold iridescent. Signed ______ 150.00
Rummer. $11\frac{1}{4}$" high, $6\frac{1}{4}$" diam. Gold iridescent. Signed ______ 175.00
Salts:
- Footed ______ 65.00
- Gold iridescent. $2\frac{1}{2}$" diam. Ruffled edge. Signed ______ 65.00
- Master ______ 90.00

Sconces, Wall. 3 green feathers. Signed. Pair ______ 650.00

Shade, Gas. 7'' top diam., 2½'' base
diam. Signed ------------------ 85.00
Sherbet. Lily pad design. Signed -- 160.00
Tazza. 6'' diam. Morning Glory
blue. Signed ------------------ 500.00
Toothpick Holder ---------------- 80.00
Tumbler. Signed ---------------- 175.00
Urn. 2'' high, amethyst and gold.
Signed "L.C.T." -------------- 140.00
Vases:
3¾'' high. Butterfly, blue and
green with allover waves and
swirls --------------------------- 250.00
6'' high. Decoration of brown
to green leaves. Signed -------- 1550.00
6'' high. Iridescent dull blue
with white, gold and green
loopings ----------------------- 450.00
6½'' high. Gold iridescent ------ 270.00
7½'' high. Signed -------------- 280.00
10½'' high. Urn-shaped, handled.
Iridescent gold shade --------- 500.00
12'' high. Lotus leaf decor, metal
base. Signed ----------------- 425.00
13½'' high. Trumpet vase, gold
iridescent with green leaves.
Signed and numbered ---------- 500.00
15½'' high. Trumpet-shaped, with
large leaves in iridescent amber
and green. Gilded metal base--- 400.00
Witches Pot. Gold with green highlights. Signed ------------------ 69.50

## TILES

Tiles fall roughly into two categories—
decorative and table. Decorative tiles were
used for fireplace fronts, floors, benches
and to decorate furniture. Table tiles were
used to hold hot dishes and thus protect
the table.

Bellflower in center. Blue and
gold -------------------------- 7.50
Buckingham Palace Scene. 7¾''
diam. Green Staffordshire, walnut
frame. 3 low wood feet, each en-
closing a marble. Hook for
hanging ---------------------- 24.00
Calendar. 1895, Boston State
House ------------------------ 15.00
Calendar, 1914. Commonwealth
Docks, Boston ---------------- 15.00
Calendar, 1925. Ship, "Flying
Cloud." Wedgwood ----------- 10.50
Castle. Blue, 5x5¼'' ------------- 6.00
Cat. 6x6'', blue and white ------- 6.75
Dutch Children. Table tile.
5¾'' square -------------------- 8.75
Elk in Woods. Geometric border,
in blue and white. 1870 Reg.
mark ------------------------- 8.50
Fireplace Tile. Colorful, floral
scrolled design. 6x6'' English---- 7.50
Floral decor on round china tile--- 8.00
Flower Pot. Blue. 5x5¼'' --------- 6.50

Tile. 6¼ x 6¼''. Framed. Delft blue-- $12.50

Flower Pot. For fireplace.
5⅛'' square. Mulberry and white-- 6.75
Gibson Girl in embossed center
decoration -------------------- 8.75
Girl with Pail. 3x5½''. Red clay,
glazed, blue, green, yellow and
brown ------------------------ 6.50
Lobster. 16'' long, 7'' wide, 1''
deep. 3 sections, unglazed ----- 10.00
Man on Barrel. Polychrome
colors. 5x5¼'' ----------------- 9.75
Old Hancock House. Stoke-on-
Trent. 6'' square, sepia decor--- 11.00
Owl. Polychrome colors, 5x5¼'' -- 12.50
Snake, 4½x6½x1''. Clay, black
glaze ------------------------- 8.00
State House, Boston, 1818.
Stoke-on-Trent. 6'' square, blue-- 21.50
Tiffany. 4'' square. Raised
medallion in green-orange ------ 16.50
Villeroy & Boch. Tea tile in blue
with white seascape in scrolls.
5¾'' -------------------------- 10.00
Water Lilies. Germany ----------- 7.75
Windmill Scene. 7'' hexagonal
tile. Marked "Delft, Germany"-- 18.00
Women and children in field
scene. White ground with black
decor. 6x6'' ------------------- 16.75

## TINSEL PICTURES

A form of primitive art made by house-
wives and children from colored tinsel paper. The pictures mainly depicted flowers,
birds, Bible scenes, landscape and costume
subjects. The art enjoyed its greatest popularity from about 1825 to 1875.

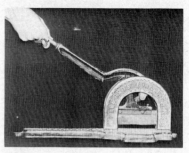

Tobacco Cutter. Five Bro's Tobacco
W'ks _____ $10.00

## TOBACCO JARS

The tobacco jar was, in most cases, a combination holder and humidor for cigars or pipe tobacco. In the past the containers were made of pottery, china, wood, metals and other materials.

Majolica. Pirate with green hat, black hair, blue shirt _____ $35.00

| | |
|---|---|
| Arab. 7'' _____ | 40.00 |
| Buffalo Pottery. Deldare ware ____ | 85.00 |
| Bulldog. "Old Sport." Bristol. Light brown with pipe on reverse _____ | 36.50 |

Bowl of flowers. Vari-colored. 13¼ x 18'' _____ $140.00

| | |
|---|---|
| Bowl of Flowers. 9½x12'' _____ | 35.00 |
| Bowl of flowers in center. Black background, in molded walnut frame, gold liner. 26x36'' _____ | 48.00 |
| Flowers and Birds. Original pine frame with applied grapes. 13½x14½'' _____ | 35.00 |
| Jacob's Dream. Bible scene. 9½x12'' | 33.50 |
| Roses, buds and leaves. 8x10''. Framed _____ | 32.00 |
| Roses. On black background, in gold frame. 12½x16½''. Fine condition _____ | 35.00 |
| Roses. Wild, with buds and leaves, white background, narrow gilt frame, coat hooks on either end. 10¼x22½'' _____ | 33.50 |

### TINWARE, See TOLE

### TOBACCO CUTTERS

Plug tobacco and snuff were the popular types of tobacco before the cigarette came into vogue. Chewing tobacco was received in "sheets" by the merchant and was cut into small squares with a tobacco cutter before being sold to the public.

| | |
|---|---|
| "Black Beauty." Like new _____ | 19.50 |
| Brown Mule Cutter. Iron _____ | 8.50 |
| Climax Plug. Cast iron _____ | 8.00 |
| "Drummond." Drummond Tobacco Co., St. Louis _____ | 8.00 |
| Five Brothers Tobacco Co., Louisville, Kentucky _____ | 8.00 |
| Griswold Tobacco Cutter. Ordinary type _____ | 8.00 |
| Imp Thumbing Nose on Blade. Iron _____ | 37.50 |
| Tobacco Cutters. Ordinary types. Each _____ | 7.50 |

| | |
|---|---|
| Colored boy with straw hat _____ | 37.50 |
| Colored boy with turban _____ | 35.00 |
| Egyptian Queen. 4'' high. Color-ful, with evil mien _____ | 37.50 |
| Elephant. Majolica _____ | 34.50 |
| Girl's Face. Majolica. Blonde hair, purple tam cover _____ | 40.00 |
| Gnome on top of barrel. Woodlike texture _____ | 32.50 |
| Indian. Majolica. 10'' to top of feathers _____ | 42.50 |
| Indian Chief. Majolica. 5'' high, dark gray _____ | 34.50 |
| Indian Girl Head. Small, color-ful _____ | 30.00 |
| 'ron. Round with fluted sides, tall finial on lid _____ | 19.50 |
| Lion Head. Austrian _____ | 33.50 |
| Man. Seated in chair, with gout. 8½'' high, Staffordshire-type ___ | 57.50 |
| Man with Skull Cap. England ____ | 42.50 |
| Monk, Jolly. Bisque _____ | 40.00 |
| Monkey Head. Majolica. Pipe and sports hat, green with pink at base _____ | 48.50 |
| Negro Jockey. Majolica. 4½'' high, pink and yellow cap with white beak, white collar and green bow tie _____ | 40.00 |
| Pewter. 7'' to top of round finial on cover. 16½'' circ. Marked "Copenhagen Pewter 439'' _____ | 22.75 |
| Pipe on Lid. Majolica. Green and pink _____ | 33.50 |
| Ram's Head. Majolica _____ | 40.00 |
| Red Indian Cut Plug Tin Tobacco Jar. Shape of bald headed man, blue vest, white apron _____ | 25.00 |
| Rookwood. Shades of brown with yellow. Spray of clover. 5¾'' high _____ | 57.50 |
| Royal Bayreuth. Tapestry ware. Cows in field _____ | 70.00 |
| Satan Head with Bee on Head. Red with popping white eyes_____ | 25.00 |
| Sea Captain. Majolica Pipe in mouth _____ | 33.50 |

## TOBY JUGS

According to an historian, the term "Toby Jug" is probably secured from the character "Uncle Toby" in Sterne's "Tristram Shandy", and the following verse is connected with the jugs:

"Old Toby Philpot,
A thirsty old soul,
As e'er drank a bottle
Or fathomed a bowl."

They were used as containers for ale and beer in England and America in the 18th and 19th centuries.

| | |
|---|---|
| Cat Toby. 9'' high, full figure____ | 67.50 |
| Coachman. 9'' high, full figure, drinking cup hat _____ | 150.00 |

| | |
|---|---|
| Toby Jug. Man astride barrel. Decor in greens, blue and orange. 8½'' high. Late _____ | $98.50 |

Delft:
| | |
|---|---|
| 9'' high. Man with beard, marked, with lid. Early _____ | 350.00 |
| 10'' high. Full figure of seated woman. Early _____ | 375.00 |
| 11'' high. Full figure of man taking snuff, bug on nose. Early _____ | 400.00 |
| English. Primitive, standing 8'' man, 9'' woman. Pair _____ | 360.00 |
| Englishman. 9'' high, seated figure with angel handle and tricorne hat _____ | 200.00 |
| George Washington Head. 9'' high, patented 1892 _____ | 145.00 |
| Lambeth-Doulton. 14'' high, brown glaze man sitting on barrel ____ | 175.00 |
| "Madam Philpot." (So-called). Delft-type in blue, white, yellow and brown. 8¼'' high. Top of hat | |

is removable lid. Circa 1760-1780 — 375.00
Man holding pipe and jug. Green
  coat and hat, yellow trousers,
  brown background. 10½'' high __ 200.00

Toby Jug. Lord Nelson. 12'' high.
  Blue coat, yellow trousers _____ $395.00

Man in green; dark red and brown
  costume, astride barrel. Late ___ 80.00
Napoleon. 10'' high. American,
  made in Trenton, N. J. _____ 215.00
Ralph Wood-type. 8'' high. Seated
  man holding cup almost to his
  mouth _____ 320.00
Ralph Wood-type. 8'' high. Seated
  man with tricorne hat _____ 295.00
Royal Bayreuth Coachman _____ 50.00
Santa Claus. 7'' high, red and
  white color. Late _____ 67.50
Scroddle. 5½'' high _____ 185.00

Toby Jug. Willow ware decor
  around sides and back. 5½'' high.
  Late _____ $95.00
Staffordshire. 5'' high. Late,
  squat, embossed figure _____ 115.00
Staffordshire. 10'' high. Man in
  sitting position with a glass in
  one hand and pitcher in other.
  Green coat, yellow trousers. Dark
  brown, green and yellow spatter
  design on top and bottom _____ 300.00
"Toby Philpot." Pratt Ware. 11''
  high. Brown coat, green pants,
  black and green base _____ 340.00

## TOLE
### (TINWARE, ETC.)

The term was originally used to designate items made of sheet iron and decorated. Usage of the term through the
years has caused it to be applied to decorated tin articles as well.

Bathtub. 27'' diam., 13'' deep ____ 45.00
Boxes:
  Book-shaped _____ 16.00
  Covered, large, original stencil__ 21.50
Cake Pan. Angel _____ 12.75
Candle Holder. Wall. 18th Century 58.50
Candle Molds:
  8-candle _____ 20.00
  12-candle _____ 27.50
  Tin, round. Scarce _____ 40.00
Candle Snuffer and 10'' decorated
  tray. Tin _____ 30.00
Candlestick. Saucer-type push-up __ 12.50

Candle Mold. 12-candle. Oblong __ $27.50

**Canisters:**
Coffee. Pair _____ 12.00
Tea. Pair _____ 12.50
Tea. Queen Anne Style. 4¾" high
excluding knob, original decor __ 97.50
Card Rack. For post cards, octago-
nal, hangs from ceiling on a chain 20.00

**Coffee Pots:**
Large _____ 18.50
Very large. Green, with original
flowers _____ 25.00
Comb Case _____ 25.00
Container. Handled, with litho-
graphed picture of snake charmer 19.50
**Cookie Cutters:**
Chick, 4" high _____ 5.00
Dog, 3½" long _____ 5.00
Dutch Man and Woman _____ 5.00
Horse, 7" long, 4" high _____ 5.00
Rabbit, 6" long, 3½" high _____ 5.00
Rooster, 4½" high _____ 5.00
Dipper. Long handled, 26" long __ 8.75
Dispatch Case _____ 7.50
Ear Trumpet. With carrying case __ 28.50
Foot Warmer. Round, pierced ____ 15.00
Gun Powder Container. Tin, 9x12"__ 18.50
Jack-O-Lanterns. Pair _____ 15.00
Lamp. Black, gold handle decor __ 17.50
**Lanterns:**
Cone-shaped, pierced, with orig-
inal snuffer and candle _____ 27.50
"Minor's Patent." 5" high, fold-
ing _____ 18.50
Lunch Basket with Tray _____ 6.50

Deed Box. 9" high, 10½" wide. Old
stencilled decor _____ $65.00

Match Box Holder. Large _____ 4.50
Match Box, Wall. Fluted edge ____ 5.00
Match Safe. Double _____ 6.00
Measure. Pint _____ 5.00
Mold. Full size turkey, with
cover. 5x9" _____ 27.50
Mustache Curling Set. Small, with
alcohol burner, etc. _____ 15.00
Nutmeg Grater. 1854 _____ 4.75
Pitcher, Water. Brown with floral
decor _____ 25.00

Coffee Pot. 12½" to top of handle.
Black with orange and green
decor _____ $15.00

**Plates:**

6" National cigars, portrait center ------------------------- 6.00
10" Baseball scene, early ------ 9.50
10" Woman holding water jug -- 7.50
10" Woodland scene, stag in foreground ------------------- 7.50

**Pudding Molds:**

Quart capacity, tapered-pail shape, bullet-fluted sides, star bottom, handled friction lid ___ 15.00
Quart capacity, shape of sponge cake, fluted sides, horn center, bail on friction lid ------------- 15.00

Rattle, Baby's. Whistle handle, porcelain mouthpiece. Painted designs on tin rattle part -------- 12.00
Scoop ----------------------------- 6.00
Snuff Box. 1 oz. size. Murray Sons & Co., Belfast, London, Glasgow 4.00
Soap Bubble Pipe --------------- 1.75
Spice Box. 3x3x2½" high. Stencilled "ALLSPICE" --------------------- 5.50
Spice Boxes. 6 round boxes in open handled container ------------- 15.00
Syrup Pitcher. Pint, lift lid ------- 9.00
Tray. Chippendale style. 19x25", deep well, original gold leaf and scroll border, flower spray in center -------------------------- 42.50
Wash Bowl and Pitcher ----------- 32.50
Wood Box. 17½" high, 16" wide, 24" long. Chippendale type ---- 225.00

## TOOLS—HAND

Before the days of power tools, carpentry and cabinetwork were done with hand tools. A variety of special tools was available to the craftsman—ranging from the adz to the wooden square. Some of these tools are now used for decorative and practical purposes.

Axe. Broad. Carpenter's --------- 7.00
Caliper. Iron, hand wrought ------ 8.75
"C" Clamp. Hand wrought ------ 8.75
Chisels, Hand. Cabinetmaker's. From ⅛" to 2", round knob wood handles. Set -------------------- 16.50
Hammer, Adz. Cooper's. Curved___ 4.00
Knife. 22", hand forged, double-edge. Tanner's bream knife for scraping hides ------------------ 5.50
Lumber Gauge Measure. Iron ----- 4.50

**Planes:**

Block. 8" ----------------------- 4.00
Grooving ---------------------- 7.00
Molding ----------------------- 7.50
Plow, carved-out handles, adjusted by wood nuts on threaded wood rod, beechwood ---------- 15.00
12x1". Wooden dado, carved handle ------------------------- 4.50
Wooden molding --------------- 3.50

TOP: Molding Plane ----------------- $7.50
BOTTOM: Grooving Plane ---------- $7.00

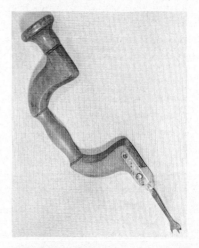

Wood Auger with bit. 13" -------- $37.50

**Squares:**

Framing square, 2 feet --------- 6.00
T-square and Bevel Gauge ------ 5.75
Wooden square. 21", light ------ 4.00
Wheelwright's wrought iron measuring wheel ----------------------- 8.50
Wood Mallet. Refinished --------- 7.00

## TOOTHPICK HOLDERS

Coal Hod. Clear glass. 2¼" long __ $12.00

**Blue:**
Cube. Hat _____ 12.50
Daisy and Button. Hat _____ 15.00
Daisy and Button with V _____ 12.50
Fine Cut. English Hobnail.
Brimmed hat _____ 8.75
Footed, with opalescent spot ____ 10.00
Hobnail _____ 12.00
Opaline. 2½" high _____ 24.00
Ribbed, opalescent _____ 15.00
**Canary:**
Daisy and Button. Hat _____ 12.00
Daisy and Button. Pail _____ 12.00
Thousand Eye _____ 16.50
**Clear:**
Bird with tall holder on back __ 9.00
Butterfly _____ 9.00
Coal Hod. 2¼" long _____ 12.00
Gypsy kettle, with green eyes __ 11.50
Snake on trunk _____ 8.50
Cranberry. Ribbed, opalescent quilt 19.50
Francisware. Scarce _____ 24.00
Green Milk Glass. Seashell _____ 15.00
Ruby Thumbprint _____ 11.50
Vaseline and Clear Scroll with 3-leg
cane band _____ 8.75
**White Milk Glass:**
Basketweave _____ 9.50
Diagonal Bar. 2" high _____ 7.75
Escalloped Drape. 2⅛" high ____ 9.00
Monkey and Hat. 3¼" high, 3"
long, 1¾" wide _____ 15.00
Santa Claus. 3½" high, 1⅞" top
diam. _____ 45.00
Seashell _____ 9.50
Tramp's Shoe. 1⅞" high _____ 9.75
Uncle Sam's Hat. White milk
glass bottom, painted red screw-
type rim _____ 12.75

## TOURAINE PATTERN CHINAWARE

The pattern was made by Henry Alcock & Co., Ltd. at Cobridge, England. The business, prior to 1875, was operated by Henry's father, John Alcock. Henry produced the pattern sometime after 1880 and it was popular until 1900 or later.

The ware is semi-porcelain with a dark blue decoration and a faint gold band within about one-half inch of the border. The pattern is not a scarce one but appears to be in demand by collectors.

Plate. 10" diam. _____ $9.50

Creamer _____ 10.00
Cup and Saucer _____ 11.50
Dish, Vegetable:
Oval, 8½" _____ 11.00
Round _____ 10.00
Pitcher, Milk _____ 14.50
Plates:
6½" _____ 6.00
8¼" _____ 7.00
10" _____ 9.50
Soup _____ 6.75
Platter. 12" _____ 18.50
Relish Dish. Oblong _____ 6.75
Saucer. 6½" _____ 4.00

## TOYS

**Autos:**
"Auto Van." Tin, Circa 1925____ 27.50
Grocery Delivery. 10" long. Wood
and tin. Not wind-up type _____ 28.50
"Leapin' Lena." Tin, mechanical.
Circa 1920-1925 _____ 22.50
Model "T" Ford Coupe. Circa
1926 _____ 18.50
"Phaeton." Tin. 14x6". Early ___ 54.50
Tin. 7" long, wind-up type ____ 29.00
Tin and wood, friction drive.
Early _____ 57.50

Touring. Tin, mechanical, 11" long _____  30.00

Auto. Coupe. Iron _____ $25.00

**Bell Toys:**
Balky Mule. Tin, wind-up _____  22.50
Clown. Rings 2 bells _____  62.50
Goat. Tin with cast metal wheels  62.50
"Landing of Columbus." Cast
iron _____  75.00
Monkey on Log. 6" long. Iron __  65.00
Buggy. 6½", one horse and driver__  42.00
Bus. 12" long. Iron _____  44.50
Cap Pistol. "Super." Late, circa
1920-30 _____  18.00

See-Saw. "The Wizard" _____ $75.00

**Circus Items:**
Auto. "Overland." 7½", with
hippopotamus and driver _____  85.00
Auto. "Overland." 7½", with lion
and driver _____  87.50
Clown. 5", wood, on stick.
Hinged to do tricks. Dated
1880 _____  34.50
Donkey and Clown. Tin, 7½" long,
wind-up type _____  21.50

Driver and two horses. Revolving
head of Chinaman on top. 16" long__ $75.00

Lion Cage. Tin, 12x7½", 2 lions
and driver _____  72.50
Wagon. "Overland." Iron, 2
horses, driver and lion _____  80.00
Wagon. Iron, 9x4½", Royal Circus,
bear in cage, driver and two
horses _____  75.00
Wagon. 15¼" long, tin and wood
with lithographed scene of circus
on wagon. 2 horses _____  30.00
**Cows:**
Calfskin. 10" long, 7" high, on
rollers. Moos when head is turned  39.50
Papier-mache. 12" long, 8½"
high. Pull-toy, on wooden base,
metal wheels _____  32.50
Cream Separator. Tin, Delaval,
6¼" high _____  18.00

Driver and two horses _____  $27.50

Delivery Wagon. Single horse ____  72.50
Ding Dong Dell _____  79.50
Dog. In house, chases cat _____  62.50
**Dump Carts:**
13", 2-wheel cast iron horse and
driver, heavy tin body _____  50.00
13" long. Iron, with one horse,
dated 1881 _____  58.00
Elephant. Wood body covered with
paper, moving tin legs. "Jumbo"
on blanket _____  27.50
**Engines:**
Iron. 20" long, with tall stack
and tender and 2 open coal cars.
Dated 1880 _____  80.00

Train and 2 cars. Tin _____ 54.50
Train and 3 cars. "Penna. Railroad." 30" long, original paint __ 85.00
Fire Engines:
  9" long. Buddy-L. Cast iron, with
    driver. Original red paint _____ 62.50
  14½" long. Motorized, 2 hoses for
    drawing-up water, eagle ornament. 2 iron men drivers, bell
    rings on back when wheels turn__ 85.00
  19" long. Iron, hook and ladder,
    3 horses and driver _____ 85.00
  Pumper-type with boiler. 3 horses _____ 80.00
Fire Hose Wagon. Driver and 2
  horses _____ 85.50
Frog, Jumping. Tin, with wind-up
  mechanism _____ 18.00
Garage. Tin, with 2 wind-up cars__ 32.50
Ice Wagons:
  Iron. 9½" long, 4½" high _____ 62.50
  Iron. 12½" long, 2 horses _____ 59.00
Iron. Flat. Swan-shaped _____ 24.00
Locomotive. "H. CLAY." Dated
  1854, 16½" high, 27" long _____ 140.00
Man Playing Billiards. Mechanical,
  tin _____ 45.00
Man Sawing Wood. Tin _____ 40.50
Manure Spreader. 2 horses _____ 69.50
Monk on Tricycle. Tin, wind-up __ 32.00
"Paddy Rides the Pig." Tin, dated
  1903, mechanical _____ 27.50
Patrol Wagons:
  10" long. Iron, 2 horses _____ 52.50
  14" long. Iron, 2 horses _____ 65.00

Sewing Machine. Hand operated __ $22.50

Pistols:
  Cap. 3½" long, patented 1887 __ 24.50
  "Chinese Must Go." Mint condi-

tion, in original box and wrapper _____ 79.50
Dog. Cap _____ 30.00
  Mfd. by: J. D. Frary, Meriden.
  Iron, shoots corn _____ 16.50
Pull-Toy. Iron, hearts in wheels____ 32.50
Sewing Machine. 6x5" _____ 20.00
Sleigh and Driver with Horse.
  Cast iron, 14" long. Scarce ____ 89.50
Steam Engine. 10", brass tank,
  6¼" long by 2¼" diam. On cast
  iron base _____ 40.00

Six holes, square top ____$55.00

Stoves:
  Coal. Iron, 6 covers, lifter,
    coal hod, shovel, kettle, frying
    pan and turning grate _____ 67.50
  Gas Range. Iron _____ 35.00
  Iron. "Royal", 9x5x5", 4 round
    and 1 oblong covers, with kettle,
    frying pan, coal hod _____ 55.00
Tractor. Fordson, with driver ____ 35.00
Truck. 11" cast iron dump-type,
  International Harvester, with
  driver _____ 59.50
Wagons:
  "Brownie Farm." No driver, 4-
    horse wagon _____ 70.00
  Coal. Iron, driver, chute and
    shovel _____ 67.50
  Dairy. 15¼" long. Tin and wood
    with horse _____ 27.50
  Fire Chief's. 14", 1-horse and
    chief _____ 75.00
  Fire Ladder. 30", 3 horses and
    2 men _____ 85.00
  Grocery, Special Delivery. 15¼"
    long. Tin and wood with horse
    on wheels _____ 27.50
  Hay. 13½", 2 oxen and darky
    driver _____ 77.50
  Hay. Wooden-type. 11x21¼",
    original paint. Circa 1895 _____ 40.00
"Wild Mule Jack." Pull-toy.
  Monkey rider, hearts form wheel
  spokes _____ 40.00
Windmill, Steel. 17" high. With
  tank _____ 42.50

**FIRE ENGINE.** Black horses, driver in uniform, bright colors. 16½'' long, 6¾'' high _____$80.00

**HOOK AND LADDER.** Three horses, gong, with driver and ladders. 33½'' long _____$85.00

**HOOK AND LADDER.** Three horses, with driver and ladders. 20'' long _____$80.00

## TRIVETS

A trivet is usually a three-legged stand with a flat-surfaced top used to hold irons—the type used in bygone days to iron clothes.

Brass. Leaf and Scroll design. 8½" long, footed _____ $18.50

| | |
|---|---|
| Arrows. (2) piercing heart _____ | 19.50 |
| B & D _____ | 9.00 |
| Beaded hearts, flowers and scroll. Handled _____ | 9.75 |
| Club Pattern. Brass, hexagonal, footed _____ | 22.50 |
| Colebrookdale _____ | 8.00 |
| Crab. With legs, heart handle ____ | 12.75 |
| Criss-cross _____ | 8.75 |
| Doves and Grapes. Brass _____ | 25.00 |
| Eastern Star _____ | 10.00 |
| Enterprise _____ | 7.75 |
| Fanner _____ | 8.50 |
| Fern _____ | 9.50 |
| Fox and Geese Track. Iron _____ | 11.00 |
| Fox and Grapes. Brass _____ | 21.50 |

| | |
|---|---|
| Fox and Trees. Footed, brass _____ | 24.00 |
| Good Luck _____ | 9.00 |
| "H" in center _____ | 5.00 |
| Harp _____ | 10.00 |
| Harp. Brass, English _____ | 20.00 |
| Hearts: | |
| 12, 8" diam. _____ | 10.50 |
| 12, star center, long handle ____ | 22.50 |
| Horseshoe. Rose center _____ | 12.50 |
| Imperial _____ | 8.00 |
| Jenny Lind. Iron _____ | 14.50 |
| "K" in center _____ | 4.75 |
| Loop. Brass, English _____ | 18.00 |
| Lyre and Berry design. Iron _____ | 19.50 |
| Pennsylvania Dutch type, with long handle and 3 slender peg legs. Heart center and small heart at handle end _____ | 18.00 |
| Rose center. Lacy iron _____ | 8.75 |
| Round. Claw feet, lacy iron _____ | 7.50 |
| Shield. Brass, English _____ | 17.50 |
| Snake and Eagle Head. Iron _____ | 18.00 |
| Spade center. Lacy iron _____ | 9.00 |
| Star. Brass _____ | 10.50 |
| Streeter _____ | 6.50 |
| Sunflower _____ | 8.00 |
| Swastika center _____ | 8.00 |
| Triangular. Footed _____ | 6.50 |
| Triple-eight pattern. Brass, on 3 feet _____ | 18.00 |
| Turtle _____ | 12.75 |
| Washington, George. Brass _____ | 30.00 |

## TUCKER CHINA

Tucker China is believed to be the first commercial American porcelain. William Ellis Tucker, son of a china merchant in Philadelphia, produced his first items in 1825. In 1828 Thomas Hulme joined him as a partner. Their ware was marked Tucker & Hulme. The partnership lasted a little over a year at which time Hulme withdrew.

Tucker died in 1832 and the business passed into the hands of Judge Joseph Hemphill and Joseph Tucker, a brother of William's. In 1837 Judge Hemphill withdrew from the firm but Tucker continued for about a year. He opened an importing business in chinaware and closed the factory.

The ware is similar to Sevres porcelain and is all hand-decorated—no transfer designs were used. The most common items are vases, pitchers and creamers, although dinner services were produced.

| | |
|---|---|
| **Cups and Saucers:** | |
| Demitasse. Landscape scene ____ | 56.00 |
| Tea. Handleless _____ | 62.50 |
| **Dishes:** | |
| Oval, covered _____ | 125.00 |
| Round, covered _____ | 125.00 |
| **Plates:** | |
| 6¾" diam., each with different landscapes in sepia. Set of 6 ____ | 69.50 |

| | |
|---|---|
| 7¼'' diam. | 42.50 |
| 8¼'' diam. | 46.50 |

Platters. Decoration of rosebuds, arrow-shaped blue sprig, green leaves:

| | |
|---|---|
| 7x10½'' | 75.00 |
| 12x17¼'' | 130.00 |

Urns. 10¼'' high. Gold painted base, floral decoration around bowl, gold decorated handles. Pair ____$600.00

Urns:
3½'' high. Flower decoration, blue band and gold trim on white background. ¼'' gold decoration on base. Pair _____ 200.00
10¼'' high. Gold painted base, floral decoration around bowl, gold decorated handles. Pair ___ 600.00

## VALLERYSTAHL GLASS

The town of Vallerystahl, Lorraine, France, has been an important glass-making center since about 1500 A. D. In 1870 the province and the factory fell into the hands of Germany as the result of the Franco-Prussian War. It was returned to France in 1918 and continued as such until 1939 when the factory was destroyed by bombs in World War II. The glass in which collectors are most interested today was imported into the United States beween 1850 and 1915.

Bottles, Perfume. Blue, bulbous, swirl ribbed, swirled stoppers and covered powder jar. Gold star decorations. Pair _____ 70.00
Camel Dish, Covered. Camphor glass, marked _____ 67.50
Dish, Covered. 6½'' high, 5½'' diam. Dolphin feet, large shell finial on lid, decorated with small shells, green milk glass _____ 68.50
Dish, Covered. Milk glass with tortoise and rider _____ 72.50
Ducks:
4½'' high. Brown top, painted green base _____ 55.00

Swimming. 6'' size, white, marked _____ 49.50
Fly on Walnut. White, scarce. Marked _____ 60.00

Duck. 4½'' high. Brown top, painted green base _____ $55.00

Hens:
7'' long. Milk glass _____ 40.00
Large, covered, milk glass. Gilt decor _____ 49.50
Salt Dip. Ram's head. (Illustrated in Warman, Milk Glass Addenda, Plate 146-D). White _____ 20.00
Set. 7'' Chicken covered dish, 5 egg cups with standing chick bases; 2 basket salt dips and 10'' tray with wells for each. Milk glass _____ 110.00
Vase. Hand holding flower container. Milk glass with gilt trim ____ 52.50

## VAN BRIGGLE POTTERY

The Van Briggle Pottery Co. was established in 1901, at Colorado Springs, Colorado by Artus Van Briggle who worked with the Rookwood Pottery in Cincinnati for several years. The pottery is still in operation at Colorado Springs, Colorado.

Bowl. 3½'' high. Flares from 3¼'' top opening to broad squat 6½'' diam. base. Heart design in relief with deep wine, blue and bluish-green shaded mat coloring _____ 22.50
Candlestick. Deep blue, saucer-type. Signed by artist _____ 20.00
Candlesticks. Pair _____ 18.00
Rose Bowl. 4'' high. Green to blue leaf decor _____ 12.50
Vases:
4½'' high. Green to blue, leaf

decor _____ 12.50
10'' high. Blue _____ 15.00
11'' high. Brown and green with
3 molded Indian heads at top,
each with a different expression   35.00

## VASA MURRHINA GLASS

A type of Victorian Art Glass first made
by the Cape Cod Glass Company, it contains flecks of mica or other metals. It was
named for Roman Murrine ware which was
composed of a glass in which metals,
precious stones and·the like were imbedded.

Vase. 8'' diam., 5¼'' high. Mottled
brown and white exterior; aquamarine interior _____ $40.00

Baskets:
Pink with dark red, silver flecks,
ruffled top, applied clear handle.
Medium size _____ 75.00
Good colors, clear thorn handle.
Large size _____ 80.00
Bowl. 9'' diam. Mottled pink, red,
blue, yellow and green with mica
flecks throughout on a white body   92.50
Creamer and Sugar Bowl. Cobalt
blue, gold flecks, melon ribbed,
amber knobs and handles _____   67.50
Decanter. 12½'' high. Cranberry
color with gold flecks, hour glass
shape. Applied ribbed handle,
matching stopper, 3 lip top ____   62.50
Ewer. 10'' high. Pink with silver
flecks, white lining, applied clear
leaf handle, 3 rows of shells ____   80.00
Fairy Lamp. 4½'' high. Zebra-type
shade with white lining. Exterior
mottled with green, red, blue,
yellow and white with silver mica
crystals. Pressed glass holder___  150.00
Finger Bowl. Cranberry and opalescent with silver flecks _____   50.00
Finger Bowl and Plate. Crimped

scalloped rims, iridescent colors
of cranberry, gold and green___   65.00
Mug. Amber with gold flecks ____   35.00
Pitchers:
5½'' high. 3'' widest diam. White
lining, casing mottled in green,
red, yellow and sprinkled with
silver mica dust. Applied reeded
crystal handle _____  125.00
8'' high. Mottled cranberry with
silver flecks, white lining, clear
applied handle _____  135.00
10½'' high. Opaque white lining,
outer casing splashed with red,
flecked allover with silver mica.
Molded in cabbage rose design.
Applied crystal handle _____  145.00
12'' high. White lining, outside
splashed with blue and brownish-
gray, silver mica flecks. Applied
clear crystal handle _____  135.00
Small.· Red, green, yellow, blue
and orange sprinkled with ''green
(chrome) aventurine crystal.''
Swirl ribbed, with clear applied
reeded handle. Sandwich origin__  120.00
Rose Bowls:
3½'' diam., pink with gold and silver flecks _____   50.00
Pink and white with silver flecks.
Artichoke pattern _____   54.50
Salt Shaker. White and rose with
gold mica flecks. Artichoke pattern _____   27.50
Sugar Shaker. Squatty. Pink and
white with silver flecks _____   55.00
Syrup Jugs:
5'' high. Cabbage rose-shape.
White background with green,
rose and white mottling. Applied
clear crystal handle, pewter top   65.00
Clear and cranberry with gold
flecks _____   57.50
Toothpick. 2'' high. Cobalt blue
with gold flecks _____   28.50
Tumblers:
Blue and white with silver flecks   32.50
Pink and maroon with silver
flecks _____   35.00
Vases:
4½'' high. Rainbow colors with
gold and silver flecks _____   57.50
6½'' high. Rainbow striped spatter with mica flecks, clear
spiral rigaree. Cased. Pair ____   85.00
8'' high. Turquoise and yellow
with silver flecks _____   65.00
8¾'' high. Rainbow hued, silver
mica. Fan-shaped, turned down
top with applied clear ribbon
edging, cased white lining _____   69.50
10½'' high. Ruffled top _____   72.00

## VENETIAN GLASS

Venetian Glass was made on the island

of Murano, near Venice, from the middle of the 13th century until around 1900. The factory was owned by the Republic. The glass is colored, thin and fragile, yet beautiful and contains much lace work.

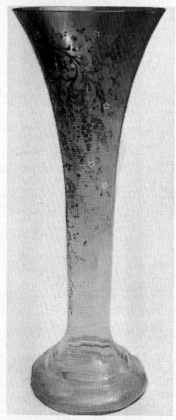

Vase. 18'' high. Red top blending to clear. Gold decoration with small white flowers _____ $97.50

Bottle, Scent. Twisted filigree stripes of white and goldstone. Cork-type stopper, 4'' high _____ 40.00
Candlesticks:
   5'' dolphin. Clear glass flecked

with gold _____ 18.00
   9¾'' high. Cactus tail-type for one candle. Large, many petaled glass blossoms. Round cup-like base _____ 48.50
Candy Dish. 6'' diam., enameled pink roses, green leaves. Gold on cover and small pink roses around wide rim _____ 23.50
Candy Jar, Covered. 10½'' high, enamel ribs, pink enamel flowers in orchid and blue, wreath ____ 35.00
Centerpiece. Small. Oval mirror base, cornucopia center, shell sides, ribbed clear to white glass 78.50
Champagne. Dolphin-type, made in Venice in 1869 _____ 80.00
Chandelier. Blown scrolls of unusual design extend from center stem, 6 arms and drip cups. Applied decor in blue, pink and orchid, gold washed _____ 425.00
Compotes:
   4¼'' diam., 2¾'' high. Red, with pedestal base and gold decor __ 42.50
   10'' diam., 8'' high. Blue, with gold overlay _____ 87.50
Cordial Set. Decanter, tray, 8 hollow stem wines, gold and enamel decor on clear. Set _____ 70.00
Cups and Saucers:
  Demitasse:
   Blue, lacy _____ 34.50
   Pink _____ 37.50
  Punch. Green with gold decor __ 30.00
  Wine. Blue with enamel flowers__ 25.00
Ewer. Latticino striped in pink and clear, with gold. 4½'' widest diam., 12'' to top of handle ____ 100.00
Glass, Hoch. 7½'' high, clear stem, cranberry bowl with gilt and flower decor _____ 72.00
Goblet. 8'' high, 3¼'' top diam. Cup and foot of latticino glass, turquoise blue and goldstone in a chaplet-bead design, goldstone in a filigree design. Hollow knob stem with gold dustings. Applied dragon with yellow eyes and rose-pink tongue _____ 112.50
Pitcher, Water. Bulbous shape. Enameled valley lilies. Wide gold band with enameled dots. 6 gold band tumblers with standing pink lilies and leaves. Set _____ 65.00
Rummers:
  Amber. Floral decor _____ 78.50
  Ruby. 8½'' high, half of bowl covered with gold leaf _____ 84.50
Salt, Master. Shape of swan. Pink body with gold decor _____ 32.00
Vases:
   4'' high. Green glass body with applied pieces of red colored cane (like shredded coconut) with blue and white enameled flowers 74.50

9½" high. Pale rose bottom shading to deep peach, rose pleated top, applied green leaves _____ 92.50

11¼" high, 7" diam. Blue and clear with gold outlining the blue _____ 110.00

18" high. Red top blending to clear. Gold decoration with small white flowers _____ 97.50

Folded handkerchief vase. Filigree. Large _____ 38.50

Wine Set. 11" amber decanter, pewter lid, and 6 5½" wines. Set 135.00

## VERLYS GLASS

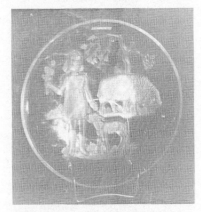

Concave Plate. 13½" diam. Clear with frosted figures of child and sheep in relief _____$150.00

Bowl. 12½ x 4½ x 3" wide. Clear with frosted doves in relief _____ $65.00

## VERRE DE SOIE GLASS

Verre de Soie Glass was produced by the Steuben Glass Company around the 1905-10 period. Its development was reportedly under the supervision of Frederick Carder who originated Aurene Glass shortly after the turn of the present century.

Verre de Soie (Glass of Silk) is an iridescent type of glass. This iridescence was produced by using a metallic chloride spray which caused the glass to develop a satiny finish with the appearance and feel of silk.

Some collectors and dealers who are not familiar with its original name call it White Carnival Glass. Production was discontinued about 1930.

Cologne Bottle. 7" high. With glass stopper _____ $75.00

Basket. Small, white with pink iri-
descence, blue handle _____ 45.00
Bowls:
  $4\frac{3}{4}$'' diam., with 6'' matching
  dish underneath _____ 65.00
  8'' diam. _____ 95.00
Candlesticks. Twisted stems. Pair __ 55.00
Compote, Jelly. 4'' high, $4\frac{1}{4}$'' across
  top _____ 35.00
Dish. 6'' diam., hat-shaped. Marked
  ''N'' _____ 42.50
Goblet _____ 46.50

Bowl. 8'' diameter _____ $95.00

Rose Bowl _____ 42.50
Shade, Gas _____ 22.50
Sherbet. Ground pontil _____ 16.75
Sugar Bowl, Covered. Engraved ___ 65.00
Vases:
  Bud. $5\frac{3}{4}$'' high. Pair _____ 57.50
  6'' high. Jack-in-the-Pulpit ____ 60.00
  $6\frac{1}{4}$'' high _____ 70.00
  7'' high. Bulbous base, short
  neck with $3\frac{1}{4}$'' diam. flaring rim__ 75.00
  12'' high. Fan-shaped and ruffled
  $9$x$5\frac{1}{2}$'' top, 5'' stem, 7'' deep
  bowl, 4'' diam. flat base _____ 85.00
Wine. Etched with flowers and
  leaves _____ 30.00

## VILLEROY & BOCH

A firm of potters was originated by
P. J. Boch in Luxembourg before 1880.
The firm was later known as ''Boch and
Buschmann.'' Still later, N. Villeroy came
in as a partner and the firm was operated
as ''Villeroy & Boch.'' This later firm made
the famous ''Mettlach'' steins and other
ware bearing the name.

Beaker. With handle. 5'' high, $2\frac{1}{2}$''
  wide. Tan color, woman holding
  pitcher in one hand, pheasant on
  platter in other. ''Wohlbekomm's
  #2327'' _____ 32.50
Bowl. $10\frac{1}{4}$'' diam., with 2 handles,
  Flower and fan, blue border ____ 30.00
Bread Board. $5\frac{1}{2}$x$8\frac{1}{2}$''. Marked
  ''Villeroy & Boch, Dresden''_____ 40.00
Butter Dish. Covered. Design in
  heavy relief _____ 55.00

Plaque, Hanging. 17'' diam. White
  with blue decoration _____$175.00

Cheese Board. $4\frac{1}{2}$x$7\frac{1}{2}$''. Marked
  ''Villeroy and Boch, Dresden'' __ 39.00
Cider and Donut Set. 6 tumblers,
  2 plates and tall pitcher. Dark
  taupe background with pictures of
  uniformed handle bar mustached
  players. Labeled ''Catcher,''
  ''Pitcher,'' ''Batsman.'' Set _____ 89.50
Cup and Saucer. Ramekin type.
  Dresden pattern _____ 7.50

Salt Box. $9\frac{1}{2}$'' high at back. Wood
lid, blue decor _____ $59.50

**Plaques:**

Mettlach. (V. & B.). 14", "Rock of Gibralter." Norcap, Dec. 149 12" diam., blue and white. Harbor scene _____ 43.50 60.00

**Plates:**

8¾" diam. Sports scenes. Mustard brown background with decor in white and tan. Pair _____ 29.50

9½" diam. Blue and yellow decor. Marked "Villeroy & Boch Wallerfangen #952" _____ 18.00

9½" diam. Dresden Blue Onion pattern _____ 20.00

12" diam. Scenic, marked "Villeroy & Boch Mettlach." Pierced for hanging. Dutch scene in browns and blues _____ 65.00

Salt Box. 9½" high at back. Wood lid, blue decor _____ 59.50

Tureen. 16" high with 17" diam. platter. Heavy relief design, 4 qt. size _____ 395.00

## WASH SETS

In the days before the advent of modern plumbing the wash set was an essential part of every bedroom. Wash stands were made especially for their accomodation.

Wash Bowl and Pitcher. Pink roses and green leaves on white ground. 16½" diam. _____ $40.00

Begonia leaves in natural green color, illuminated with gold, goldtraced handles. 12-piece set ____ 60.00

Ironstone, white, undecorated. English _____ 35.00

Limoges. Wash bowl and pitcher. Floral decoration _____ 57.50

Maddock, John. English, 7-piece set. Bulbous pitcher, covered chamber. Green leaves and scrolls _____ 67.50

Meakin. Pink hollyhocks, leaves and buds. 4-piece set _____ 50.00

Minton China. 15½" diam. wash bowl, 11½" high pitcher. Bluish-white background, green decoration _____ 55.00

Set. Green ivy vines and leaves. 7-piece set _____ 65.00

Staffordshire. Wash bowl, pitcher. Named "Spring," "Summer," "Winter," "Autumn" _____ 72.00

Wash Bowl and Pitcher. Blue and white. Circa 1880 _____ $45.00

Wash Bowl. Pink roses and water lily bouquets, embossed blue edge _____ 14.50

Wash Bowl and Pitcher. Large cabbage roses and small yellow roses. Devon Furnival England. Reg. No. _____ 59.50

Wash Bowl and Pitcher. 5-piece set. Brown roses and vine decor ____ 62.50

Wash Bowl and Pitcher. Yellow, shading to white, wide gold-shot top _____ 42.50

Wash Bowl and Pitcher. White to pale blue with yellow iris decor 45.00

Wash Bowl and Pitcher. Pink body with copper lustre decoration. Ship scene in center of floral decor. Homer Laughlin china ____ 44.50

## WATCH FOBS

Watch fobs were popular in the Victorian era and through the 1920's. The wrist watch replaced the pocket watch and the need for a fob. The fob was not only a decorative item but was useful in pulling the watch from a vest pocket. The earlier fobs were made of silk with metal fastenings and decorations. Later, the advertising fob appeared with a leather strap.

Keystone Watch Cases _____ $3.50

Allis-Chalmers Tractor Division ____ 7.50
Echo Springs Whiskey advertisement
  fob _____ 4.50
Keystone Watch Cases _____ 3.50
Marblehead, Mass. 30th Anniversary 4.00
Motorcycle. Inscribed "Perfect
  Score Gypsy Jaunt." 1928 _____ 4.75
National Assn. of Ice Industries___ 3.50
Newport, Maine, Centennial. U. S.
  Flag in colors on front _____ 5.00
Ohio Power Shovel Co. With
  enameling _____ 6.00
Silk. With gold decorations. Circa
  1895 _____ 10.00
State of Massachusetts Seal _____ 3.75
Woodsman of the World _____ 4.00
Woolworth Building, N. Y. _____ 5.75

## WATCHES

American Watch Co. Closed plain
  silver case, dated 1884, stem
  wind. Running _____ 40.00
Diana Chronometer, French. Open
  face engraved silver case, stem
  wind. Circa 1880. Numbers 1 to
  12 on raised translucent medallions, 13 to 24 outside ring.
  Running _____ 77.50
18K Gold Watch. Engine turned
  face with Roman numerals. Key
  wind, 2¼'' diam. Geo. III type.
  Made by Robert Roskell, Liverpool. Circa 1815 _____ 125.00
Elgin. Ladies'. 14 karat, dated
  Dec. 1891. Engraved hunter case.
  Marigolds and leaves around
  scenic medallion _____ 55.00

18K Gold Watch. Engine turned
  face with Roman numerals. Key
  wind, 2⅛'' diam. Geo. III type.
  Made by Robert Roskell, Liverpool. Circa 1815 _____ $125.00

Elgin. Open case, heavy silveroid,
  engraving of deer on back. Circa
  1890, key wind, thick crystal,
  old black ribbon chain _____ 50.00
Elgin National Watch Co. For lady.
  14 karat closed engraved gold
  case. Stem wind and set _____ 75.00
French Lapel Button Watch. Made
  in 1917, dial ¼'' diam., stem
  wind _____ 42.50
Gold Watch. 18 karat. Small, man's,
  made in Geneva, sold by Sontag.
  Case engraved and decorated
  with blue enamel. Key wind and
  set _____ 92.50
Hampden. Ladies'. Gold, 25-year
  case _____ 75.00
Manufactured by Crescent. Nickel
  case, 3 oz., screw bezel, solid
  back, swing ring, locomotive design _____ 25.00
Mickey Mouse. Round, made by
  Ingersoll _____ 55.00
Railroad Watch. Silveroid case,
  porcelain face, Trenton Watch
  Co. _____ 39.50

Stop Watch. Gold, open-face, engraving of horse's head on back. Near mint condition _____ 65.00

Swiss Watch. Small, closed engraved sterling silver case. Decorated dial, gold hands, stem wind. Running condition _____ 45.00

## WATERFORD GLASS

The factory was established at Waterford, Ireland, in 1729. Chandeliers, candelabra, boat-shaped and turn-over bowls, drinking vessels, etc., were produced. It was a flint-type glass commonly decorated by cutting. The characteristic of the glass made before 1830 is the dark color. The color became whiter and more brilliant after that date. The factory closed in 1852 as the Irish glass industry was a dying business. The last maker of the old Irish Cut Glass died in 1896. In 1952, 100 years after the Waterford Glass Co., Ireland, closed, it was reopened and is now in production.

Plate. 6'' diam. _____ $24.00

Chalice, Covered. 16'' high, long stem, round foot, high finial. Cut allover (Deer and Castle) _____ 150.00

Cruet. 12'' high, cut. Spire stoppers. Pair _____ 75.00

Decanters:
    9'' high, applied handle _____ 55.00
    10'' high. Cut allover. Original mushroom stoppers. Pair _____ 89.50

Goblet. Large _____ 40.00

Jar, Covered. 10'' high, 5½'' diam. 82.50

Lamps, Hurricane. 27'' high, cut base, stem and bobeches. Double button cut spear prisms. 18th Century. Pair _____ 400.00

Lustres. Cut, 12½'', 9'' prisms with cut ball on end. Pair _____ 310.00

Pitcher. 10½'' high, clear glass ___ 75.00

Plate. 6'' diam. _____ 24.00

Salt, Master. Diamond shape, footed _____ 22.50

Salts. Oval. Pair _____ 40.00

Tumbler. Cut _____ 20.00

Urns. 9½'' high. 4 round pointed ends extend above the rim. Square base, cut. Pair _____ 95.00

Vase. Cornucopia in silver holder. 15'' high _____ $145.00

Vases:
    9'' high. Cut. Heavy. Pair _____ 125.00
    10¾'' high. Cut, footed. Circa 1810 _____ 115.00
    12¼'' high. Flared top, petal-shaped base _____ 90.00
    15'' high. Cornucopia in silver holder _____ 145.00

Wine Glass. 5½'' high. Heavy diamond-cut pattern _____ 25.00

## WAVECREST GLASS

The glass is made of opal or milk glass and has a satin finish. It was made in France but was imported into the United States and decorated in the Sevres manner by the C. F. Monroe Co., Meriden, Connecticut, from about 1894 to 1905. The mark is "Wavecrest" with the initials of the company "C.F.M. Co." Some items bear the name "Nakara" and "C.F.M. Co."

Box. Hinged cover, 3'' high, 3½'' diameter _____ $75.00

Biscuit Jar. Enameled blue flowers on pink and white background, raised scroll pattern. Silver plated cover and handle _____ 89.50

Bowls:
2¼'' high, metal rim. "The CFM Co." on bottom _____ 57.50
3½'' diam. Three ornate legs. Signed _____ 65.00
7½'' diam., 6'' high. Has brass ring and feet _____ 95.00

Boxes:
4'' square, hinged cover. Raised blue shell, yellow floral decor, satin lining _____ 100.00
Collars and Cuffs Box. 7'' square, 6'' high, satin lined _____ 130.00
Hinged cover, 3½'' high, 3½'' diam. _____ 75.00
Jewel. 7'' diam., brass hinged cover, pink floral decor on cover and sides, embossed in light blue _____ 135.00
Letter, 6'' high x 4½''. Enameled violet decor _____ 115.00
Powder. 4'' square, round bevelled glass mirror on cover. Pink flowers on green background ___ 80.00
Scroll design with floral decorations. Medium size _____ 120.00
Card Holder. 1¼x4x2½'' high. Gold plated collar. Pink enamel flowers _____ 25.00
Cigar Humidor. Metal cover, 6x8'' 100.00
Cracker Jar with Lid. 7½'' high, fully decorated _____ 175.00

Dish. 7'' diam., gold ormolu rim, baroque handles. Pink and blue with enamel amethyst flowers __ 85.00
Flask. Floral decor _____ 65.00
Hair Receiver. Brass top, raised enamel decor _____ 55.00
Jar, Covered. 6½'' high, melon ribbed with pansy decor _____ 125.00
Pin Tray. No handles _____ 20.00
Planter. 9x3x4''. Ferns and floral decor _____ 100.00
Salt and Pepper Shakers. Pair ____ 49.50
Stationery Holder. 6¼x3¼x4¼'' high. Hand painted pansies and raised swirls, gold plated rim _____ 75.00
Sugar Bowl, Creamer and Syrup Jug. Resilvered tops. Set _____ 150.00
Syrup Jug _____ 125.00
Tray. 7'' round. Blue and pink flowers _____ 85.00

Vases:
6½'' high. In footed ormolu holder. Pink and blue pansies and raised shell, gold decor _____ 85.00
7'' high. Bulbous, low. Heavy gold ormolu butterfly side handles, running leaf intaglio decor _____ 95.00
8½'' high. Oval, cream, white and gold with pink apple blossoms and gold beaded rim _____ 125.00
9'' high. Metal base, cream with pink blossom decor _____ 140.00
11'' high. White and blue. Sprays of yellow cosmos front and back. Metal collar and feet _____ 195.00

## WEATHER VANES

The weather vane indicates the direction of the wind and was often made in the shape of animals or other objects.

Auto. Open top, circa 1915. Driver wearing duster and goggles. Milk glass ball, copper red _____ 185.00
Chicken and Letters. Tin. Iron rods, wood shaft. Old decorations. Pennsylvania-Amish type _____ 295.00
Copper:
Deer _____ 300.00
Rooster on arrow _____ 260.00
Copper figure and ball. Brass letters and Cardinal arms, spire 3 feet long. Complete, ready for mounting:
Cow. 28'' long, 18'' high _____ 265.00
Fish. 26'' long, 9'' high _____ 250.00
Horse. 31'' long, 16'' high _____ 285.00
Rooster. 18'' long, 24'' high ____ 260.00
Eagle. Zinc. 37'' wingspread, 54'' long. N.E.S.W. _____ 275.00
Horse. Copper. Bullet hole in horse. Needs refinished _____ 175.00
Horse. Running atop iron N.E.S.W. 95.00
Ram. Gold leaf _____ 265.00

Tin chicken and letters. Iron rods,
wood shaft. Old decorations.
Pennsylvania-Amish type _____ $295.00

## WEDGWOOD

Josiah Wedgwood founded a pottery at
Burslem, England, in 1759. A new factory
was built at Etruria around 1770 and it is
still in operation. Basalt and Jasperware
are the products of principal interest to
collectors today. In 1878 the plant resumed
the manufacture of porcelain—dinnerware,
etc. A small quantity of porcelain had
been made around 1800 but was discontinued. A considerable amount of Jasperware is still being imported into the United
States but is incised "Wedgwood, England"
on the base. For Wedgwood listings, see
"Basalt" and "Jasperware."

Jasperware Teapot with very light
powder blue ground, raised white
figures form designs by Flaxman.
Impressed "Wedgwood" _____ $100.00

## WELLER WARE

Weller Ware was first made in Steuben-
ville, Ohio, in the early 1890's by W. A.
Long and was called "Lonhuda." In 1896,
S. A. Weller, Zanesville, Ohio, purchased
the pottery. The name was changed to
"Louwelsa" and it was produced in quantity. Many pieces resembled Rookwood
which had floral decorations on a dark
ground underglaze. Most items were marked
"Weller."

Plaque. Wm. McKinley. 4½'' diam.__ $15.00

Bowl. 12'' diam., candlesticks
  (pair) and flower holder (shape
  of flying fish). Green with blue
  decor. Each piece marked.
  Matching set _____  49.50
Cruet. 7'' high. Cherry blossom
  decor _____  45.00
Flower Frog. 4½'' diam., bluish-purple fish on top. Matte glaze ____  18.50
Flower Pot. 8'' top diam., 6'' bottom diam., 7'' high. Black with
  U. S. flag on obverse and reverse _____  38.50
Jardiniere. 9'', apples _____  40.00
Jug. Dickensware (Weller), 5''
  high, 3½'' diam. 2 chess players  75.00
Lamp Bases. Harp shades. 19'' high.
  Blue with colorful pink flower
  decor and green vines. Electri-
  fied. Pair _____  45.00
Mugs:
  5½'' high, handled. Indian "Black-
  bird" _____  24.50
  5½'' high, handled. Indian "Tame
  Wolf" _____  24.50
Pitchers:
  2½'' high, 6'' across flat pitcher.
  Brown glaze with berries and
  autumn colored leaves. Marked
  Louwelsa Weller _____  29.50

| | |
|---|---|
| 12" high. Tankard. Indian "Chief Hollow Horn Bear" _____ | 59.50 |
| 13½" high. Tankard, slender. With deer in forest _____ | 65.00 |
| 21½" high, 7" square base. Full figure of blonde woman in relief, green and pink coloring. Signed "Weller Art Nouveau MAT" ____ | 75.00 |

Pitcher. 11½" high. Emerald green at bottom up to ¾ of the way; remainder grey at top. Pink interior _____ $40.00

| | |
|---|---|
| Plaque. Wm. McKinley. 4½" diam. | 15.00 |
| Punch Powl. 13" diam., 6½" high. Shades of rich brown and green fruit decor _____ | 80.00 |
| Umbrella Stand. 20" high, 10" diam. Red, green and gold tulips | 40.00 |
| Urn. 7" high. Dark brown to orange. Flower and leaf decor. High glaze _____ | 39.50 |

Vases:

| | |
|---|---|
| 3½" high. Brownish with cherries. Louwelsa _____ | 12.00 |
| 6¼" high. Handled, nasturtium decor _____ | 39.50 |
| 7" high. Double bud vase with acorn and oak leaf decor. Signed | 25.00 |
| 7½" high. Dickensware Weller. Man playing golf. Brownish-green background _____ | 75.00 |
| 8" high. 4 handles at neck, gray background with grapes in relief | 42.50 |
| 8½" high. Louwelsa, floral decor, artist's initials _____ | 45.00 |

Vase. 9½" high. Green body with panels of lighter green leaves and brown stems _____ $38.50

| | |
|---|---|
| 10½" high. Louwelsa, Indian. Signed by A. Dunlavy _____ | 50.00 |
| 11½" high. Bottle shaped vase. Dickensware Weller. "Domby & Son" _____ | 95.00 |
| 12" high. Varigated green and tan ground with blue plum decor | 50.00 |
| 16" high. Decorated with berries. High gloss, Louwelsa _____ | 65.00 |
| 16" high. Floretta, grape decor in relief _____ | 65.00 |
| 17" high. Louwelsa, rose decor, signed by artist _____ | 70.00 |

## WESTERN FRONTIER ITEMS

Western Frontier items available now date from about 1850 to 1890. It was in this period that the great migration to the West took place.

| | |
|---|---|
| Branding Iron. Massive, used for crates. AWF & Co. Ex. _____ | 60.00 |

Buckles:

| | |
|---|---|
| Bronze. Wells Fargo & Co. 1877 pattern Union Pacific Train, with classic old iron horse on the face _____ | 10.00 |
| Bronze. Wells Fargo & Co. 1902 pattern, with names San Francisco and Sacramento in face _____ | 10.00 |
| Clip corners and detailed stage-coach loaded with WF Mine workers _____ | 15.00 |
| Clip corners. Part of State pattern with exact replica of famous | |

Currier & Ives "Express Train" embossed in heavy brass face, with Wells Fargo name ........ 20.00
Wells Fargo & Co. Bankers & Forwarders. 1886 pattern. AC&CRR gold train with full company name ........................... 10.00
Wells Fargo & Co. "Alert & Faithful", with a WF guard dog protecting a strong box and safe 15.00
Wells Fargo & Co. "Alert and Faithful" stagecoach under attack ........................... 15.00

Key. 6". Old ranch-type. Iron ...... $6.75

Charcoal Iron ........................... 4.50
Colt, Wells Fargo. 5 shot, 3" barrel with WF & Co Val Verda address and Colt NY address ... 350.00
Cup, Drinking. Copper, marked Wells Fargo & Co Sutter Creek... 20.00
Key, Jail or Ranch. Old and large, 6" long ........................... 1.50
Knife. WF & Co. die set, circa 1870 45.00
Mail Bag. US embossed like Pony Express type ........................... 50.00
Pistol, Boot. Steel. "WF & Co. — Express Bldg SF" on barrel. With under hammer ........................... 100.00
Plate. Small, heavy brass. Adams Express Co. Two loop fittings on the back, for use as buckle or badge ........................... 12.00
Scale, Brass. Enamel finish. With words "Adams Express Co." 97 Broadway New York and Great Eastern, Western & Southern Express and "London" engraved in the pans ........................... 200.00
Sign, Metal. Yellow, 2'x1', bears the words "Wells Fargo & Co. Bankers and Express Forwarders" 27.50
Spurs, Iron. Spanish. 2½" rowels. Pair ........................... 3.50
Vest, Steel. Made to fit under overcoat. Covered in soft hide and bears name "Butterfield Stage

Co." Transit Overseas, W.B. & Co. 1859, Paris. Weighs 27 pounds. "Smiths & Tower's" number 4. pattern armour .......... 1000.00
Wax Seals. Wells Fargo. Western States ........................... 55.00

## WILLOW WARE

The ware derives its name from the design or pattern. The scenes are in the Chinese tradition and are usually done in medium or light blue, although some examples are made in red.

The pattern is probably one of the most popular ever used by the Staffordshire potters and by potteries located elsewhere.

Compote. 8½" diam., 4¾" high. (Doulton's, Burslem) ........... $25.00

Butter Pat ........................... 2.25
Butter Tray. 5" diam., ½" deep ... 9.50
Cereal Bowl. "Alfred Meakin" .... 4.50
Cup and Saucer. "Allertons" .... 10.00
Cup and Saucer. Handleless. Early Staffordshire ........................ 16.50
Egg Cup. Double ........................ 7.00
Gravy Tureen. Covered, on tray .. 30.00
Ladle. For large tureen .......... 25.00
Pitcher, Milk. Covered. Ridgway, England ........................ 18.50
Plates:
7" diam. "W. R. Ridgway & Co." ........................... 7.50
8" diam. ........................ 8.50
8½" diam. ........................ 8.75
Platters:
12½x15½". "England" .......... 21.00
17" diam. ........................ 29.50
Salt Shaker ........................ 8.00
Sugar Bowl. Covered. "Ridgway".. 21.00
Teapot. Doulton ........................ 55.00
Tureens:
Covered, on tray. 2-quart size. "Ridgway" ........................ 72.50
Large, with cover and ladle .... 95.00

Platter. 14½'' diam. Theo. Hughes.
England _____ $8.50

Vegetable Dish. Square sided, 5½''
high, 9½'' square. Marked ''Ye
Olde Willow.'' Staffordshire England. Late _____ 15.00

## WOODENWARE

A general term which serves as a ''catch
all'' for wood items of dairy and kitchen
use of the 19th century.

Cottage Cheese Bowl. 7'' diam.
Hole in bottom for drainage ____ $22.50

Barber Pole, Hanging. 22'' long,
original decorations _____ 95.00
Bellows. Pine _____ 24.50
Boot Jack _____ 6.00

Bowls:
  14x23''. Original paint _____ 29.50
  15'' diam. Burl. Refinished _____ 69.50
  16'' diam. Maple, old _____ 25.00
  22'' long, 8'' deep, turned _____ 35.00
  Cottage Cheese Bowl. 7'' diam.
  Hole in bottom for drainage ____ 22.50
Box. 2½'', oval, covered _____ 4.75
Buckets:
  Oaken, for well _____ 9.50
  Sugar _____ 8.00
Butter Bowls:
  Medium size, plain _____ 11.00
  11½x23''. Original green paint___ 27.50
Butter Molds:
  Cow _____ 10.75
  Flowers and leaves _____ 8.50
  Round, medium _____ 7.50
  Round, large, with leaf design __ 9.00
  Sheaf of Wheat _____ 8.50
Butter Paddle _____ 5.75
Cheese Box. Large _____ 14.50
Churns:
  Barrel, with crank _____ 29.50
  Dasher-type, with handle _____ 25.00
  Side-wheel _____ 20.00
Clamps. 18'' heavy jaws, marked
  ''T. B. Minor'' _____ 15.00
Cranberry Picker _____ 65.00
Cutting Board. Handled _____ 6.75
Darning Egg. With handle _____ 3.75
Dumbbells:
  Eagle. Carved, on gilt ball.
  7½'' high, wingspread 11'', good
  detail _____ 95.00
  Pair _____ 9.50
Flour Scoop _____ 7.75
Foot Warmer. Charcoal pan _____ 10.00
Forks:
  11'' long _____ 7.00
  Hay, 2-prong _____ 12.00
Grain Measure. 9'' diam., 5'' high 5.50
Grain Scoop _____ 10.00
Hat Stretcher _____ 9.00
Hobby Horse. 41'' long, 33'' high,
  in swing standard _____ 69.50
Indian Clubs. Pair _____ 10.00
Ink Sander _____ 9.75
Inkwell. Glass insert, holes for
  quill pen _____ 7.50
Keg. Labeled ''Kentucky Rifle Gun-
  powder'' _____ 15.00
Knife Boxes:
  Pine, refinished _____ 25.00
  Walnut, refinished _____ 28.50
  Walnut, rough _____ 10.00
Ladle. With holes _____ 6.75
Ladle. Curly maple, refinished ___ 14.00
Lemon Squeezer _____ 5.50
Meat Pounder _____ 4.00
Merry-Go-Round Wood-carved
  Horse. Pony size _____ 495.00
Mortars and Pestles:
  6'', maple _____ 27.50
  Spice _____ 14.50

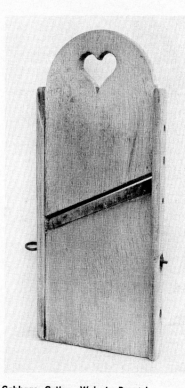

Cabbage Cutter. Walnut. Pennsyl-
vania-Dutch-type with heart cut-
out on handle. 18'' long _____ $35.00

Ox Yokes:
  With bows _____ 48.50
  Without bows _____ 37.50
Peck Measure. Iron band _____ 7.50
Pepper Mill _____ 14.00
Pie Lifter. 2-prong _____ 4.50
Plane. Early _____ 15.00
Potato Masher _____ 3.50
Pump. 48'' high. Barrel-type, wood
  plunger and spigot _____ 20.00
Rolling Pin. Large _____ 6.75
Rolling Pin. Curly maple, with
  handles _____ 14.50
Rolling Pin. Pine, one-piece type__ 3.00
Salad Bowl. Oblong _____ 18.50

Salt Boxes:
  Hanging, pine. Pennsylvania Dutch
    type. Refinished _____ 42.50
  5½x6½x6'' high. Covered, pine.
    Refinished _____ 25.00
Sap Bucket. 11½'' diam. Handle
  added. Refinished _____ 18.00
Shoe Lasts. Hand-carved. Set of 4__ 8.50
Shoes, Dutch. Leather trim _____ 9.50
Shovel, Grain. Large, all wood __ 49.50
Shutters, House. Pair _____ 18.00
Spoons:
  Refinished _____ 6.75
  Rough _____ 5.50
Stirring Paddle. Primitive _____ 4.00
Sugar Box. Covered, burled _____ 14.50
Sugar Scoop _____ 7.50
Sugar Tub. Medium _____ 18.00
Wagon Jack _____ 16.50
Wagon Seat _____ 75.00
Washboard. With rolls _____ 16.50
Yoke, Shoulder. Hand hewn with
  chains and hooks _____ 20.00

## ZSOLNAY PORCELAIN

    The factory was established at Funf-
kirchen, Hungary in 1855. The items are
of soft paste, usually enameled in many
brilliant colors and highly glazed.

Bowl, Oval. Flared rim, gold-traced
  Persian flowers, white background. 14½'' long, 10'' wide, 7½''
  tall. Signed _____ 130.00
Dip and Chip Set. All enameled.
  Signed _____ 98.00
Ewers. 10'' high, face handles. Pair 130.00
Jug. Large Persian shape. Gold-
  traced birds of paradise and
  florals. Burnt orange background.
  13½'' high. Signed Z. W. Pecs__ 95.00
Pitcher. 8'' high. Iridescent enameled, long spout. Signed _____ 80.00
Planter. Large, oval, flared rim.
  Gold-traced brilliant Persian flowers, white background. 14½''
  long, 10'' wide, 7½'' high.
  Signed _____ 130.00
Tea Set. Teapot, sugar, creamer, 2
  cups and saucers, mint dish. All
  enameled. Signed _____ 95.00
Vases:
  5'' high. Iridescent, red color,
    signed _____ 40.00
  9½''. White ground with various
    colors of flowers. Signed _____ 69.50

# Index

- NOTES -